HANDBOOK OF
LOCAL
AREA
NETWORKS

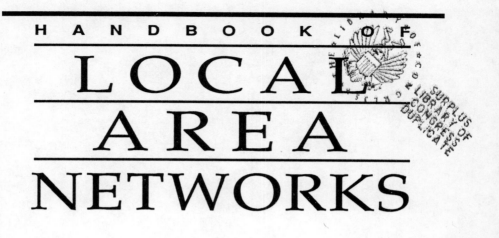

HANDBOOK OF
LOCAL
AREA
NETWORKS

John P. Slone and Ann Drinan, *Editors*

With a Foreword by Mark Freund

AUERBACH PUBLISHERS
Boston and New York

"A Decision Support System for Evaluating Investments in Local Area Networks" reprinted from *Manufacturing Review* 1, 3 (1988). Used with permission.

Copyright to "SNA and LANs: The Gateway Function" held by Kevin Tolly.

Printed in the United States of America

Auerbach Publishers
210 South Street
Boston MA 02111 USA

Contributors

Robert E. Blackshaw
Corporation for Open Systems, McLean VA

Robert J. Bond
Managing Partner, Romac & Associates, Wellesley Hills MA

Paul J. Brusil
Principal Scientist, The Mitre Group, Bedford MA

Richard A. Cerny
President, Backbone Networks Corp, Worcester MA

Peter Cluck
National Audit Consultant, Pansophic Systems, Inc, Conshohocken PA

William Collins
Consulting Engineer, Codex Corp, Mansfield MA

James W. Conard
President, Conard Associates, Reston VA

Lorne A. Dear
Deputy Assistant Auditor General of the Air Force, San Bernardino CA

Terence H. Dineen
Engineer, Hewlett-Packard Co, Chelmsford MA

Victor A. Duarte
Principal Software Engineer, Pilot Executive Software, Boston

Donald Dytewski
LAN Products Program Manager, Intel, Hillsboro OR

Phillip R. Evans
Director of Telecommunications, FMC Corp, Dallas

Mark Freund
President/CEO, Interconnect Network Consulting Group Inc, Santa Monica CA

Frederick Gallegos
Management Science Group Manager, US General Accounting Office, Los Angeles

Chris Gladwin
Manager of Emerging Technologies, Martin Marietta, Chantilly VA

v

Thomas R. Halsell
   Controller, Yum Yum Donuts Inc, City of Industry CA

Gilbert Held
   Director, 4-Degree Consulting, Macon GA

Vincent C. Jones
   Computer Networking Consultant, Tenafly NJ

Celia A. Joseph
   Consultant (Independent), Concord MA

Kimberly E. Kirkpatrick
   Lead Engineer, The Mitre Group, Bedford MA

Robert Klenk
   Senior Systems Analyst, Medical Center of Delaware, New Castle DE

Paul J. Leach
   Apollo Fellow, Hewlett-Packard Co, Chelmsford MA

David P. Levin
   President, Netcomm Inc, New York

Hampton R. Liggett
   PhD Student, North Carolina State University, Raleigh NC

Daniel C. Lynch
   President, Interop Inc, Mountain View CA

Leo J. McLaughlin III
   Manager of Microcomputer Engineering, The Wollongong Group, Palo Alto CA

Nathaniel W. Mishkin
   Senior Consulting Engineer, Hewlett-Packard Co, Chelmsford MA

James F. Mollenauer
   President, Technical Strategy Associates, Newton MA

John Morency
   Technical Director, Open Network Systems (DEC), Littleton MA

Nathan J. Muller
   Consultant Relations Manager, General DataComm Inc, Middlebury CT

Kurudi H. Muralidhar
   Principal Scientist, Industrial Technology Institute, Ann Arbor MI

Fritz E. Nelson
   Technical Writer, Martin Marietta, Chantilly VA

Asghar I. Noor
   Independent Consultant, Natick MA

Mikhail Orlov
   Director of Marketing, Diversified Communications Technologies Inc, Abington MA

Joseph N. Pato
Consulting Engineer, Hewlett-Packard Co, Chelmsford MA

Richard Pitkin
Principal Engineer, Digital Equipment Corp, Littleton MA

Ladan Porooshani
Software Engineering Manager, Digital Equipment Corp, Littleton MA

David K. Porter
Consultant Software Engineer, Digital Equipment Corp, Littleton MA

Robert A. Prichard, Jr
Network Planning Manager, Public Service Company of Colorado, Denver

Andy Richter
Systems Analyst, Vanderbilt University, Nashville

Floyd E. Ross
Senior Staff Engineer, UNYSIS, Paoli PA

Hugh W. Ryan
Partner, Andersen Consulting, Chicago

Lewis F. Saettel
Systems Analyst/Network Manager, Vanderbilt University, Nashville

Leland W. Seeton, Jr
Principal Engineer, Digital Equipment Corp, Wilton NH

John P. Slone
Senior Consultant, Martin Marietta, Orlando FL

Cheryl Snapp
President, Snapp & Associates Inc, Orem UT

William Stallings
President, Comp-Comm Consulting, Prides Crossing MA

William G. Sullivan
Professor, Virginia Polytechnic Institute and State University, Blacksburg VA

Joseph J. Tardo
Consulting Engineer, Digital Equipment Corp, Littleton MA

Stephen A. Thomas
Lead Engineer, AT&T Tridom, Marietta GA

Kevin Tolly
Principal, Virtual Systems of New Jersey Inc, Sea Girt NJ

Jeffrey Earl Tyre
Regional Engineering Manager, Rockwell CMC, Santa Barbara CA

Larry van der Jagt
Chief Engineer, Knowledge Implementations Inc, Warwick NY

Contributors

John L. Wheeler
    Owner, Wintergreen Information Services, Webster NY

Geoffrey L. Wyant
    Sabre Software, Cambridge MA

Stephen E. Young
    President, ImageAbility, Westford MA

Contents

Contents

Foreword
On LANs and Organizational Strategy

When an organization is successful, it is implied that that organization is also competitive. Currently, however efficient the manufacturing plant, however skillful the engineering department, however responsive the distribution channels, or however timely the marketing division, competitiveness and the overall success of an organization will depend increasingly on the implementation of strategically effective information strategies.

Differentiating between the strategic and the tactical implementation of technology is still a fundamental issue in the automation of corporations in the US. Most current applications of technology are tactical rather than strategic, and organizations that have used powerful computer and communications technology to automate repetitive or computationally intensive tasks have been slow to adopt information systems technology as an integral element of corporate strategy. This is short-sighted.

HISTORY

Information systems have traditionally been implemented according to an organization's functional structure. Accounting systems, for example, have been implemented for accounting, manufacturing systems installed in manufacturing, and sales information systems for sales departments.

This approach made sense with respect to the popular management models of the years following World War II, wherein hierarchical organizations segregated their functional responsibilities. During the 1990s, however, a trend toward the flattening of the organization will continue, with the removal of many of the traditional management layers from the middle of the organizational chart. The more team-oriented companies that result are proving that they can be more responsive to their markets, employees, and their competition.

To become more competitive, corporate executives need to better understand the dynamics of their organizations. Tactical information regarding a manager's departments or division is insufficient. An executive needs to understand the dependences that exist (and continually change) between these functional groups.

NETWORK COMPUTING

Information systems for the 1990s must be altered to support the change in corporate management structure, and with local area networks (LANs) it is possible to build information systems not subject to the hierarchical boundaries of the traditional corporation. LANs are particularly important because they permit the implementation of these systems while preserving 85% or more of the corporation's traditional mainframe (i.e., functionally oriented) investment.

To see LANs as a tool of strategic value, however, requires a change of outlook. LANs also have traditionally been used in a departmental or functionally oriented computing context, as systems subordinate to the corporate mainframe. LANs should move to the top of the information processing structure and be distributed horizontally across the entire enterprise. The users follow the LANs to the top, and the new representation takes on a peer-to-peer rather than a hierarchical aspect.

LANs can then become a network computing stratum, or platform, that encompasses the entire corporate enterprise. The functionally oriented mainframes remain, but a method is now available to access all that corporate information from wherever the user may reside in the organization. Access is no longer limited to the users who were part of any specific mainframe's hierarchy. Through LAN gateways, users can, theoretically at least, access all the organization's data.

A single window to the enterprise can be created. Applications can now be developed that reside on the local network computing platform and can access any corporate data and synthesize it into a global picture for management.

SUCCESSFUL NETWORK IMPLEMENTATION

Successful strategic LAN applications require careful adaptation of the technology to the current organizational computing environment. LANs are not a substitute for host computing, they are an augmentation. An incremental investment in LAN technology can produce enormous rewards from both the new technology and the current computing environment.

In practice, the effective strategic implementation of LANs relies on an understanding of several key aspects of the technology. Two of these, throughput and network management, are discussed in the remainder of this foreword, and should be kept in mind as the chapters in this handbook are referred to.

THROUGHPUT

System performance in a computer has always depended on movement of data between the machine's multiple components. Applications tend to be referred to specifically as CPU bound or I/O bound. CPU-bound applications are those that are computationally intensive and likely to saturate the central processor of a particular computer while the communications bus sits idle, waiting for the CPU to finish its task. I/O-bound applications are jobs that are communications intensive and tend to leave the CPU sitting idle.

A LAN is composed of many CPUs and communications channels. In addition to the I/O buses of the machines, the LAN architecture itself is a communications channel between many CPUs. Optimizing the performance of a corporate LAN requires skillful balancing of these different processing and communications resources. The common term that is increasingly being applied to such design methodologies is scalability. This refers to scaling LANs and internetworks to the business function (whether departmental or enterprisewide) and to the application. The goal of the LAN designer is no different from that of the mainframe and application designers: to optimize the balance between the different system components to maximize the performance and throughput of the system.

Optimization of LAN performance can be dramatically more complex than the optimization of mainframe performance. This is particularly true as LANs become larger. The traditional approach with microcomputers, optimizing the components, should be avoided. The LAN is a system of many components (and subcomponents), so it is essential that the approach be to optimize the aggregate system. It is not necessarily appropriate to buy the newest, biggest, and best technology. A higher return on computing dollars will be realized by planning ahead and designing a balanced LAN. It has long been accepted, for example, that the faster the file-server CPU (e.g., 80206, 80386, or 80486), the better the performance of the LAN as a whole. The reality is that the file server is not the LAN's primary bottleneck. Many high-powered servers operate at only 35% CPU use and 15% I/O bus use because the single network interface card plugged into them is saturated. Many network operating systems will support two or more network interface cards on a single server. Using them is one method of balancing loads and minimizing bottlenecks.

Some network operating systems no longer assign much more than file and print service to the central network engine. Applications (particularly with client/server architectures) are being moved to application servers. It is conceivable that on an optimized LAN, CPU capacity in the file server will be smaller than it will in the separate data base and communications servers.

The key for the LAN is to be applications driven. The business will drive the applications requirements, and the LAN, or network computing platform, should be optimized to the processing and communications loads created by that application.

NETWORK MANAGEMENT

After the issue of throughput is addressed, the other key design requirement is the need for a well thought–out network management strategy.

If there is one single thing to keep in mind regarding network management, it is that while supermanagers, single-console management systems, and industry standards are desirable, developing a thorough LAN management methodology is essential. Fully integrated network management tools are in the offing, but the current LAN management tools can, if properly orchestrated, provide effective LAN management. Currently, the network manager has to be the integrator.

Another requirement is that LAN management strategy has to be proactive as well as reactive. The bottleneck balancing tactics described previously are an example of proactive LAN management, because optimizing the performance of a LAN is a continuous task.

MANAGEMENT INVOLVEMENT

The real challenge to network managers is helping business management better understand the capabilities and benefits of this technology, so that the organization can gain a higher return on its investment.

One way to ensure business management's participation in technology management (and, equally important, bring technologists into the business perspective) is to form a LAN operating committee. This committee should include end-user management (e.g., vice-presidents of marketing, distribution, sales, manufacturing, and accounting) as well as data communications or MIS management. The goals of the committee need to be explicit, and an effective leader must be appointed to chair the committee and keep it on course. Business managers need to better understand what these networking technologies can enable the company to do and conversely, network managers need to better understand management's goals for the company. A successful committee can produce better communications, a more cohesive corporate vision, and broader support and acceptance of the enterprisewide LANs. Without such orchestration, it is possible that the LANs will become targets or tools of corporate political maneuvering.

Networking computing platforms should enable companies to achieve this single window to the enterprise. Automating the existing process, the traditional approach, should give way so that traditional processes can be changed. This is why LANs have such strategic potential. It is necessary that network managers start to manage this technology using this new perspective.

MARK FREUND
President, Interconnect
Network Consulting Group

Introduction

Twenty years ago, in *Future Shock*, Alvin Toffler asserted that the world needed a new symbol of technology to take the place of the classic symbol, the assembly line. The microprocessor arrived as if on cue. It heralded the arrival of the information age and within a few years established itself as this new symbol. It is now a challenge to find any example of modern technology that does not use microprocessors; they are in kitchen appliances, television sets, VCRs, and stereos. In cars, they manage engines, transmissions, and braking systems and perform diagnostics. Few offices lack at least one personal computer (which could not exist without microprocessors), and even what used to be the classic symbol of technology, the assembly line, has been revolutionized. Microprocessor-controlled robots and machine tools are used in every type of manufacturing function.

DEFINING LOCAL AREA NETWORKS

The activities of microprocessor-controlled robots and machine tools are coordinated by way of local area networks, or LANs. LANs of this type have always had a symbiotic relationship to microprocessors. In fact, LANs are unique in the communications world in that they were designed from the beginning to operate primarily in support of, and to be operated and controlled by, microprocessors. To many computer scientists, the relationship between LANs and microprocessors is so close that the technologies are practically interchangeable. Some people consider a LAN to be an extension or peripheral of a microprocessor, while others, adopting a different perspective, believe a LAN includes all the microprocessors connected to it.

Wherever the conceptual boundary between that amorphous entity called a LAN and the microprocessor is placed, few will disagree that LANs and microprocessors have already made significant contributions and that they will continue to produce changes in production, work, and communications. It is for this reason that this book, which is about LANs, was developed.

There are many schools of thought concerning the precise scope of LANs, and little progress has been made in reaching a consensus. Some of us just hope the argument will go away, avoiding the adoption of any definition that might wrongly limit what constitutes a LAN, and that might as a consequence hinder innovation.

This book therefore defines LANs in the broadest possible way, and as a look at the table of contents will reveal, covers a very wide range of LAN topics. It is hoped that through the inclusion of such a diversity of topics, some readers' horizons will be broadened, problems will be seen and solved from slightly different perspectives, and perhaps someone's creativity will be stimulated.

HOW TO USE THIS BOOK

The reader's objective will determine how to get the most out of this handbook. For the reader in search of an educational manual or textbook, the organization is such that if the chapters are read sequentially, cover to cover, the topics will unfold in a logical, orderly progression. For the reader with a general grasp of most of the subject matter, but who needs more focused information, each section is organized to provide complete coverage of a topical area with a minimum of dependence on other sections. Last, for the reader with very specific needs, each chapter can be read independently.

Such specific needs may take several forms, and accordingly the handbook contains several types of chapters. The first such type presents basic, fundamental concepts, or information about stable technologies. Other chapters deal with more dynamic, time-sensitive subjects. These have been included to the greatest extent practical in a publication of this form, but within a strict guideline. The information presented bears on significant trends, and time-sensitive details are identified for the reader. A third type of chapter, case studies, describes what other people have done in certain situations with the technologies available to them. Some case studies are presented as standalone chapters; others are embedded within chapters as illustrative material.

For any reader, it is suggested that the section introductions be read first. The overall organization of the book will then be clearer and the reader will be given a summary of the information presented in each chapter. For all readers, this handbook is not meant to be simply read once and shelved. Every effort has been made to include only chapters that will contribute to the book's usefulness on a continuing basis, and the intent is for this book to be kept handy and referred to many times. Most of the chapters are well illustrated, and many include such useful features as checklists and lists of suggestions. An index facilitates the location of specific items of interest.

LANs have permanently changed the organizations that rely on the tools of information processing, and these changes are not fully understood. All of us in industry face challenges as we attempt to adapt. Whether the specific challenge at hand can be characterized as LAN management, management within a LAN environment, or simply coping, the response must be multifaceted and multidisciplined. It is our sincere hope that this book will assist the reader in preparing a thoughtful, insightful response to whatever the challenge may be.

ACKNOWLEDGMENTS

The editors wish to express their most sincere appreciation and gratitude to all the contributors to this volume, including the many authors of individual chapters and the countless others who have made indirect contributions in the form of suggestions for revisions and improvements or author referrals. Without their many hours of planning, preparation, and execution, and more important, without their willingness to share their ideas and experiences with others in our industry, this book would never have been possible.

We would like to thank the staff at Auerbach Publishers, especially Pam Kirshen, Kim Horan Kelly, and Paul Berk, all of whom have worked closely with us on the book's development and production and who at times provided the encouragement needed to see it through to completion.

JOHN P. SLONE
ANN DRINAN

Section I
Strategic Issues

Competitiveness in today's global economy is dependent on the skillful and appropriate application of automation technology. Local area networks have a unique and important role to play in the state of automation during the 1990s and, by inference, in the competitiveness of organizations throughout the decade. To best achieve a competitive edge through the application of any technology, it is first necessary to view that technology from a strategic perspective.

Section I of this handbook examines strategic issues associated with LANs, beginning in Chapter I-1, "Incorporating Local Area Networks into Long-Range Planning." This chapter argues that networks should be developed with a top-down perspective so that communications management can more readily support the organization's strategic business objectives. Specific steps in the strategic planning process are explained, as are the LAN-related issues that should be considered during the process.

LANs will play an integral role in the automation of factories, providing the key to efficiency and competitiveness. Chapter I-2, "Using LANs to Automate the Factory Floor," addresses this application. This chapter discusses the similarities and differences between factory floor and office communications and highlights several specific technologies targeted at providing local area communications in the factory.

One aspect of local area networks that is often overlooked or considered too mundane but that is of strategic importance is building wiring. Chapter I-3, "Strategies for Wiring Buildings," discusses the various media available for this task. The chapter presents cogent reasons for considering factors other than the initial acquisition cost of the cable itself. Included is a description of a building wiring plan as actually implemented by a major northeastern university.

1

I-1
Incorporating Local Area Networks into Long-Range Planning

ROBERT A. PRICHARD, JR

During the last five years, requirements for communications within functional units of an organization have accelerated, while transparent communications between functional units have had to be maintained. These demands have driven network users to seek ease of connection and less reliance on proprietary operations. Gone are the days when separate networks were used to meet individual requirements within an organization. Today, a single intelligent network must integrate the individual unit requirements and facilitate transparent communications.

This chapter can help the communications manager select LAN solutions to meet the organization's current needs while successfully integrating the LAN into the overall communications network architecture. This process requires a top-down planning sequence that defines the specific LAN solution in the context of the strategic direction of the entire communications network.

STRATEGIC PLANNING

The strategic planning process is composed of three basic tasks:

- Projecting communications system requirements into a three- to five-year time frame.
- Establishing a flexible systems development process capable of responding to internal and external change.
- Defining expected system results to ensure that the system design produces them within the specified time.

Strategic systems planning is very different from conducting a technical system analysis to determine the performance of a particular system that will be used as the corporate network standard. If operational and performance issues are allowed to dominate the LAN selection process, the result will be a bottom-up model that meets technical criteria but that most likely does not fit

3

the existing network. Technical system analysis is vitally important, but analysis is only a subset of strategic systems planning. Once the strategic system issues are in place, a strict technical analysis can be performed with confidence that the solution will meet short- and long-term goals.

Modeling's Role in Strategic Planning

Building a model to describe a corporate communications system has two parts:

- The selection of a starting point.
- The definition of the process used to describe the system.

The process for describing the system can follow inductive or deductive reasoning. With the inductive (or bottom-up) approach, the designer moves from the specific to the general. In other words, the designer starts with an application and fits the network to it. With the deductive (or top-down) approach, the designer moves from the general to the specific. This approach starts with the network and fits the application to it.

Two factors affecting the selection of a communications system modeling and planning approach are the corporation's organizational structure and its technological maturity.

The communications system plays a specific role in the organization's ability to deliver the goods and services that keep it in business. The perceived importance of this role determines where the communications function resides in the organizational structure and also determines management's response to capital expenditure requests for system improvements. Budget items are generally evaluated on the basis of four types of requirements:

- Legal requirements—New legislation or the amendment to existing legislation affecting the way the corporation does business. These legislative changes may require modification of the communications systems.
- Operational requirements—Requirements that come from system users (e.g., system reliability, security, performance, and interconnection with other service or supply companies).
- Economic requirements—Requirements that will result in cost avoidance or reduced expenses. These requirements are evaluated with economic analysis methods to determine whether they will improve the profitability of business operations.
- Customer service requirements—Requirements necessary to improve the corporation's image among its customers. Management views these requirements as critical to the corporation's strategic positioning in a competitive marketplace. Internal communications systems generally require some modification to take advantage of new interface options with customers.

The second factor affecting the modeling approach is technological maturity, which is defined as the level of communications system sophistication that

4

can be supported internally by the corporation. It can be measured by observing how the communications system design and operations functions are performed. If the design function is predominantly vendor controlled or if the maintenance and operations functions are predominantly controlled by an outside source, technological maturity is low.

A high level of technological maturity is present when an organization uses a standards-based network development plan that is not vendor specific or driven by vendor product change. This type of network design allows for multiple vendor equipment and does not require hardware-intensive solutions or nonstandard software fixes for compatibility.

In operations, technological maturity is demonstrated by using internal personnel to cost-effectively provide operations and maintenance functions. Contractors or supplemental help are used at the discretion of the corporation during peak periods, not routinely.

In actual communications systems development, a staff's degree of technological maturity will fall at some intermediate point between total vendor control and total internal control, as shown in Exhibit I-1-1. The modeling approach used to plan the long-range development of the communications system will determine the direction of movement along this continuum. Bottom-up modeling is generally used when the trend is toward vendor or outside control. The top-down approach is generally used when the trend is toward internal control.

Bottom-Up Modeling. Bottom-up modeling views the network through the application, as illustrated in Exhibit I-1-2. The application, not the network, is the corporate resource. The user application, based on the installed (and mostly vendor-specific) hardware, drives the selection of equipment and technology. Because the majority of local network applications required little outside connectivity in the past, the premise worked well and provided the re-

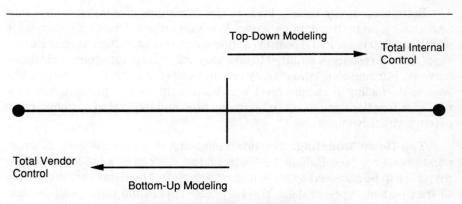

Exhibit I-1-1. The Control Continuum

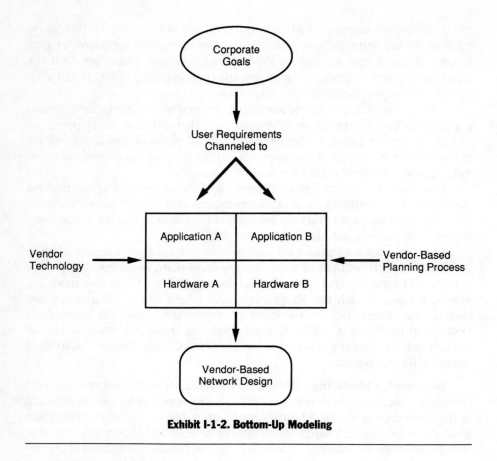

Exhibit I-1-2. Bottom-Up Modeling

quired computing resources and communications at the facility or campus level.

Bottom-up design usually leads to the development of multiple, separate LANs, voice, and other data networks. The exception is when a single vendor provides all services. In the postdivestiture environment, a single vendor cannot supply all the resources required to operate a major corporate communications network. Furthermore, connectivity requirements for LANs are no longer isolated at the facility or campus level. With bottom-up systems planning, communications functions are likely to be fragmented and integrated systems transparency virtually impossible.

Top-Down Modeling. Top-down modeling views the network as a corporate resource (see Exhibit I-1-3): individual devices or local networks are resources to be accessed by the entire organization. The network must be able to transport all types of data. The particular application remains important; however, the local network is designed within the context of the larger cor-

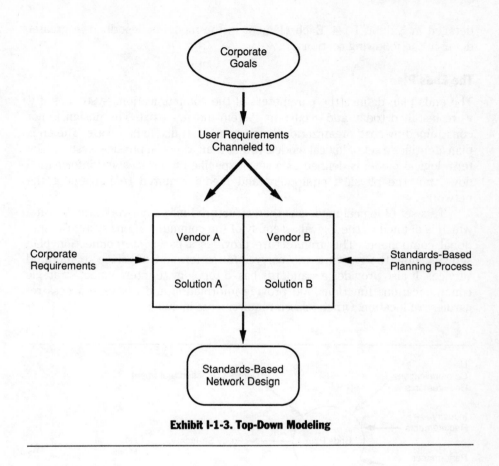

Exhibit I-1-3. Top-Down Modeling

porate network. The network provides the connectivity and the hardware required for protocol-independent data, voice, and image transmission.

Top-down modeling supports a corporation's strategic planning efforts. The network is a corporate resource, and it should be designed with a standards-based architecture such as that provided by the Open Systems Interconnection (OSI) model. An OSI-based architecture will have several strategic advantages. One is transparency of operation between the different types of systems on the network. This means that LANs can be selected to meet user needs without compromising access to the entire communications network. Another is the division of the OSI model into lower layers, which provide end-to-end data transfer resources, and upper layers, which provide applications-oriented information transfer resources. This allows corporate responsibilities for these functions to be divided along the lines of the OSI model. The result will be smoother operation of the corporation's communications services.

The elements composing the top-down strategic planning process are detailed in Exhibit I-1-4. Each element in the model is described in greater detail in the following sections.

The Ends Plan

The ends plan defines the parameters of the communications system as if it were installed today and a current system did not exist. The design is not constrained by cost, organizational structure, or available hardware. The ends plan identifies a set of logical models rather than a special physical system. The term logical model is defined as a set of specified interfaces and information flows, not the physical equipment and media required to implement the network.

This set of logical models is then structured into a network architecture, which is defined as the logical assembly of the communications system's functional components. The architecture provides a basic interconnection plan showing how the network will carry information and interface to required services. It also provides a standards-based topology to interconnect strategic communications functions and provide information and resource access regardless of location. Other related requirements include:

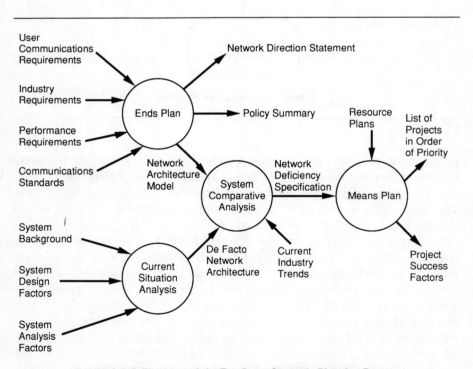

Exhibit I-1-4. Elements of the Top-Down Strategic Planning Process

- Connectivity among systems, hardware, and procedural elements.
- A single system image to any user or vendor subsystem, regardless of its function or geographic location.

There are four categories of input to the ends plan:

- User communications requirements—These are the resource requirements expressed by the working units that maintain the customer interface or the organization's production of goods and services. They are often based on vendor suggestions and may not reflect an understanding of the strategic needs of the organization. User communications requirements usually are the basis for budget item requests.
- Industry requirements—These are specific to the corporation's business (e.g., the use of Manufacturing Automation Protocol/Technical and Office Protocol (MAP/TOP) in the automotive industry, or the migration to the proposed Utility Communications Architecture in the power utility industry).
- Performance requirements—These are driven by operational or customer service issues. Generally, they are technical items relating to response time, throughput, graphics support, nodal delay, or related performance issues. Customer service requirements may be such items as call routing, voice response, direct data base access, or the average response speed.
- Communications standards—These are driven by operational, industry, or economic issues. They allow seamless interfaces, feature and function transparency, and system integration. Standards requirements generally promote operational efficiencies within the communications network; they also can assist in the development and execution of disaster recovery procedures.

The output from the ends plan process becomes input for the system comparative analysis. The primary output is the following written material:

- The network direction statement—This document provides the basic principles that guide network development. Such areas as network structure, network composition, network capacity, and risk evaluation are addressed in this document.
- The policy summary—This document outlines corporate guidelines for communications system responsibility. The system design, installation, and maintenance functions are described in the policy summary.
- The network architecture model—This is the set of models and the supporting documentation that define the logical assembly of the communications system. The network architecture model includes the architecture plan showing how the network will carry information and interface to the required services.

The Current Situation Analysis

Usually, a company has a communications system already in place, which may be as simple as leased telephone services from the local common carrier or as complex as a multinode, nationwide voice and data network. This existing system and the basic services that the business must provide are the starting points for the analysis of the current situation.

The communications manager requires three types of information to conduct a thorough situation analysis: system background, system design factors, and system analysis factors.

System Background. The system background provides specific knowledge about why certain equipment is in place and how it was selected. The decisions made and approved by management in the past are an indication of company policy.

System Design Factors. These are the constraints existing at the time of the system design, including the state of technology, corporate business direction, public communications policy and regulation, and general economic climate. Following is a more detailed examination of each of these factors:

- State of technology—Changes in technology most directly affect system design. For example, new standards and larger function sets are continually introduced for LANs. Examples of the new standards include the IEEE 802.6 (metropolitan area networks) and 802.9 (integrated voice/data LANs) as well as the ANSI standard on FDDI (fiber distributed data interface).
- Corporate business direction—The business supported by the communications system may take various directions over time. Changes may result from changing markets in which the primary product or service is obsolete or changed, or the corporation may be involved in mergers and acquisitions in which new subsidiaries are being acquired or sold. Most often, changes occur with the natural turnover of management personnel. For example, a conservative management will hold system levels at the status quo, concentrating mainly on operation and maintenance issues. On the contrary, an aggressive management will demand that the system design accommodate the merging of new technologies and new systems of companies acquired in the course of business. The particular mode of the company will have a major impact on system design and strategic planning.
- Public communications policy and regulation—Common carriers (local and long distance), services, and tariffs represent real costs for operating the communications network and heavily affect the design of the network architecture. In the past, common carriers have had little impact on LANs. Today, however, twisted-pair wiring is an option for LAN traffic in the 10M-bps range. Therefore, the cost of and jurisdiction over local wiring in the plant have become strategic issues.

The communications manager may also need support from the local or long-distance carrier if the distributed processing environment requires some combination of private and public network facilities. Although LAN technological advancements allow for the use of bridges, routers, and gateways to create communications access, the actual communications media may span tens or hundreds of miles. Most companies must lease these types of transmission facilities from a common carrier. And even when the company has a large internal network that supports LAN connectivity and distributed processing, common carriers still can have a significant effect on the company's strategic plan for disaster recovery. The communications manager must design a network architecture that permits the company's system to interface directly with the common carrier at multiple points to provide prompt service restoral using carrier transmission facilities.

The general economic climate affects the pace of communications growth. In robust economic times, the growth rate accelerates; conversely, in depressed times it slows. The economic climate combined with the phase of communications system maturity determines the corporate communications network growth and may be used to estimate future expansion. The communications manager can evaluate the economic climate and its impact on the company's network by addressing the questions listed in Exhibit I-1-5.

System Analysis Factors. System analysis factors are used to compare the network and its performance against management's expectations. The communications manager must provide answers to the following questions:

- Technical—How is the network configured today? Who is connected to it? What services are provided to users, maintenance and operations personnel, and network designers? What situations are supported well, marginally, or not at all? Where are the supported locations? How are they

---

- What is the current pace of economic activity in the company's industry?
- Are demand factors pushing production of a particular set of goods or services?
- Are profits increasing or decreasing?
- Are additional facilities being added to compensate for the growth pattern?
- Are consolidations and reorganizations occurring?
- If the market is surging, is the observed growth actual or just a swell?
- Can a slowdown that will leave an excess of facilities be predicted?
- Do communications requests advance linearly with new service requirements, or is there some lag between the two?
- How much lead time is required for new communications services?
- What types of services may be required for related systems issues (e.g., safety, reliability, and spare capacity)?

Exhibit I-1-5. Questions for Evaluating the Impact of the Economic Climate on System Expansion

connected? What types of services are required at each location, and why is each location important to the company? When will new service requests be issued and for which locations? What is driving the changes?

- Cost—How much of the overall enterprise budget is communications expenditures? Is that amount increasing? If so, at what rate?
- Performance—What is management's view of the services provided by the communications group? How do they compare with the costs, reliability, and response times of services contracted from common carriers or other outside sources?
- Profitability—How would the corporation's profitability be affected if services remained fixed at the current level? Could the current grade of service continue to be provided with no capital expansion?
- Capacity—How does the current system's capacity compare to projected future requirements as outlined in the company's strategic business plan? (This comparison should be based on quantifiable items that directly relate to performance requirements.) When will the current system be unable to meet the company's performance requirements?

The System Comparative Analysis

The output of the current situation analysis process is a de facto network architecture. This architecture and supporting documentation are used as input to the system comparative analysis, which is a process that analyzes the differences between the de facto network architecture and the network architecture model developed in the ends plan. The output of the process is a network deficiency specification.

There are three kinds of input to the system comparative analysis: the ends plan network architecture model, the de facto network architecture, and the evaluation of current industry trends. The ends plan network architecture model and the de facto network architecture have been addressed already. The communications manager must evaluate the following three categories of current industry trends:

- Standards—Standards are the doorway to the future. General knowledge of the types of standards and their applications is more important than global technical knowledge of specific standards. Because standards help define the interfaces and protocols required to design or maintain the network architecture, understanding them will help the communications manager gain advantage in competitive bidding situations, clarify vendor claims, and identify potential implementation problems.
- Technology developments—New technology developments must be monitored by the communications manager. Reading current materials, obtaining information directly from vendors, and attending trade shows and industry conferences are all methods for staying informed of new developments.

- Product evaluations—Product evaluations are a direct source of information because they can provide specific benefits and performance as well as functional and interface information. In the process, the communications manager will get to know the vendors and the local marketing groups and learn about product support and customer service. To properly perform the evaluation process requires a considerable amount of the communications manager's time.

A properly designed corporate network architecture should not be designed around one vendor's product or product line. The best network for the corporation is one designed with flexible, standards-based interfaces and protocol transport facilities that will provide the widest range of options possible.

The output from the system comparative analysis procedure is the network deficiency specification. This document identifies the deficiencies between the de facto network architecture and the ends plan network architecture model, with consideration given to the business and evolving industry trends. The deficiencies are summarized in descending order of importance as follows:

- System architecture deficiencies.
- System standards deficiencies.
- System technology deficiencies.
- Transmission system deficiencies.

The Means Plan

The means plan process creates a document that specifies projects to be implemented and the period of time for implementation. The goal is to balance network deficiencies and corporate resources to provide optimum user, application, or technology solutions while maintaining alignment with the strategic or long-term communications plans.

The network deficiency specification and the resource plans are the input to the means plan. In strategic communications system planning, the communications manager will use the resource plans to schedule time, personnel, and money.

A project schedule must be prepared, incorporating time for the following activities:

- Documentation preparation, which includes system design, technical specification development, and financial justification preparation.
- Management approval.
- Vendor selection and product evaluation.
- Procurement and equipment production.
- Personnel training, equipment installation, test and acceptance, and production cutover.
- Project finalization, including closing out all related project jobs or tasks,

finalizing all vendor payments, checking red-lined construction drawings for accuracy, ensuring that all planned services are cut over to the new system and that previous services are terminated, checking all as-built drawings for accuracy and ensuring that they are posted to the master drawing file, and providing for the turnover of system responsibility to operations and maintenance personnel.

Personnel also must be scheduled. Generally, engineering and operations personnel have direct responsibilities, with approval and support roles being played by management, finance, and procurement personnel. Engineering personnel provide system design, system specifications, and system documentation packages. Operations and maintenance personnel provide new system training, installation, testing and acceptance, and cutover. Contingency personnel planning is required to ensure that skilled replacement personnel are available should personnel substitution be necessary.

The size of the project budget determines whether the project must be capitalized or expensed. Generally, capitalized items are part of the budget cycle, whereas expensed items are charged against a single budget line item. For capitalized items, funding approval must be obtained from management; the funding approval documentation often contains a lease-versus-buy comparison. Disbursement schedules also must be prepared to allow for actual cash flows during the year.

The output from the means planning process is a document containing a list of projects in order of importance and a list of individual project success factors. The first list sequences projects according to their strategic importance. Each project targets an identified network deficiency (or multiple deficiencies) and through implementation moves the de facto architecture toward the ends plan architecture model.

The list of project success factors identifies measurable performance indicators. Each project is measured by how much it narrows the distance between the de facto network architecture and the ends plan architecture model. Other internal or external factors, however, can influence the project's success in reducing the gap between the current system and the desired system. The gap may be even wider after the project is implemented, which is the result of circumstances that have changed in a dynamic environment. The project success factors measure whether the new system accomplished its specified design criteria independent of other influencing factors.

SELECTING LAN TECHNOLOGY

Today's communications environment requires that LANs maintain communications system integrity and present a single system image to all users. Communications system integrity allows any resource a communications path to any other compatible resource in the network. To the application, the network appears as a single, broad highway with no contention for communications resources. LAN technology, therefore, must be integrated into the network architecture using standard interfaces and protocols.

Using the top-down strategic planning approach, the communications manager can be sure that LAN operating features will function correctly after the LAN is connected to other internal or external facilities. Top-down planning also allows for modular network growth, economic use of existing facilities in technology transition, less vendor control, and individual project cost justification.

Network Layers

Networks, as defined in strategic plans, can be separated into the layers illustrated in Exhibit I-1-6: facility or campus networks, hubs and hub networks, metropolitan area networks (MANs), and wide area networks (WANs). Each of these network layers uses a different combination of the three basic types of LAN technologies: PBX, baseband, and broadband.

Facility and Campus Networks. A facility can represent any organizational unit. It may be a single building or part of a building or multiple buildings in a contiguous geographic location, organized around some common function.

PBX networks are used in the campus or facility for local low-speed connections to asynchronous or synchronous hosts. The highest concentration of LANs will be in the campus or facility, because this is where user groups cluster. Baseband LANs are used most frequently; broadband LAN use is less frequent but can be extremely effective in some campus environments and high-rise or multiple-building complexes.

Hubs and Hub Networks. A hub is a facility with access to the next level of network services or higher-speed transmission links. The same combinations of LANs may be found in the hub as in the facility or campus environment. A hub network is the group of facilities or campus networks supported by a hub. The hub is the service gateway for passing traffic from facilities to network resources and vice versa. The classification of a particular location as a hub or a facility is based on the types of services provided, switching capabilities, and media access. The focus for the communications manager is on functions, not physical hardware, though generally the two are parallel.

Metropolitan Area Networks. The MAN connects the hub nodes. It can be a T1, DS3, or higher-speed network and is usually transported by optical fiber or digital microwave. The IEEE Standard 802.6 for MANs and the ANSI standards for FDDI are two examples of proposed industry standards in this area. Both baseband and broadband technologies are used for MANs. The common carriers are looking at a robust high-speed MAN, called switched multimegabit data service (SMDS), to transport both voice and data traffic.

The private MAN does not fit every application. Some organizations are not large enough to support a private network with multiple hub locations; other

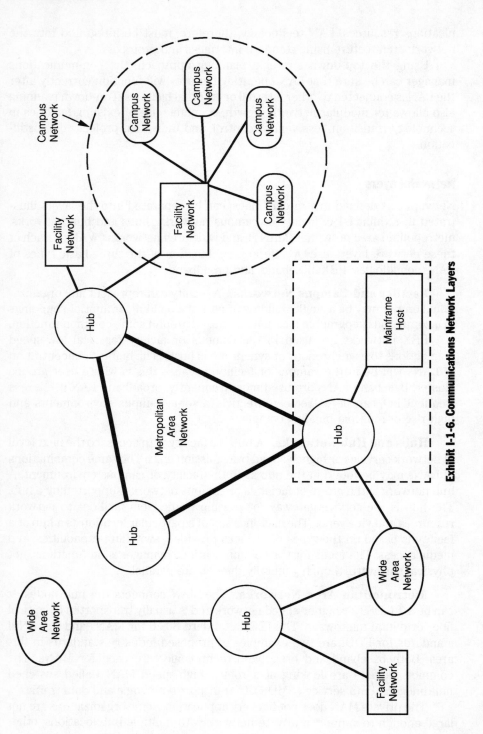

Exhibit I-1-6. Communications Network Layers

networks use common carrier facilities to connect hub nodes and use LANs primarily as internal communications networks within facilities or campuses.

Wide Area Networks. The WAN is used to transport data over large geographic areas. These systems may be public or private and may contain elements of digital or analog microwave, terrestrial land line, optical fiber, or satellite carriers. The WAN has no impact on a LAN unless the LAN belongs to a network that has a distributed architecture and wide geographic range. In that case, transport of data may be required from one LAN to a second LAN using the WAN. The communications manager should look at this contingency when planning, even if the application is not a current requirement.

System Justification

The technical alternatives for LAN service should be evaluated as a system justification analysis. System justification is composed of technical and economic justification.

Technical justification is a written document that focuses on whether a LAN is appropriate for servicing needs and on which particular LAN configuration provides the best technical solution. Answers to the following questions provide an information framework for a complete technical analysis:

- User profile—Who are the users, and what are their job descriptions? What departments will use the LAN, and which group will use it the most? How many people will use the network?
- Distribution profile—What kind of geographic distribution of services is required? Are users located in the same facility? If so, how are communications services distributed? What transmission resources are available within the facility? How difficult are new installations? If the users are not in the same facility, are they in a campus environment, or distributed differently? What communications media is available between the locations? Are there any related restrictions or factors (e.g., unavoidable costs, tariffs, or local regulations) that affect the distribution of services?
- Traffic profile—What volume of traffic must be supported? How much of it is internal and how much external? When are the primary and secondary hours of operation, and when are the typical peak periods? What is the distribution of transaction types (e.g., file transfers, print jobs, communications, common applications access, and data base inquiries) on a regular day and during peak times? What is the maximum acceptable response time for the individual user? How many I/O transactions will the file server process? Will local printers attached to terminals or network printers be used? How much memory is required to support network operations? How many and what size of records will be stored? What retention and access guidelines will be used? How much system downtime can be tolerated?

- System profile—Which technology best meets both user and network requirements? What hardware is required to implement the system? Is it deliverable today? Are the external communications services delivered through a communications server or by a gateway device attached to a terminal node? What external host access is required? How will nodes be attached to or deleted from the network? What hardware is required for each new node installation? Does the network configuration allow for easy troubleshooting and diagnostics?

Economic justification is the balance to the technical justification. The lowest-cost system in today's dollars should not drive system selection; it should be selected on the basis of the best combination of cost and performance.

Objective evaluation is not always easy. Soft dollar savings from a LAN (e.g., productivity improvements) are difficult to measure in real terms. For example, costs that are avoided by installing a new system may be masked by additional service requests. The new service requests combined with the up-front cash outlays may in fact cause the system costs to rise for a period of time. If management has approved the project on the basis of cost reduction statistics alone, the communications manager's recommendation may be criticized. Therefore, the communications manager must understand the company's financial planning methodology and the manner in which cost analyses are presented to management to represent new system costs appropriately.

Following are basic cost factors to be considered when preparing an economic analysis:

- Hardware costs—The type and cost of the supporting hardware, including file servers, print servers, communications servers, peripherals (e.g., printers, plotters, digitizers, and high-resolution monitors), and storage devices must be documented.
- Software costs—The costs of the supporting software must be documented, including the cost and availability of site licenses for applications software.
- Communications and networking costs—Costs to be accounted for include bridges, routers, gateways, cabling, transceivers, transceiver cables, modems, user and network interfaces, concentrators, and cross-connect hardware.
- Maintenance costs—This area is often overlooked when calculating system costs. Up-front costs are incurred in training maintenance personnel in LAN operation and troubleshooting. In addition, test equipment and troubleshooting and analysis software must be purchased. Furthermore, there are ongoing maintenance costs. How much labor is required to move, add, or change a terminal within the network? How many people will be used to maintain network performance levels? What other duties and responsibilities do the maintenance personnel have? Will such equipment as bridges, routers, or gateways be required to add communications func-

tions? Is special cabling required for every installation? Is the addition or deletion of a network node disruptive to the entire network?

- Management costs—LAN management is an often overlooked cost. LAN managers are responsible for resource and functional operations management. Resource management includes creating and maintaining records for locations, types, and numbers of devices; software revision levels; global addressing schemes; physical configurations; network problems; and other associated functions. Functional operations management includes the addition and deletion of workstations, network hardware and software, file server setup, access identifications, and user assistance. Depending on the network's size and type and on the relative sophistication of the users, 20% to 100% of one person's time will be required for network management. More time will be required during the initial installation, with requirements decreasing as the users become more familiar with network operation.

Installation and Integration Requirements

Much of the information used to prepare an installation and integration plan is compiled in the process of completing the technical system justification. The five component parts are a technical plan, a procurement plan, an implementation plan, a cutover plan, and postcutover operations.

The technical plan lists technical specifications defining the product to be procured for the selected network. Exhibit I-1-7 provides an example of the information required in the technical plan.

The technical plan should also address whether the installation will be turnkey with contracted maintenance, turnkey with internal maintenance, or an internal installation with internal maintenance.

The procurement plan is the documentation required to meet the company's purchasing policies. When preparing the procurement plan, the communications manager should:

- Make vendor requests—Vendor requests will be one of three types: a request for information (RFI), a request for proposal (RFP), or a request for quotation (RFQ). The RFI is used as a technical and financial screening document to narrow the field of possible products. The RFP is a more formal document requiring detailed system configuration information and firm system pricing. The RFQ is the document used when a system has been selected but additional hardware is needed. This document is used to compare pricing from different vendors with the same product.
- Compare vendor packages—The vendor bids should be compared on price/performance ratios, not just on low dollar amounts. Most important, the comparisons should be done in the context of the whole communications system. If all of the RFPs represent different products and vendors, the comparison process may be complete at this point. A second round of comparisons on the basis of an RFQ may be required to competi-

LAN Type
- Broadband, baseband, or PBX
- Access method
- OSI level 1 and 2 standards supported

Network Architecture
- Architecture type
- Control protocol
- Topology
- Transmission medium
- Data rate
- Maximum network length
- Maximum number of workstations supported
- Types of workstations and emulation packages supported

Communications Capabilities
- Gateways, bridges, routers, and brouters supported
- Data communications equipment required
- Electrical and mechanical interfaces supported
- Communications link support (speeds and interfaces)
- OSI level 3 and 4 protocols supported
- Microcomputers supported
- Mainframe link

Operating System Functions
- Operating system platform
- Internal functions:
  - —File locking
  - —Record locking
  - —Print spooler

Communications Media
- Backbone cable type
- Topology of work area
- Cable lengths
- Wiring access closets
- Distribution wiring to terminals
- Connectors required
- User interfaces required
- Communications and interface equipment

Additional Information
- Vendor information
- Product history
- Testing and troubleshooting capabilities
- Configuration aids
- Security and LAN management provisions
- Training for maintenance personnel and LAN managers
- Documentation:
  - —User's manual
  - —Technical reference manual

Exhibit I-1-7. Technical Planning Information for LAN Installation

tively bid the same product.

- Select a vendor and finalize negotiations—The communications manager, along with a group of support personnel, should choose a vendor and forward the documentation to management for required approvals. Once approval is given, final delivery, support, and payment schedules are negotiated with the vendor.

The implementation plan is the project's preinstallation action plan; its primary focus is physical site preparation and coordination. Dates are established for all interdepartmental functions, vendor activities, and contracted services. Key elements of the implementation plan include:

- Facilities preparation.
- Internal departmental coordination.
- Detailed wiring plans and installation.
- Equipment configurations.
- Circuit ordering, installation, and testing.
- Equipment installation and testing.
- Customer and user training.

The cutover plan provides detailed installation procedures and a timetable for bringing the system online. Vendor and user responsibilities during cutover will vary depending on the installation and maintenance agreement.

The postcutover operations plan is used to describe network test and acceptance procedures and how to install live traffic on the network. Acceptance may come after traffic is running on the network and all of the network functions have been demonstrated. Once the acceptance agreement is signed, payment should be made to the vendor.

LAN Management Requirements

The LAN will change over time. To manage it properly, the communications manager must control its growth and ensure that its design remains consistent with the long-range plans for the entire communications network. The areas of network administration, network expansion, and network security all must be managed.

The network administration function seeks to maintain consistency between the LAN protocols and communications network protocols. Its goal is to provide transparency for all applications. The communications manager must monitor the protocol stacks used in the LAN applications to ensure that these same protocol stacks are supported by the communications network's transport mechanism. Most applications will require access to another system or to a remote resource at some time, and if the communications path must be patched together with nonstandard interfaces, the network's integrity has been compromised.

As the user community requests additional LAN applications, the communications manager has the responsibility to strictly enforce technical design parameters in network expansion interconnection. Specifically, the physical interfaces (both electrical and mechanical), the transmission media, and the protocols must be consistent. Sloppy electrical and mechanical interfaces create noise generators that corrupt data and reduce throughput. Improperly selected transmission media will have the same type of limiting effects, though the symptoms may be different and more difficult to diagnose. The critical task for the communications manager is to maintain consistency in network expansion so that the maximum performance is obtained from the whole communications network.

In today's distributed communications environment, security is a key issue. The connectivity that supports multiple network access can be used to gain unauthorized access to any network in the communications system. Therefore, multiple levels of security are required in the network. The communications manager is responsible for implementing network security within a consistent framework.

SUMMARY

To incorporate LANs into long-range or strategic plans, the communications manager should:

- Communicate to corporate management the need for long-range, strategic communications system planning—Management support must be obtained for a project to develop a strategic communications system plan.
- Develop a framework for top-down modeling—If no strategic plan exists, the bottom-up modeling process is probably in place. Tough issues must be addressed to change the systems modeling process.
- Communicate the importance of a standards-based communications network architecture for integrating LANs into long-range planning.

I-2
Using LANs to Automate the Factory Floor

CELIA A. JOSEPH

During the last decade, manufacturing organizations, like many other businesses, sought increased efficiency through automation. True gains in efficiency, however, require that automated pieces communicate with one another to create an integrated information system. The need for integrated, automated manufacturing systems is driving the many changes in factory communications.

This chapter is an overview of factory communications LANs. It addresses the requirements for factory floor LANs, outlines current standards, and summarizes the main media and transmission techniques in use.

FACTORY COMMUNICATIONS REQUIREMENTS

Today's factory LANs must operate in a computer-integrated manufacturing (CIM) environment in which the goal is to integrate and automate all manufacturing information and processes.

CIM can be divided into four areas:

- The business data processing function—This function administers and controls information related to the business aspects of manufacturing. For example, this function includes material and parts planning, production scheduling and capacity planning, item tracking, status reporting, and maintaining purchase orders and supplier information.
- The computer-aided design (CAD) function—This function provides tools for turning designs into computerized representations. With CAD tools, engineers can analyze the dynamic behavior of parts and systems before they are built.
- The computer-aided manufacturing (CAM) function—This function automates the extraction of information from CAD drawings for numerical control and robot programs. The CAM function may also include automated process planning.
- The flexible manufacturing system (FMS) function—This function encompasses highly automated tools for manufacturing cells, material plan-

ning, material handling, and scheduling. These tools facilitate quick adjustments to production schedule changes and efficient use of manufacturing resources.

CIM implementation requires many types of automation and communications. The communications requirements are best defined by a model of manufacturing functions, including the frequently used Reference Model for Factory Automation developed by the International Standards Organization (ISO). As illustrated in Exhibit I-2-1, the ISO model defines a hierarchy of manufacturing-related functions, with the enterprise level as the highest level and the equipment level as the lowest.

Implementing the ISO model requires diverse computing and communications capabilities. A hierarchical LAN architecture, which permits different LANs to be used as needed, is gaining popularity. Exhibit I-2-2 is an example of how different LANs can be used to fulfill specialized requirements. For example, the enterprise LAN could be a Technical and Office Protocol (TOP) LAN, the factory backbone LAN could be a Manufacturing Automation Protocol (MAP) broadband LAN, the section and cell LANs could be MAP carrierband LANs, and the controller-to-device connections could be made using a FieldBus LAN.

Some factory communications needs can be met by products for office LANs. The enterprise and plant facility levels, for example, could use office LAN products. Others, such as the cell, station, and equipment levels, differ the most from office communications and require specialized facilities.

FACTORY FLOOR LANs

Factory floor production has several characteristics that require special communications capabilities. These characteristics include:

- An unfriendly environment—The factory floor can be a harsh environment; it can be dirty, dusty, wet, or subject to electromagnetic interference (EMI). Dirt, dust, and water are obvious enemies of electronic components, and EMI can induce voltages that interfere with the electrical signals used to transmit data.
- Real-time processing—Many manufacturing operations (e.g., process control) require real-time communications, which usually translates into two basic needs: deterministic (i.e., predictable) response times and clock synchronization throughout the network. Office LANs are inadequate because of the variability that can be induced by changes in network resource loading or the probabilistic (i.e., unpredictable response times) nature of the network protocols. Real-time communications also requires that the communications components be synchronized; however, time synchronization across LAN components can be difficult.

Level	Hierarchy	Area of Control	Responsibility	Basic Functions
6	Enterprise	Managing the corporation	Achieving the enterprise's mission and managing the corporation	• Corporate management • Finance • Marketing and sales • Research and development
5	Facility or plant	Planning production	Implementing the enterprise functions and planning and scheduling production	• Product design and production engineering • Production management (upper level) • Procurement (upper level) • Resource management (upper level) • Maintenance management (upper level)
4	Section or area	Allocating and supervising materials and resources	Coordinating production and obtaining and allocating resources to jobs	• Production management (lower level) • Procurement (lower level) • Resource management (lower level) • Maintenance management (lower level) • Shipping • Waste material treatment
3	Cell	Coordinating multiple machines and operations	Sequencing and supervising shop floor jobs and supervising various supporting services	• Shop floor production (cell level)
2	Station	Commanding machine sequences and motion	Directing and coordinating the activity of the shop floor equipment	• Shop floor production (station level)
1	Equipment	Activating sequences and motion	Taking action on commands to the shop floor equipment	• Shop floor production (equipment level)

Exhibit I-2-1. The ISO Reference Model for Factory Automation

223367

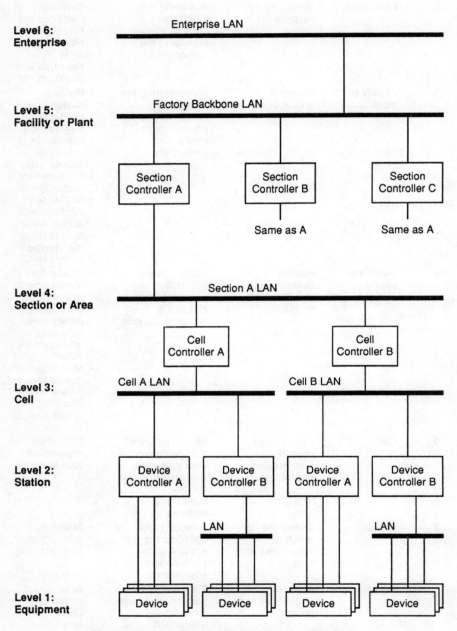

Level 6:
Enterprise — Enterprise LAN

Level 5:
Facility or Plant — Factory Backbone LAN

Section Controller A

Section Controller B

Same as A

Section Controller C

Same as A

Level 4:
Section or Area — Section A LAN

Cell Controller A

Cell Controller B

Level 3:
Cell — Cell A LAN   Cell B LAN

Level 2:
Station — Device Controller A   Device Controller B   Device Controller A   Device Controller B

LAN

LAN

Level 1:
Equipment — Device   Device   Device   Device

Exhibit I-2-2. A LAN Hierarchy for a Factory Floor System

- Fault tolerance—Once a manufacturing run has started, any downtime translates directly into lost product and financial waste. Communications equipment, protocols, and associated manufacturing applications must be able to withstand and recover from faults.
- Priorities—To ensure rapid response times or high throughput requires giving some applications priority over others in accessing and using communications resources.
- Special applications—The factory floor communications system may need to support special applications. Examples include messaging between manufacturing controllers and their associated devices and graphics data exchange between CAD/CAM systems and controllers.

Standards

Because of the simple nature of many factory floor devices (e.g., sensors and actuators), the first factory communications products were designed to provide a cheap, rugged, and simple method of communication between the devices and their controllers. As manufacturing devices grew more sophisticated, so did the communications products, and the vendors offering unique solutions proliferated. As with office communications, linking the proprietary factory communications products from different vendors was difficult and expensive.

Several standards applicable to the factory environment are under development. Each differs in the factory communications functions it provides. Exhibit I-2-3 compares the various standards to the ISO Open Systems Interconnection (OSI) Reference Model for communications. For each—Bitbus, FieldBus, MAP/TOP, MiniMAP and Ethernet—the shaded areas indicate the aspects of the OSI model that are implemented by the standard.

Bitbus. Bitbus is a low-cost method for connecting distributed intelligent devices to a central host in an electrically harsh environment. It is a serial protocol for the rapid transfer of very short control messages (2 to 248 bytes) among nodes in a control network. The hardware uses Intel Corp's 8044 microcontroller. Bitbus is sometimes considered another type of FieldBus network because, like FieldBus, it connects devices to device controllers. Therefore, it serves levels 1 and 2 of the ISO Factory Reference Model, and its functions equate to the physical and data link layers of the ISO/OSI Reference Model. However, some experts feel that Bitbus's lack of an application layer is a significant drawback.

Bitbus operates only in a single-master–multiple-slave arrangement; it is not suitable for peer-to-peer communications. Bitbus runs on twisted-pair wire and can operate at 62.5K bps for up to 13.2 km, or at 375K bps for up to 900 m. Its protocol is based on a subset of IBM's Synchronous Data Link Control (SDLC) and RS-485.

The IEEE Project 1118, which used the existing Bitbus protocol as a starting point, is developing a serial data communications standard for micro-

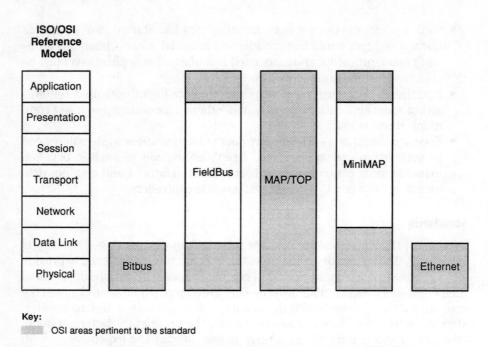

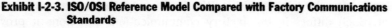

Key:

OSI areas pertinent to the standard

**Exhibit I-2-3. ISO/OSI Reference Model Compared with Factory Communications
Standards**

---

controller devices on a multidrop bus. To date, IEEE 1118 has produced two
documents—one for functional requirements and one that gives a data overview and architecture. Some experts view IEEE 1118 as a formalization of the
Bitbus master-slave protocol.

FieldBus. FieldBus is the standard initiated by the International Electrotechnical Commission (IEC) PROWAY Working Group to standardize communications for industrial LANs. In the factory LAN hierarchy depicted in Exhibit
I-2-2, FieldBus would be used between the devices at level 1 and the device
controllers at level 2. It provides OSI capability equivalent to the physical, data
link, and application layers. FieldBus is intended to simplify the current complexity of point-to-point cabling between devices and controllers and to provide
improved communications capabilities.

Several standards organizations are working on standards of the FieldBus
type. These include the Factory Instrumentation Protocol (FIP) in France,
Process FieldBus (PROFIBUS) in Germany, MIL-STD-1553 developed by the
US Air Force and the US Navy, and the Instrumentation Society of America's
ISA SP-50. Exhibit I-2-4 compares several characteristics of each of these
standards with Bitbus.

		FieldBus Type			
	ISA SP-50	MIL-STD-1553	FIP	PROFIBUS	Bitbus
Speed	≤100K bps	1M bps	3M bps	9.6K–500K bps	62.5K–375K bps
Hamming Distance	*	2	3	2 or 4	1
Broadcast Supported	*	Yes	Yes	Yes	No
Message Length	*	2–64 bytes	2 bytes	246 bytes or fewer	2–248 bytes
Control	Peer-to-peer	Central controller	Single-bus arbitrator	Master-slave, multiple masters	Master-slave
Encoding	*	Manchester	Manchester	Non-return-to-zero	Non-return-to-zero inverted
Number of Stations	256	31	60	32 or 122	28
Distance	750 m/ 1,900 m	6 m	1 km	0.4 to 2.4 km	13.2 km/900 m

Note:
* To be determined

Exhibit I-2-4. FieldBus Standards Compared with the Bitbus Standard

The FieldBus standards have common characteristics because they address similar requirements, primarily the replacement of existing 4-mA to 20-mA systems. For example, the ISA SP-50 standard defines two systems called H1 and H2:

- H1 is a digital replacement for existing 4-mA to 20-mA systems—It is intended for short distances, operates at low speed, and uses low-cost wire in a star topology.
- H2 is a higher-performance system suitable for logic applications—It provides support for longer distances, higher speeds, and peer-to-peer communications and uses a bus topology. Some experts expect the H2 FieldBus to be a low-cost subset of IEEE 802.4. H2 will contain protocols equivalent to the OSI physical, data link, and application layers. Its applications layer will be based on the work done by ISA dS72.02 for a process control application layer.

MAP/TOP. MAP and TOP are two specifications for standard communications interfaces; both potentially can satisfy all levels of the ISO Factory Reference Model. MAP and TOP specifications were formulated by a General Motors (GM) task force established in 1980 to investigate the interfaces among incompatible proprietary communications systems. The first version of MAP was produced in 1982.

Boeing, faced with problems similar to GM's, adapted MAP for its own needs and produced TOP. The original MAP and TOP specifications were based on the work then in progress in various ISO standards committees. Version 3.0 is the most current version of MAP/TOP specifications. The MAP/TOP users group has frozen the specifications at Version 3.0 until 1994 to encourage vendors to develop products that conform to them.

MAP and TOP support all seven protocol layers of the ISO/OSI Reference Model. To accommodate the process control industry, MAP also has a three-layer protocol Enhanced Performance Architecture (EPA), which includes the physical, data link, and application OSI protocol layers. Systems that include a seven-layer protocol stack and a three-layer EPA stack are called MAP/EPA systems. Systems that have only a three-layer EPA stack are called miniMAP systems. Exhibits I-2-5, I-2-6, and I-2-7 illustrate the MAP, TOP, MAP/EPA, and miniMAP protocol stacks.

A distinguishing feature of MAP and TOP is the wide variety of applications they support, including the following:

- Messaging between controllers and associated devices—This application is used primarily by MAP and is based on the Manufacturing Message Specification (MMS). MMS specifies the syntax and semantics for general manufacturing messaging but does not contain application-specific information. Application specifics are being defined separately in MMS companion standards, such as those being developed for robots, programmable logic controllers (PLCs), numerical controllers, production management, and process control. MMS has more than 80 services that provide connection management, device information sharing, program upload and download, program management, variable access, resource management, operator communication, event management, and journal management.
- File transfer—Both MAP and TOP use the ISO standard file transfer, access, and management (FTAM). FTAM defines abstract, distributed file storage and provides basic services for read, write, create, erase, locate, and transfer functions.
- Virtual terminal—The ISO Virtual Terminal (VT) capabilities allow terminal users to connect to and access heterogeneous host systems, regardless of the type of terminal used.
- Mail—The TOP specification includes an electronic mail capability called the Message-Handling System (MHS). This is based on CCITT recommendation X.400. MHS has two services: a basic message transfer service (MTS) and an interpersonal message (IPM) service. MTS supports general, application-independent message transfers; IPM uses the MTS to provide electronic mail service to users.
- Directory services—The ISO Directory Services provides for centralized or distributed directories of network resources. It also provides security features (e.g., controlling who may access certain directory resources).
- Network management—ISO's network management development was in

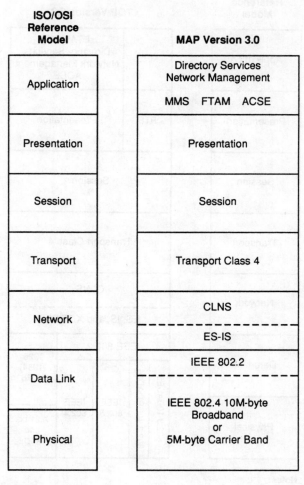

ISO/OSI Reference Model	MAP Version 3.0
Application	Directory Services Network Management MMS FTAM ACSE
Presentation	Presentation
Session	Session
Transport	Transport Class 4
Network	CLNS - - - - - - - - - - - - - - ES-IS
Data Link	IEEE 802.2 - - - - - - - - - - - - - - IEEE 802.4 10M-byte Broadband or 5M-byte Carrier Band
Physical	

Notes:

ACSE	Association control service element
CLNS	Connectionless network service
ES	End system
FTAM	File transfer and access method
IS	Intermediate system
MMS	Manufacturing Message Specification

Exhibit I-2-5. MAP Layers Compared with the ISO/OSI Reference Model

ISO/OSI
Reference
Model

TOP Version 3.0

ISO/OSI Reference Model	TOP Version 3.0		
Application	MHS	FTAM VT Directory Services Network Management ACSE	
Presentation	RTS	Presentation	
Session	Session		
Transport	Transport Class 4		
Network	CLNS		
	ES, IS, and X.25 PLP		
Data Link	IEEE 802.2		X.25 (1984) LAPB
	802.3 10BASE5 / 802.3 10BROAD36	IEEE 802.5 / IEEE 802.4	
Physical			X.21 bis and X.21

Notes:

ACSE	Association control service element
CLNS	Connectionless network service
ES	End system
FTAM	File transfer and access method
IS	Intermediate system
LAPB	Link access protocol–balanced
MHS	Message-Handling System
PLP	Physical layer protocol
RTS	Reliable transfer system
VT	Virtual terminal

Exhibit I-2-6. TOP Protocol Layers Compared with the ISO/OSI Reference Model

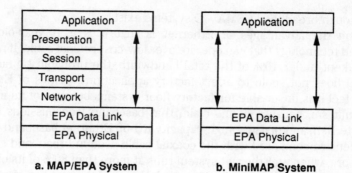

Application		Application
Presentation		
Session		
Transport		
Network		
EPA Data Link		EPA Data Link
EPA Physical		EPA Physical

a. MAP/EPA System   **b. MiniMAP System**

Exhibit I-2-7. MAP Enhanced Performance Architecture (EPA) and MiniMAP Protocol Stacks

preliminary stages when MAP and TOP capabilities were defined. In part because of this, MAP and TOP include only three network management functions: configuration, fault, and performance management. Furthermore, the management information protocol and service specified in MAP and TOP are an older version of the ISO CMIS/CMIP. As the ISO was in the preliminary stages of defining managed objects, MAP and TOP also created their own definitions of the objects to be managed, incorporating work from the IEEE 802 efforts.

- Interchange formats—TOP includes several information exchange formats useful for CAD/CAM applications, including the Product Definition Interchange Format (PDIF), the Initial Graphics Exchange Specification (IGES), and the Computer Graphics Metafile Interchange Format (CGMIF).

Ethernet. Ethernet is a de facto standard for factory floor systems because of its widespread use. Ethernet's functions correspond to the OSI physical layer and the lower part of the data link layer. It has been used for almost all levels of the ISO Factory Reference Model, though its main use has been for the station, cell, and section or area levels. Ethernet can be used in combination with higher-level protocols and applications; for example, it can be used as the basis for TOP networks.

In an Ethernet system, there is no central controller; control is distributed throughout the network. Ethernet uses carrier-sense multiple access with collision detection (CSMA/CD) algorithms to control access to the network. *Carrier-sense capabilities* means that if one station senses that another station is transmitting, it will wait until the transmission ends before beginning its own transmission. If two stations transmit at the same time, the collision detection algorithms ensure that all stations recognize the collision and control who will transmit first. Ethernet typically uses baseband modulation tech-

33

niques, though broadband CSMA/CD systems exist.

Among the advantages of Ethernet is that it is a 10-year-old, well-established technology that can operate over low-cost coaxial cable. If network loads are kept under 10% of the total bandwidth, the probabilistic nature of CSMA/CD does not seem to affect factory applications. Critics of Ethernet, however, feel it is unsuitable for factory floor systems because of its inherent nondeterminism, because of the claim that baseband transmissions may be sensitive to EMI, and because high-capacity RG-59 Ethernet baseband cable is quite expensive compared with the coaxial cable used in broadband systems. Furthermore, when an Ethernet system runs at more than 80% of its capacity, its performance may degrade significantly because of the number of collisions and retransmissions that occur. Research by Digital Equipment Corp, a major vendor of Ethernet systems, has been published in an effort to refute some of the preceding criticisms.

Transmission Techniques and Media

Two main transmission techniques are in use in factory floor systems—baseband and broadband. Baseband and broadband techniques can be used on a variety of media, including twisted-pair cable, coaxial cable, and optical fiber. The characteristics of these techniques and media applicable to the factory environment are summarized briefly in the following sections.

Baseband Transmission. In baseband systems, the bits of the data stream are represented by low and high voltage levels. This one data stream occupies the entire bandwidth of the transmission medium. Typical transmission rates are 1M to 10M bps in segment lengths to 1,000 m. Some baseband transmission techniques (e.g., those used in Ethernet) are susceptible to electrical noise. Other transmission techniques (e.g., carrierband) use a radio frequency carrier to provide effective noise immunity.

Broadband Transmission. Broadband uses multiple frequencies to transmit multiple data streams on a single cable. Broadband provides a total bandwidth in the range of 300 MHz to 400 MHz, which is usually divided into smaller, individual channels of 1 MHz to 12 MHz. Broadband networks can span 10 km or more. Broadband is highly immune to noise interference, which makes it a wise choice for factory environments. Although the cable for broadband is relatively inexpensive, such components as the head end (remodulator) and modems can be expensive.

Twisted-Pair Cable Media. Twisted-pair cable is usually found in telephone systems; however, it is also the basis for Bitbus and FieldBus LANs. Noise interference can be a problem with twisted-pair cable unless it is shielded, which increases its cost considerably. Twisted-pair cable is also limited in bandwidth and the distance it can carry signals.

Coaxial Cable Media. Coaxial cable shields the conductor and protects it from noise. With broadband transmission techniques, coaxial cable can provide enough channels to satisfy a wide variety of applications. For example, broadband coaxial systems can simultaneously carry data, voice, and video.

Fiber-Optic Media. Fiber-optic networks can transmit at rates of millions of bits per second, and the systems on the network can be kilometers apart. Furthermore, fiber-optic systems are immune to electrical interference, making them ideal for factory environments. The lack of standards for fiber-optic systems, however, has hampered their adoption.

FUTURE DEVELOPMENTS

This section presents an overview of anticipated changes in factory communications. These are divided into near-term changes (what forward-thinking firms are installing), mid-term changes (expected in the next three to five years), and long-term changes (promising research areas).

Near-Term Changes

Changes in communications technology are being made throughout manufacturing enterprises. Some current trends are communications integration, the development of manufacturing infrastructures, and the use of microcomputer LANs for manufacturing.

Communications Integration. Products that support the enterprisewide communications needed to implement CIM are being offered by several vendors, including IBM, Digital Equipment Corp, and Hewlett-Packard. Integrated communications in an enterprise requires hardware and software products in three areas: connectivity, information transfer, and information applications.

LANs, wide area networks (WANs), or combinations of the two may be needed for connectivity throughout the organization. Information transfer products are readily available using any one of several protocol suites (e.g., OSI, SNA, DECnet, and TCP/IP). Products are also available that transfer information between protocol suites. Common applications to permit information sharing can be a more difficult problem, because different portions of an enterprise usually select their information processing applications separately. The key to this problem is a common information architecture; otherwise, integrating different applications will result in a hodgepodge of translation products.

Manufacturing Infrastructures. Connectivity is a vital ingredient in developing the infrastructure necessary to improve US industrial competitiveness and to reduce manufacturers' reliance on outside suppliers. One way such infrastructures are developing is through groups of small and medium-sized manufacturers bidding collectively on projects. The Flint River Project in Michigan is an example. In this project, 30 to 40 smaller, specialized companies combine their resources with those of a central firm to establish a flexible manufacturing network. For such an infrastructure to work, the organizations must coordinate their activities, ideally using both voice and data links to support the integration of such activities as design, scheduling, and production. This type of integration may not be feasible because of cost, but facsimile communications (sometimes called fax net) is a low-cost first step.

Microcomputer LANs. A new trend is to use microcomputers as low-cost, automated tools at the station and cell levels. As more microcomputer-based systems are used, the need to integrate them increases. Off-the-shelf microcomputer LANs are an inexpensive method of providing integrated communications. LANs also are easy to use as gateways to other factory, engineering, order entry, and office computer networks because of the availability of microcomputer products.

Mid-Term Changes

Mid-term changes will be a product of current research and standards now being completed. Some potential mid-term changes are new applications, mobile communications, distributed data management, growth in manufacturing infrastructures, and applications management.

New Applications. Several useful application standards are nearing completion. These include the following:

- The Product Data Exchange Specification (PDES)—The PDES defines a standard for the exchange, description, and format of the data necessary to fully describe a product and its manufacturing process.
- The Remote Data Access (RDA) standard—RDA provides a structure for the exchange of data base manipulation instructions and the exchange of the resulting data.
- The Office Document Architecture (ODA)—The ODA is an international standard that defines the syntax of document types, including memoranda, letters, invoices, forms, and reports. The ODA also defines what these documents can contain and how this content is exchanged. ODA documents can contain text, graphics, and sound.

Mobile Communications. Use of such mobile machines as automated guided vehicles (AGVs) will require mobile communications. Current research is focusing on developing through-the-air methods of communications suitable for factory environments. Possibilities being investigated include spread-spectrum packet-radio techniques and optical methods using infrared.

Distributed Data Management. As an enterprise migrates to integrated communications, its information storage methods require revision. Most organizations store information in several separate repositories. The information must therefore be reentered when it is being transferred between the different parts of an organization. The results are highly redundant data storage as well as concurrency problems (i.e., determining which copy is the most current) when data updates are needed.

One example of consolidation is the Industrial Technology Institute's Network Object Server for MMS applications. The Network Object Server is a central repository for the MMS information required in a manufacturing cell. It reduces the communications needed to coordinate the actions of devices in the cell, facilitates the distribution of up-to-date data, and reduces the overall communications processing needed.

Growth in Manufacturing Infrastructures. As firms working collectively in a manufacturing infrastructure gain experience, their integration tools can become more sophisticated. For example, a fax net could be gradually replaced with integrated communications using a combination of LANs and WANs.

Applications Management. With the growing use of distributed manufacturing applications comes the problem of managing distributed resources. This problem is compounded if the applications are developed by different vendors. A new area of research is applications management, which seeks to adapt techniques developed for managing distributed network resources to distributed applications.

Long-Term Changes

Long-term changes in manufacturing communications will be based on new research in manufacturing. Two promising research areas are distributed data and control integration and total communications integration.

Distributed Data and Control Integration. Centralized data repositories may be inadequate for large, flexible, highly integrated manufacturing systems. An architecture based on artificial intelligence concepts—one providing both distributed control and distributed knowledge bases—may be more efficient and reliable. Researchers are investigating the use of separate information management elements and decision-making or control elements. The information is managed using distributed, hierarchical knowledge bases, with one knowledge base for a particular function or group of similar functions. The decision-making or control system performs most of the tasks of a traditional control system. The information management and the decision-making or control systems will be implemented through distributed systems that are parallel yet independent.

Total Communications Integration. Although CIM solves many information-flow problems, it creates others, the biggest of which is how to integrate the diverse communications methods used in various parts of an enterprise. The development of one communications method usable throughout an organization is being researched. Such a method must support real-time and nonreal-time traffic and meet other requirements as well. Systems based on optical fiber may be one solution to total communications integration.

SUMMARY

The automation of the factory floor is a technical challenge in its own right, and becomes even more complex in the context of the trend toward networks that encompass the operation of the entire enterprise or organization. This chapter has reviewed some of the special requirements that factory LANs must meet (e.g., resistance to hostile environmental conditions, real-time processing, fault tolerance) and described the LANs that have been developed to meet these requirements. As development work continues, manufacturing LANs that provide more automation functions at lower cost, integrate more easily into enterprise (and larger) networks, and interoperate more closely with the business data processing and CAD manufacturing functions will become more widely available.

I-3

Strategies for Wiring Buildings

MIKHAIL ORLOV

Today's complex networking environment offers many challenges to the network manager's planning and decision-making abilities. Expanded voice, data, and video applications have stretched the limits of the voice-grade telephone wire that once satisfied all communications requirements and have prompted network managers to search for strategic solutions to future network wiring requirements.

Among the factors affecting overall LAN performance—access methods, hardware interfaces, software protocols, and communications media—the communications media and its fundamental performance characteristics are the most difficult to change. Installing a building wiring system is an expensive and disruptive undertaking. Therefore, the selection of an effective, generic wiring system that has the ability to support current networking technologies as well as future, higher-performance networking requirements is a critical long-term, strategic decision.

Building wiring has a life span many times greater than the equipment it connects. Generations of communications controllers, phone sets, mainframe hardware, and software will come and go, but the wiring will remain. The communications media is the least changeable element of a communications network.

This chapter reviews the elements of a building wiring system and discusses in detail the pros and cons of the most commonly used wiring media. It concludes with a case study of a building wiring plan.

ELEMENTS OF A BUILDING WIRING SYSTEM

The office, horizontal, riser, and campus backbone wiring make up the building communications network. Exhibit I-3-1 is a diagram of these various wiring elements, which have the following characteristics:

- The office wiring connects any desktop terminal device (e.g., a phone, workstation, or facsimile transmitter) to the wall outlet—Typically, it consists of a wall-mounted modular jack and the line cord. The office

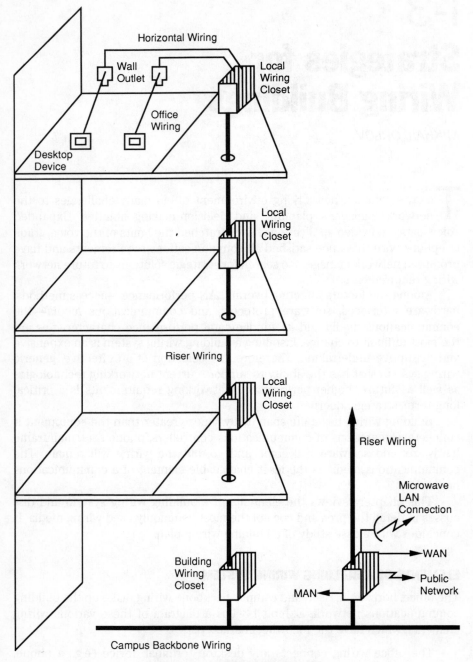

Horizontal Wiring

Wall Outlet

Local Wiring Closet

Office Wiring

Desktop Device

Local Wiring Closet

Riser Wiring

Local Wiring Closet

Riser Wiring

Microwave LAN Connection

WAN

Public Network

MAN

Building Wiring Closet

Campus Backbone Wiring

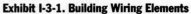

Exhibit I-3-1. Building Wiring Elements

wiring is the interface between the user's equipment and the building network.

- The horizontal wiring, which is sometimes called horizontal distribution, connects the office wiring to the local wiring closet (sometimes called the communications closet or riser closet)—The local wiring closet houses the wire termination equipment that provides the access for connecting riser and horizontal wiring.
- The riser wiring (sometimes called the building backbone or communications riser) connects the local wiring closets and the building wiring closet.
- The campus backbone wiring connects multiple building sites that cannot be spanned by a single LAN—A building wiring closet is the interface between the riser wiring, the interbuilding campus backbone wiring, and such off-campus networks as metropolitan area networks (MANs), wide area networks (WANs), and public networks.

In considering the building wiring for communications needs, planners should not ignore the fact that, as a rule, a building networking system is not a standalone system but a part of the campus network. Campus network environments include those that are used for educational, research, commercial, and military purposes.

The building wiring system is managed by an administration system that includes two main components: a labeling system and a tracking system. The labeling system consists of physical labels placed on jacks, equipment, and connectors to document moves and changes as they occur. The tracking system is a data base used to document the wire and equipment used in new installations, moves, and changes. Records produced by the administrative system assist in fault isolation and provide valuable information control for service and installation personnel.

WIRING MEDIA

Building wiring, which accounts for approximately 30% of the building networking system value, uses three types of transmission media. Twisted-pair copper wire is a common medium for office and horizontal distribution. Optical fiber is associated with riser and campus backbone wiring. Various types of coaxial cable can be used for all of the wiring elements.

Transmission characteristics—bandwidth, delay distortion, and signal-to-noise ratio—describe communications media performance. Bandwidth, which is the range of frequencies carried, is the most important transmission characteristic. When a digital signal (i.e., a square wave consisting of a sine wave of a fundamental frequency and numerous harmonics) passes through a cable of limited bandwidth, the high-frequency harmonics attenuate, rounding the wave and ultimately causing distorted transmission and possible errors.

The speed at which information travels is measured in bits per second (bps) and is called the data rate. The bandwidth and data rate are interrelated because the greater the bandwidth, the higher the maximum possible data rate. The data rate also depends on the length of a communications channel. The bandwidth of a medium, and hence its data rate, is often referred to as channel capacity.

Bandwidth-intensive applications (e.g., cooperative processing, distributed data bases, bit-oriented graphics, and full-motion video) require wiring systems capable of operating at high data rates.

Exhibit I-3-2 lists the characteristics of various communications media, including the total data rate supported, the bandwidth, and the repeater spacing for digital transmission.

Delay distortion has a profound effect on the data rate. It occurs when the digital signal's various frequency components arrive at the receiver at different times. The higher the data rate, the more critical the delay variation becomes. Delay distortion can cause signal components of one bit position to spill over to another, thereby creating transmission errors. The communications media should support uniform propagation of the digital signal's frequency components to minimize delay distortion.

Bit error rate (BER) is a measure of the communications channel's noise immunity. The bit error rate depends on the signal-to-noise ratio. The better the quality of a communications medium, the higher the signal-to-noise ratio and the lower the bit error rate. The higher the signal-to-noise ratio, the greater the distance a signal can be transmitted without degradation of the bit error rate.

Twisted-Pair Cable

Twisted-pair cable is the most pervasive communications medium. It is used for both conventional analog voice communications and digital data transmission. Examples of twisted-pair LANs include the 10BASE-T Ethernet on unshielded twisted-pair cable, the 4M-bps IEEE 802.5 token ring, the 16M-bps IBM Token Ring on both shielded and unshielded twisted-pair cable, the 256K-bps Apple-Talk, the 1M-bps 1BASE5 Ethernet, and the 2.5M-bps ARCnet.

Distortion, interference, and noise are network artifacts that cause alterations in signal shape; all are undesirable, and their effects must be considered when choosing a twisted-pair cable. Of all the communications media, twisted-

Medium	Total Data Rate	Bandwidth	Repeater Spacing
Twisted-Pair Cable	10M bps	500 kHz	100 m
Coaxial Cable	500M bps	550 MHz	1–10 km
Optical Fiber	2G bps	2 GHz	10–100 km

Exhibit I-3-2. Transmission Characteristics of Common Communications Media

pair cables are the least immune to noise. Reasonably good noise immunity can be achieved, however, if the twist length is significantly shorter than the wavelength. In balanced twisted-pair systems operating at frequencies below 100 kHz, noise immunity can be the same as with more reliable media (e.g., coaxial cable).

The conductor thickness of twisted-pair cable is measured according to the American Wire Gauge (AWG). Twisted-pair cable gauges for a typical office environment are 24 and 26 gauge; however, 22 and 28 gauge are also used.

Electrical Properties. Three electrical properties of twisted-pair cable determine the quality of the transmitted signal:

- Capacitance.
- Attenuation.
- Cross talk.

Whenever two conductive surfaces or wires are brought into close proximity and separated by a dielectric (i.e., any insulator, including air), a capacitor is formed. Capacitance is the measure of a capacitor's ability to store an electrical charge and its resistance to sudden changes in the magnitude, or voltage, of that charge. The two wires of a twisted pair form a capacitor; their capacitance is called mutual capacitance. It must be kept low to minimize loss of signal quality. Capacitance also exists between adjacent pairs within the same cable.

In high-frequency data communications applications (e.g., LANs), mutual capacitance distorts the square wave shape of the signal, causing errors in data transmission. The larger the capacitance, the higher the distortion and, consequently, the higher the potential error rate. Exhibit I-3-3 depicts the effect of mutual capacitance on digital signals.

Attenuation is the reduction in strength of a transmitted signal as it travels along the cable. A combination of capacitance, inductance, and resistive losses in the cable causes attenuation. Attenuation is directly proportional to frequency and is expressed in decibels (db) per unit of length of the conductor.

In voice communications, as attenuation increases, the volume at the

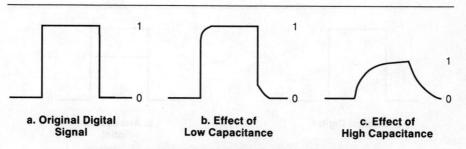

a. Original Digital Signal   b. Effect of Low Capacitance   c. Effect of High Capacitance

Exhibit I-3-3. The Effect of Mutual Capacitance on Digital Signals

receiver decreases until the signal can no longer be understood by a listener. Attenuation of a digital signal reduces the height, or voltage, of the square wave (see Exhibit I-3-4). If attenuation causes a signal to fall below a certain threshold, the receiver may fail to distinguish between on (represented by 1) and off (represented by 0) states, or it may confuse the signal with noise. Low attenuation is essential for high-quality, error-free data transmission, particularly over long lengths of twisted-pair cable.

Exhibit I-3-5 illustrates the combined effect of capacitance and attenuation on a digital signal. With high capacitance and large attenuation, a signal is produced in which the on and off states are almost indistinguishable, therefore causing error.

Cross talk is a type of noise on a wire pair; it reduces the signal-to-noise ratio, thereby interfering with signal reception. Its cause is interference between signals on adjacent wire pairs, and its severity usually increases as the space between wire pairs decreases. Cross talk can be reduced by careful arrangement of the twisted pairs within the cable, but it cannot be eliminated.

To prevent cross talk when providing high data rate services (e.g., T1, which transmits data at 1.544M bps) on conventional 24-gauge twisted-pair cable, the transmitting and receiving paths must be on separate cables. When different communications services (e.g., 10M-bps Ethernet and voice) coexist in the same bundle, the twisted-pair cable intended for these multiple services should meet pair-to-pair cross talk requirements. Ringing and dialing signals on telephone circuits should be prevented from interfering with the data transmission, and the high-frequency energy radiated by the data signals should be prevented from entering the voice network.

Jitter. Jitter is an inherent characteristic of the cable and other elements of the circuit. Excessive jitter makes it impossible to correctly extract the clock signal from transmitted data and causes errors in data reception. It can be measured in nanoseconds (ns) or as a percentage of the data transmitted. If the jitter, as a percentage of data transmitted, rises above a certain level, errors and subsequent retransmissions will cause the network to slow or fail.

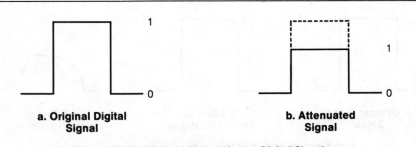

a. Original Digital Signal   **b. Attenuated Signal**

Exhibit I-3-4. The Effect of Attenuation on Digital Signals

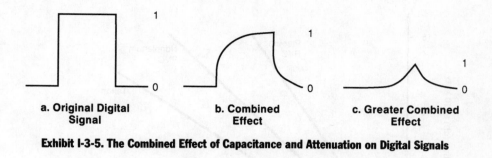

| a. Original Digital Signal | b. Combined Effect | c. Greater Combined Effect |

Exhibit I-3-5. The Combined Effect of Capacitance and Attenuation on Digital Signals

The main causes of jitter are insufficient bandwidth, amplitude and delay distortions, capacitance, and cross talk and other types of noise. Jitter on twisted-pair wiring is caused in particular by the attenuation of all the components along a transmission line (i.e., patch cables, termination panels, and cross-panel patch cords) and by the impedance mismatches between these components.

The higher the data rate, the more rigorous the limits on jitter. For example, the 1M-bps Starlan LAN (IEEE 802.3 1BASE5) specification allows a maximum jitter budget of 32 ns. The specification of the 10M-bps Ethernet (IEEE 802.3 10BASE5) allows a maximum jitter budget of 18 ns, of which 12.5 ns (or about 70% of the total jitter tolerated) results from the coaxial cable. The proposed specification for 10M-bps Ethernet on unshielded twisted-pair cable (IEEE 802.3 10BASE-T) limits the jitter budget to 11 ns.

Insulation Materials. The materials used to insulate twisted-pair cable directly affect cable performance as follows:

- Capacitance is directly related to the dielectric constant of the insulation and its thickness—The lower the dielectric constant and the thicker the insulation, the lower the capacitance. Lower capacitance allows higher data rates and longer transmission lines.
- Attenuation is directly proportional to the mutual capacitance and, therefore, to insulation—Exhibit I-3-6 shows, for 24-gauge wire transmitting a 10-MHz signal, the relationship between attenuation and transmission distance for different types of insulation. For example, a LAN with an allowable attenuation budget of 10 db that uses plenum-rated PVC-insulated cable has a maximum distance of about 85 m. A LAN using Teflon-insulated cable supports a maximum distance of 170 m. Sometimes, using a cable with higher-quality insulation solves a distance problem.
- Cross talk is essentially independent of the type of insulation used. As discussed previously, however, the signal-to-noise ratio can be improved by selecting an insulation that provides for low capacitance and low attenuation.

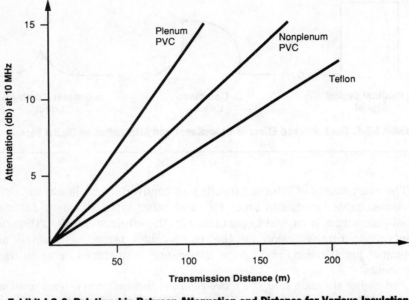

Exhibit I-3-6. Relationship Between Attenuation and Distance for Various Insulation Materials

- Jitter is heavily dependent on the type of insulation material used, as detailed in Exhibit I-3-7. At 10 MHz and 20 MHz, frequencies relevant to LANs, cables insulated with Teflon contributed least to jitter.

Insulation materials affect the relationship between data rates and transmission distance, as shown in Exhibit I-3-8. For example, at a 5% fixed jitter rate (which is a commonly used standard) and a transmission distance of 300 ft, the

	Jitter[2] (ns)		
Insulation[1]	**1.0 MHz**	**10 MHz**	**20 MHz**
Teflon	2.2	2.4	2.7
Nonplenum PVC	2.0	6.0	7.5
Plenum PVC	1.5	5.8	6.0

Notes:
[1] Insulation materials 6- to 7-mil wall on 24-AWG unshielded four twisted-pair cable.
[2] Jitter was measured on an average of three 100-m cable samples suspended in the air. An eye pattern measurement of pseudorandom Manchester-encoded signals was used.

Exhibit I-3-7. Comparison of Insulating Materials' Contribution to Jitter

maximum data rate to be supported for a plenum PVC–insulated cable is approximately 11M bps compared with 19M bps for a Teflon-insulated cable.

Special hardware can compensate for poorly insulated cable. For example, attenuation-induced jitter can be reduced by incorporating an equalizer. Equalizing techniques can also be used to offset delay distortion. Reliance on special hardware will, however, increase the cost of the building wiring system and decrease its design flexibility. Use of high-quality cable is preferred.

Optical Fiber

Optical fiber technologies are classified as single mode or multimode. Single-mode fibers have a small core (a diameter of 8 or 9 microns). Multimode fibers have a larger core (a diameter of 50 to 100 microns). The large core allows many modes of light propagation, hence the name multimode fibers. Bandwidth and attenuation of a single-mode fiber are both superior to that of multimode fiber. Exhibit I-3-9 shows the single-mode and multimode fibers.

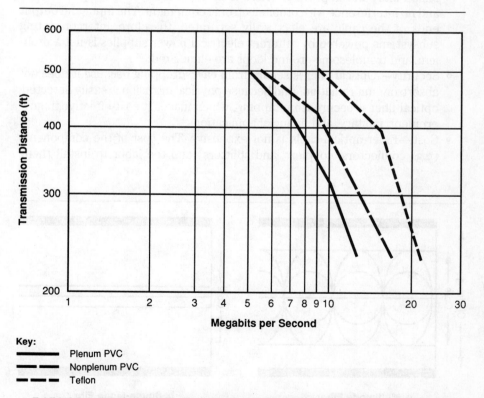

Key:

▬▬▬▬	Plenum PVC
▬ ▬ ▬	Nonplenum PVC
▬ ▬ ▬	Teflon

Exhibit I-3-8. Relationship Between Data Rates and Transmission Distance for Various Insulation Materials

Optical fiber is attractive for building wiring systems for the following reasons:

- Capacity—Optical fiber's vast bandwidth allows it to support data rates in the gigabit range, therefore meeting current building wiring requirements for nearly all users and providing spare bandwidth to accommodate future services. Multimode optical fiber can support transmission rates to 100M bps over distances of 2 km without a need for repeaters.
- Reliability—Optical fiber signal transmission is not affected by the electromagnetic interference and radio frequency interference (EMI/RFI) found in factories, hospitals, and areas close to airports. No shielding against EMI is needed. When properly jacketed, fiber-optic cables operate reliably in corrosive or otherwise harsh environments and over wide temperature ranges (e.g., under flammable conditions in which electrical codes and common sense prohibit the use of twisted-pair and coaxial cable). It can withstand temperatures of up to 1,000° C. Data reliability is very high. Bit error rates over optical fiber are on the order of 10^{-9} (i.e., one in every billion bits) and improving. There is no cross talk between optical fibers and no interference with other electronic equipment. The input and output ends of the cable are electrically separated; therefore, interconnecting subsystems powered by different electrical power supplies is not a problem, and troublesome ground loops are eliminated.
- Security—Optical fiber is secure from eavesdropping because it does not absorb or emit radiation. And because physical intrusion is easily detected, optical fiber is secure from tapping, which makes it cost-effective in government, military, and financial applications.
- Cost—Fiber-optic cable is not expensive. The cost of the components (e.g., connectors, couplers, and splitters) and the labor to install them,

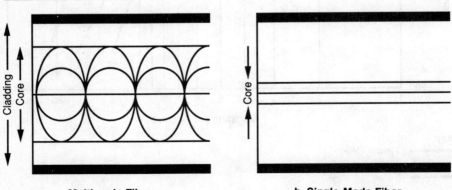

a. Multimode Fiber   b. Single-Mode Fiber

Exhibit I-3-9. Types of Optical Fiber

however, is relatively high. Optical fiber is cost-effective when its special properties (e.g., bandwidth and noise immunity) are critical to system design. Fiber-optic cables are also lightweight and easy to handle, and they make efficient use of installation space.

Applications. Optical fiber is well-suited for back-end LANs used in computer rooms to interconnect mainframes, mass storage devices, and high-speed printers. The key requirement in these applications is multimegabit file transfer capacity between devices. Only fiber-optic cable meets these criteria.

Another application for fiber-optic cable is the connection between LANs located in different parts of a building or across a campus. A campus backbone must sustain high loads and high-peak data rates. Even the traditional office environment, which once depended on low- to medium-speed devices, may now require data rates beyond those of conventional LANs. Such applications as color graphics, cooperative processing, full-motion video, sensing and imaging, and medical treatment and diagnostics require a higher capacity medium than coaxial cable.

Metropolitan area networks (MANs) able to carry both voice and data are becoming a reality. The MAN standards group (IEEE 802.6) is considering fiber-optic cable as the wiring medium.

Coaxial Cable

Coaxial cable is the dominant LAN medium within buildings and for campus backbones. Such advantages as wide bandwidth, immunity to external noise and cross talk, and predictable, controllable, and less frequency-dependent electrical characteristics have made coaxial cable the medium of choice. However, recent work with twisted-pair and fiber-optic cable, including the use of unshielded twisted-pair cable to transmit data off the backbone network at 10M bps (over a limited but acceptable distance of 100 m) and drastic cost reductions in fiber-optic backbones are reducing coaxial cable use in new LAN applications. Exhibit I-3-10 shows the actual and predicted use of all three media.

In building wiring systems, coaxial cable will gradually give way to twisted-pair cable as the main medium for office and horizontal wiring and to optical fiber as the basic component of riser wiring and the campus backbone.

LAN Medium	Late 1980s (Actual)	1995 (Projected)
Twisted-Pair Cable	42%	50%
Coaxial Cable	56%	27%
Optical Fiber	2%	23%

Exhibit I-3-10. Growth in the Use of Optical Fiber and Twisted-Pair Cable for LANs

Baseband and Broadband Systems. Coaxial cable is composed of an inner conductor of solid wire and an outer shielding conductor that is usually grounded. Between the two conductors is a dielectric material. For LAN applications, coaxial cable is usually classified as that used for baseband or broadband transmission. The use of the terms baseband and broadband to characterize coaxial cable is peculiar to the LAN industry; in signal theory, *baseband* refers to transmission in its original form, without modulation, and *broadband* refers to any channel with a bandwidth greater than a voice-graded channel (4 kHz). The primary distinction between the two types of cable is the impedance—for baseband it is 50 ohms, and for broadband it is 75 ohms.

As with the cable, there are several distinctions between baseband and broadband transmission systems. In baseband LANs, there is no signal modulation. Taps, often called transceivers, place digital signals encoded directly onto the cable using Manchester or Differential Manchester techniques. The signal occupies the entire bandwidth of the cable; therefore, only one channel is in operation at any time. The usual maximum data rate is 10M bps, though there are exceptions.

In broadband systems, the signals are first modulated onto a carrier and then impressed on the cable using a radio-frequency (RF) modem. Multiple carriers can be supported in a frequency-division multiplexed fashion. The forward and reverse channels can be carried on the same or different cables.

Broadband LANs offer greater bandwidth than baseband LANs because each cable has multiple channels. A 300-MHz midsplit system can support bandwidths of 110 MHz to 120 MHz in each direction and can achieve data rates of up to 5M bps for each 6-MHz subchannel (6-MHz channels are a standard taken from the cable television industry). Six to eight 6-MHz channels are used by most LANs to provide aggregate data rates of 30M bps to 40M bps. One notable exception is Applitek Corp's UniLINK, which can achieve aggregate data rates of up to 200M bps. Its tremendous bandwidth makes it a valuable backbone component.

A broadband LAN can support thousands of connections, but it must be balanced to compensate for the insertion loss (i.e., loss of signal strength) across such passive components as taps, splitters, or couplers and for cable attenuation loss. Amplifiers are usually placed at 0.5- to 1.5-km intervals to regenerate the signals. The actual practical distance for most broadband LANs is 55 to 60 km.

Baseband LANs can support 100 devices on a single cable segment; however, the maximum number of devices per segment is based on a proprietary system specification or even on a standard. Broadband LANs are more flexible, with the number of devices on a segment determined more by the designer's decisions about use of amplifiers and repeaters. Like broadband systems, baseband systems suffer insertion loss. A repeater compensates for signal degradation; the maximum number of repeaters is five. The number of interconnected devices can be a few hundred, but the total is limited by practical considerations (e.g., access).

Coaxial cable provides superior noise immunity over standard twisted-pair cable. Its noise immunity is affected by the application and the environment. Baseband systems usually provide immunity of 50 to 60 db; broadband systems operate with noise immunity of 85 to 100 db.

The security issues for broadband and baseband are similar to those for twisted-pair cables, but coaxial cable is easier to tap outside the wiring closet than is twisted-pair cable. Coaxial cable does not emit as high an amplitude signal as twisted-pair cable, so intercepting the signal is more difficult.

COST OF INSTALLING WIRING SYSTEMS

The actual bare wire cost accounts for approximately 30% of the total building wiring system's cost. Of this cost, horizontal distribution constitutes one third.

Building wiring can be installed using two basic methods. It can be installed in space above the ceiling (in the plenum), or it can be installed in conduit or troughs under the floor. Network planners usually prefer to install wiring in the plenum to avoid the additional cost of conduit and because the space provided by floor troughs is limited. The National Electrical Code (NEC), however, states that unless cables installed in plenum space meet fire-resistance and low smoke-production requirements, they must be enclosed in metal conduit.

In particular, twisted-pair cable made with PVC must be installed in conduit. PVC is not classified as fire-resistant, low-smoke insulation. Among the low-smoke, low-flame cables, those insulated with Teflon have one significant advantage: they provide superior electrical performance for all communications services. Exhibits I-3-11 and I-3-12 list nonelectrical properties of various insulation materials.

Twisted-Pair Cable Considerations

Inexpensive twisted-pair cable is available but must be used with conduit. Low-smoke, low-flame types are more expensive but can be installed in the plenum without conduit. Bare cable costs are deceptive, however, because the cable is a very small part of the entire installation. After the costs of conduit, conduit connectors, couplings, and straps are added to the cost of the conduit-type cable, its cost is double that of the plenum cable.

Coaxial Cable Considerations

The installation cost of coaxial cable exceeds that of conventional twisted-pair cable. Baseband coaxial cable is usually less expensive than broadband, and the cable called thin baseband cable (a type of 50-ohm baseband cable) is less expensive than multiple-shield ⅜-in standard Ethernet cable. In all cases,

Property	Insulation	
	PVC	Teflon
Oxidation Resistance	E	O
Heat Resistance	G-E	O
Flame Resistance	E	O
Low-Temperature Flexibility	P-G	O
Abrasion Resistance	F-G	E
Water Resistance	E	E

Notes:
O   Outstanding
E   Excellent
G   Good
F   Fair
P   Poor

Exhibit I-3-11. Comparison of Selected Insulation Materials

---

however, the hardware required for installation and the installation itself are the significant cost components.

In general, broadband systems are more complex to install, certify, and maintain than are baseband systems. Preventive maintenance involves periodic testing and alignment of LAN parameters (e.g., the signal volume at wall outlets, various signal-to-noise ratios, and the signal volume at amplifiers). In addition, building code restrictions may affect the labor costs for installing coaxial cable. For example, conduit may be necessary, floor troughs may need to be modified, or dry-wall partitions may be required for taps, splitters, or transceivers.

Fiber-Optic Cable Considerations

Installing fiber-optic cable differs little from installing copper wire or coaxial cable. Like other types of cable, fiber-optic cable allows the use of various methods of cable distribution, including cellular and duct raceways and conduit systems. There are, however, advantages to fiber-optic cable installation:

- There is no danger of electrical short circuits between conductors.
- Fiber-optic cable can withstand hot and cold temperature extremes.
- Building codes are easily satisfied.
- Fiber-optic cable is thin and lightweight, so it can be installed in existing

---

Insulation Material	Normal Low	Normal High	Special Low	Special High
PVC	− 20° C	80° C	− 55° C	105° C
Teflon	− 70° C	200° C	N/A	260° C

Exhibit I-3-12. Nominal Temperature Range of Insulations

conduits or in other cable runs—A 10-fiber cable has a diameter of less than ⅜ in and generally can fit into crowded conduits.
- Fiber-optic cable neither produces nor is affected by cross talk, so it can be installed alongside any other cable.
- When installed above ground between buildings, fiber-optic cable is not susceptible to lightning, airport radar, or any other source of noise, nor is it affected by water.

Single-mode fiber is more subject to signal loss at splices or cable taps and connections than is multimode fiber. Therefore, multimode fiber is recommended if there is no immediate demand for gigabit data rates. If single-mode fiber capacity becomes necessary, the addition of the new cable should not pose installation problems.

The network manager who installs optical fiber must analyze many cost and performance trade-offs. For example, the network manager must determine the power budget (to ensure that the proper signal level is maintained throughout the system), decide on the interconnection method (e.g., tapping versus splicing, or fusion versus elastomeric), choose an installer, and control the quality of installation (e.g., ensure that the bending radius, physical alignment of fibers, and insertion loss are acceptable).

Evaluating the cost of a fiber-optic cable installation is complex. Although the cable itself is not expensive, the line components and the labor required to install them are costly. For example, a typical contractor's rate for making a fiber-optic connection is $75 to $90 an hour. Fiber-optic cable may cost as much as $8 per foot of wire, whereas twisted-pair cable might cost only $2 a foot.

The superior performance of optical fiber can make it a cost-effective choice for current and future communications needs. Its ability to handle a high volume of traffic, its noise resistance, and its small size and flexibility all provide near-term benefits as well as the capacity for future growth without costly media replacement.

CASE STUDY

Boston University's Information Technology Network and Systems Engineering Group and its Office of Telecommunication have developed a cable distribution plan to suit the near- and long-term needs of the university. The plan objectives include the following:

- To establish minimum requirements for voice and data communications in new construction and renovation projects.
- To streamline the planning and construction processes for voice and data wiring.
- To provide guidelines for space planners, architects, and contractors.
- To maximize the life cycle of wiring for new and renovated buildings.

A description of some aspects of this cable distribution plan follows.

Networking Services and Requirements

Communications services required by building tenants include:

- Telephone service from the local exchange carrier or telephone company.
- A broadband cable television connection for data and video.
- A local area network connection for high-speed internetwork transport.
- Fire alarm, security, and environmental controls.

Telephone service is provided by the telephone company over twisted-pair cable trunks; in the future, however, service might be brought in on telephone company optical fiber, demultiplexed, and distributed within buildings over twisted-pair cable.

Broadband cable television service is distributed over a single coaxial trunk cable with a spare redundant cable. Broadband service on the main campus includes two data bus channels (one for the campus terminal network and one for Ethernet), point-to-point links, and several video channels.

Fire alarm, security, and environmental controls use telephone company twisted-pair cable. The main campus has a fiber-optic, high-speed, token-ring data network that supports data transport between Ethernet building networks.

Many buildings on the main campus have access to one or both campus backbone networks. The service area of these backbone networks is expanding and will eventually reach all locations within the main campus.

The fiber-optic ring backbone is a high-speed network that transports data at eight times the raw signaling speed of the intrabuilding Ethernet networks. The fiber-optic network currently supports Ethernet but is adaptable to future data and voice communications technology.

Main campus telephone service is Centrex provided by New England Telephone; it is distributed directly to every building on campus over twisted-pair trunks. These trunks terminate in interconnection panels located in the building closet and riser system and are cross-patched directly to the telephone riser or an electronic key system, which is then connected to the telephone riser. Centrex requires one pair (for tip and ring signals) for each circuit.

Two types of electronic key systems have been installed to date—DataStar and Merlin. Other electronic key or PBX equipment will be installed in the future as the university's plans for telephone service develop and as new technology is introduced.

Building Cabling

Unshielded twisted-pair cabling is the primary cabling service throughout the university buildings. Installation is in a star configuration, radiating from the local wiring closet to the individual station wall outlets. Unshielded twisted-pair distribution does not preclude other cabling distributions. Ethernet is usually required in science and engineering buildings and is being used in many other buildings for networked workstations.

Access Points. Telephone company twisted-pair trunks and the campus backbone network coaxial cable and fiber-optic trunks typically enter a building at a single point. Trunk lines running between buildings are installed in a buried conduit system with necessary access vaults.

Suitable space for a 60-by-36-by-18-in heavy gauge metal cabinet is provided at the backbone network service access point. Optical-fiber and broadband are terminated at the building entrance, protecting these services from damage that might be caused by activity within the building. Conduits continue from this access point cabinet to the closet and riser system entrance. Conduits, which are grounded at the access service point to the termination cabinet, have the following characteristics:

- They are made of galvanized metal with a diameter of at least 4 in and a minimum bend radius of 12 in.
- A minimum of four conduits are required to provide building service—One is reserved for telephone cable service, one is reserved for broadband and fiber-optic service, and two are reserved for future use.

Local Wiring Closets. The university's network closets are combined riser and equipment closets and accommodate interconnection panels and rack- or wall-mounted electronic equipment. Trunk distribution enters the closet and riser system through the building wiring closet (typically in a basement), and passes through the riser system to network closets on floors above.

Closets are adjacent to the main hallway and are vertically aligned on each floor to simplify the riser system. Vertically aligned closets require only sleeves through the floor and ceiling, which must be appropriately fire-stopped.

Communications cabling is kept separate from electrical cabling for safety and performance reasons. Closets are not located within 10 ft of high-voltage power distribution without appropriate shielding.

Riser System Cabling. The university's riser cabling requires five 4-in sleeves. Fire-stopping for the sleeves is critical. After the cable is installed, the sleeves are fire-stopped with a removable, properly rated substance. Typically, grounding is provided through the riser system for the closet's grounding panels and equipment.

Interconnection Panels. Unshielded twisted-pair interconnection panels provide cross-patching between station distribution cabling and riser cabling and between station distribution and communications equipment for both voice and data. The university's unshielded twisted-pair interconnection panels are AT&T spec 110 high-density panels. Circuits are four-pair. The punch-down sequence and color codes are in accordance with AT&T's Premises Distribution System. Cross-patching uses 110 patch cords. Station distribution panels are field terminated, and riser distribution panels are connected with the telephone company's 50-pin connectors.

The university's typical interconnection panel is laid out as follows. The station distribution cabling is in the center of the closet wall and is flanked on the left side by the telephone riser interconnection and on the right side by the data communications equipment interconnection.

Panels for services other than unshielded twisted-pair (e.g., thin Ethernet) are designed on a case-by-case basis. Thin Ethernet, however, requires substantial wall space on the auxiliary interconnection panel area; therefore, space should be reserved for any future Ethernet installations.

Station Cabling. Each station wall outlet consists of a standard twisted-pair station outlet, an optional thin Ethernet station outlet, and an empty spare outlet. Empty gang boxes are used when future expansion will be required. If installed as part of the construction or renovation project, double gang boxes with pull strings save effort and expense when the cable is installed through finished walls and ceilings.

Individual cables leave the closet at exit sleeves above the door and follow common hallway routings to the point where the station circuits branch off to wall outlet locations. Sleeve placement in fire walls must be provided to gain access to all rooms and must be properly fire-stopped after cable installation. Cable bundles are tie-wrapped and secured to the building structure at least 3 in above the suspended ceiling using J straps spaced 5 ft apart.

The university has had difficulty distributing cabling in partitioned areas. Many partitions are not designed to accept standard-sized outlet boxes for cable termination. Typically, patch cords have been run through partition channels from wall-mounted outlet boxes. If partitions are not attached to the wall, cabling must be introduced through utility poles from above ceiling drops.

Floor Distribution Capacity. Each closet can handle the communications requirements of 10,000 sq ft of usable floor space. Floors with more than 10,000 sq ft allow for a second network closet. One station wall outlet is provided for every room or office of less than 200 sq ft, with a minimum of two station outlets for each room larger than 200 sq ft. Spare outlet empty gang-boxes are installed at the same density as the active station outlets.

Documentation and Maintenance. The Information Technology Network and Systems Engineering Group receives floor plans for final approval and for checking conformance to plan during wiring installation. Copies of the floor plans are provided to contractors with final markups for station outlet locations. The installation contractor then delivers an as-built drawing to the group on completion of cable installation and certification.

Building wiring installed according to approved floor plans will be maintained by the group. Those buildings not conforming to the group's specifications and not approved by the group before construction may not be eligible for maintenance service.

Floor plans for any new university building must be reviewed by the group. The group will also review communications requirements with the building's proposed tenants. When detailed plans are complete, the wiring is ready to be submitted for bid by qualified subcontractors.

Oversight

The group oversees wiring installation, handles contractor questions, and determines conformance to standards and to the plan. Contractors are required to guarantee their installation for one year and to repair defects reported by the group. Furthermore, the group has the authority to visit the job site during work in progress and to accept or reject installation of closets and wiring.

ACTION PLAN

The Building Industry Consulting Service International (BICSI) publishes a Telecommunications Distribution Methods Manual. BICSI, which is an organization of communications service planners primarily from the communications industry, provides services to the construction industry for communications wiring. Its manual, though brief and somewhat limited in scope, is a helpful reference for the development of a building wiring system.

As a rule, network managers who do not follow a single, vendor-based standard but use the best of the standards appropriate for satisfying users' particular needs will have the greatest success in creating a cost-effective, uniform wiring plan.

Section II
Needs Assessment, Selection, and Implementation

Once it has been determined that LAN technology is appropriate for the organization, the data communications manager must begin the formidable task of translating the idea into equipment, software, and services. A conceptual system design is needed. After it is established, an assessment of alternatives can take place. Such an assessment should consider technical, strategic, and cost implications. When it is completed, the results of the assessment must be clearly communicated to senior management. Finally, the data communications manager, when given the approval to proceed, must plan for and carry out the actual implementation.

Section II provides guidance for this stage in the life cycle of a LAN. Chapter II-1, "Needs Assessment in Data Communications Networking," presents a methodology for developing the conceptual system design from a strategic perspective. Such a perspective allows the design to take shape unencumbered by current technological limitations, costs, or operational issues. The chapter also presents an overview of several LAN-related technologies as they pertain to networking in general.

Chapter II-2, "Assessing LAN Technologies," provides a closer look at LAN technologies themselves, including some useful insight into the pros and cons of each. The technologies considered include those pertaining to media and cable plants, topologies, LAN software, standards, and interconnections. Requirements and risks are then presented in a discussion of LAN selection criteria.

Chapter II-3, "Planning for a LAN Implementation," focuses on the issues associated with planning the actual LAN installation. Meeting the users' communications needs requires much more than a mere assessment of technologies and standards followed by equipment and media selection. Coordination of the personnel involved is a critical element. Selection of a network coordinator ensures that user needs can be identified and incorporated into the planning process. Once identified, these needs contribute significantly to the selection of the appropriate media. Furthermore, to ensure success, the media installation and certification must be carefully planned and closely supervised. Finally, it is important to provide for long-term maintenance after installation.

More often than not, decisions regarding communications technology in general and LANs in particular can be reduced to a set of cost figures and a score representing such nonmonetary issues as strategies and technology-related matters. Not surprisingly, the alternative with the best nonmonetary score rarely represents the lowest-cost alternative. That leaves the data communications manager with the unenviable tasks of having to choose between cost and technology and then relating that decision to senior management. Chapter II-4, "A Decision Support System for Evaluating Investments in Local Area Networks," describes an innovative software package that can help managers resolve this kind of conflict. This system helped a manufacturer in the Midwest justify the added expense of a technically superior solution related to its manufacturing LAN system requirements.

Chapter II-5, "Building an Integrated Local Area Network Environment: A Case Study," takes a somewhat different approach. This chapter details the decision-making process and the cost factors associated with developing a LAN for a company with a diverse set of communications requirements.

Finally, Chapter II-6, "Design of an 802.3 Ethernet Network," discusses the factors that went into the LAN expansion at Vanderbilt University's School of Engineering. The chapter also discusses matters of practical importance regarding several LAN-related components.

II-1
Needs Assessment in Data Communications Networking

JOHN P. SLONE

During the 1980s, dramatic changes in the communications world took place. During the first half of the decade, the breakup of the century-old Bell System, accompanied by the Federal Communications Commission's (FCC's) philosophical shift from regulation to deregulation to no regulation, was among the most significant. Subsequently, new companies emerged, providing not only a plethora of communications products (e.g., modems and multiplexers) but communications services (e.g., value-added networks [VANs], very-small-aperture terminal [VSAT] satellite transmission systems, and transnational fiber-optic networks) as well.

During the second half of the decade, there was a fundamental shift in focus. As basic technologies matured and the postdivestiture environment stabilized, users of communications technologies shifted their attention to strategic issues. Wideband nationwide networks became popular, the use of LANs became commonplace, and decades-old communications architectures had to be reviewed, frequently undergoing dramatic changes.

These changes have created much opportunity, and sophisticated users of data communications services have had ample opportunity to restructure their networks for cost efficiency, service improvement, or access to new markets. Not surprisingly, however, many users have been left behind, feeling confused, bewildered by conflicting claims, and deprived of control.

This chapter addresses the needs and concerns of all but the most sophisticated users. It describes how to assess the needs of new or existing data communications applications from a strategic perspective and translate them into a functional, cost-effective, and adaptable design for the 1990s.

DATA COMMUNICATIONS NETWORK PLANNING STEPS

Data communications network planning is grouped into four stages: requirements definition, strategic planning, network design, and implementation. The following are suggested steps for each of these stages:

- Requirements definition consists of the following activities:
  —Assessing existing network resources.

   —Defining existing communications requirements.
   —Defining known future requirements.
 • During strategic planning, the following tasks must be performed:
   —Defining the ideal network, disregarding cost or technical requirements.
   —Performing a gap analysis to highlight differences between the existing and ideal networks.
   —Surveying available data communications technology in terms of generic solutions.
   —Performing a preliminary analysis of possible generic solutions and their approximate costs.
 • Network design comprises the following steps:
   —Specifying communications requirements and proposed alternatives.
   —Developing requests for proposals for specific hardware, software, and transmission components.
   —Evaluating vendor responses by technical merits.
   —Evaluating the best technical solutions on the basis of financial considerations.
   —Making final selections and negotiating terms.
 • During implementation, the following tasks are performed:
   —Developing a phased installation plan beginning with limited pilot installations for testing and acceptance.
   —Graduating to large-scale migration on acceptance.
   —Fine-tuning the installation during and after migration.

The first three stages are discussed in depth in the following sections.

CONSIDERATIONS IN THE REQUIREMENTS DEFINITION PROCESS

Any reliable network design begins with a thorough understanding of the requirements, which is best gained by assessing and documenting existing network resources and requirements. Known future requirements (e.g., new applications that have been approved but not implemented) should be included as well. The following sections highlight the major factors to be considered in this stage.

Compiling Profiles

The following profiles are helpful in defining network requirements:

 • User—Compiled by job category.
 • Use—Compiled by determining online available hours, typical use fluctuations, and priorities.
 • Geographic—Compiled by determining geographical distribution and density by user communities.
 • Applications—Compiled by determining the application's importance to the organization, revenue impact, and response time requirements.

- Hardware—Compiled by determining types of devices and their locations.

User Profile. This profile documents both actual and potential system users by job category. An example of such users and their impact on the network may include the following information:

- Executive—Extremely light use, light traffic, stringent response time expected but not always essential.
- Management—Occasional use, moderate traffic, moderate response times, often heavy electronic mail use.
- Knowledge workers—Frequent use, moderate to heavy traffic, moderate response times, frequent bursty traffic (e.g., image or file transfer).
- Engineers—Very frequent use, light to moderate input, heavy output, productivity closely tied to response time.
- Clerical—Very frequent use, heavy input and output, productivity dependent on response time.
- Administrative—Moderate to occasional use, light to moderate traffic, response time not critical.

Use Profile. The use profile documents such factors as online availability requirements and typical peak loading times. For typical businesses, peak use periods occur during regular business hours and near the end of each month. For colleges and universities, peaks occur at such specific events as registration, midterm, and end of term. Regardless of the nature of the network, however, as a network grows in size and diversity of users, the statistical nature of large numbers tends to flatten out the peaks and valleys, yielding a more predictable and stable use base.

Geographic Profile. Geographic distribution, concentration, and density have significant effects on network design. For example, a business that clusters most users in a single building or campus environment is likely to rely heavily on private facilities (e.g., LANs and PBXs). A business that clusters users in a limited number of buildings in a metropolitan area is a prime candidate for a public or private metropolitan area network.

Beyond the local or metropolitan environments, geography and traffic flow jointly determine the possible solutions. Businesses with concentrations of manufacturing and engineering locations are likely candidates for wideband facilities (e.g., T1 and higher), with network concentration at certain key locations. On the other hand, businesses with widely scattered users (e.g., banks, retail stores, restaurants, or hotel chains) are more likely to benefit from using VANs or VSAT services. Finally, other users may be best served by such traditional networking techniques as dial-up communications or dedicated point-to-point or multipoint circuits. The geographic profile highlights factors most likely to influence such network decisions.

Applications Profile. To design an effective communications network, it is essential to understand how important the application is to the user organization. For example, it costs an airline or brokerage firm thousands of dollars in lost revenue if its network goes down, even for a few minutes. A university, on the other hand, would be inconvenienced but would suffer little if any permanent damage.

Response time variations also have distinct effects on different organizations. For example, slow response in an automatic teller machine would hardly be noticed by banking customers. A similar slowdown in a chemical plant's process control network, however, might contribute to a catastrophic environmental disaster if a message to close a critical valve were delayed by even a few seconds.

Recently, new applications significantly affecting network design have begun to emerge. In particular, infrequent but high-bandwidth tasks (e.g., image processing and file transfers) enable the shared use of a high-bandwidth service. Multimedia applications (e.g., voice and text, data and video) make varying bandwidth demands; moreover, they require a system that will assign priorities because the different information signals have varying time sensitivities. The design of a network to meet requirements of these types is radically different from network design in a traditional terminal-to-host environment.

Hardware Profile. Although the hardware profile is still an important consideration in network design, it is less of a concern than it was a few years ago. Most network services can accommodate various types of hardware, software, and protocols. The factors to consider are those affecting the total traffic load at any given time. For example, interactive terminals with low data volumes place little demand on the network. At the other extreme, engineering workstations, page printers, and host-to-host connections place heavy demands on the network.

Traffic Flow

Estimating traffic flow can be useful if certain underlying assumptions are kept in mind. Generally, terminal users can estimate the number and frequency of transactions and the length of each transaction to and from the workstation. Estimating printed reports and intermachine file transfers is also important. Perhaps the most difficult traffic to estimate accurately is the sporadic traffic associated with file transfers and image processing, especially between peer workstations. To calculate such traffic, which generally comes in bursts, the communications manager should first make reasonable estimates of the number of files—documents, spreadsheets, and engineering drawings—that will be transmitted by a typical user during a typical day. Then the typical sizes for these files should be estimated. The typical number of files is then multiplied by the typical size; the product is multiplied by the size of the user community to yield a realistic traffic pattern.

When overhead (e.g., protocol overhead and network management information) is added to this network, a picture of the total traffic flow over the network emerges. Figures should then be adjusted to show the peak traffic volume on the basis of time of day and seasonal adjustments. Finally, a considerable margin should be added for growth, especially for ad hoc traffic.

For smaller networks, total traffic and estimated response times can be calculated manually. Larger networks, however, require modeling packages. Such factors as line speed, number of terminals per controller, and number of drops on a circuit can significantly affect response time and user satisfaction.

Communications Other Than Data

Traditionally, most organizations have kept data communications segregated from other types of communications (e.g., voice and video). Recent technological changes have made this distinction less logical. To understand the overall picture, it is appropriate to assess other communications needs along with the need to communicate data.

Voice, in particular, is an important concern. In most organizations, the majority of communications expenditures are still for voice, which consumes most of the bandwidth. Generally, data is the fastest-growing element of any network and requires more complicated design and management techniques. Current growth trends indicate that, for most organizations, expenditures and bandwidth requirements for data will soon exceed those for voice (see Exhibit II-1-1). It is important to plan now for merging the two technologies when appropriate.

Relatively few organizations now employ any type of video technology, but their number is growing. Simply because of its high bandwidth requirements, video is also an important consideration. Whenever facilities are installed to support video, both voice and data can usually be added at a low additional cost.

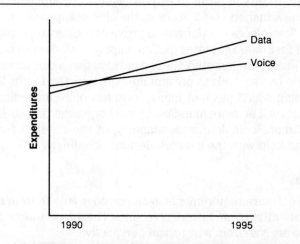

Exhibit II-1-1. Current Growth Trends of Voice and Data

For example, if a company installs a closed-circuit television system for security reasons, such a system probably uses coaxial cable. This same cable can be developed into a fully featured broadband LAN.

THE STRATEGIC PLANNING PERSPECTIVE

Many of the problems apparent in data communications networks today are the result of shortsighted planning (e.g., planners considered current needs, added a percentage for growth, and then reacted to changes when necessary). When networks evolve in this manner (which is not uncommon), capacity problems, redundancy, and network management issues can choke the network within a few years. Such problems can be avoided through strategic planning.

Although strategic planning received a lot of press coverage during the 1980s, it is still not well understood. Often missing in strategic planning endeavors is the proper perspective—a critical element. Strategic planning should not become bogged down in discussions of growth, cost, organizational issues, and technical feasibility. Instead, it should be undertaken from the perspective of designing a network from scratch, as opposed to adjusting the current network to fit future needs. This perspective allows a company to develop a vision and to find a means to accomplish it. Past planning efforts have primarily worked in reverse, centering on the means, with no ultimate destination.

The Value of Information

During the strategic planning stage, an organization should assess the value of its own information in general and the relative value of different types of information. Such an analysis can provide protection in the event of a system failure, for example, by determining whether certain networking elements should be given priority in terms of responsiveness or redundancy.

An extreme situation could occur at the chemical processing plant mentioned earlier. Two pieces of information arrive at the central computer simultaneously. The first message states that an employee worked an hour overtime and should be justly compensated; the second says that a certain valve needs to be closed within two seconds to prevent an explosion. Obviously, there is little doubt concerning which piece of information has more immediate value. Although examples will be more mundane in most organizations, such an analysis can lead to a more complete understanding of the nature of a company's information and help with the network design accordingly.

Future Growth

An estimation of future requirements must consider growth from the strategic perspective rather than from historical records. The information industry is still too dynamic to analyze from a historical perspective.

For example, a plan developed a decade ago on the basis of historical records could not have accounted for the explosive growth of microcomputers. Developed strategically, however, the plan might have addressed the need to process large amounts of information in a custom-tailored application at the desk and the subsequent need to exchange composite, processed information with peers. This may well have resembled today's microcomputer LAN environment. Therefore, it is important for organizations to consider the future without being encumbered by existing technology.

The Need for an Architecture

The final stage of strategic network planning is the development of an architecture. Without one, the network grows without direction. An architecture provides the framework for future networking decisions and allows growth and change in one network segment without adversely affecting others.

As shown in Exhibit II-1-2, the sample architecture divides the network roughly along geographic boundaries. The wide area network (WAN) is located in the center, surrounded by several metropolitan, campus, and local networks. The local networks can be connected either directly to the WAN or, if appropriate, through a metropolitan or regional network. The end users and applications are shown around the perimeter.

There is no standard framework for defining an architecture, and there is also no right or wrong architecture. The worst mistake is to have no architecture at all.

NETWORK DESIGN

Networks generally have specific characteristics of user concentration or distribution that lend themselves to certain networking alternatives. For example, large communities of users in a small area lend themselves to various local area networking techniques. Large communities located in or near major sites tend to be well served by a hub-and-star arrangement. Small offices scattered throughout a region of the country (e.g., the mid-Atlantic or New England states) may be best served by multidropping. Widely scattered, small offices (e.g., banks or hotel chains) are ideally suited to the VSAT approach. The following sections discuss several alternatives and how to compare them.

Networking Alternatives

Traditionally, users have had few network alternatives. A few vendors offered a choice between dedicated and switched (dial-up) services, with a handful of pricing schemes and little to differentiate among services. The current networking market, however, is vastly different and still evolving. New service vendors are entering the market, and those already in existence are offering more options. Users can choose from a variety of digital and analog services; terrestrial or satellite transmission; fiber, copper, or radio technology; and

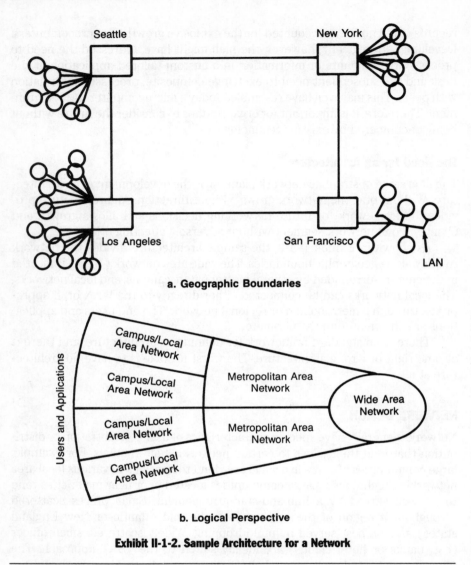

a. Geographic Boundaries

b. Logical Perspective

Exhibit II-1-2. Sample Architecture for a Network

dedicated, circuit-switched, or packet-switched approaches. Prices can be distance-, volume-, speed-, or time-sensitive or can reflect a combination of these factors. In addition, users can select from various levels of quality on the basis of individual requirements.

Networking Techniques

Many traditional networking techniques—specifically multidropping, multiplexing, and concentration—use dedicated leased lines to realize certain economies of scale. Each is described further in the following sections.

Multidropping. This networking technique connects a small number of locations on bridged data lines (see Exhibit II-1-3), with each station or controller on the line polled for traffic. Disadvantages of multidropping include:

- Line turnaround and protocol polling severely limit the amount of traffic and number of stations that can share a line.
- The bridged data link is often difficult to troubleshoot and maintain.
- One defective station can affect the entire line, totally preventing communications on the line.

Multiplexing. Multiplexing provides line sharing for parallel circuit requirements. For moderate-sized networks, it offers economies of scale through the use of regional hubs, such as the network shown in Exhibit II-1-4.

Multiplexing is convenient because multiplexer hardware is relatively transparent to the network. Statistical time-division multiplexing is particularly effective because it dynamically allocates bandwidth according to need. Most multiplexers have sophisticated diagnostic and control capabilities, and many provide forward error correction on the line.

Nevertheless, multiplexing has some inherent limitations. For example, in a statistical time-division multiplexing environment, buffering can introduce delays that dramatically alter traffic response patterns. In particular, a polled network (e.g., a binary synchronous 3270-type network) is especially vulnerable to such delays.

Concentration. Concentration is similar to large-scale, sophisticated multiplexing (see Exhibit II-1-5). Typical remote concentrators include IBM 37XXs and similar devices from other companies (e.g., NCR Comten and Amdahl). Concentrators are comparably priced to front-end processors and very large multiplexers. They generally accommodate multiple protocols, use moderate-speed trunks (e.g., 56K bps), have highly efficient compression algorithms, and provide remote polling of stations.

In addition to these three traditional techniques, several newer networking techniques are now available.

VSATs. One of the newer networking techniques is VSAT (see Exhibit II-1-6). In a typical VSAT network, a host computer is connected to a master earth station. The master station transmits signals to a satellite, which relays them to several very small, inexpensive earth stations at the user sites.

VSAT is a radical departure from traditional networking techniques in several ways. For example, VSAT is especially well suited to unbalanced communications applications that require more data to be sent to terminals than are received from them. In addition, VSAT does not provide the high-speed transmission that is traditionally associated with satellites. Typical VSAT systems currently transmit at maximum speeds of 56K bps. Finally, VSATs provide highly economical, distance-insensitive communications to remote locations that previously could not be reached because relatively low-volume transmission requirements made it economically infeasible.

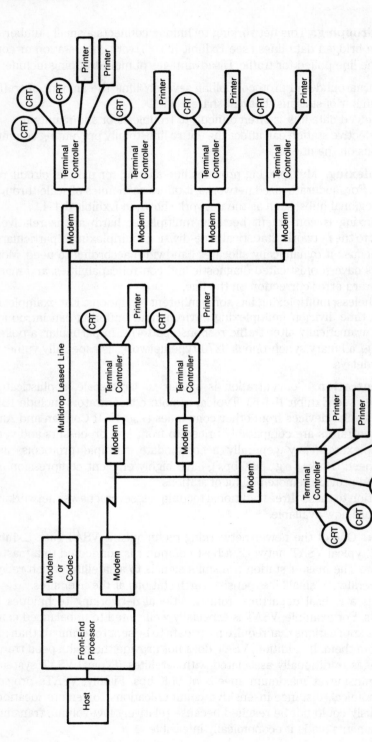

Exhibit II-1-3. Multidrop Leased-Line Configuration

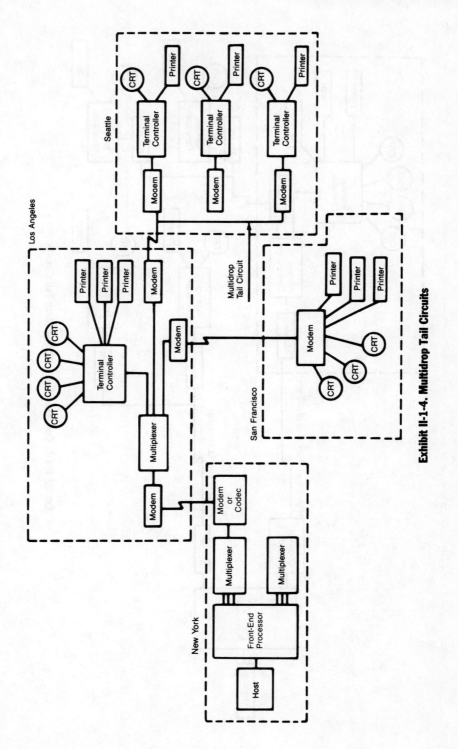

Exhibit II-1-4. Multidrop Tail Circuits

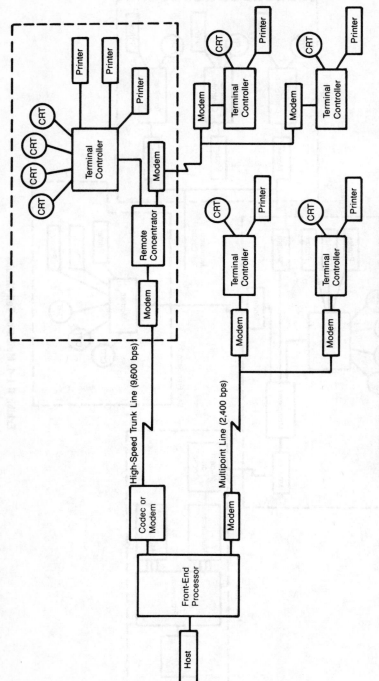

Exhibit II-1-5. Concentration with Multidrop Tail Circuits

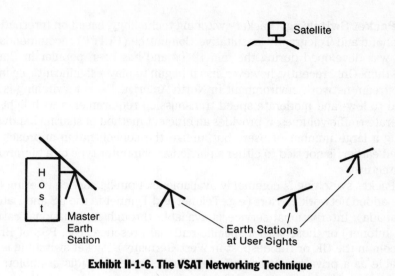

Exhibit II-1-6. The VSAT Networking Technique

Channel Extension. Another nontraditional networking technique that has found a market is channel extension. It is also a radical departure from traditional networking in that the front end (which was originally developed to off-load the communications responsibility from the host) is bypassed entirely. Channel connection is usually restricted to a distance of 200 ft—that is, in or very close to the computer room. Channel extension provides the means to overcome that limitation.

By using channel extenders, users can conceivably have a locally attached printer running at optimum speed across the country. Pricing for channel extension is extremely distance-sensitive. For short distances (e.g., across the street), channel extension can be achieved by using inexpensive passive extenders and dedicated fiber. For moderate distances (e.g., across town), inexpensive passive extenders still work, provided a very high quality transmission medium (e.g., fiber) is employed. One drawback to using passive extenders is the lack of error control. Transmission errors are treated as channel errors by the host, and the consequences can be catastrophic.

To overcome this limitation, active channel extenders must be employed. Active channel extenders emulate the controller at the host end, take responsibility for data integrity across the circuit, and re-create the channel appearance at the remote end. These extenders are considerably more expensive but prove effective over most media, including fiber, microwave, and leased T1 channels. Despite apparent cost, active channel extenders are often the best—or only—solution to such applications as high-speed file transfers between geographically distributed hosts. The expense can be brought into perspective by considering alternative costs (e.g., expenses associated with contingency planning and the devastating effect of not planning for contingencies).

Packet Switching. Packet-switching technology, based on International Telephone and Telegraph Consultative Committee (CCITT) recommendation X.25, was developed during the mid-1970s and has been popular in Europe since then. Only recently, however, has it begun to play a significant role in the mainstream network environment in North America. Packet switching is well suited to low- and moderate-speed transmission requirements with light and moderate traffic volumes. It provides an efficient method of sharing bandwidth among a large number of users but, unlike the concentration approach discussed earlier, is not tied to either a particular computer type or a hierarchical architecture.

Packet switching is commonly available as a public service offering from value-added network carriers (e.g., Telenet and Tymnet in the US and Datapac in Canada). International service is available through multinational carriers (e.g., Infonet) or those with a specific national presence (e.g., PSS of British Telecom in the UK or Bundespost in West Germany). Packet switching is also available as a private network offering. Packet assembler/disassemblers and switches may be obtained from US public carriers or from several other manufacturers, including Amdahl, BBN, Northern Telecom, Siemens, and Telematics.

Another alternative that is gaining popularity in packet networking is the so-called hybrid network, which consists of both a public portion and a private portion. A typical hybrid packet network consists of a public VAN offering coupled with several packet assembler/disassemblers and one or more privately owned packet switches that may or may not be directly connected to each other (see Exhibit II-1-7). The switches may be obtained from the public carrier or a private switch manufacturer. In this arrangement, the organization benefits from both the ubiquity of the public service and the economy and control of a private network.

LAN Interconnection. With the widespread use of LANs, it is common to need to interconnect LANs across a wide area. Two primary technologies are available for this purpose: bridges and routers. Bridges are usually employed to provide connections between LANs of the same type. They operate at the data link layer of the Open System Interconnection (OSI) model and are therefore transparent to higher-layer protocols, making them suitable for linking LANs that employ multiple higher-layer protocols (e.g., TCP/IP, XNS, and DECnet). Most bridges currently provide traffic filtering to isolate local traffic within local LAN segments.

Unlike bridges, routers can connect LANs of the same or different types. Routers operate at the network layer (layer 3) and are therefore not transparent to layer 3 protocols. As such, if multiple layer 3 protocols coexist on the LANs, multiple routers or multiprotocol routers must be implemented.

Bridges and routers are typically used with leased digital facilities (e.g., 56K bps or T1) but can be readily used in conjunction with multiplexers. Other networking technologies can also be used to interconnect LANs (e.g., using concentrators to interconnect token-ring LANs or using X.25 gateways to

74

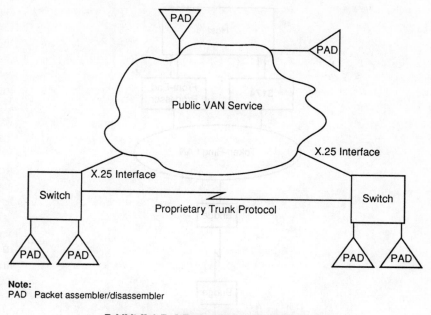

Note:
PAD   Packet assembler/disassembler

Exhibit II-1-7. A Typical Hybrid Packet Network

interconnect LANs over a packet network), but such techniques are usually employed in lieu of, rather than in conjunction with, bridges and routers.

LANs as an Alternative to Channel Extension. With the advent of reliable LAN interconnections, it has become possible to extend the LAN into the computer room rather than extend the channel to the user site. For example, in an IBM network, user workstations may be attached by a token ring to a 3174 controller. That token ring can be bridged to another token ring located in the computer room. Channel-attached 3174s or 3745 front-end processors can be attached to that ring. Exhibit II-1-8 illustrates this type of network. By establishing a terminal-to-host session through this configuration, the remote user can receive near-local response times, just as if the workstation were connected to an extended channel.

Although LANs are presented here as a true alternative to channel extenders, the data communications manager should examine channel extension product offerings thoroughly before dismissing them altogether. Some of these products, though marketed as channel extenders, are in fact examples of proprietary LANs bridged together. It is likely that the distinction among these technologies will continue to blur over the next few years.

Fast Packet and Frame Relay. Many new networking technologies are beginning to emerge. Among the most promising are the technologies of fast packet switching and frame relay. Together, these technologies represent an

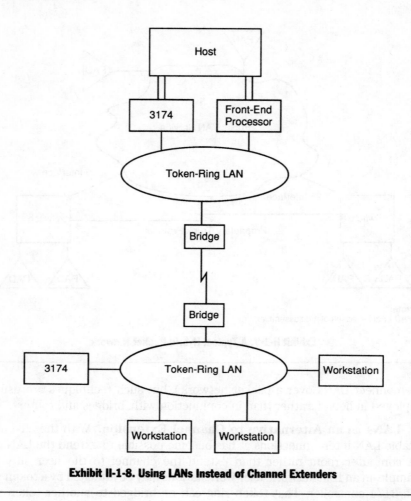

Exhibit II-1-8. Using LANs Instead of Channel Extenders

entirely new paradigm for wide area networking that is known in the broadband ISDN world as the asynchronous transfer mode.

In a fast-packet/frame-relay environment, each frame of information carries sufficient information to allow intermediate switches to route it to its final destination. Frame relay is implemented within layer 2 so that link-level integrity (e.g., error checking and recovery) remains the responsibility of the end devices, just as if they were connected by dedicated facilities. It is anticipated that because of this implementation approach, in-transit delay will decrease to tens of milliseconds. In a general sense, fast packet and frame relay are analogous to the media access control sublayer of the IEEE 802 LAN protocols. To complete a connection, a higher-layer protocol must be employed in the end devices. For LANs, that protocol is the 802.2 logical link control. For WANs, such protocols as link access procedure-D are likely candidates.

Fast packet and frame relay provide an efficient ability to share wideband facilities (e.g., 155M bps to 600M bps), making such applications as switched high-definition television possible. When used in conjunction with lower-speed facilities (e.g., T1 or T3), this technology allows the typical large corporation to integrate such diverse applications as front-end-processor–to–front-end-processor trunks, LAN interconnections, packet-switching trunks, and voice tie lines over shared communications facilities. These same applications can currently share bandwidth with traditional time-division multiplexers, but each device is assigned a relatively narrow slice of bandwidth with this approach. With fast packet/frame relay, the entire bandwidth is available for use by any of the devices when needed and is released for use by others when it is no longer needed.

Comparing Network Costs and Alternatives

Many factors must be considered to fully understand a networking decision. Uppermost are the costs associated with various alternatives; for a true comparison, all associated costs must be compared. These costs include hardware, software, transmission media, and management expenses. In addition, it is sometimes possible to calculate the dollar value of response time. For example, it may appear on the surface that installing multiple channel extenders and a private fiber-optic system will be expensive, but it may prove cost-effective in a broader context.

Such was the result of a study performed for a large metropolitan government in the Southeast. A combination of fiber optics and channel extension, along with digital distribution from three primary locations, was estimated to cost $1.8 million. The alternative was to continue to grow as in the past, using multidrop leased circuits as well as modems, multiplexers, front-end processors, and (in one location) a remote concentrator.

Over a period of five years, the cost of not installing the fiber-optic system amounted to just over $2.1 million—or an additional $60,000 annually. In addition, response time with the first option decreased from an average of five or six seconds to slightly less than one second, resulting in a real cost reduction because of decreased overtime for clerical workers.

SUMMARY

A needs assessment should begin with a compilation of profiles describing the scope of the design problem and documenting existing resources. Following the profiles, it is important to view networking requirements strategically. From this point, a gap analysis can be performed, priorities established, and designs developed, compared, and implemented.

Many options should be considered, including all possible consequences of each alternative—not just the initial cost. Finally, the primary concern of any network design should be to meet the needs of the end-user community.

II-2
Assessing LAN Technologies

JOHN P. SLONE

The communications needs of the information age are staggering and only beginning to be fully understood. Microcomputers, minicomputers, and robotic systems are becoming standard fixtures in office and manufacturing environments as organizations apply information-based technologies to strengthen their positions in an increasingly competitive market. In fact, information has become such a competitive necessity, it has essentially reached commodity status.

Like any commodity, however, information has value only when it is exchanged or applied. Therefore, communications managers are faced with a rapidly increasing number of information-producing and information-based devices that must communicate with each other. It is no longer practical to install a dedicated connection between each pair of devices that need to communicate. More sophisticated solutions are needed to keep costs down, ensure open connectivity options, and maintain efficient operations; LANs can provide such solutions.

Different people have different concepts of what a LAN is, but in this chapter, it is any electronic communications system that transports information within a limited geographic area (e.g., an office, a department, a building, a campus, or even an area of a city). Similarly, there is little agreement on what type of equipment constitutes a LAN. To some people, the term *LAN* applies only to a coaxial-based network that connects computers, terminals, and servers. Others might use the term to refer to two microcomputers that are connected with a piece of wire. Still others would include telephone systems, video switching systems, and point-to-point channel extenders in their definition. Using the broadest definitions of LANs and LAN technology, this chapter describes the LAN's role in providing communications, examines the available LAN technologies, and presents LAN selection criteria.

LAN: STATE OF THE ART

The technical foundation for LANs is nearly complete. Development efforts currently focus on using networking technology rather than on creating networks. Development of applications software is a key issue for the future of local area networking. Because the basic LAN technology has matured, communications managers who choose to install a LAN can take advantage of the new productivity-enhancing applications as they become available.

LANs are designed to be economical, and they usually reduce costs quickly because with their use, equipment and cabling can be shared, fewer and less frequent reconfigurations are required to accommodate additional devices, and employees can work more efficiently. For example, in the past, employees had to use two terminals to access two dissimilar computers. If a LAN is installed, only one workstation is needed.

These are only a few of the advantages of LAN technology. As applications are developed to take further advantage of LAN capabilities, productivity improvement tools that were inconceivable before the introduction of LANs will be readily available. An early example of such a tool is an application with which users at different workstations can simultaneously view, discuss, and modify identical screens of text, data, and graphic information. Changes made on one workstation are displayed simultaneously on all the screens.

LAN Categories

There are many ways to view LAN technologies and to categorize LANs. One of the more common ways is to group them by transmission and switching technologies.

Baseband LANs. Baseband LANs were the first to be used on a large-scale basis. The distinctive feature of the baseband LAN is its use of a single transmission medium and a single transmission channel. Because of this, baseband LANs are usually more restrictive than others in terms of transmission distance, the number of workstations the network can support, and the network's total information capacity.

Baseband networks, however, are usually less expensive to implement than other types, especially for small networks. In addition, baseband LANs use digital transmission techniques, which are inherently less expensive than analog techniques and enhance transmission reliability. Furthermore, recent advances in baseband technology have made significant progress toward increasing the information-handling capacity of baseband LANs. Finally, because baseband LANs were the first to be widely used, such support equipment as bridges, gateways, servers, and test equipment is readily available.

Broadband LANs. Broadband LANs employ many of the technologies used by the cable television industry. For example, broadband LANs and cable television generally use the same coaxial cable, amplifiers, splitters, couplers, and taps. To adapt this technology for data transmission, radio frequency modems are used to convert the digital data signals into analog signals. These signals fit on one of the many cable channels in the same way that different television channels are carried on commercial cable systems.

Broadband LANs have fewer limitations on the number of workstations, transmission distance, and information capacity than baseband LANs. More devices can communicate at once (i.e., one per channel). In addition, broadband LANs can be used to simultaneously transmit information in different formats (e.g., data and video).

Because they are more complex than baseband networks, broadband LANs are usually more expensive to install and maintain. The use of analog transmission techniques also has its inherent disadvantages. Nonetheless, broadband networks are an excellent choice for many applications.

Switch-Based LANs. Switches of different types, including PBXs and telephone companies' central offices, can also be used as LANs. Because almost every office employee requires a telephone and extra wire pairs are usually installed with the pairs used for the telephone, it makes sense both logistically and financially to use existing wiring. Such switches also provide the basis for a common, integrated directory as well as an architectural association between voice and data systems.

Another advantage of switch-based LANs is their ability to provide both circuit and packet switching on a single network. Circuit switching is more suitable for calls that transmit large amounts of data for a relatively long period of time, whereas low-volume, interactive traffic is more efficiently served by packet switching. Neither baseband nor broadband LANs are well suited for circuit switching.

Until recently, the primary disadvantage of using voice-switching technology as a LAN technology was the limited bandwidth of twisted-pair wire as compared with other transmission media. To a large extent, this disadvantage has been eliminated by new technqiues that allow much faster transmission rates. During the early 1980s, transmission rates higher than 64K bps were considered impractical. Currently, however, the upper limit is in the multimegabit-per-second range and continues to advance. In addition, the aggregate bandwidth of a large switch greatly exceeds that of other LANs.

The most significant disadvantages of a switch-based LAN are organizational because of the traditional split between the voice and data communications departments. Although many organizations are merging these two areas, industrywide cross training has yet to occur. Consequently, applications that take advantage of this combined technology have been slow to develop. In the meantime, other types of LANs continue to expand and strengthen their footholds in the marketplace.

Hybrid LANs. Several other types of LANs are available, but they are primarily hybrids or adaptations of the types discussed. For example, an architecture referred to as a hierarchical star, short-bus network is configured like a PBX but functions like a baseband LAN because all the devices must contend for the baseband bus located inside the switch.

Another hybrid is a combined voice and data version of FDDI (fiber distributed data interface), a high-speed fiber network standard being developed by the American National Standards Institute (ANSI). This network is technically a baseband system because all devices share a single digital channel on a single medium. However, because of its 100M-bps bandwidth and its integration of voice and data, FDDI is not appropriately classified as a baseband network in the traditional sense.

The development of a hybrid system that is tailored to meet the needs of an organization is often advisable. In many organizations, small LANs have already been installed in departments in several locations. As the communications needs of these relatively small communities expand, a larger network can be installed as a backbone to link the smaller networks. In such cases, baseband networks usually serve the needs of individual departments, broadband LANs are found on factory floors, and a broadband LAN, PBX, or higher-speed baseband LAN connects the smaller LANs.

LAN Technologies and Components

Communications managers exploring the use of LANs must also evaluate the underlying technologies and components. These are discussed in the following sections.

Media and the Cable Plant. In general, local area networks use one of three transmission media: twisted-pair wire, coaxial cable, or fiber-optic cable.

Twisted-pair wire has the largest installed base of the three primary media because it is used in telephone wiring and is also the least expensive. Shielded twisted-pair wire has excellent electrical characteristics and therefore has sufficient bandwidth for most data applications, though it is somewhat more expensive than telephone wiring.

Although coaxial cable has a smaller installed base than twisted-pair wire, it is fairly well known: coaxial cable has been used extensively in the past to support IBM 3270 terminals, and it is found in virtually every home served by cable television. Coaxial cable is also the transmission medium used for many popular baseband and broadband LANs.

The most commonly cited advantages of coaxial cable are its high bandwidth and resistance to noise interference. A single cable can support a network of thousands of workstations and several video channels. The cable can also be easily tapped. Although this simplifies reconfiguration efforts, it makes the network vulnerable to security violations. And because the electrical characteristics of coaxial cable vary, the coaxial cable installed for one application is not necessarily adequate for another application. Other disadvantages of coaxial cable are its cost and size. Some types are bulky and therefore difficult to work with. Installation can be expensive, especially if extra conduit is needed for support.

Unlike the other media, fiber-optic cable transmits signals by using light rather than electrical impulses. Although its user base for LAN applications is the smallest, fiber-optic cable is the most promising of the three media for the long term because of its relatively low cost, long life expectancy, security, immunity to noise, and extremely high capacity. In addition, recent break-throughs in the field of electro-optic circuits and processing create a tremendous potential for optical systems in general.

For many years, fiber-optic systems have been used for long-distance transmission and private bypass systems. Only recently has it become economical to use fiber-optic cable for transmission over shorter distances. This is largely a result of improvements in light-emitting diode (LED) technology, which offers a cost-effective alternative to laser technology, which was previously required.

Access Methods. Some method of arbitrating network use is needed. Unlike traditional networks, which were designed around a master-slave concept, LANs are designed to facilitate peer-to-peer relationships. Therefore, a scheme that allows devices to share the network as equals is required. Many such schemes have been developed; they can be categorized as either statistical or deterministic.

Statistical contention schemes allocate resources on a first-come, first-served basis. The most common of these schemes is carrier-sense multiple access with collision detection (CSMA/CD). Each device waits until the channel is idle before transmitting data and then listens to its own transmission to verify that no other station seized the idle channel at the same time. In the event of a collision, both devices stop transmitting for a random period of time before trying again. Other contention schemes are available, including CSMA without CD and schemes that use separate channels or buses to handle contention. Statistical schemes add very little overhead to the network when lightly loaded, but response times can degrade significantly during periods of heavy loading.

Statistical schemes are well suited for most interactive, terminal-to-host traffic and file transfers. For applications in which precise timing is required, however, deterministic schemes have been developed. The most commonly known deterministic scheme is token passing. This is the scheme used for IBM's Token Ring Network and the Manufacturing Automation Protocol (MAP). Another common scheme is the slotted ring. Both systems guarantee that each device on the network has a chance to transmit within a given time frame. As a trade-off, deterministic schemes require more precise implementation and add a fixed amount of overhead to the network.

Topology. Although network topology is critical to such considerations as network efficiency and propagation delays, it is primarily a concern of the engineering community. Each topology currently used (i.e., star, ring, and bus) permits logical connections between any pair of devices on the network, which is the users' only concern.

Because the topology is usually chosen on the basis of such factors as the medium and access method used, communications managers should not be overly concerned with it. For example, a twisted-pair network requires a star topology if a PBX is used to control access. A ring topology is needed in a network that uses token-ring access, and coaxial networks are almost always installed with a bus topology. Fiber-optic systems are installed in either a ring or a star configuration.

LAN Software. Communications managers should encourage the use of software that provides high-level connections. Most microcomputers are not bought to be used as terminals. Therefore, though software that provides terminal emulation may be adequate for the short term, it is not a long-term solution. Software should provide for more sophisticated methods of exchanging information and sharing the processing load among attached devices.

Interconnection Technologies. Of all the LAN technologies, none provides more flexibility to the network designer than interconnection technologies. The ability to interconnect LANs in a mix-and-match fashion allows small LANs to be tailored to the needs of individual work groups yet remain part of the overall network. Similarly, when work groups are too far apart from each other to accommodate the technical limitations of their LAN, a second LAN can be installed and the two can be connected.

Interconnection devices are usually categorized as bridges, routers, or gateways. Although these types are frequently confused, each has a distinct purpose. The differences can best be understood by considering the OSI reference model.

Bridges, which perform link-layer services (level 2 in the OSI model), are used to provide connections between two LANs of the same type and to overcome distance limitations. Routers, which are also used to link LANs, perform network layer (level 3) services (e.g., routing decisions and sometimes address translations). Unlike bridges, routers can connect LANs of either the same or a different type. It is not uncommon to find bridging and routing functions combined into a single unit (a bridge/router) that connects the two LANs and filters the traffic.

Unlike the other interconnection technologies, gateways usually interconnect LANs with non-LAN technologies. As such, they perform application layer (level 7) services. A common example is a device that emulates the functions of a 3174 cluster controller, thus acting as a 3270 gateway. Exhibit II-2-1 illustrates the differences between these three types of interconnection technologies.

LAN Standards

Progress in the area of LAN standardization has been tremendous during the past few years, especially at the lower layers of the OSI model. (Upper-layer standards are being developed for general use and as such are also applicable to the LAN environment.)

The IEEE has been the leader in LAN standardization, and the results of its efforts have been organized into the 802 family of standards. The 802 family

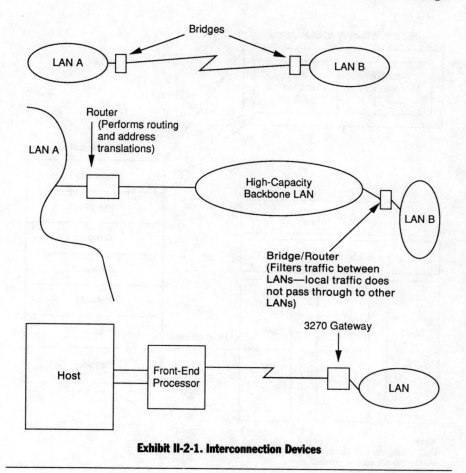

Exhibit II-2-1. Interconnection Devices

incorporates several important standards, including the 802.2 logical link control; the 802.3, 802.4, and 802.5 media access control and physical layer standards; and the 802.10 standard for interoperable LAN security. Exhibit II-2-2 shows the relationship of these standards to the OSI model.

Although the IEEE has taken the lead in general-purpose LAN standardization, ANSI has taken the lead in high-performance LAN standardization with FDDI, a standard for a 100M-bps fiber-optic ring. In addition, liaisons have been established in other areas, such as between the 802.1 LAN management group and the ANSI committee on OSI management.

In addition to these standards development activities, the international community is incorporating the IEEE and ANSI work, primarily through the ISO, and there are several industry (i.e., de facto) standards significantly influencing the marketplace. Communications managers should be aware of such industry standards as the US Department of Defense standards (e.g., TCP/IP) and keep them in mind when developing a LAN strategy.

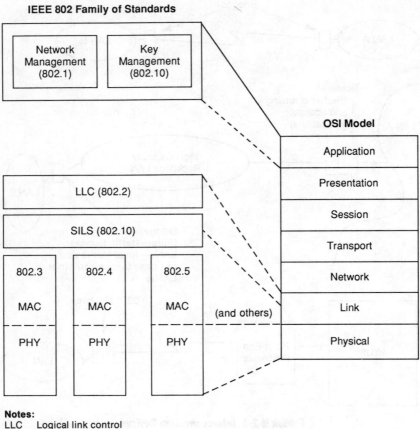

Notes:
LLC   Logical link control
MAC   Media access control
PHY   Physical layer
SILS   Standard for interoperable LAN security

Exhibit II-2-2. The Relationship of LAN Standards to the OSI Model

LAN SELECTION CRITERIA

The technical foundation for the LAN market is almost complete. Therefore, the next several years will be marked by consolidation, refinements, improvements, and new tools that take advantage of LAN environments.

Before an organization decides to install a LAN, it should first determine its needs. For example, if an organization is trying to gain a competitive edge by automating its factory, it should consider installing a LAN. If an office has just added or is planning to add a significant number of microcomputers, a network can greatly enhance office productivity. A mundane example is that a LAN can minimize the use of the so-called sneakernet—that is, it can reduce the number of employees who must walk around the office carrying diskettes. Similarly, if an organization has various dissimilar computer systems, a network can bridge the gap between them by facilitating terminal switching, protocol conversion, file transferring, and peripheral sharing.

The earliest LAN proponents promoted the economic advantage of the networks. For example, a common cable plant would reduce costs. Terminals could have access to multiple mainframes. Expensive peripherals (e.g., high-quality printers) could be shared by all the devices on the network, and employee productivity could be improved. These arguments are still valid in the current business environment, but communications managers should also consider the role a LAN can play in the strategic positioning of the organization. For example, an organization may be planning to add new product lines to gain a certain market share during the next few years. A network designed to encourage communication and sharing of ideas may greatly increase the number of new product innovations.

Similarly, an organization committed to reducing overall cost without sacrificing quality can benefit from a LAN implementation. For example, a LAN can provide university researchers with access to new resources while minimizing costs and adding a new technology that can be incorporated into an expanded curriculum.

Technical Considerations

Because LANs are designed to solve so many diverse problems, technical considerations are often influenced by the type and nature of information to be carried. For example, a network carrying such information as file transfers and interactive terminal traffic would be well served by a baseband network employing a statistical contention scheme. A network transmitting information for an automated manufacturing facility would require a deterministic access method. If an organization has both requirements, the best solution may be a broadband network that accommodates the interactive traffic on one channel using a contention scheme, file transfers on another channel, and factory information on a third channel using such an access method as token passing. If an organization's needs center on enhanced communication between employees, a PBX that allows audio and data conferencing, augmented with an electronic mail system, may be the logical choice.

If the LAN's technical requirements are not clearly indicated by the type of information being carried, cost may be the deciding factor. However, no blanket statement can be made concerning which technology provides the best value. Such diverse factors as building design, local fire codes, and the type of telephone system in use can significantly influence this decision. For example, in a building with open areas that contain modular furniture, a coaxial-based system may be the most economical solution. In an old building with no space for installing new cable, a switch-based system may be the only choice.

The organizational structure can also significantly influence the type of network installed. In some organizations, rifts between the staffs of the voice and data communications departments may discourage the use of a PBX LAN. If these two departments' employees are cooperative, however, a switch-based solution is a natural extension of other cooperative efforts, whereas a coaxial cable or fiber-optic network would seem impractical because of the need to hire new employees or to teach new skills to existing staff members.

Highly centralized organizations are natural candidates for centralized LANs (e.g., broadband and switch based). Highly distributed organizations with clearly defined, autonomous communities of interest are natural candidates for a more distributed LAN approach (e.g., a set of small work-group LANs connected by a high-speed backbone LAN). In addition, before choosing a network, communications managers should consider speed, response time, and throughput requirements as well as distance requirements, the number of workstations to be supported, and estimated traffic patterns. These issues are described in the following sections.

Speed, Response Time, and Throughput Requirements. The type of traffic expected has a major influence on speed and throughput requirements. For interactive terminal traffic with moderate amounts of file transfer activity, a CSMA/CD baseband network might be the best choice. If heavy file transfers and interactive traffic between channel-attached controllers are anticipated, a LAN employing a deterministic access scheme may be more appropriate.

Distance. Baseband networks are usually limited to a distance of a few thousand feet. Broadband networks can deliver high-speed traffic reliably for miles and do not require bridging techniques for moderately long distances. Other networks can be modified to accommodate longer distances through the use of bridges, but some degradation of service is usually encountered.

Number of Workstations. Broadband networks can support a large number of workstations economically. Supporting a relatively small number of workstations on a broadband network, however, is not usually cost-effective.

Traffic Patterns. If user communities are located within well-defined geographic boundaries, several community-oriented baseband networks connected by a high-capacity backbone network would probably provide for the best use of network resources. For widely dispersed user communities, a network composed entirely of broadband networks might be more appropriate. As a result, traffic within a given community of interest would be confined to a single channel rather than a geographic area.

Management Considerations

The installation of a LAN involves several risks, described in the following sections. Communications managers should assess these risks and take steps to minimize them. With proper planning and coordination, most problems can be avoided.

Externally Induced Instability. An environment characterized by frequent moves, construction, and hardware reconfiguration is more detrimental to a broadband LAN than to other LAN types because of the constant need to readjust the electrical properties of the cable plant.

Single Points of Failure. Single points of failure (e.g., single pieces of hardware and heavily loaded cable runs that place a high degree of dependence on single components) can usually be avoided through the use of redundancy. For example, the installation of duplicate cables into a heavily loaded area, with workstations intermingled on the two cables, can minimize service disruption in the event of a single cable cut. Some LANs (e.g., IBM's Token Ring Network) provide for automatic rerouting of the traffic by reversing the traffic direction if a component fails.

High-Density Traffic. High-density traffic presents a degree of risk by potentially degrading performance in parts of the network. To minimize this risk, communications managers might consider isolating high-traffic areas through the use of work area networks (e.g., small baseband networks) that access the primary network through a router.

Competing Technologies. This risk factor is sometimes introduced when an alternative network is advocated by a separate organizational entity, resulting in competition between the two groups. For example, a data communications department might install a broadband network, and a voice communications department might offer data communications services on a PBX LAN. The cooperative use of high-level system interfaces between the networks can minimize the negative impact of such a redundant arrangement.

Network Complexity. Network complexity varies by size and type. Baseband coaxial networks are usually the least complex; broadband coaxial and PBX LANs are usually the most complex. Before embarking on a LAN project, communications managers must assess the complexity and the readiness of their organization to handle the task. They may need to hire new, more skilled employees or develop new talent in existing employees, as appropriate.

Planning for Change

LANs must be developed properly to accommodate changes as they occur. The types of changes that can occur and should be considered in the planning stages fall into four categories: growth, mobility, technology, and applications.

Growth can be partially determined from historical data, strategic and business plans, and such sources as applications backlogs and interviews with departmental representatives. However, new technology, price breakthroughs, new applications, and changing business conditions can significantly alter even the most thorough estimates. An additional source of change is the latent demand that frequently surfaces as a result of the turnpike effect—that is, the increase in network demand arising as a result of new capabilities offered by the network. Because of the difficulty in predicting change, communications managers must ensure that the network installed will not run out of capacity in the near future.

Communications managers must also consider mobility when planning a network. Broadband networks can be reconfigured to accommodate movement of the work force; however, each change in the cable plant requires careful engineering. For this reason, highly mobile work forces might be better served by a PBX LAN. Some technological changes, however, cannot be accommodated by a PBX LAN. For example, new technologies that increase bandwidth requirements (e.g., graphics or video) may exceed the capacity of a PBX. In these cases, multiple reconfigurable baseband LANs might better serve user needs.

Cost Considerations

Communications managers should recognize that the following factors contribute to the cost of any LAN:

- Cable plant and hardware expenditures.
- Personnel costs associated with the design and engineering of the system, which includes the traditional network engineering functions of traffic engineering and port allocation as well as technology-specific functions that vary with the type of LAN selected.
- Installation costs, including an allowance for the cost of bringing electrical properties into compliance with specifications and the usual costs of cable and conduit installation.
- An incremental cost for operational support and modifications.
- Technical personnel and user training.

All these factors should be evaluated during the project life cycle rather than at installation to obtain an accurate estimate of network costs.

SUMMARY

The maturity of LAN technology suggests that it should be considered in organizations that depend on efficient information handling. To make a sound decision, communications managers who are contemplating the role of LANs must:

- Understand the organization's strategic objectives and communications needs and then determine whether to deploy a LAN.
- Define the type and nature of the information to be carried on the LAN.

- Consider only LAN types appropriate for the organization's information and equipment and that are compatible with the organizational structure.
- Use LANs conforming to international standards, unless there is a compelling reason to use a proprietary system.
- Identify and address security risk factors during the initial design of the LAN.
- Consider external requirements (in addition to local information requirements), including the need to access resources external to the LAN and the need to access LAN resources from outside the LAN.
- Consider costs during the expected life of the network, including all identifiable direct and indirect cost factors.
- Make provisions to readdress the network plan periodically to ensure that needs continue to be addressed over time and that new technologies are incorporated at the appropriate time.

II-3
Planning for a LAN Implementation

DONALD DYTEWSKI

Before a LAN can be planned and installed, the communications manager should learn as much as possible about current communications technologies and trends. Successful installation of a LAN requires consideration of such factors as data rate, throughput, standards, cabling schemes, future expansion, maintenance, and cost. An understanding of technical issues alone, however, is not sufficient; the organization's communications objectives must be understood as well.

Planning does not ensure that the network's specifications will not change. Even a well-planned system is likely to change almost as fast as it can be installed. This evolution can be caused by personnel turnover, growth, economics, and technological change. This chapter describes how a network strategy can account for this inevitable change and still lead to installation of the newest, most up-to-date LAN.

LAN STANDARDS

Along with the wide variety of data communications equipment installed today are numerous ways of providing connectivity over LANs. Methods of LAN implementation seem endless considering the many different protocols, interfaces, and media.

Proprietary networks have been around for a long time, and some are so well accepted that they have become de facto standards. Examples include Ethernet, DECnet, SNA, and ARCNET—all of which use different cabling schemes and interfaces. Unfortunately, attempts to integrate these systems often lead to problems. Communications devices have different languages (i.e., protocols) as well as different cabling systems. Even when the cable type appears to be similar, the signal electronics and data formats can be incompatible. Therefore, it can be expensive for an organization to attempt facility integration. Communications vendors are often blamed for making integration difficult. Fortunately, the need to provide compatible communications equipment has led to the development of communications standards, which specify how devices should interconnect over a particular medium.

The IEEE Project 802 began a decade ago to address these kinds of concerns, and it successfully established standards for the bottom two layers of the OSI model (the physical and data link layers). Several IEEE standards have come out of this effort, including:

- 802.2—Logical link control.
- 802.3—Carrier-sense multiple access with collision detection.
- 802.4—Token-passing bus access method.
- 802.5—Token-passing ring access method.

Except for IEEE 802.2, these standards specify the requirements for the physical and medium access control layers. As a result, there is an increasing degree of order in the world of LANs.

IEEE 802.3, however, exemplifies how even a standard can change. Originally, the 802.3 specification used a 50-ohm coaxial cable as the medium (10 BASE 5). Today, the same standard includes provisions for using broadband media (10 BROAD 36) and has recently been amended to include twisted-pair wiring (10BASE-T). In addition, other groups are considering fiber-optic cable as an alternative medium for the 802.3 specification.

How much attention, then, must be given to standards? Standards-setting activities are clearly important, because they attempt to reflect industry advances. Therefore, in the future, there will be not only additions to existing standards but a clear migration path allowing vendors and users to advance with the standards.

Network Planning

Network planning begins with the selection of a network coordinator. Similar in function to the system manager of a computer center, the network coordinator is often called the communications manager. Regardless of title, this person must act as the control point for everything related to the cable system. The network coordinator meets with department heads to discuss current and future communications needs, confers with corporate staff members on plant-wide communications strategies, and plans and oversees installation of the network. Once the network is installed, the coordinator is responsible for expansion and maintenance.

The coordinator evaluates the communications needs of the site. To phase the network into the overall communications structure of the facility, the coordinator must:

- Develop a detailed implementation plan.
- Define data paths.
- Define applications and equipment requirements.
- Account for external factors.
- Select the proper media.

Developing the Implementation Plan

A detailed implementation plan ensures that all communications requirements are incorporated, that specific project milestones are met, and that task responsibilities are carefully assigned. If the project encompasses more than one group or department, it is wise to form a project team, with the network coordinator acting as project manager. Responsibilities of this team include reviewing network requirements and quotations and tracking the project and the costs incurred during installation and system checkout. Although the project can begin within the confines of a single department, an overall plan is necessary to prevent individual departments or divisions from having different networks that can obstruct the corporation's communications strategy.

Defining Data Paths

A second consideration in network planning is the type of data and where the data must be distributed or shared over the network. A variety of connections need to be defined, including:

- Terminal to host.
- Host to printer.
- Host to host.
- Personal computer to host.
- Personal computer to file server.
- Personal computer to gateway.
- Factory-floor devices to host.

Each connection contributes to the overall network load, which determines how fast a user can enter and use data. Terminal traffic is usually considered a light load because it is limited by the input speed of the terminal operator. It should be noted, however, that terminals also receive information (e.g., graphics), and this increases the load to a moderate level. Host-to-host communications can involve large file transfers. Although these may occur infrequently and are of short duration, they still constitute a heavy load on the network. To obtain a rudimentary value for bandwidth use, the amount and duration of network traffic must be estimated. This value aids in selection of the network type and the method of traffic separation. Some consulting firms perform network simulation; however, the simulated system must be modeled very closely to the actual system to be of any value. An accurate simulation requires a great deal of computing power and is very expensive.

Identifying the various data paths helps plan cable routes and determines where bottlenecks can occur. For example, there may be five workstations in a computer-aided design and computer-aided manufacturing (CAD/CAM) department that, while confined to a local Ethernet segment, must also have access to a higher-level host. Typically, CAD workstations create a heavy load on the network because of large graphics file transfers.

One method of connecting workstations to the host—on another sub-network—is by a bridge. Although the load imposed on the bridge may not cause a problem at first, department expansion resulting in the addition of stations to the network could create a bottleneck. These conditions must be considered during the planning phase. In this particular situation, additional cable or taps could be provided to allow another bridge to be added as necessary. Other alternatives include installing a higher-capacity bridge or a bridge with expansion capabilities. Failure to consider future scenarios can make expansion inconvenient and costly.

Defining Applications and Equipment

A third planning consideration is the need for a clear definition and understanding of the equipment connected to and the applications running on the network. These considerations dictate the network's topology as well as the interfaces used.

To understand networking requirements, it is important to communicate with as many groups within the organization as possible. Manufacturing may need production information on an hourly basis, whereas order services may need only a daily production report. The information uncovered provides a better sense of how to organize the existing applications and how to distribute data over the network efficiently.

One way to develop a communications architecture is to segment the network so that it conforms to the structure of the organization. This does not necessarily mean that each department must have its own network but that the network reflects the way business is transacted both within and between groups. This process identifies network users and the resources they need to access. Once this level of detail is known, a structured approach can be taken to implement the LAN.

A manufacturing department and a service department are good examples of different environments that can increase effectiveness by using a LAN to share data. For example, order services uses terminals that are connected to a host computer with point-to-point links, and production planning uses personal computers to track inventory requirements and production schedules. Order services generates daily reports for production planning, and production planning sends monthly reports detailing inventory status to order services.

By installing a network, order services could keep its terminals—which would then be networked by terminal servers—and production planning could retain its personal computers on a file server network. Access to production and inventory reports would be granted to any member of the production planning department. If production planning needs to review order status (e.g., to schedule production runs), an asynchronous gateway to the order services' host computer could be used. In addition, reports to order services' host computer could be transferred daily, which would enable the department to serve customer needs better. The resultant elimination of the interdepartmental information lag and the reduction of paperwork becomes even more evident when departments are geographically dispersed.

A comprehensive organizational network of this type must provide for connection to many devices, including:

- Host computers.
- Terminals.
- Printers.
- Personal computers.
- Programmable controllers.
- Numerical controllers.
- Robots.
- Bar-code systems.
- Vision systems.

Connecting these end devices to the network can create problems, not only because each product could have a different manufacturer but because each method of connection could also be different. Ideally, each vendor would offer a standard direct network connection from its device; unfortunately, in practice this is not the case. Sometimes the end device has no backplane interface. In other cases, the end device simply is not designed to have any communications capabilities other than an RS-232 connection.

If a direct connection is not available, other methods of connecting the end device to the network exist. For example, a serial or parallel port may be available. This may not be the most efficient method of connection to the network, but it does provide connectivity. Some of these connections might use an internal protocol (e.g., high-level data link control or synchronous data link control). It is imperative, however, that the network interface unit be able to accept these types of protocols transparently. If not, a gateway may be needed to convert from one protocol to the other. A final consideration when the communications manager is investigating connection methods: a migration plan should be formulated in the event that a better method of connecting the device to the network becomes available (through either the vendor or a third party) in the near future.

Accounting for External Factors

The following external factors must be considered during the network planning stage:

- Expansion—A critical issue is personnel and equipment relocation. As many as 50% of office personnel might move within one year. The cabling system can offer better utility if taps are placed at convenient locations.
- Ease of installation—This usually depends on the type of facility. Conducting a site survey before the cable system is designed helps identify problem areas, alternative cable routes, and component placement.

- Maintenance—Two maintenance levels exist: the maintenance of the cable system and the maintenance of the end devices on the network. Maintenance of end devices is contingent on the type of equipment that is installed.
- Standards—Currently, much is being done both in the IEEE groups and with the manufacturing and automation protocol and the technical and office protocol (MAP/TOP) to define standards, not only for the protocols to be used but for the cabling systems themselves. ANSI is working on specifications for the FDDI, which specifies optical fiber and connector types. The cable system designer must be aware of these standards so that the actual cabling system conforms to the chosen standard.
- Cost—When all other factors have been addressed, the one major remaining factor is cost. Although initial costs are the primary concern, future requirements must also receive serious consideration.

SELECTING THE PROPER MEDIA

The network must be flexible enough to allow for expansion or relocation of personnel. Ideally, a new terminal or computer could be added by simply plugging it into the existing LAN; proper planning and the right type of cabling make this possible. Yet there are drawbacks with cable systems that already have this capability (e.g., broadband). Short descriptions, including both benefits and drawbacks, of popular cabling types are covered in the following sections. Each description evaluates the type of cable according to cost, area of coverage, noise immunity, maximum data rate, and maintenance.

Twisted-Pair Cable

Although twisted-pair cable is typically used for connecting such point-to-point devices as terminals and host devices because of its low cost, it is increasingly being used for LANs (e.g., token-ring and Ethernet networks). As a result, a current point of interest is whether the spare twisted-pair cabling in telephone cables can be used to support LANs. Telephone twisted-pair wiring would save money because the cable is already installed. Limitations on cable length, noise susceptibility, and maximum data rate, however, may outweigh any benefits.

In terms of quality, the twisted-pair wiring used for telephones may not equal the wiring used for data communications. For this reason, it must be physically checked before it can be considered for data communications use. For a fee, some vendors and cable service companies will assess the condition of existing telephone twisted-pair wiring to see whether it is suitable.

Even when using twisted-pair wiring of a data communications grade, there are limitations to data rate, distance, and noise susceptibility. Typical data rates for twisted-pair LANs are from 56K bps to 1M bps, though new technology is pushing the upper limit for twisted pair to 10M bps.

Twisted-pair wiring maintenance requires such simple tools as a volt-ohmmeter or an oscilloscope. An electrician or technician can usually resolve any problem with minimal effort.

The network coverage area is affected by the length of permissible cable runs, which is determined by the cable's attenuation characteristics. Attenuation reduces signal strength; its effects become more severe as the data rate increases. To allow longer cable runs, signal regenerators are used to boost signal strength; however, this is possible only if the cable provides significant noise immunity. Twisted-pair cable used for LANs allows runs from 300 ft to 1,000 ft, which is usually sufficient. Most offices are located within 300 ft of a wiring closet.

Because it was designed to handle voice rather than data communications, standard twisted-pair wiring does not offer much shielding from noise. Static on the line during a voice conversation is considered a nuisance only; when data is transferred, however, noise can corrupt data and a retransmission may therefore be required. An excess of retransmissions causes network inefficiency, but shielded twisted-pair wiring is available to overcome this noise sensitivity. Although the shield provides better noise immunity, it also increases the cost of the cable.

Baseband Coaxial Cable

Like twisted-pair wiring, several varieties of baseband coaxial cable exist. Although costs vary according to quantity purchased, type of insulation, and customer discount, the baseband coaxial cable used for thickwire Ethernet is relatively expensive—more so than either twisted-pair or broadband coaxial cable. This is one of the main reasons for the popularity of running Ethernet over twisted-pair wiring.

Baseband coaxial cable has advantages, however. First, the shielding and electrical characteristics of the cable offer superior noise immunity as opposed to twisted-pair cable. Second, the attenuation of the cable is typically less than that of twisted-pair cable, so signals can travel farther without distortion. Typically, the data rates used on baseband coaxial cable are between 1M bps and 10M bps.

It is usually more difficult to maintain baseband coaxial cable than twisted-pair cable because of the type of connectors used. Special tools are required to install or replace connectors on baseband cable, which is also more difficult to splice than twisted-pair cable.

Because of the cost advantages of twisted-pair wiring, many users are converting from baseband coaxial cable to twisted-pair cable by using baluns. A balun matches the impedance between the two media and provides a cost-effective connection for some devices (e.g., terminals). There are at least two drawbacks to this: first, the use of twisted-pair cable limits the distance of the connection; and second, the immunity to noise decreases. In addition, it is necessary to determine whether the device to be connected to the balun (e.g., a terminal) will be compatible.

Broadband Coaxial Cable

Broadband LANs are often used in very large facilities (i.e., larger than 500,000 ft^2) and differ from baseband LANs in the type of coaxial cable used and in the transmission method. A 75-ohm coaxial cable between 0.500 in and 0.750 in in diameter is typically used for the main trunk line. The cost of cable varies from moderate to high depending on the type of insulation used. The cable should be routed in a way that permits use of the least expensive type of insulation. Broadband LANs use radio frequency (RF) transmission, whereas baseband coaxial LANs transmit the digital signal without additional modulation. Because of the use of RF transmission, the data being transmitted is usually above the minimum noise level in typical factory and office environments.

Broadband coaxial cable can support multiple services over a single cable because broadband data communication systems divide the cable's available bandwidth into several frequencies, or channels, which are each 6 MHz in bandwidth. This standard arose from broadband use in the cable television industry. The ability to split the cable bandwidth into many channels enables several services (e.g., a security system, data communications, and video conferencing) to be placed on different channels on the same cable.

Compared with twisted-pair and baseband cabling, broadband coaxial cabling has the widest bandwidth (44 MHz), allowing a single cable to support thousands of nodes over several miles at data rates in excess of 10M bps. Broadband cable also has excellent noise immunity because of its electrical characteristics and the use of RF transmission.

Despite its bandwidth advantages, broadband cabling is relatively expensive and is more difficult to install and maintain than other media. Only one standard (IEEE 802.4) specifies the use of broadband cable. IEEE 802.3 mentions using broadband cable, but only as an option. Although the MAP specification cites IEEE 802.4, proponents are working to have other media and media access techniques selected to provide less expensive communication interfaces.

Fiber-Optic Cable

Fiber-optic cable has been making significant inroads into the LAN marketplace. Although optical fiber is most often used for point-to-point connections for intrafacility communications, a wide variety of fiber-optic cable types and active components are currently being used for fiber-optic LANs.

Fiber-optic cable offers technical advantages over other media types: it has extremely high bandwidth, very high noise immunity, and effective security, and it can cover a large area. The main drawback to fiber-optic cable is its relatively high cost, which is explained in part by its other drawbacks (i.e., the special tools and specially trained technicians needed to install and maintain it). These obstacles, as well as continuing investigation into such issues as connectors, offer some insight into why standardization for fiber-optic LANs has taken longer than for LANs using other media.

Work is currently being done by ANSI to standardize the FDDI, a 100M-bps fiber-optic token-passing network. Even when products conforming with FDDI are readily available, they will probably be too expensive to use as a common interface for such devices as personal computer workstations. In addition, the throughput provided by the network is not needed for a personal computer workstation environment. FDDI is more likely to be used for graphics CAD workstations and host computers and as a backbone network in a manner similar to the way broadband is used today.

DESIGN AND INSTALLATION

This section and the next will review the design, installation, and maintenance requirements of a typical broadband cable network. The network coordinator plays an active role in the installation of the network, which usually consists of the following four steps:

- Site survey.
- Cable system design.
- Cable system installation.
- System certification.

System design and installation can run more smoothly if the network coordinator is familiar with the details of all of these steps, because each one involves a considerable information exchange.

The Site Survey

During the site survey, a cable designer visits the facility in which the system will be installed, meets with the network coordinator to determine the locations of access points, and reviews building floor plans to look for potential installation problems. For the cable network to be a true utility, the access points should be located throughout the building. This makes it easier—and less expensive—to relocate equipment. Certain components (e.g., amplifiers and power supplies) must be serviced occasionally as part of an effective preventative maintenance program. Therefore, it is wise to locate these devices in easily accessible areas that are nevertheless physically removed from locations where they could be damaged. The topography of the cable system has a direct bearing on installation costs and mean time between failure of the components.

The cable type chosen (specifically, its insulation) must be appropriate to the cable route and must comply with applicable building codes and laws. In the US, most local building codes are based on the National Electrical Code, which lists specific types of cables for different locations. In the case of any conflict, local codes take precedence.

From 50% to 75% of the total cost of a broadband system is incurred during installation of the cable. One factor that affects cost is cable routing; it is obviously more expensive to route the cable high above a factory floor in trusses than above ceiling tiles in an office.

In a facility that cannot afford any network downtime, redundant cabling, which presents an added expense, may be required. The redundant cable should connect the same points as the main cable but must take a different route. This reduces the chance of accidental damage to both trunk-line cables. A second cable design is therefore needed. This type of installation is costly and makes the system more complex.

Different redundancy levels exist. Total redundancy can be provided by installing two complete, separate cable systems, or the redundant segments can be limited to the system's active components. For a broadband system, active components make up 25% to 33% of the total system cost. These cost trade-offs must be weighed against the cost of network downtime.

Cable System Design

The information gathered during the site survey is used to create a full two-way cable system design. Because data applications require two-way communications, inbound and outbound channels are necessary. The available bandwidth of the cable system can be split in several ways. A midsplit system will provide 17 channel pairs with a frequency offset of 192.25 MHz; a high-split system can provide as many as 24 channel pairs with a frequency offset of 192.25 MHz. The decision of whether to use a midsplit or high-split system depends on the devices attached to the network.

Other parameters to be considered during the design phase include frequency response, carrier-to-noise ratio, distortion, and hum. These are specified in the MAP/TOP broadband medium specification.

Site survey information is also used in producing cable layout drawings (provided for the customer along with the bill of materials) so that device locations, access locations, and routing paths can be identified for the cable runs. This helps to determine the location of taps, placement of amplifiers and couplers, and correct tap values. The cable system design usually represents from 3% to 10% of the total cost of the network. The cost depends on the complexity of the system and on how much of the design involves duplication of similar cable segments (e.g., feeders).

Cable System Installation

After the design is complete, the installation of cabling can begin. This entails not only the cable installation but certification, system testing, and maintenance. The network coordinator must work closely with the installer. If the cable system is designed for use in a factory, the installation may have to be scheduled during production downtimes. If it is to be installed in an office environment, it may have to be scheduled to avoid regular business hours. If greater emphasis is placed on design, layout, and installation, however, the amount of downtime and expansion costs will be significantly reduced.

To help maintain schedules and control costs, labor requirements should be coordinated before installation. A materials inventory should be completed to reduce the possibility of materials shortages.

Some vendors offer preinstallation training classes for maintenance personnel to teach them an initial understanding of the system and its upkeep. It is also worthwhile to keep maintenance personnel involved in all later stages of installation, because they will be required to answer future questions and repair breakdowns.

Knowledgeable supervision during installation ensures that design specifications are being followed correctly. Simple matters (e.g., kinks in the cable and improper connections) can create havoc in even the most well-designed cable system and can delay start-up of the cable system, which leads to added installation and check-out costs.

Cable System Certification

To gain certification, the cable system must be activated, tests must be performed, and measurements must be taken to see that the actual cable system meets the design criteria. Activation is the process of applying power to the active components. The system is checked for correct voltage levels, opens, and shorts. Then a more complex series of tests and measurements is run. These may include a system sweep, checks of forward and reverse path loss, and determining the carrier-to-noise ratio, hum modulation, and distortion. These tests should be well documented, perhaps by taking photographs of a spectrum analyzer screen at the various test points, and the documentation should be kept on file. The test results aid in troubleshooting problems that may arise later.

Twisted-pair networks do not require as extensive a checkout as a broadband system before the LAN is put into service. It is wise, however, to examine the cable for termination to the correct equipment, noise, opens, and shorts.

MAINTAINING THE NETWORK

Proper maintenance of a broadband network requires:

- Trained personnel.
- Proper test equipment.
- Spare network components.
- Preventive maintenance.

Maintenance personnel must know the cable system and the devices connected to it. The cable television industry is one source of trained, qualified people, or current employees can be trained on broadband cable principles. A service contract with an outside vendor is another possibility.

An in-house service facility will need test equipment (e.g., a volt-ohmmeter, spectrum analyzer, sweep signal generator, and signal level meter). This equipment, or most of it, must be portable. If a contractor is hired for maintenance work, it may not be necessary to have all the preceding items of test equipment, but emergency tools should be kept on hand so that simple operations may be performed.

A stock of spare parts and equipment will minimize expensive network downtime. Downtime can be costly because network devices are of so many types and are themselves costly. The cable system designer can make recommendations to help to keep inventory costs down. Usually, spare boards for box-level devices should be kept on hand. The decision of whether to keep other spare parts in inventory (e.g., coaxial cable, amplifiers, taps, couplers, and fittings) depends on how critical the part is or on its mean time to repair and mean time between failure. A small test network should be maintained so that pass or fail tests can be performed on cable system parts and even on some of the communications devices.

The network coordinator and the maintenance department should set up a regular maintenance schedule. Weekly head-end checks, for example, can reveal the overall condition of the cable system. With a spectrum analyzer, noise, signal levels, and distortion can be checked. Quarterly section sweeps performed with a sweep generator may help detect unusual attenuation in a particular section to the cable.

The whole network cannot always be brought down to do a full sweep of the spectrum; therefore, individual sections should be brought down when possible to check the system's condition. It is wise, however, to perform a complete annual sweep. The holiday season or any planned shutdowns are opportune times to schedule preventive network maintenance that could otherwise be disruptive. Having a set plan for preventive maintenance reduces the risk of marginal performance or major network failure.

SUMMARY

The final selection of a LAN medium or cable system can still generate controversy; however, the following generalizations apply:

- With newer technologies comes higher capacity at lower cost—Two examples are fiber-optic systems and 10M-bps Ethernet, which functions on twisted-pair cable.
- Systems should be based on existing standards—This makes migration to new technologies much easier.
- A network coordinator is critical to the successful implementation of a LAN.
- Preventive maintenance can keep the network running smoothly and increase its contribution to organizational productivity.

II-4

A Decision Support System for Evaluating Investments in Local Area Networks

WILLIAM G. SULLIVAN • HAMPTON R. LIGGETT

A successful computer-integrated manufacturing implementation depends on effective communications among multivendor, heterogeneous programmable devices and realistic evaluation techniques for assessing the benefits (i.e., performance) and costs of automation. Many technical options for meeting the communications challenge exist, but the basic requirements for a manufacturing LAN must first be understood. These requirements are usually articulated during the evaluation process—and they tend to be fuzzy, difficult to quantify, and difficult to communicate to senior management.

This chapter develops and demonstrates the application of an innovative procedure for evaluating (i.e., justifying) automated manufacturing technology. It focuses in particular on LAN solutions to the problem of integrating information on the manufacturing shop floor.

A LAN is the nervous system of an integrated manufacturing system. Data from robots, programmable controllers, mainframes, personal computers, and other intelligent devices flows from node to node on the network to allow integrated control of manufacturing processes.

In planning a manufacturing LAN, questions arise concerning the practical value of a LAN versus other media for communication among programmable devices. For example, why not continue to hardwire programmable logic controllers and various shop floor devices as these connections are required? Should computer tapes be hand-carried from the design engineer to manufacturing engineering? Even when manufacturing LANs are accepted as essential to a company's strategic well-being, difficult-to-resolve questions arise concerning proprietary versus nonproprietary communications protocols; baseband, broadband, or fiber-optic transmission media; and different LAN topologies.

The most critical factor in determining both the necessity of an industrial LAN and its proper architecture is the issue of manufacturing control. To achieve control of an integrated manufacturing facility (e.g., General Motors'

Factory of the Future prototype in Saginaw MI), the communications medium must be capable of:

- Passing commands among the cell controllers, materials-handling controllers, and the factory control system.
- Receiving status and monitoring data from the various manufacturing components.
- Downloading and uploading application programs to and from programmable devices at the cell level.
- Transferring scheduling information and manufacturing status reports between the scheduling system and the factory control system.

Therefore, the realization of integrated control in a modern automated manufacturing facility lies in a real-time communications system supported by an industrial LAN, which allows direct access to a shared manufacturing data base for such functions as scheduling, process planning, design, inventory control, cost estimating, and accounting.

Manufacturing LANs can be classified under three general headings:

- Open or nonproprietary systems, including those that conform to MAP.
- Closed or vendor-specific (i.e., proprietary) implementations.
- Systems that combine proprietary and nonproprietary LANs.

In an open system both the hardware and the software have operating parameters for data exchange that are defined by recognized standards (e.g., IEEE 802.4). Devices that conform to these standards can communicate with other devices, regardless of the vendor. Closed communications systems, on the other hand, are designed for the interconnection of single-vendor–supplied devices on the basis of proprietary protocols. Such a system does not support equipment from different vendors without extensive (and often customized) enhancements. Different proprietary systems can be connected by gateways, but the interaction of these heterogeneous protocols may have a detrimental effect on a system's overall performance.

The advantages of an open strategy (e.g., one-wing MAP) are long-term flexibility, interoperability, stable specifications, the availability of products conforming to the specifications, and international acceptance as a standard. The primary advantage of a closed-system architecture is that a total solution to the integration problem—including software, hardware, and installation—can be provided by a single vendor. For applications that are expected to involve only minor changes in the future and do not require the high degree of flexibility inherent to an open system, a closed system may provide the least-cost solution. In addition, a closed system may be the best choice when response time considerations are a critical design parameter (e.g., in the process industries).

Because manufacturing LANs may have numerous designs and implementations, a systematic, thorough evaluation of the trade-offs between costs and performance is essential. Many systems integrators argue that LANs are a necessary factor in the successful operation of any modern manufacturing facility and should be accepted without detailed justification. This point of view ignores two important issues. First, a manufacturing LAN may not always be an appropriate solution, and second, considerable analysis is needed to make the best choice among the many available LANs and configurations.

The basic challenge therefore involves evaluating the costs versus the performance of proposed solutions to factory communications problems. This is not a simple situation amenable to traditional engineering economic analysis. Traditional cost measures (e.g., present worth and payback) simply fail to consider the benefits and costs that arise from such factors as network flexibility, expandability, and maintainability. This, in turn, has the effect of relegating a strategic decision to the level of a simple cost analysis and often leads to suboptimal results. The key problem is how to adequately address the non-monetary factors, which are not easily quantifiable in terms of dollars but which have a tremendous impact on the success or failure of a given investment opportunity.

OVERVIEW OF THE DECISION SUPPORT SYSTEM

The decision support system requires data from a structured group process for assessing new technology (e.g., the Nominal Group Technique or the Kepner-Tregoe method). To take the strategic (and typically long-term) needs of the company into account, the evaluation committee is composed of principal users of the LAN. The decision support system guides the committee through the methodology by which the most suitable LAN is selected for a given manufacturing application.

An overview of how the decision support system fits into higher-level planning activities is provided in Exhibit II-4-1. The step numbers indicate the menu options in the software that perform the indicated tasks. It is assumed that the organization has a strategic plan and a technology assessment process in place before using this system. Therefore, the analysis starts with a set of feasible LAN alternatives (step 2). This initial set of LAN alternatives has been subjected to critical performance requirements, producing a subset of LAN alternatives in which trade-offs among desired attributes must be examined to make a final recommendation. After the problems are defined, a list of strategic attributes is developed (step 3). These attributes are the nonmonetary aspects of networking that the evaluation committee feels are essential to effective manufacturing communications.

Exhibit II-4-2 is a sample list of attributes. These attributes are non-monetary because there is no market mechanism conveniently available by which dollar values can be assigned to them. An average ranking is developed to reflect the importance of each attribute in meeting the company's strategic objectives (steps 4 and 6), and an average performance score is computed that

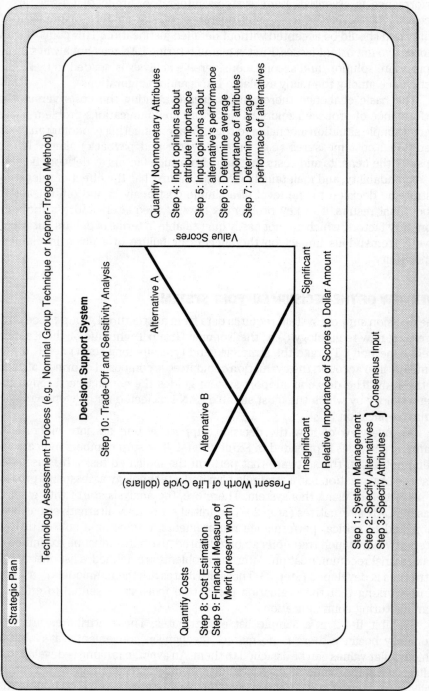

Exhibit II-4-1. Overview of the Decision-Making Process

Attribute	Benefit
Flexibility	Rapid response to the introduction of new product lines and design changes to existing products
Expandability	Allows removal of existing components and addition of new components with minimal disruption to usual operations
Implementability	Feasible with respect to existing technology and accomplishable within a reasonable time frame
Reliability	Ability to operate continuously with minimal interruption from system failure
Integrity	Minimize transmission errors
Security	Protection of data from access and alteration by unauthorized personnel
Functional Abilities	Minimize both response time to interactive users and turnaround time on batch jobs
Accessibility	Provide easy access to the manufacturing data base for all authorized personnel
Manageability	Minimize required number of system operators by eliminating specialists for each system
Integration	Interconnection of all corporate functions to one data base
Risk Level	Minimize the risk level of invested assets; should improve, not worsen, the corporation's competitive position

Exhibit II-4-2. Sample Listing of Nonmonetary Attributes Used in Strategic Evaluation of Manufacturing LANs

represents how well each alternative performs with respect to each attribute (steps 5 and 7). These two measures are combined to form the value score (step 10), which represents an unbiased, explicit, and consistent appraisal of benefits derived from each alternative. The larger the value score, the better the alternative is in terms of its strategic (nonmonetary) importance. Steps 4 through 10 of Exhibit II-4-1 have been coded for machine computation and can be made resident on an IBM personal computer.

As the nonmonetary aspects of each alternative are being considered, the life cycle costs (e.g., investment and annual recurring costs) are quantified using estimation forms (step 8) and present worth analysis (step 9). The monetary and nonmonetary attributes of each alternative are then displayed graphically so that sensitivity analysis can be performed, if necessary, to identify the preferred alternative. (Sensitivity analysis is a key feature of the design support system and is illustrated later in this chapter.)

To ensure that careful consideration is given to all essential attributes in evaluating alternative LANs, the following basic principles of investment management must be considered:

- Short-term goals must be tied to strategic plans.
- The evaluation process must be explicit and consistent.
- The evaluation process must be consensus based.
- Performance attributes are subjective and quantitative.

- The risk assessment is critical.
- Performance tracking is essential.

The procedure reported in this chapter embodies these six principles. A decision-by-consensus committee that includes management, in-house computer specialists, and end users quantifies benefits and appraises the costs of a factory communications system. Concerning the first and fourth principles, short-term goals are typically tied to strategic plans through the types of attributes considered. A group consensus method is used to ensure fairness and consistency of participation by all disciplines involved in the selection process (the second and third principles). Risk assessment is possible through what-if sensitivity analyses and risk-specific attributes included in the investigation (the fifth principle). Performance tracking may be accomplished by periodic reappraisals of selected projects (the sixth principle).

The evaluation summarized in Exhibit II-4-1 can also be accomplished with spreadsheet software. A decision support system, however, offers an important advantage over spreadsheets in its ready-made ability to lead users through multiple paths. This allows consideration of issues important to each member of the evaluation committee. Consequently, users are encouraged to develop insight into the design and analysis of LAN solutions while reducing their judgments to numbers in a realistic and credible manner.

APPLICATION OF THE PROCEDURE TO AN INDUSTRIAL PROBLEM

The remainder of this chapter describes each of the steps in Exhibit II-4-1. They are applied to a LAN evaluation problem fashioned after the experience of a large manufacturer in the Midwest. First, the problem is described, and then the need for evaluation of the alternatives by multidisciplinary committee is demonstrated. Each of the 10 steps in Exhibit II-4-1 is subsequently illustrated for this particular problem.

Problem Statement

A large manufacturer of heavy equipment is experiencing declining sales, market share, and profits. Management views modernization and automation of the production facility as essential to ending this downward spiral and regaining the company's position as a market leader.

A primary issue to be considered in the automation of the facility is the control of manufacturing processes. Several types of workstations for CAD, geometric modeling, and analysis are used in the product design phase, and both computer numerical control (CNC) and direct numerical control (DNC) devices are used in manufacturing. Management believes that a LAN, by facilitating communications among cell controllers, mainframes, workstations, and production equipment, can contribute to the following innovations in the manufacturing process:

- Writing of numerical control programs offline, at CAD workstations, and downloading of the programs to production equipment.
- Relaying of production control and schedule information from the cell controllers to mainframes and other equipment.
- Automatically sending design changes that originate at CAD workstations to process planning and manufacturing resource planning departments.
- Using a single, integrated manufacturing data base to supply information for all corporate functions.

A graphic representation of information integration through one network design is given in Exhibit II-4-3. A bus topology is shown here, although ring, star, and point-to-point topologies are considered. Several network interface units (NIUs) are included to establish connections among a wide assortment of heterogeneous devices. The topology proposed in Exhibit II-4-3 uses a broadband coaxial cable plant that supports MAP. This is one of the alternatives considered by the evaluation committee, as described in the following section.

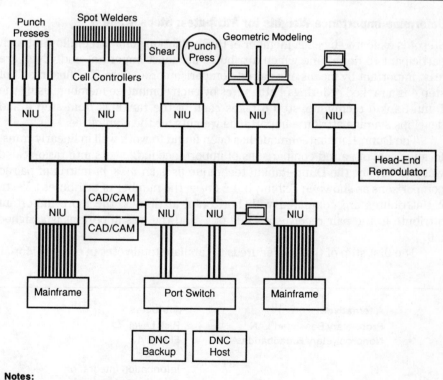

Notes:
DNC   Dynamic network controller
NIU   Network interface unit

Exhibit II-4-3. Computer Network Schematic for a Manufacturing Firm

The Evaluation Committee

Because the decision to implement a LAN has important strategic implications and involves high front-end costs, a decision support system was developed and used to facilitate the evaluation process. A committee was formed to ensure that all of the affected areas of the corporation had their interests properly represented and to allow the input of each individual to ensure that all critical attributes are considered.

Specify Alternatives and Attributes: Steps 2 and 3

As discussed earlier, the committee applied a group technique to develop a consensus regarding which LAN configurations and performance attributes should be included in the analysis. Step 1, system management, provides the committee chairperson with file management and other utilities, whereas steps 2 and 3 are used to enter the alternatives and attributes into the computer program. Exhibit II-4-4 indicates the alternatives and attributes that were selected.

Determine Importance Weights for Attributes: Steps 4 and 6

Step 4 is executed by each member of the evaluation committee, allowing each participant to determine which attributes are most important and which are least important by means of a paired-comparison procedure. The final result of step 4 is a ranked ordering of attributes by each committee member. Using the Dunn-Rankin technique, step 6 takes each of the rankings from step 4 and develops average attribute importance weights for the committee.

The Dunn-Rankin technique has been found to work well in linearly transforming sets of paired comparisons of importance judgments into ratio-scaled weights. Briefly, the Dunn-Rankin technique uses an $m \times m$ matrix of paired comparisons as shown in Exhibit II-4-5 (m = the number of attributes). Vertical attributes are compared with horizontal attributes; the more important attribute in the pair receives a value of 1, and the less important is assigned a 0.

The first step of this procedure is to tabulate total votes in each cell for all

Alternatives	Attributes
Proprietary Baseband LAN	Risk Level
Nonproprietary Broadband LAN	Flexibility
	Security
	Information Integration
	Expandability
	Implementability

Exhibit II-4-4. Alternatives and Attributes

Attribute	Security	Flexibility	Expandability	Integration	Risk Level	Implementability
Security	—	6	6	7	7	8
Flexibility	4	—	5	6	7	7
Expandability	4	5	—	6	7	6
Integration	3	4	4	—	6	6
Risk Level	3	3	3	4	—	6
Implementability	2	3	4	4	4	—
Column Totals	16	21	22	27	31	33
n	10	10	10	10	10	10
R_i	26	31	32	37	41	43

Exhibit II-4-5. Dunn-Rankin Matrix Developed by Evaluation Committee

committee members. The attributes are then arranged in ascending order along the horizontal and the vertical axes of the matrix. The number of committee members, n, is added to each column total to produce a rank-sum R_i for each attribute (see Exhibit II-4-5). The following parameters are calculated as an intermediate step in obtaining the Dunn-Rankin weights (W_i) shown in Exhibit II-4-6:

$$R_{\min} = n \qquad R_{\max} = mn \qquad R_{av} = \frac{n(m+1)}{2}$$

The expected value of standard deviation (s) is calculated as:

$$s = \frac{mn(m+1)^{1/2}}{12}$$

The normalized ratio of each attribute (Z_i) is calculated as:

$$Z_i = \frac{(R_i - R_{av})}{s}$$

The weight of each attribute (W_i) is calculated as:

$$W_i = \frac{(Z_i + |Z_{\min}|) \times 100}{(Z_{\max} + |Z_{\min}|)}$$

The normalized weight of each attribute—Nor(W_i)—is calculated as:

$$\text{Nor}(W_i) = \frac{W_i}{\sum_{i=1}^{m} W_i}$$

The independence of attributes is an extremely important assumption underlying the Dunn-Rankin technique. For any nontrivial set of paired comparisons, total independence among the performance attributes may be unattainable. This problem can be largely overcome by carefully and concisely defining each attribute.

	Minimum	Security	Flexibility	Expandability	Integration	Risk Level	Implementability	Maximum
				Attribute				
$R_i - R_{av}$	−25	−9	−4	−3	2	6	8	25
Z_i	−4.23	−1.52	−0.68	−0.51	−0.34	1.01	1.35	4.23
$Z_i + Z_{min}$	0	12.71	3.55	3.72	4.57	5.24	5.58	8.46
W_i	0	32	42	44	54	62	66	100
$Nor(W_i)$	—	10.67	14.00	14.67	18.00	20.67	22.00	—

Exhibit II-4-6. Calculations and Results of the Dunn-Rankin Technique

Determine the Performance Scores for Each Alternative: Steps 5 and 7

An integer rating scale of $+5$ to -5 is used to assess how well each alternative meets the requirements of each attribute. In step 5, each committee member is asked to select a number from this 11-point rating scale to indicate his or her perception of how each alternative performs relative to each attribute:

- 5—Extremely beneficial to meeting the firm's strategic goals.
- 3—Beneficial to meeting the firm's strategic goals.
- 1—Slightly beneficial to meeting the firm's strategic goals.
- 0—Neither beneficial nor detrimental (indifferent).
- -1—Slightly detrimental to meeting the firm's strategic goals.
- -3—Detrimental to meeting the firm's strategic goals.
- -5—Extremely detrimental to meeting the firm's goals.
- 75—Signifies a pass on rating this alternative-attribute pair.
- Entries other than those shown (e.g., 4 or -2) are allowed as long as the entry is an integer from -5 to $+5$.

Individual responses from step 5 are used to develop an average rating in step 7. These composite results are shown in Exhibit II-4-7.

Cost Estimation and Present-Worth Calculations: Steps 8 and 9

The next step involves the estimation of life cycle costs for each alternative. These costs are calculated using the front-end investment costs of the proprietary baseband and the nonproprietary broadband alternatives, which are developed from the worksheets shown in Exhibits II-4-8 and II-4-9.

After initial costs were determined, the committee applied a rule of thumb that annual hardware maintenance charges for a computer network are approximately 10% of the initial costs and the software maintenance costs over the LAN's life cycle are expected to be approximately 150% of the initial costs. The annual hardware maintenance costs are therefore estimated to be $16,455 for the proprietary baseband LAN and $20,061 for the nonproprietary broadband LAN. Software and communications costs are $243,075 for the

	Proprietary Baseband LAN	Nonproprietary Broadband LAN
Security	2.4	3.6
Integration	-1.2	4.6
Expandability	1.6	4.9
Implementability	4.0	2.8
Flexibility	1.5	4.2
Risk Level	2.0	1.8

Exhibit II-4-7. Average Rating for Each Alternative

Component	Cost Estimating Factors				
Site Architectural Survey	$150 per work area drop	×	9	=	$ 1,350
Intrabuilding Connections	$35 per ft	×	1,900	=	66,500
Cable Installation	$20 per ft	×	2,075	=	41,500
Equipment:					
Transceivers	$200 each	×	9	=	1,800
Network interference units	$750 per port	×	9	=	6,750
Radio frequency modem	$750			=	750
MAP board and software	$10,000			=	10,000
Interface board	$2,700 each	×	2	=	5,400
Interface software	$10,000			=	10,000
CAD emulation package	$250 per unit	×	2	=	500
Network Manager	$20,000			=	20,000
	Total				$164,550

Exhibit II-4-8. Proprietary Baseband LAN Initial Cost Estimation

proprietary baseband LAN and $300,917 for the nonproprietary broadband LAN. A summary of the present worth of each alternative, assuming a 15% discount rate and a life expectancy of 10 years, is shown in Exhibit II-4-10.

Compute the Overall Value Score and Conduct a Sensitivity Analysis: Step 10

The importance weights developed in step 6 and the average performance scores obtained from step 7 are combined to develop a single nonmonetary

Component	Cost Estimating Factors				
Site Architectural Survey	$150 per work area drop	×	9	=	$ 1,350
Intrabuilding Connections	$35 per ft	×	1,900	=	66,500
Cable Installation	$20 per ft	×	2,075	=	41,500
Equipment:					
Taps	$19 each	×	9	=	171
Splitters	$10 each	×	9	=	90
Network interface units	$4,000 each	×	9	=	36,000
Radio frequency modems MAP (head end)	$5,000 each			=	5,000
Network Manager	$20,000			=	20,000
Network Analyzer	$30,000			=	30,000
	Total				$200,611

Exhibit II-4-9. Nonproprietary Broadband LAN Initial Cost Estimation

	Proprietary Baseband LAN	**Nonproprietary Broadband LAN**
Initial Investment	$164,550	$200,611
Hardware Maintenance	16,455/year	20,061/year
Software Maintenance	243,075	300,917
Present Worth at 15% a Year	$488,954	$602,210

Note:
All dollar amounts represent debits.

Exhibit II-4-10. Summary of Present Worth

---

value score for each alternative. This score represents the advantages of each alternative with respect to difficult-to-quantify considerations. An additive weighted model is used to combine the importance weights and the performance ratings for two reasons: first, ease of understanding and application; and second, credible results have been obtained through extensive use of importance weights and the average performance score in actual practice. The model uses the attribute weights developed in step 6 and the performance scores from step 7 as follows:

$$\text{SCORE}_j = \sum_{i=1}^{m} \text{Nor}(W_i)\,R_{ij}$$

where:
$\text{Nor}(W_i)$ = the normalized weight of attribute i
R_{ij} = the performance score for alternative j against attribute i
m = the number of attributes

These calculations yield overall value scores of 178 for the proprietary baseband LAN and 351 for the nonproprietary broadband LAN.

Monetary (present-worth) and nonmonetary (value-score) considerations are now presented on a summary graph. Present worth is plotted on the left axis, and the value score is plotted on the right axis. This graph provides insight into which alternative ought to be recommended by displaying differences between the monetary and nonmonetary aspects of each. The scales of both axes are fixed so that the percent changes between the maximum and minimum extremes of present worth and the value score are identical.

Exhibit II-4-11 summarizes data pertinent to the current analysis; higher values on both axes are indicative of improved performance. The five boxes at the bottom of the graph constitute a legend explaining the significance of the point where the lines cross. If the lines cross to the right of the middle, the analysis is weighted toward quantifiable costs; therefore, nonmonetary judgments must be more important than monetary considerations when recommending a more costly alternative. If the lines cross to the left of the middle, the analysis is weighted toward nonmonetary factors.

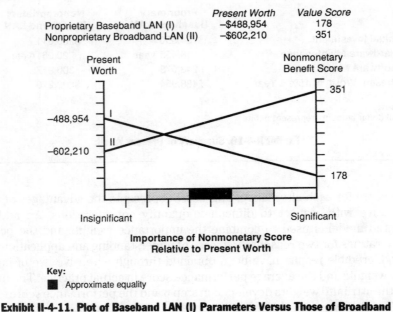

	Present Worth	Value Score
Proprietary Baseband LAN (I)	–$488,954	178
Nonproprietary Broadband LAN (II)	–$602,210	351

Exhibit II-4-11. Plot of Baseband LAN (I) Parameters Versus Those of Broadband LAN (II)

The ratio property of the scale allows for quick identification of the differences in alternatives. For example, the right-hand enclosed area on the graph in Exhibit II-4-11 is much larger than the left-hand enclosed area. This means that the relative difference between the nonmonetary attributes is much larger than the relative difference between present worths. Alternative II (nonproprietary broadband LAN) is more costly than alternative I (proprietary baseband LAN); however, a large increase in nonmonetary benefits could more than offset the cost advantage of alternative I. In this case, monetary considerations would have to be much more important than nonmonetary attributes before the least-cost alternative would be recommended.

Because subjective data and rough cost estimates for first-of-a-kind technology are used in this analysis, the capability for conducting sensitivity analyses is also built into step 10 of the software. This allows the responsiveness of one alternative versus that of another to be investigated over possible ranges of error for estimated quantities. To conduct a sensitivity analysis, the value score and present worth are varied by a predetermined amount and the resulting impact on the point of indifference (i.e., the crossover point) is noted. If the value score and present worth for the nonproprietary broadband LAN are decreased (made worse) by 20%, as shown in Exhibit II-4-12, the point of indifference moves toward the right-hand side of the graph. This illustrates the possible effect of a 20% negative bias in nonproprietary LAN parameters, which

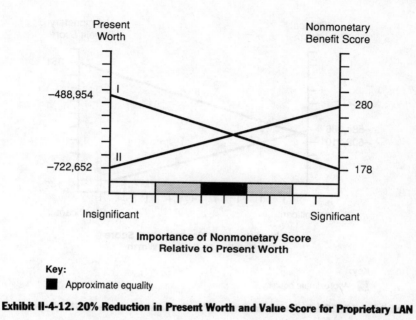

Exhibit II-4-12. 20% Reduction in Present Worth and Value Score for Proprietary LAN

serves to reduce the desirability of this alternative and increases the relative importance of the value score in the final recommendation that the company makes.

Conversely, when the value score and present worth of the proprietary baseband LAN are decreased by 20%, the indifference point moves to the left-hand side of the graph, as shown in Exhibit II-4-13. This indicates that a proprietary LAN should be recommended under these conditions only when present worth dominates the decision-making process relative to nonmonetary considerations.

When the point of indifference lies to the left (as in Exhibit II-4-13), a compelling case can be made for selecting the nonproprietary broadband LAN alternative. If, in this situation, it is decided to choose a proprietary baseband LAN, this decision simply means that practically all the weight has been placed on present worth. The opposite could be true if the nonproprietary broadband LAN is selected when the point of indifference lies at the far right side of the graph. Such a group judgment can shed considerable light on the corporate values actually used in making strategic decisions.

SUMMARY

The decision support system described in this chapter is a tool for evaluating capital investments in technology in which strategic considerations often out-

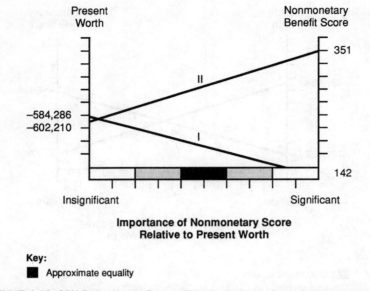

Importance of Nonmonetary Score
Relative to Present Worth

Key:
■ Approximate equality

Exhibit II-4-13. 20% Reduction in Present Worth and Value Score for Nonproprietary LAN

weigh short-term financial measures of profitability. The software facilitates the gathering and analyzing of pertinent data used to make judgments in a group decision-making process. Furthermore, the procedure encourages iterative updating of shared data within the evaluation committee. It also encourages team building that involves senior management, which improves the likelihood that management will accept the new technology.

For the application of the design support system described in this chapter, it was discovered that a 20% error in estimating costs and value scores did not reverse the preliminary conclusion to adopt a broadband LAN. This conclusion depended on the relative importance of strategic benefits and short-term profitability that had been established a priori by the management of the company presented in the example.

II-5
Building an Integrated Local Area Network Environment: A Case Study

DAVID P. LEVIN

The successful implementation of a local area network is a direct result of much analysis and planning. There are budget limitations as well as the need to make a thorough study of users, hardware, software, applications, and future expansion opportunities and requirements. This chapter presents a case history of the activities and processes undertaken by one particular organization to create an integrated LAN environment.

Servco (a fictitious name used throughout this chapter to represent a real company) is a professional service organization that recently relocated its headquarters. In the process, the firm wanted to upgrade its computer and communications facilities to include a microcomputer LAN. To accomplish this goal, Servco enlisted the help of a consultant company that used the needs assessment methodology to plan the firm's new LAN.

USER PROFILE

The information processing resource users within the organization can be divided into several groups. The first major group comprises the secretaries, whose microcomputer use consists of producing documents using word processing programs. Their total network use is moderate to heavy. The second major user group consists of junior professionals (considered the power users), whose network use is also moderate to heavy. The third user group comprises the senior professionals, whose moderate microcomputer use suggests limited network use. The final major user group is the graphics department. It makes use of high-powered microcomputers, and its network requirements are for high-volume, low-frequency access.

All of the firm's document production is based on microcomputer technology. The firm's staff comprises well-paid, highly motivated individuals. To support the firm's business needs properly, these users demand a high level of network reliability, capability, and capacity.

USE PROFILE

The use requirements of the microcomputer LAN are extensive. Although the typical 10-hour workday runs from 8:00 AM to 6:00 PM, many staff members work much later. Others perform international operations, necessitating around-the-clock network availability. As the deadline for the production of a final document approaches, the LAN should allow the firm to divide the document into several pieces for additional work, then reassemble and print it on a short schedule. Typical peak use periods occur during the late morning and late afternoon, and Friday is the peak day. Network availability and uptime in both day and evening hours are as critical on the weekend as they are during the week. The peak season is early fall, starting in early September.

SPACE PLANNING PROFILE

The firm's new headquarters is a multifloor high-rise building built during the mid-1960s. All electrical and communications wiring is run in floor trenches, with separate trenches for the electrical and communications systems.

LAN users are evenly distributed among several adjacent floors in the building. Each floor has one base building communications closet. All the closets are vertically aligned within the building.

APPLICATIONS PROFILE

The applications programs running on the LAN are fundamental to the work of the organization. Although technically the organization can revert to using its microcomputers in a standalone mode, operations without the LAN are not acceptable.

The primary application on the LAN is word processing, with the application program running on the local microcomputer and the files stored on a central file server. Spreadsheets are shared in a similar fashion. Additional file-sharing requirements include graphics files and inclusion of files in electronic mail messages.

HARDWARE PROFILE

The organization's microcomputers are manufactured by IBM, Compaq, Toshiba, and Apple. IBM and IBM-compatible microcomputers use the 80286 microprocessor and are equipped with the PC AT bus or the microchannel architecture bus. All of the MS-DOS microcomputers have at least 640K bytes of random access memory. Video adapters include color graphics adapter, extended graphics adapter, and video graphics adapter models.

The number of Toshiba laptop computers in use at Servco is growing and will continue to do so. As a result, management wants to provide for connection of these devices to the LAN. This means buying either Toshiba's Ethernet card or an external expansion box that accommodates any full-length expansion card. The advantage of the Toshiba Ethernet card is that it fits inside the laptop—adding less than one pound to the unit's total weight. A one-card expansion chassis is also very popular because it allows the user to choose from a variety of third-party network interface units without changing the expansion chassis.

Additional hardware requirements include the need to share laser printers and plotters throughout the office, regardless of the location of the target printer. Several microcomputers have facsimile interface cards and the number of these devices will probably grow in the future.

GROWTH REQUIREMENTS

Exhibit II-5-1 details Servco's local and remote communications requirements in the areas of local data communications, remote data communications, local video, facsimile, copier use collectors, access control, and paging and imaging terminals.

Type of Communications	Required at Time of Move	Supported in 2 Years	Supported in 10 Years
Local Data Requirements			
Single-channel MS-DOS micro LAN	X	X	X
Multichannel MS-DOS micro LAN		X	X
Single-channel Ethernet LAN	X	X	X
Multichannel Ethernet LAN			X
MS-DOS micro to value-added network		X	X
MS-DOS micro to TWX-telex network		X	X
TWX and telex terminal to access line	X	X	X
Single-channel Apple micro LAN	X	X	X
Multichannel Apple micro LAN		X	X
Remote Data Requirements			
Local micro LAN to remote LAN		X	X
Local micro to remote at 1.2K bps and 2.4K bps	X	X	X
Local asynchronous terminal to remote host		X	X
Local Video Requirements			
Video training			X
Video teleconferencing			X
Security surveillance	X	X	X
Other Requirements			
Facsimile transceiver to line	X	X	X
Copier use collector to micro			X
Paging terminals	X	X	X
Imaging terminals		X	X
Access control	X	X	X

Exhibit II-5-1. Servco's Local and Remote Communications Requirements

Initially, Servco requires a single-channel MS-DOS microcomputer LAN (e.g., IBM's PC LAN or IBM Token Ring), a single-channel Ethernet LAN, a single-channel Apple microcomputer LAN, and support for TWX and telex terminals that access the value-added network carrier's transmission line. Servco will require multichannel LANs in the future as the computational power of its microcomputers and the number and complexity of applications increase and as imaging technology is integrated into information processing technology.

Remote data communications requirements are initially limited to local microcomputers accessing remote information sources by 1,200-bps and 2,400-bps modems. Within two years, Servco will require the ability to connect its headquarters LAN to remote microcomputer LANs. The company will also require that its microcomputers emulate asynchronous terminals and connect to remote host computers.

Video security surveillance is required by Servco at move-in time. Within 10 years, the firm wants to use video teleconferencing and video training.

Servco requires support for other forms of communications including facsimile transceivers and paging and access control. At move-in time, however, these devices are accommodated by dedicated twist-pair cabling.

CABLING SUPPORT FOR LOCAL COMMUNICATIONS REQUIREMENTS

The cabling alternatives that can support Servco's local communications requirements are outlined in Exhibit II-5-2. Servco chose four local cabling network alternatives: twisted-pair cabling, broadband coaxial cabling with twisted-pair cabling, baseband Ethernet with twisted-pair cabling, and broadband and baseband coaxial cabling with twisted-pair cabling. For each of the four alternatives, the support provided is indicated as yes with full-function support, yes with limited-function support, or no support.

Twisted-pair cabling is universally used for connecting voice telephones to a PBX and to an auxiliary transmission line. Twisted-pair cabling supports single-channel LANs, including the Ethernet, token-ring, and AppleTalk architectures. It also supports microcomputers and TWX and telex terminals connecting to carrier access lines. Twisted-pair cabling is effective for connecting facsimile transceivers to an access line, for employing copier use collectors, and for paging networks.

Twisted-pair cabling provides limited-function support for video teleconferencing communications. Codecs costing $30,000 or more are required to convert video signals to a data stream of less than 1.6M bps to travel over this type of cabling. Limited-function support of imaging terminals is provided because only a portion of today's imaging products use this type of cabling.

Twisted-pair cabling does not support video security surveillance or video training communications. In addition, it does not support multichannel LANs, regardless of network architecture, because the baseband signaling cannot

| | LAN Cabling Alternatives | | | |
	A	B	C	D
Cable Components				
Twisted-pair cabling	Yes	Yes	Yes	Yes
Baseband coaxial cabling	No	No	Yes	Yes
Broadband coaxial cabling	No	Yes	No	Yes
Local Data Communications Requirements				
Single-channel MS-DOS micro LAN	Y	Y-F	Y-L	Y-F
Multichannel MS-DOS micro LAN	N	Y-F	N	Y-F
Single-channel Ethernet LAN	Y-F	Y-F	Y-F	Y-F
Multichannel Ethernet LAN	N	Y-F	N	Y-F
MS-DOS micro to value-added network	Y-F	Y-F	Y-F	Y-F
MS-DOS micro to TWX-telex network	Y-F	Y-F	Y-F	Y-F
TWX-telex terminal to access line	Y-F	Y-F	Y-F	Y-F
Single-channel Apple micro LAN	Y-F	Y-F	Y-F	Y-F
Multichannel Apple micro LAN	N	Y-F	N	Y-F
Local Voice Communications Requirements				
...n to PBX switch	Y-F	Y-F	Y-F	Y-F
...tation to telephone company demarcation	Y-F	Y-F	Y-F	Y-F
...o Communications Requirements				
...ning	N	Y-F	N	Y-F
...conferencing	Y-L	Y-F	Y-L	Y-F
...urveillance	N	Y-F	N	Y-F
...ms of Communications				
...transceiver to access line	Y-F	Y-F	Y-F	Y-F
...e collector to micro	Y-F	Y-F	Y-F	Y-F
...rminals	Y-F	Y-F	Y-F	Y-F
...erminals	Y-L	Y-F	Y-L	Y-F
...ntrol	Y-F	Y-F	Y-F	Y-F

	...ed-pair cabling only
	...band coaxial cabling with twisted-pair cabling
C	Baseband Ethernet with twisted-pair cabling
D	Broadband and baseband coaxial cabling with twisted-pair cabling
N	No support
Y-F	Yes, with full-function support
Y-L	Yes, with limited-function support

Exhibit II-5-2. Cabling Support for Servco's Local Communications Requirements

provide frequency division multiplexing and separate signaling bands.

Baseband coaxial cabling does not provide any additional support beyond twisted-pair cabling. It is more cost-effective for large-scale Ethernet networks with more than 100 nodes attached. Baseband coaxial cabling does not support multichannel LANs; network segmentation, however, is supported. Both broadband coaxial cable with twisted-pair cabling (alternative B) and broadband and baseband coaxial cable with twisted-pair cabling (alternative D) provide full-function support for all of Servco's local communications requirements.

SPECIFIC CABLING NETWORK ALTERNATIVES

Exhibit II-5-3 details the capabilities of four cabling network options considered by Servco. Two twisted-pair-only alternatives were considered. The first twisted-pair-only alternative (option 1) uses cable that is compatible with IBM Type 2 cabling specifications.

Type 2 cable consists of four pairs of 24-gauge solid copper cable and two pairs of 22-gauge solid copper cable separately shielded. The 24-gauge cable is typically used for voice communications, facsimile equipment, and auxiliary telephone transmission lines. The 22-gauge cable is typically used for most data communications, access control, and single-channel LANs.

The second twisted-pair-only cabling alternative (option 2) uses a custom-designed eight-pair, 22-gauge solid copper cable with a foil shield. This cable has the same capabilities as the IBM Type 2 cable. The third cabling option

	Option 1	Option 2	Option 3	Option 4
Budget Item				
Twisted-pair cabling	IBM Type 2	22-gauge	24-gauge	24-gauge
Coaxial network	None	None	Broadband	Ethernet
Voice Communications Services				
PBX sets at 64K bps	Yes	Yes	Yes	Yes
ISDN basic rate	Yes	Yes	Yes	Yes
ISDN primary rate	Yes	Yes	Yes	Yes
T-carrier	Yes	Yes	Yes	Yes
Data Communications Services				
3270 CRT to 3274 2.5M bps	Yes	Yes	Yes	Yes
ASCII CRT to mini 19K bps	Yes	Yes	Yes	Yes
10M-bps micro LAN, one channel	Yes	Yes	Yes	Yes
16M-bps micro LAN, one channel	Yes	Yes	Limited	Limited
10M-bps micro LAN, two channels	No	No	Yes	No
10M-bps micro LAN, five channels	No	No	Yes	No
CAD/CAM network, one channel	Yes	Yes	Yes	Yes
CAD/CAM network, two channels	No	No	Yes	No
CPU network, one channel	Yes	Yes	Yes	Yes
CPU network, multichannel	No	No	Yes	No
Other Communications Services				
Video surveillance	No	No	Yes	No
Video teleconferencing	Yes	Yes	Yes	Yes
Video distribution	No	No	Yes	No
Facsimile equipment	Yes	Yes	Yes	Yes
Digital image services	Limited	Limited	Yes	Limited
Access control	Yes	Yes	Yes	Yes

Exhibit II-5-3. Servco's Cabling Network Alternatives and Their Capabilities

(option 3) is a hybrid of broadband coaxial and twisted-pair cabling using eight-pair, 24-gauge solid copper cable with foil shielding. The broadband coaxial cabling was originally designed for community antenna television and supports data and video communications.

The third cabling option is somewhat limited in its support of single-channel 16M-bps microcomputer LANs because the 24-gauge twisted-pair component supports fewer than the maximum of 260 stations. The broadband and twisted-pair cabling hybrid provides the most robust support for a variety of data, video, and imaging communications.

The fourth option (option 4) is a hybrid of baseband Ethernet and twisted-pair cabling using eight-pair, 24-gauge solid copper cable with foil shielding. This option provides limited support of single-channel 16M-bps microcomputer LANs and limited support of digital imaging services. No support is provided for multichannel LANs, however, regardless of network architecture and device type. This baseband coaxial and twisted-pair cabling hybrid does not support video surveillance or distribution services.

CABLING NETWORK COST ALTERNATIVES

Exhibit II-5-4 details the costs associated with the four cabling options described in Exhibit II-5-3. Twisted-pair cabling materials are divided into feeder cable, station cable, other cable, and other components. Twisted-pair cabling materials for option 1 total $39,700—the most expensive alternative because of

Budget Item	Option 1	Option 2	Option 3	Option 4
Twisted-pair cabling	IBM Type 2	22-gauge	24-gauge	24-gauge
Coaxial network	None	None	Broadband	Ethernet
Twisted-Pair Cabling Materials (thousands of dollars)				
Feeder cable	$ 6.2	$ 4.4	$ 3.2	$ 3.2
Station cable	23.3	11.1	9.7	9.7
Other cable	5.2	5.2	4.7	4.7
Other components	5.0	5.0	5.0	5.0
Coaxial Network Cabling Materials (thousands of dollars)				
Cabling	$ 0	$ 0	$ 3.6	$ 4.4
Cabling components	0	0	6.4	49.9
Cabling Installation Labor (thousands of dollars)				
Twisted-pair network	$14.0	$12.0	$12.0	$12.0
Coaxial network	0	0	8.0	6.0
Total Cabling Costs (thousands of dollars)	$53.7	$37.7	$52.6	$94.9

Note:
* Based on a configuration of 200 outlets evenly distributed among three adjacent floors using plenum-rated cable and unionized electrical workers.

Exhibit II-5-4. Servco's Cabling Network Alternatives and Costs*

the high cost of IBM Type 2 cable. Options 3 and 4 have the lowest twisted-pair cabling materials cost, at $22,600. The cost of twisted-pair materials for option 2 is $25,700, which is close to the cost of options 3 and 4, but option 2 provides the additional functions of option 1.

Coaxial network cabling materials include cabling and cabling components. There are no coaxial cabling costs for options 1 and 2. Broadband coaxial cable is slightly less expensive than the baseband coaxial cable required for Ethernet thick-wire cabling (used for vertical runs between floors) and Ethernet thin-wire cabling (used for horizontal runs). Servco requires three thin-wire loops per floor to connect approximately 65 outlets per floor.

The broadband coaxial cabling components are considerably less expensive than those for an equivalently sized Ethernet baseband network. Broadband coaxial cabling components include eight port taps that cost approximately $50 each. Servco's Ethernet baseband network requires a $260 tap and transceiver for each of the 160 outlets. Although Servco's Ethernet network design is somewhat less expensive in terms of labor costs for the coaxial network, the additional cabling component costs make this alternative the most expensive by a sizable margin of approximately 80%.

Cabling labor costs include twisted-pair network and coaxial network installation. The labor costs for installing twisted-pair cabling are equal for all options except option 1, because the heavier Type 2 cable generally costs approximately 15% more to install.

Option 2, which uses custom-designed 22-gauge twisted-pair cabling, is the least expensive of the four alternatives, with a total cost of $37,700. Options 1 and 3 are equally priced at approximately $53,000, but option 3 is preferred because of its more comprehensive support for Servco's future communications requirements. Option 4 is the most expensive alternative, costing $94,900, but it does not offer the support of option 3. Although option 2 is the least expensive alternative, option 3 provides the best price/performance ratio.

THE COMPUTER AND COMMUNICATIONS RELOCATION BUDGET

Servco elected to install option 3, the broadband coaxial and twisted-pair hybrid. Exhibit II-5-5 summarizes Servco's relocation project budget estimate for computer and communications expenses on the basis of a final configuration of 125 telephone instruments, 40 MS-DOS microcomputers, 30 Apple microcomputers, three video surveillance cameras, and six controlled access doors.

The budget for the telephone PBX switch and associated station equipment was $80,000, with an additional $6,000 for a standalone call accounting device. Cabling materials, including two controllers for the Apple microcomputer network along with tools and supplies, were budgeted at $37,000, with an additional $20,000 for installation by unionized electrical workers. A small uninterruptible power supply able to handle the telephone PBX switch, access control equipment, and LAN components was budgeted at $8,000.

Item Description		Budget Amount (thousands of dollars)
Telephone PBX switch and station equipment		$ 80.0
PBX call-accounting hardware and software		6.0
Communications cabling materials		37.0
Twisted-pair cabling materials	$22.6	
Coaxial network materials	10.0	
Apple star controllers	3.4	
Tools and supplies	1.0	
Communications cabling labor		20.0
Twisted-pair network	12.0	
Coaxial network materials	8.0	
Uninterruptible power supply (UPS)		8.0
LAN-related components		46.0
Compaq 386/110 2M-byte server	9.5	
Tape backup unit	1.7	
Novell NetWare 2.15	2.8	
Novell UPS card and Apple package	0.5	
Network interface cards	30.0	
Installation of LAN hardware and software	1.5	
Video surveillance network interface equipment		6.0
Access control equipment		16.0
Consulting project management fee		12.0
Network design and certification	5.0	
Project implementation	7.0	
Subtotal of project budget items		231.0
Sales tax and shipping charges		20.0
Contingency (at 5%)		11.0
Total Project Budget		$262.0

Note:
* Budget estimates are based on a configuration of 125 telephones, 40 MS-DOS microcomputers, 30 Apple microcomputers, three cameras, and six access doors.

Exhibit II-5-5. Computer and Communications Relocation Project Budget Estimate*

Servco chose a Novell LAN operating system using Zenith Z-LAN 4000 network interface boards. A Compaq Deskpro 386 with 2M bytes of random access memory and 100M bytes of hard disk storage, costing $9,500, was chosen as the initial file server. A tape backup unit, Novell's uninterruptible power supply interface card, and Novell's NetWare Version 2.15 with Novell's Apple network support product were all added to the file server. The cost of the server with these options totaled $16,000. Forty network interface cards were purchased at a cost of $750 each. The overall budget for LAN-related components totaled $46,000.

Servco budgeted $6,000 for video surveillance network interface equipment and $16,000 for access control equipment. Servco's cost for network design, network certification, and project management was $12,000.

The computer and communications project budget items came to a subtotal of $231,000. An additional $20,000 was budgeted for sales tax and shipping charges. Contingency was budgeted at 5% or $20,000, to accommodate addi-

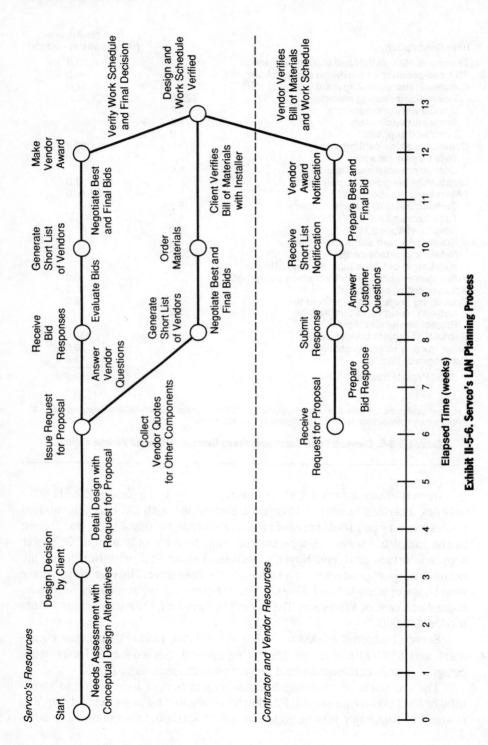

Exhibit II-5-6. Servco's LAN Planning Process

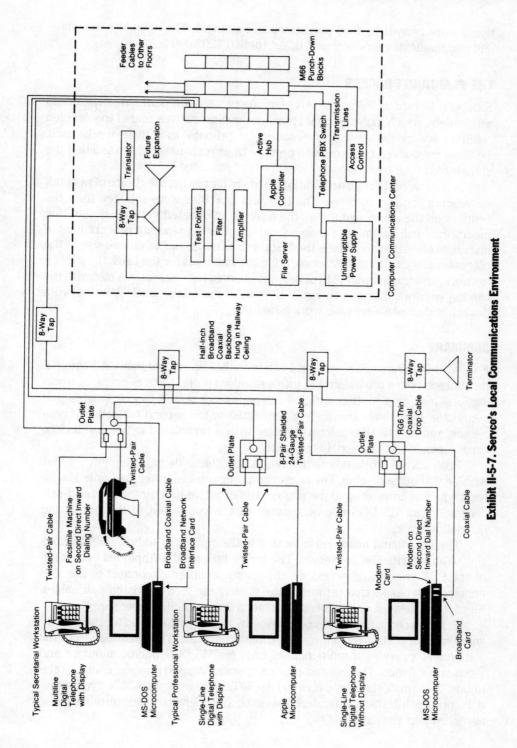

Exhibit II-5-7. Servco's Local Communications Environment

tional work caused by field conditions and changes. The complete computer and communications relocation budget totaled $262,000.

THE PLANNING PROCESS

Exhibit II-5-6 shows Servco's LAN planning process. Preparation of the needs assessment, which included conceptual design alternatives, and of the detailed cabling network design with the request for proposal took three weeks each. Vendors were given two weeks to prepare their responses, and evaluating the vendor bids took two weeks.

Servco went through an additional step of narrowing the choice of network installation vendors to three. The best and final bids were solicited from the vendors on the shortened list on the basis of an updated network design that incorporated all last-minute changes. Servco selected separate procurement of materials and labor to reduce the installer's markup and to ensure use of the highest-quality materials. After ordering the materials for the LAN, the cabling network, and the telephone PBX network, Servco representatives met with the cabling network installer to verify the bill of materials, finalize the network design, and create a realistic work schedule.

SUMMARY

Exhibit II-5-7 shows Servco's local communications environment. All communications services are integrated into a standard outlet plate. Secretarial workstations include a multiline digital telephone connected to one twisted-pair connector, a facsimile transceiver connected to the second twisted-pair connector, and an MS-DOS microcomputer with a broadband network interface card attached to the coaxial connector.

Professional workstations include a single-line digital telephone, either with or without a display. The microcomputer used is either an Apple Macintosh, which is connected to the star controller active hub through twisted-pair cabling, or an MS-DOS microcomputer that is connected to the broadband coaxial network.

The broadband head end is located in the computer and communications center along with the file server. The active hub for the Apple network, telephone PBX switch, and access control microcomputer all connect to the M66 punch-down blocks that terminate the station and feeder twisted-pair cables. All of these devices are connected to the uninterruptible power supply.

Servco's communications requirements for the present and for the next 10 years are supported by the hybrid cabling network. The broadband coaxial component provides a multichannel LAN for MS-DOS microcomputers and video surveillance. The twisted-pair component supports access control, telephone, voice mail, the single-channel AppleTalk network, IBM 3270-type terminals, printer interface extenders, facsimile transceivers, telex terminals, and asynchronous terminals.

II-6
Design of an 802.3 Ethernet Network

ANDY RICHTER • LEWIS F. SAETTEL

T he decision to upgrade the Ethernet network at the School of Engineering at Vanderbilt University required the consideration of several design goals and conditions:

- Incorporating an existing installed base of SUN workstations.
- Providing transparent user access to platforms from different vendors.
- Supporting reduced-function workstations.
- Sharing printers, plotters, and tape drives to reduce network costs.
- Providing electronic mail and file transfer within and outside the network.
- Allowing access to other networks, including CSnet, Bitnet, and Usenet.

The School of Engineering had already installed a small Ethernet network. It consisted of 25 68020-based SUN workstations connected by ThinLAN cable. The constant use of these workstations made it necessary to incorporate this segment into the new network with no loss of functional transparency to the user and no downtime.

The network design had to provide high connectivity for various types of workstations and peripherals. The School of Engineering is a diversified research facility that relies on outside sources for research support, and these sources bring into the school's network a variety of computer equipment. An investigation established that the existing 68020-based network and most of the high-end and reduced-function workstations in use were supported by Ethernet.

The network staff then needed to locate a suitable Ethernet vendor. Some of the vendors considered were Digital Equipment Corp, SUN Microsystems, and Hewlett-Packard (HP). Each of the vendors was provided with an initial proposal that stated the desired configuration and predicted growth over a four-year period. The vendor had to meet these use requirements and provide the lowest cost of ownership over the four years.

SUN and Hewlett-Packard most closely matched these requirements. The initial prices of SUN workstations were lower, but the cost of ownership of the Hewlett-Packard workstations proved to be less expensive over the four years.

Hewlett-Packard also manufactures a variety of networking equipment for the implementation and technical support of an Ethernet network. For these reasons, Hewlett-Packard was chosen as the primary vendor for workstations, file servers, peripheral devices, and equipment for the construction of the Ethernet LAN.

Computer models 318, 330, 350, and 840 from the HP 9000 Series were chosen for the network. The 9000 Series 300 workstations run a virtual memory version of UNIX called HP-UX. HP-UX provides electronic mail, can transfer files between various platforms, can access other networks both within and outside the university, and allows the sharing of peripheral devices.

The initial network configuration consisted of one backbone segment connecting two networks of more than 100 80286-based HP Vectras each. The network covers two buildings, one with six floors and one with three floors. Exhibit II-6-1 represents the network configuration in each of the two buildings. The two buildings are connected by the campus broadband network. The two 80286 networks are standalone HP ThinLAN networks. The 80286 platforms use an HP ThinLAN interface card with either HP ThinLAN server software or HP ThinLAN user software. The HP ThinLAN networks are also configured as single-segment networks with multiple file servers. Exhibit II-6-2 shows the connection of clients and servers on the ThinLAN networks.

INTERCONNECTION

Computers and peripherals on an Ethernet network may be connected by ThickLAN or ThinLAN segments, or a combination of both. ThickLAN and ThinLAN have a number of requirements or restrictions that must be followed to stay within the specifications of an Ethernet or IEEE 802.3 network. These specifications and the estimates for the growth rate of the School of Engineering governed the initial design of the network. Some of the specifications for the ThickLAN and ThinLAN segments are described here.

ThickLAN

A ThickLAN segment, sometimes known as a backbone segment or cable, consists of a thick coaxial cable fitted with a 50-ohm terminator on each end. Only one end of the backbone must be grounded to prevent electrical hazards and to prevent noise from ground loop currents. The cable is available with either a PVC or Teflon sheath. The Teflon sheath is required by most building fire codes if the backbone is not installed inside conduit.

To prevent reflections, the backbone cable must be a multiple of 2.5 m in length, with a maximum length of 500 m. ThickLAN coaxial cable is available with or without premarked 2.5-m intervals. Use of the premarked cable increases the ease of installation.

To connect devices to the backbone, a media access unit (MAU) is placed

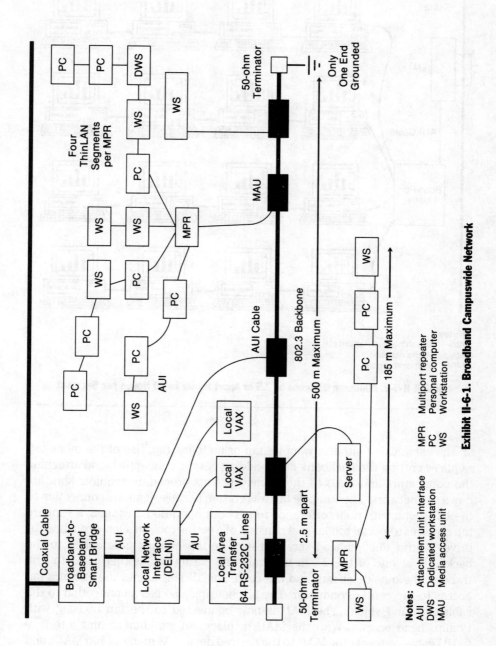

Exhibit II-6-1. Broadband Campuswide Network

Notes:
AUI   Attachment unit interface   MPR   Multiport repeater
DWS   Dedicated workstation   PC   Personal computer
MAU   Media access unit   WS   Workstation

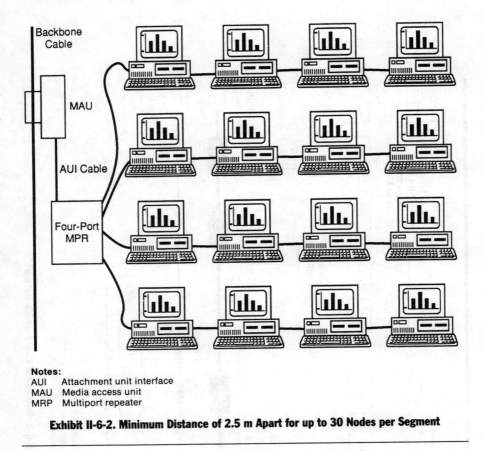

Notes:
AUI   Attachment unit interface
MAU   Media access unit
MRP   Multiport repeater

Exhibit II-6-2. Minimum Distance of 2.5 m Apart for up to 30 Nodes per Segment

on the cable using either a vampire tap or an inline tap. Use of the inline tap requires cutting the backbone cable, adding N-type connectors, and attaching the connectors and MAU to the inline tap. This procedure requires shutting down the network. The vampire tap was chosen because it allows connection to the backbone with no interference to network operation. Installing a vampire tap requires a special toolkit that consists of a coring tool, an allen wrench, a nut driver, and a Phillips-head screwdriver. The tap housing is attached to the backbone at one of the 2.5-m intervals; the coring tool is then used to drill through the outside sheath and the cable shield. This allows the vampire tap access to the center conductor. The tap housing also has a connection to the cable's ground shield. The MAU is now connected to the tap housing with Phillips-head screws. With the MAU in place, an attachment unit interface (AUI) cable connects the MAU to the desired device. As many as 100 MAUs and 1,024 devices may be installed on a 500-m backbone segment.

ThinLAN

ThinLAN cable is also coaxial type but is less expensive to use and easier to install. The requirement that the segment length be a multiple of 2.5 m also applies to ThinLAN, but the segment length is limited to 200 m. Vendors may impose additional restrictions. ThinLAN segments are fitted at each end with a 50-ohm terminator. Neither end of a ThinLAN segment is grounded.

Many workstations and personal computers provide a ThinLAN port, which uses a BNC connector. A T connector is used with each device to attach it to the ThinLAN segment. Computers and devices that have only an AUI type of interface may be connected to ThinLAN by using a ThinMAU, a small box that has a short AUI cable for connection to the device, and a BNC T connector for connection to the cable. If the workstation already has an AUI drop cable and an MAU, the N-type connectors on the MAU can be converted to BNC with an adapter. As many as 30 devices can be connected, in a daisy chain, on one 200-m ThinLAN segment.

Repeaters

When the length of a backbone or a ThinLAN segment has to exceed specifications to reach a desired workstation or computer, a repeater may be installed. A repeater receives packets from one segment and retransmits them to the adjoining segment, allowing the maximum cable lengths to be exceeded. Another useful device is a multiport repeater, which retransmits packets it receives over each of its ThinLAN ports. Multiport repeaters are useful, for example, in corridors that need 200-m ThinLAN ports that run in opposite directions. A four-port multiport repeater directs data to four 200-m ThinLAN segments.

One standard of IEEE 802.3 Ethernet states that no packet may pass through more than two repeaters to reach its destination. For this reason, careful network planning is required. Placing file servers and multiport repeaters directly on the backbone prevents clients from transmitting through more than the maximum number of repeaters.

Bridges

A bridge provides communications between two networks. Some bridges convert broadband packets to baseband packets and vice versa; others connect two separate baseband or broadband network segments. A device known as a smart bridge connects two backbone segments and can detect which devices are on each segment. It builds an address table that it uses to determine whether packets transmitted on one side need to be forwarded to the other side of the bridge. This type of bridge reduces network congestion by restricting data to the segments of the network on which it belongs. A smart bridge may also be programmed to allow or disallow packets from specific devices or to broadcast packets.

SUMMARY

Consultations with the vendors and research into a number of network configurations led to the construction of the School of Engineering Distributed Computing Network (SEDCON), as diagrammed in Exhibit II-6-1. The network performed well until the number of servers, diskless and disk-equipped workstations, and reduced-function workstations installed on the network approached 200. At that point, connectivity slowed during busy periods. Because the largest number of SEDCON workstations are diskless, data traffic is often heavy enough to slow down the network. A few of these diskless workstations were upgraded, either by adding memory or installing fixed disk drives. This reduced the amount of data swapping over the network.

Because with a single-segment network of this type any faulty device affects the entire network, a Hewlett-Packard protocol analyzer was purchased to aid in troubleshooting. It provides useful information about the status of the network. First it showed that only 40% to 60% of the network's bandwidth can be used. This appears to be the rule rather than the exception with this type of network. The protocol analyzer can also locate, in most cases, a malfunctioning transmitter or a cable problem. The analyzer may be configured to monitor, for example, the traffic among all devices, between specific devices, or between specific protocols. The purchase of a protocol analyzer is recommended.

Another change to the network was the purchase of two smart bridges to segment the backbone into three pieces. There has been a significant improvement in speed since the smart bridges were installed.

Section III
LAN Technologies and Standards

Local area network (LAN) standards and technologies constitute a level of sophistication and complexity that rivals even the most advanced computer architecture. To the uninitiated, this array of alternatives seems like a bewildering assortment of products, each supported by a different and often conflicting set of claims by its supporters. To help the network manager who needs to make sense of it all, this section of the *Handbook* provides an orderly survey of the most important LAN technologies and standards. More specifically, this section restricts its focus to the technologies and standards that work together to create the foundation of a single LAN. Interconnection technologies and those that build on the LAN foundation are covered in subsequent sections.

LANs employ many different technologies. Some of these technologies have roots in other communications-related disciplines; some were designed specifically for LANs. Chapter III-1, "A Primer on LAN Technologies," touches on a number of these technologies by giving a technical overview, some background information, and basic trade-offs associated with each. Included in this chapter are discussions on topologies, transmission media, switching, modulation, encoding, multiplexing, and access methods.

Chapter III-2, "Wiring Media," takes a closeup look at the subject of media. The media discussed include shielded and unshielded twisted-pair wire, coaxial cable, and optical fiber. Each is considered with respect to several technical factors, including propagation characteristics, noise, and cost. The chapter concludes with a hypothetical case study.

Chapter III-3, "Fiber-Optic and Copper LANs," also examines wiring media. Particular emphasis is placed on optical fiber and on the structured cabling systems supported by major computer and communications vendors. Examples of common LANs are discussed, with particular attention to how these LANs can be supported over a structured cabling system.

The subject of premises wiring not only has caught the attention of major vendors but has also been the subject of discussion in standards organizations. In particular, the International Telephone and Telegraph Consultative Committee (CCITT) has undertaken premises wiring standardization to some degree in its integrated services digital network (ISDN) recommendations. Chapter III-4, "ISDN Standards and Premises Wiring," discusses the ISDN standards related to premises wiring. Chapter III-4 states that, even for the network manager who does not foresee a need for ISDN, these standards should be considered, because a premises wiring system conforming to ISDN will, in fact, support many non-ISDN requirements, including most popular LANs.

In any data transmission system, it is necessary to have a scheme for representing binary data as transmitted signal elements. Such a scheme is known as an encoding technique. There are many such schemes available, and the one implemented for a given system impacts both quality and cost. Chapter III-5, "Encoding Techniques in Local Area Networks," discusses the major encoding techniques used in standardized LANs today, including a description of each technique, as well as its pros and cons.

In a similar fashion, all communications systems require a means of sharing the available media. Such methods are referred to as access methods. Chapter III-6, "LAN Access Protocols," surveys access methods and protocols in general, then focuses on those specifically oriented toward LANs. The chapter also introduces the Institute for Electrical and Electronics Engineers (IEEE) 802 family of standards and provides some general guidelines for comparison.

Chapter III-7, "IEEE 802 Standards," discusses the IEEE 802 family in considerably more detail—down to the bit level in many cases. The chapter discusses how the standards fit within the open systems interconnection (OSI) reference model and provides detailed descriptions of the three most common of the 802 standards—802.3, 802.4, and 802.5. The standard for metropolitan area networks, 802.6, is also discussed briefly, followed by a discussion of internetworking 802 LANs.

Similarly, for high-speed LANs, Chapter III-8 discusses standardization of "The Fiber Distributed Data Interface" (FDDI). This chapter provides a brief history of FDDI, discusses in detail the various standards that make up FDDI, and concludes with an up-to-date status of FDDI standardization efforts.

III-1
A Primer on LAN Technologies

ASGHAR I. NOOR

Data communications requirements in early generations of computers were minimal, because of the technology's emphasis on batch processing. Increased reliance on distributed processing, and experience with wide area networks (e.g., ARPAnet), helped accelerate the development of LANs, a data communications technique that combines reliability and high bandwidth.

LAN BASICS

LANs can carry data, voice, and video simultaneously over limited distances at a high data rate without complex switching, routing, error checking, and recovery procedures.

All LANs share four common characteristics:

- Data traffic.
- Limited geographic coverage.
- High bandwidth.
- Support of distributed processing.

LANs can be grouped according to the following criteria:

- Architecture, or topology.
- Switching technique.
- Transmission medium.
- Encoding and modulation technique.
- Control and access method.

Topology, control and access method, transmission medium, and switching technique are independent of each other. In theory, any control scheme can be used with any access mechanism on any medium to support any topological arrangement using any switching technique. In practice, certain topologies are combined with certain access mechanisms and transmission facilities.

141

Topology

In the context of communications networks, topology refers to the ways that end points, or stations, are interconnected. It is determined by the layout of communications links, switching elements, and data paths between any pair of stations. Thus, the choice of topology is influenced by such factors as reliability, expandability, and performance. Unconstrained topology is the most general type, characterized by stations that are connected in an arbitrary pattern (see Exhibit III-1-1). An unconstrained topology has no significant advantages and requires a high degree of complexity at each station. As a result, LAN designers use constrained topologies, which have to meet several requirements. They must:

- Ensure proper receipt of all message traffic.
- Route traffic across the network's least-cost path.
- Minimize the length of the channel.
- Support the least expensive transmission medium.
- Provide the best possible end-user response time and throughput.

These objectives can be met by a limited number of topologies, which are discussed in the following sections.

Horizontal Topology (Bus and Tree). This is popular as a LAN architecture, and traffic flow is relatively simple to control. As shown in Exhibit III-1-2, the stations are connected to a single transmission line, through which they can communicate with each other directly. Stations are connected passively so that failure in a local station does not bring down the entire network. This topology can be implemented as a bidirectional or unidirectional system. In a bidirectional system (e.g., Ethernet) all the communicating stations are connected to a common cable on which transmission signals propagate in both directions. The interface is capable of identifying and accepting messages being

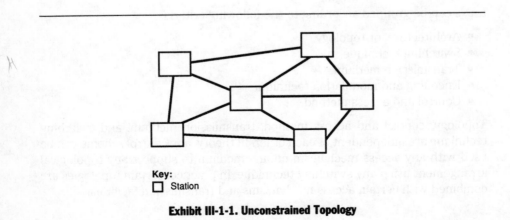

Key:
☐ Station

Exhibit III-1-1. Unconstrained Topology

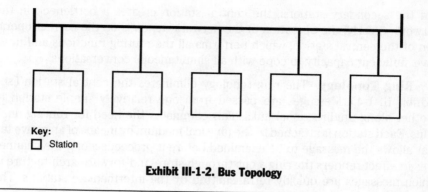

Key:
☐ Station

Exhibit III-1-2. Bus Topology

sent to it. The system using single coaxial cable with bidirectional transmission naturally supports broadcast communications.

The unidirectional system consists of two interconnected one-way channels. Stations are connected to both channels through passive taps. In the simplest case, the tap on the forward portion of the cable is used for message transmission and the tap on the reverse portion is used for message reception.

Star Topology. This is the simplest of all topologies and is very widely used (see Exhibit III-1-3). The stations do not need to make routing decisions; all messages are routed to the central station. This leads to a particularly simple structure for the secondary stations. However, the cost and the complexity involved in making the central station sufficiently reliable may offset the benefits derived from the simplicity of the secondary stations. A star topology is an obvious choice to support a number of terminals in a time-sharing system. If, however, the usual pattern of communication is not between the central station

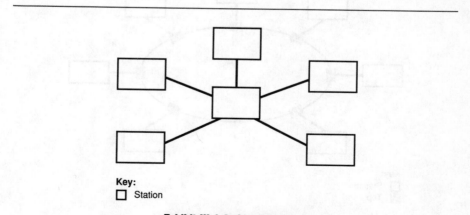

Key:
☐ Station

Exhibit III-1-3. Star Topology

and the secondary stations, the central station creates a bottleneck in the network. Clearly, the operation of the network depends on the correct operation of the central station, which performs all the routing functions and must have sufficient capacity to cope with all simultaneous conversations.

Ring Topology. The ring topology eliminates the central station (see Exhibit III-1-4). Messages are passed from one relatively simple station to another along unidirectional links. This eliminates the need for routing decisions. Each station is attached to the physical medium by means of an active tap that allows the message to be examined before it proceeds along the channel. This in effect renders the ring a cut-through store-and-forward architecture in which messages are quickly retransmitted by the intermediate stations. The delay incurred at each station can be limited to a small number of bits.

A simple access scheme consists of passing the right of access sequentially from station to station. In one implementation, a control token moves around the ring. On receiving the control token, a station may transmit its message; it then passes the token on. In another implementation, message slots circulate continuously. The slots may be empty or full; a station with a ready message waits until an empty slot comes by, marks it as full, and then uses it to send its message.

Hierarchical Topology. A hierarchical topology uses several layers, with multiple stations at one level connected to a single station at the next higher level (see Exhibit III-1-5). In a hierarchical topology, most of the interaction is assumed to exist between the successive levels of the hierarchy (i.e., between parent and child stations). Stations are dedicated to one or a few tasks;

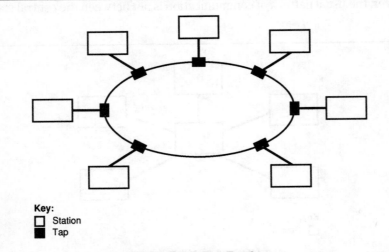

Key:
□ Station
■ Tap

Exhibit III-1-4. Ring Topology

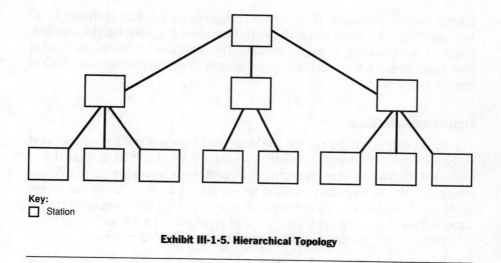

Key:
☐ Station

Exhibit III-1-5. Hierarchical Topology

these are linked to higher-level stations that integrate the output of the lower stations. This topology is often found in factory or order-entry applications.

Switching Technique

Circuit switching involves the establishment of a physical path between two parties before actual communication begins. Before transmission of a message, a reservation signal is sent toward the destination. The reservation signal travels from node to node and reserves the channel along the path. If it cannot find a free channel at any intermediate node, it waits while holding the reserved channel; when a channel becomes free the reservation is made, and it proceeds to the next node and repeats the process. In circuit switching, the transmission of data is independent of bit sequence and is time transparent. Unused capacity is not available to another node.

Unused capacity is a drawback of circuit switching that packet switching overcomes by multiplexing the use of all communications facilities among active nodes. The basic idea is to allocate some or all of the system capacity to one station at a time, but only for a very short time. The sending station is required to divide messages into small units, or packets, for individual transmission. The packet is generally subdivided into a control header part and a data part. The header contains information for directing the packet across the intermediate nodes to the destination station. An intermediate station holds a packet temporarily, until it finds a suitable route for it.

The designers of packet switching systems are faced with the problem of choosing line capacities and topologies that will result in relatively high use with relatively low congestion.

The packet switching technique can also be implemented in terms of multiaccess, or broadcast. Here, a single transmission medium is shared by all stations. Each station is given the entire channel, but only for the duration required to transmit a single packet. The multiaccess/broadcast packet switching technique statistically multiplexes the communication channel among its users.

Transmission Medium

The transmission medium is the physical path between the transmitter and receiver in a communications system. Media can be classified as guided and unguided. With a guided medium, the electromagnetic waves are guided along a physical path. An unguided medium allows signals to move in all directions. Broadcast transmission of electromagnetic waves (e.g., radio frequency, microwave, infrared) is an example of the use of an unguided medium.

Transmission media are evaluated using the following criteria:

- Physical description—The construction and materials (i.e., twisted-pair wire, coaxial cable, optical fiber).
- Transmission characteristics—These include the signaling mechanism (i.e., analog or digital), modulation techniques, capacity, and frequency range.
- Connectivity—Point-to-point or multipoint.
- Geographic scope—The maximum distance between points on the network.
- Noise immunity—How well the medium protects data from contamination.
- Relative cost—The cost of components, installation, and management.

The transmission medium establishes the physical connection between stations. The most widely used physical media for LANs are shielded and unshielded twisted-pair, coaxial, and fiber-optic cable.

Twisted-Pair Cable. The twisted-pair cable used today is generally composed of 24-gauge wire (see Exhibit III-1-6). Transmission distance is limited by such factors as the direct-current loop resistance and the alternating-current attenuation of the wire pairs, which are susceptible to radio frequency emission and pose a problem when security is important. At high frequencies the near-end crosstalk of twisted-pair telephone cable is typically 35 dB worse than that of coaxial cable. The attenuation is approximately 2.3 times that of coaxial cable.

Coaxial Cable. Coaxial cable has become a popular medium for LANs because of its large capacity, low error rates, and configuration flexibility (see Exhibit III-1-6). It is an excellent high-performance substitute for twisted-pair cable. Coaxial cable has a single center conductor, surrounded by an insulator, then a wire-mesh shield, and finally a polymer (usually a PVC) jacket. It is generally classified by its physical size and characteristic impedance. Although

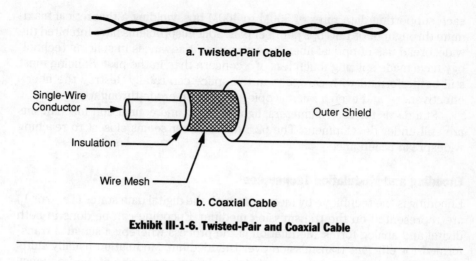

a. Twisted-Pair Cable

Single-Wire
Conductor

Outer Shield

Insulation

Wire Mesh

b. Coaxial Cable

Exhibit III-1-6. Twisted-Pair and Coaxial Cable

terms like broadband and baseband really describe signaling techniques, they often are used to describe the coaxial cable used for LANs. In baseband, the cable's bandwidth is used primarily to transmit one channel at a single frequency, on the order of 10 to 20 MHz. In broadband, the cable's bandwidth is divided to create a large number of frequency-divided subchannels.

Cable television systems usually use 75-ohm coaxial cable with a usable bandwidth of 300 to 400 MHz. Interactive communication requires bidirectional (two-way) transmission. If there is one available cable, the approach is to split it into downstream and upstream frequency bands. There are three common approaches: subsplit, mid-split, and high-split. The subsplit system uses the 50- to 450-MHz band in the forward direction and the 5- to 30-MHz band in the reverse direction. The mid-split system uses the 250- to 450-MHz band (forward) and 5- to 200-MHz band (reverse). The high-split system has a guardband between the two splits. This guardband may be used to carry some control information.

Optical Fiber. Optical fibers are made of plastic or glass and can serve as a very high-performance transmission medium. In optical fiber technology, electrical signals are transformed into light pulses by a modulator, transmitted over the fiber by a light source, then detected and converted back into electrical signals by photoelectric diodes. The fiber has enough bandwidth to sustain a data rate of several gigabits per second. The error rates are very low, and transmission is not affected by electrical or electromagnetic interference. Fiber-optic cables are very small and light. As a result, fiber is expected to become the chosen medium for LANs during the 1990s.

Light-emitting diodes (LEDs) are the light source for most LAN applications of optical fiber technology, whereas lasers are found more often in long-haul networks. A single LED is capable of transmitting four different colors, each supporting data rates of 300M to 400M bps, yielding a theoretical maximum throughput of 1.6G bps per fiber pair. Splicing problems have inhibited the widespread use of optical fiber; however, recent advances in splicing technology have made splicing much less of a concern than in the past. Splicing must still be performed with care; dirt in the splice can totally destroy the fiber's effectiveness, and even a microscopic scratch can erode throughput.

Standards for core diameters, light sources, and connection mechanisms are still under development. The 62.5-micron fiber seems closest to reaching widespread acceptance.

Encoding and Modulation Techniques

Encoding is the technique by means of which the digital data states (i.e., 0 or 1) are represented on the transmission medium. Encoding can be done in both digital and analog forms. Modulation is the process whereby a signal is transformed for efficient transmission over the medium. Modulation usually shifts the frequency content of the encoded signal from one region of the frequency spectrum to another.

Several digital encoding techniques are non–return to zero (NRZ), Manchester, differential Manchester, and duobinary. Examples of waveforms are shown in Exhibit III-1-7.

One of the simplest ways to transmit a digital signal is to use two different voltage levels. In NRZ coding (see Exhibit III-1-7a), a 0 is represented by a set negative voltage and a 1 by a set positive voltage. As a result, the signal does not revert to 0 volts unless it changes states. The disadvantage is that a sequence of all 1s or 0s will be coded as a constant voltage; this large direct-current offset will cause engineering problems on long stretches of cable.

Manchester coding (see Exhibit III-1-7b) provides a binary waveform with no direct-current offset. The midpoint transition between the two voltage levels serves as both a clock signal and data; a high-to-low transition signifies a 1; a low-to-high transition signifies a 0. Because clock and data signals are included in a serial data stream, Manchester coding is considered to be self-clocking. A modified format called differential Manchester coding (see Exhibit III-1-7c) uses a mid-bit transition only to provide clocking. Here, the coding of 0 or 1 is represented, respectively, by the presence or absence of a transition at the beginning of the bit period. The advantage of this method is that polarity is irrelevant: data is encoded as the presence or absence of a transition in either direction. IEEE 802 allows the use of either Manchester or differential Manchester coding.

Duobinary encoding (see Exhibit III-1-7d) is used to reduce bandwidth requirements during transmission; in this form of coding, a 1 is encoded as the same signal level used for the last 1 if the number of 0s between the two 1s is even. Otherwise, the 1 is encoded as the opposite basic signal level. A 0 is always encoded as a zero level.

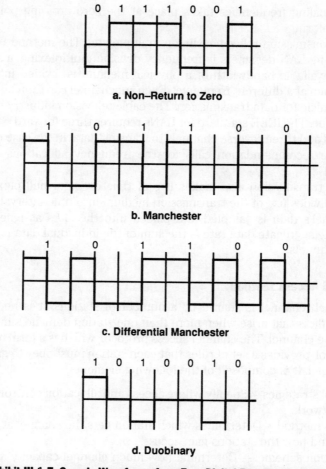

Exhibit III-1-7. Sample Waveforms from Four Digital Encoding Techniques

Two analog encoding techniques, phase shift keying and frequency shift keying, are frequently applied with LANs. In phase shift keying, two signals are shifted in phase by 180°. The transition between these two signals usually takes place at the zero crossing point to reduce the switching energy. With frequency shift keying, information is impressed on a carrier by shifting the frequency of the transmitted signal to one of a small set of defined frequencies. With a single-channel coaxial system that uses frequency shift keying, information is encoded, frequency modulated onto a carrier, and impressed on the coaxial transmission medium. Here, only one information signal is present in the media.

Phase-coherent modulation is a special form of frequency shift keying, in which the signaling frequencies are related to the data rate. Transition between the two signaling frequencies takes place at the zero crossing point of the carrier waveform.

Data transmission relies heavily on multiplexing. The method used most extensively by LAN designers is frequency division multiplexing, a system in which the available bandwidth of a physical medium is divided into several channels, each at a different frequency. Each subchannel can then be used as a separate vehicle for data transmission. The cable television industry pioneered this technique. The IEEE standard for LANs requires three forward channels to receive data and three reverse channels to transmit data. In the case of a single medium the recommendation calls for the frequency allocations shown in Exhibit III-1-8.

Digital transmission also makes use of time division multiplexing. This technique divides use of the transmission medium into time intervals or slots. Each channel's data is sampled and placed into the slots assigned to that channel. The aggregate data rate is the sum of the individual data rates of the sampled channels.

Control and Access Method

Because each channel is shared by a number of stations, it is necessary to resolve conflicts that arise when more than one station demand simultaneous access to the channel. The channel access protocol, which is a form of multiaccess protocol, provides a set of rules that each station must obey to gain access to the channel. It is composed of the following elements:

- Control strategies—Specify where access and allocation control resides in the network.
- Access method—Determines which station gets the channel at any given time, and how the stations gain access.
- Allocation schemes—Determine how much channel capacity a station is given.

Transmitting Band (MHz)	Receiving Band (MHz)	
	Q Point = 156.25 MHz	Q Point = 192.25 MHz
35.75–53.75	192–210	228–246
41.75–59.75	198–216	234–252
47.75–65.75	204–222	240–258
53.75–71.75	210–228	246–264
59.75–77.75	216–234	252–270
65.75–83.75	222–240	258–276

Exhibit III-1-8. Sub-Band Assignments for a Single-Medium Frequency-Division Multiplexed Network

A network's topology and the interconnection medium in use influence, and may even restrict, choice of access protocol. Other factors influencing the selection of the access protocol are cost, performance, and complexity. The access protocols most frequently used on LANs are shown in Exhibit III-1-9.

The access protocols differ according to the static or dynamic nature of the bandwidth allocation algorithm and the degree to which the algorithm can adapt to changing needs. Thus the principles of operation of the access protocols can be classified as follows:

- Fixed assignment.
- Random assignment.
- Demand assignment.
- Adaptive strategies and mixed modes.

Fixed-assignment techniques allocate channel access to the stations independent of their requirements. Fixed-assignment techniques take two main forms, frequency-division multiple access (FDMA) and time-division multiple access (TDMA).

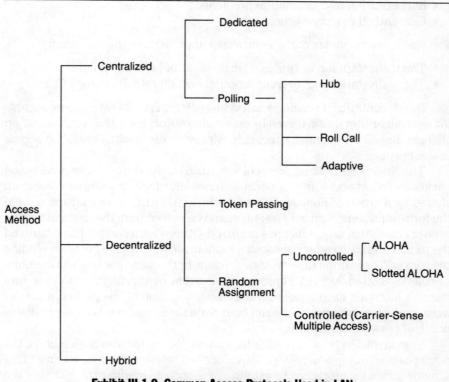

Exhibit III-1-9. Common Access Protocols Used in LANs

In frequency-division multiple access, each station is assigned a fraction of the bandwidth and confines its access to the allocated sub-band. In time-division multiple access, a time slot of predetermined duration is assigned to each station. The station has access to the entire channel bandwidth, but only during the allocated slot. From a performance standpoint, it has been established that time division is superior to frequency division. For otherwise similar systems, the delay is always longer for frequency division than for time division. Frequency division also wastes a fraction of the bandwidth to achieve adequate separation of the sub-bands. Both fixed-assignment techniques lack flexibility because neither can adjust bandwidth allocation.

Random-assignment techniques can be centralized or decentralized. In centralized schemes, channel allocation, conflict resolution, and error recovery are allotted to one preselected station. In a decentralized system, these responsibilities are shared by all the stations on the network.

A centralized scheme offers several advantages, which include:

- Better control over determination of priorities, override provisions, and bandwidth allocation.
- A simple implementation mechanism at each station interface.
- Simplification of coordination problems.
- Guaranteed response times.

The main disadvantages of the centralized approach are the following:

- The main station constitutes a single point of potential failure.
- The main station can become a bottleneck, thereby reducing efficiency.

In a decentralized scheme, each station determines its own access according to an algorithm that is driven by observable outcomes in the communication channel. Random-assignment techniques provide users with controlled access to the channel.

The first decentralized protocol was ALOHA, developed for ground-based packet radio networks. It is applicable, however, to any transmission medium shared by a group of noncoordinated users. In ALOHA, users transmit data in the form of packets; if an acknowledgment is received from the destination, the sender knows that no conflict has occurred. Otherwise, a conflict has destroyed the packet and the sender must wait a random amount of time before resending the packet. The waiting time must be random, or the same packets will continue to collide. Slotted ALOHA improved the system by dividing access time into discrete intervals, each equal to the transmission time of one packet. A sender must start a transmission at the slot boundary. Collisions, in this case, cause less waste of network bandwidth.

The inefficiency of the ALOHA system led to the development of the carrier-sense multiple access (CSMA), or the listen-before-talk, scheme. This scheme increases efficiency by requiring a station to monitor the status of the channel before transmitting. If it detects another station's transmission, the station defers its own transmission until the channel becomes idle. The station may then initiate its own transmission. It is possible for two or more stations to attempt transmission at approximately the same time, and collisions can occur. A station therefore waits a reasonable amount of time after transmission for an acknowledgment. This time depends on the maximum round-trip propagation delay and provides for the fact that the acknowledging station must also contend for the channel. In the absence of an acknowledgment, the station assumes that a collision has occurred and retransmits.

CSMA systems suffer from a number of deficiencies. When two packets collide, the medium is unusable during transmission of both damaged packets. If a packet is long in comparison with propagation time, the amount of wasted bandwidth can be considerable. This waste can be reduced if a station continues to listen to the medium while it is transmitting. CSMA with collision detection overcomes this problem by using the following algorithm:

1. If the medium is idle, transmission is initiated.
2. If the medium is busy, the station waits an amount of time drawn from a probability distribution and repeats step 1.
3. The station listens to the channel during transmission.
4. If a collision is detected during transmission, the transmission is immediately stopped and the channel is jammed by transmitting for a fixed amount of time to ensure that all stations are aware of a collision.
5. After transmitting the jamming signal, the station executes a back-off algorithm, then goes back to step 1.

The back-off algorithm is critical. If the back-off delays are too short, collisions reoccur, wasting valuable channel capacity. On the other hand, if the delay intervals are too long, the channel remains idle. With random back-off, two stations involved in a collision are less likely to collide on their next tries. To ensure back-off stability a binary exponential back-off algorithm is used. In this case, the mean back-off delay for a new packet is set to some initial value, which doubles each time a transmission attempt with this packet results in a collision. After a number of unsuccessful attempts, the station gives up and reports an error.

III-2
Wiring Media

LARRY VAN DER JAGT

Much work has been done to determine which strategies for building and campus wiring minimize life cycle costs associated with cabling. This problem is assuming increasing importance as the role of data communications grows within organizations. Given the cost associated with relocating data cabling, organizations are increasingly being wired in saturation fashion, which involves locating outlets everywhere, as is currently the case with telephone wiring. In this wiring environment various media are being combined to form hybrid networks, which use low-cost media such as unshielded twisted-pair telephone cable in short-distance, high-density applications, and connect geographically distributed areas with coaxial or fiber-optic cable.

The limitations of the various media, and the appropriate use for each, are the technical issues that are examined in this chapter.

TYPES OF MEDIA AND MEDIA IMPAIRMENTS

In any network it is the physical medium that performs the task of conveying signals from one network location to another. In an organizationwide network use can be made of simple unshielded twisted-pair telephone wiring, coaxial and fiber-optic cable, and microwave and satellite links. LAN applications usually require the wiring of a building or a campus with a physical medium (i.e., cable). Although this represents the norm for today's technology, there are indications that LANs using radio frequency transmission may soon become practical.

Signal Problems

Signal-to-noise (S/N) ratios in a LAN are rarely so low as to interfere with communications; the limiting factor is signal distortion. This distortion has a variety of sources. Mismatches in the cable characteristics and improper termination of cables result in electronic reflections that can distort or create new, unwanted data pulses. The acoustic echo in a cave or canyon is analogous to data pulses caused by reflections. Considerable problems could arise if, in a transmission between banking computers, a message was accepted multiple times because of an echo. An echoed message such as "Withdraw $100" would almost certainly cause complaints from someone. Communications systems contain safeguards against this type of problem, but the example is presented as an illustration of the potential effect of this impairment. Reflections are the most common source of problems in LANs.

Although the noise level in a LAN is usually low enough to allow satisfactory transmission, one possible exception is a network that is not properly or adequately grounded. In this situation, spurious currents can completely hide the data signal. If noise is a problem in a LAN, the grounding of the network should be examined carefully. Signal distortion can be caused by the nature of the data pulses. A data pulse typically has many frequency components, which when combined make up the actual pulse. Different frequencies may travel at different speeds across the medium. This causes signal distortion. As an extreme example, if a system were designed in which the signal representing a 1 traveled more quickly than the signal representing a 0 and the amount $001.00 were transmitted, the 1 could travel faster than the 0s and arrive ahead of them, causing the received amount to be $100.00 instead of the intended $1.00. This particular error would not occur in a real-world network, but it illustrates the problem, which is termed group delay. After ground problems and reflections, group delay is the most probable source of signal impairment in a LAN.

Unshielded Twisted-Pair Cable

The most commonly installed wiring by far is telephone wiring (i.e., unshielded twisted pair). Generally the use of telephone wiring for data communications has been limited to low-speed point-to-point links between individual computer systems. Popular standards such as the RS-232 interface allow connection of a wide variety of devices. Modulation and demodulation (modem) techniques allow for low-speed data communications over the public telephone system. It is now possible to provide higher-speed data communications over LANs using unshielded twisted-pair cable, but at high data rates planning for the electrical characteristics of unshielded twisted-pair cable becomes important.

Different varieties of unshielded twisted-pair cable have different electrical characteristics. When an existing cable plant is being considered for use in a LAN environment, it may be difficult to determine exactly what type of wire is installed and how it is routed. Tests can be performed to determine the characteristics of an existing cable plant. Such tests should be seriously considered before a new LAN is run over an existing cable plant. It is the cable's twisted construction that is responsible for its immunity to noise and low radiation characteristics; therefore no attempt to run a LAN across cable made up of untwisted-wire pairs should be made.

Propagation Characteristics. Unshielded twisted-pair cable's group delay and attenuation characteristics limit its use to relatively short distances, usually approximately 300 ft. Exhibit III-2-1 illustrates what 300 ft of unshielded twisted-pair cable does to a data pulse. The pulse duration shown is 100 ns, typical of a 10M-bps system. The pulse with the square sides is the pulse as it would look going into the cable, and the rounded pulse is the pulse as it would look coming out of the cable. The level of pulse degradation shown in the exhibit is reasonably severe; communications in the presence of this level of distortion, although possible, is not desirable. For this reason, the use of unshielded twisted-pair cable for LANs is practical only in small areas in which the individual cable runs are not expected to exceed about 300 ft. In addition, attempts to use unshielded twisted-pair cable for data rates in excess of 10M bps should be made only after evaluation of alternatives. A detailed analysis of the actual medium should also be made.

If the economics of twisted-pair cable are such that it must be used in a given situation above these data-rate or distance limitations, there are compensation techniques that distort pulses before transmission and undistort them after transmission. To use these techniques the nature of the distortion caused by a particular run of cable must be known. There are restrictions with respect to cable specifications and run lengths, and these should be well understood before an organization proceeds with such a network.

Noise Considerations. Another consideration with unshielded twisted-pair cable is noise coupling between adjacent conductors in the same cable. This problem can be particularly severe when conventional telephone wiring is combined with LAN wiring in the same cable and when ringer pulses are

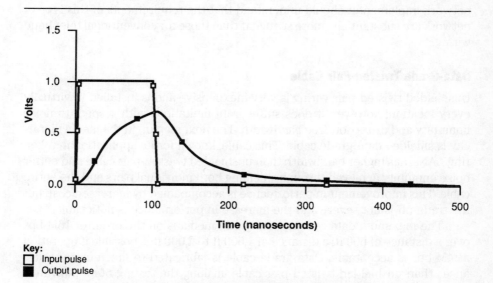

Key:
☐ Input pulse
■ Output pulse

Exhibit III-2-1. Propagation Characteristics of Unshielded Twisted-Pair Cable

present. These pulses (used to ring the telephone) can cause noise bursts in the cable pairs that are in proximity to the telephone cable pairs. Although these noise bursts may be relatively infrequent (depending on how busy the telephones are), they can cause significant disruption of LAN data traffic, particularly if the LAN software does not recover gracefully. It is advisable, when possible, to dedicate a cable to the network rather than having it carry data and voice together.

Cost Considerations. The primary reason for using unshielded twisted-pair cable in networks is to minimize the cost of the physical cable plant. Unshielded twisted-pair cable is inexpensive and easy to install. A typical price for this type of cable might be $25 per 500 ft. To connect the cable using standard phone jacks takes a trained installer only seconds, compared with minutes' worth of labor to attach connectors to other cable types. In addition, because most buildings and campuses are typically saturation wired for telephone service, it is relatively easy to provide wired data jacks everywhere a phone jack is placed.

Summary. Data transmission on unshielded twisted-pair cable over distances of 300 ft is possible at rates to 10M bps but should be undertaken with caution.

Attempts to exceed these limits may be successful but should be examined very carefully in light of alternatives. Existing cable may support network traffic but should be carefully examined using appropriate test equipment before that decision is made. If possible, separate cable should be dedicated to the network traffic. Finally, care should be taken to properly terminate the network, and the network implementer should understand that the requirements of this type of network are substantially more stringent than those for conventional telephone wiring.

Data-Grade Twisted-Pair Cable

Unshielded twisted-pair wiring is very inexpensive and is installed in virtually every location; however, it does suffer from limitations with respect to noise immunity and distortion-free bandwidth. The next step up in the media hierarchy is shielded data-grade cable. This cable, known for its application in token ring LANs, has higher bandwidth than unshielded twisted-pair cable and better noise immunity achieved through shielding both individual pairs and the entire cable. This improvement in performance is accompanied by increased cost, but the trade-off is not severe and the increase in performance is noticeable.

The maximum data rate on data-grade media is on the order of 16M bps over a distance of 600 ft; a distance of 1,500 ft to 2,000 ft is possible if operation at 4M bps is acceptable. Data-grade cable is fabricated to much closer tolerances than unshielded twisted-pair cable, making the testing of an individual cable plant for LAN suitability less important.

Propagation Characteristics. From a propagation point of view, data-grade twisted-pair cable is still limited by its group delay characteristics, although the distance limitation of 300 ft is relaxed. Attenuation characteristics of data-grade twisted-pair cable are also somewhat better than those of unshielded twisted-pair cable.

Noise Considerations. Shielding of individual pairs within a cable greatly limits the noise coupling between the pairs within a cable. This individual shielding also effectively protects against such noise sources as ring signals when unshielded voice cables are included within the overall shield of the data-grade cable. The overall shield also effectively eliminates electromagnetic interference (EMI) problems that can occur in unshielded cable systems. The elimination of these potential noise sources greatly enhances the probability of success in a network installation.

Cost Considerations. The initial installed cost of a network using shielded data-grade cable is higher than that of an unshielded system. A typical cost for this type of cable might be $225 per 500 ft for polyvinyl chloride (PVC)–insulated cable or $700 per 500 ft for Teflon-insulated cable. Teflon cable is suitable for plenum installation and is electrically stabler over a broader temperature range. This higher initial cost should be balanced by lower life-cycle costs associated with trouble-free operation and lower probability of network start-up problems.

Summary. Data-grade twisted-pair cable provides a significant enhancement in performance and a significant increase in noise immunity when compared with unshielded twisted-pair cable. If a large network is being installed, this cable should be seriously considered.

Coaxial Cable

Coaxial cable comes in a wide variety of types covering a broad range of applications. Coaxial cable can be well shielded or poorly shielded; it can be thin and flexible or thick and rigid. For the purposes of this discussion, it is assumed that high-quality, well-shielded cable is used, which is readily available from many sources and is well understood by installation personnel.

Propagation Characteristics. The attenuation characteristics of coaxial cable are superior to both unshielded and data-grade twisted-pair cable. For instance, the attenuation of a data-grade twisted-pair cable may be specified at 45 dB/km at a frequency of 16 MHz, while the attenuation of unshielded twisted-pair cable at that frequency may be twice that. By comparison, the attenuation of high-grade coaxial cable at 16 MHz might be only 20 dB/km. At 150 MHz the attenuation of high-grade coaxial cable might be in the range of 83 dB/km, a figure comparable to the attenuation of unshielded twisted-pair cable at one-tenth the frequency.

This low attenuation figure for coaxial cable is not, however, an indication that single-channel data transmission at 100M bps is possible using coaxial cable. The reason for this is that the group delay distortion exhibited by coaxial cable (i.e., the variation in propagation velocity associated with the various frequency components of the signal) limits the effective bandwidth of an individual signal to about 20M bps. When coaxial cable is used for transmission of broadband information, even though the carrier frequency may be 150 MHz, the variation in frequency around this carrier that represents the signal is only 6 MHz, and it is this variation in frequency that causes the group delay.

Noise Considerations. The overall shielding of coaxial cable makes it relatively impervious to electromagnetic interference. Its bandwidth is wider than that of either unshielded or data-grade twisted-pair cable, and it is well suited to the transmission of information modulated around a high-frequency carrier. This transmission around a carrier is the mode in which coaxial cable is used when transmitting in cable TV–type applications.

Long cable runs increase the likelihood of ground loops (i.e., differences in electrical ground potential at different locations within the network). Although this has nothing to do with the characteristics of the cable itself, the problem is more common in coaxial cable networks because they tend to be used over longer distances than twisted-pair networks.

Cost Considerations. Just as coaxial cable specifications can vary widely, so can costs. These can range from $60 to $500 per 500 ft. As these numbers illustrate, coaxial cable is not necessarily more expensive than data-grade twisted-pair cable, particularly when some of the lower grades of cable are used. Even though high-grade coaxial cable may be expensive, it is readily available and well understood. Similar to data-grade cable, the life cycle costs should be lower than for unshielded twisted-pair cable as a result of coaxial cable's superior propagation and noise performance.

Summary. Coaxial cable is well suited to applications where distances are longer and data rate requirements are in the 10M- to 20M-bps range. It is a relatively low-cost medium and is well understood by installers and others responsible for LAN operation and maintenance. It exhibits acceptable noise immunity and is particularly well suited if broadband transmission is desired.

Optical Fiber

Fiber-optic cable is currently at the top of the media hierarchy when it comes to quality of data transmission and immunity to noise. It is not, however, without its limitations, among which are its cost and the relative unavailability of individuals trained in optical fiber's installation and use. Nor is the data transmission rate unlimited, although it is almost always higher than that possible over electrical conductors. With the development of simpler termination techniques, applications suited to its superior transmission characteristics, and lower prices for the fiber and components, it is probable that in the near future optical fiber will be the medium of choice for most data transmission applications.

Propagation Characteristics. Pulses traveling down short runs of fiber-optic cable show little or no visible distortion. The bandwidth of fiber is not limitless, however, and it is affected by group delay distortion for the same reasons as other media. In a system using glass multimode fiber-optic cable and LEDs and operating in the 850-nm wavelength region, the bandwidth limitation attributable to group delay is about 1 MHz/km. Under these conditions, transmission in the 20M- to 30M-bps range over distances of 2 km is about the limit. Other types of fiber-optic transmission, such as those using laser sources in the more favorable 1,300-nm wavelength region and employing single-mode fiber, can achieve transmission rates into the hundreds-of-megabits-per-second range; however, the cost of such systems does not allow their use in most LAN applications.

A misconception about data transmission using optical fiber is that a light source can only be turned on or off, so that only digital transmission is possible. In reality, light can be modulated to transmit analog as well as digital signals. This allows for broadband transmission on fiber-optic cable similar to that used on coaxial cable. Fiber-optic video links are an example of this type of transmission.

Noise Considerations. Fiber-optic cable itself is unaffected by electromagnetic noise and electrical ground loops. This solves noise problems associated with twisted-pair and coaxial cable. The use of fiber-optic cable, however, requires detection of very small amounts of energy in the receiver circuits, and these circuits are electrical in nature. Extreme care must be taken by the equipment designer to ensure that the noise immunity gained through the use of fiber optics in these sensitive circuits is not lost. This problem is an issue of equipment design and selection, not network installation.

Cost Considerations. One of the common misconceptions about fiber-optic cable is that its cost is very high. In fact, it is possible to purchase fiber-optic cable at $150 per 500 ft, making the cost of raw cable comparable to data-grade twisted-pair or coaxial cable. The expense is in the terminations and in the transceiver components that generate and detect the light transmitted in the cable. Prices range from a few tens of dollars each for the transmitter and detector to hundreds of dollars for higher-grade components. Individuals well trained in optical media may also be in short supply, which can push up maintenance costs for a fiber-optic network. The inherent noise immunity and low-distortion transmission characteristics of optical fiber should reduce the need for maintenance, however.

Summary. Optical fiber provides, without a doubt, the best transmission characteristics of the three network media discussed. It is somewhat more expensive than the others to install, and there are fewer individuals qualified to maintain it. Optical fiber's transmission characteristics, however, are so far superior to the others that it is probable that it will some day become the media of choice in hardwired network applications. Optical fiber promises data rates in the hundreds of megabits per second over distances on the order of 500 m. It can therefore serve the present and future information transmission needs of an organization, whereas significant growth in transmission bandwidth requirements cannot be accommodated by the electrical conductor–based media.

TOPOGRAPHIES

Media can be connected in a number of topographies, or physical configurations. Another term used to describe the way networks logically connect is topology. The distinction between the two terms is that topography refers to physical connections and topology refers to the way the networking software views the network. In this section, physical connections, or topography, are considered. The particular topography that is best suited to an individual installation is a function of both the geographic makeup of the installation and the anticipated traffic requirements. If the stations to be connected by the network are uniformly spaced, one particular type of topography (linear) would probably result in minimum installation cost. If clusters of stations are scattered around the network geography, another topography might be more cost-effective. Other considerations, such as failure modes and the ability to isolate portions of the network, enter into the analysis used to decide on the best topography for an individual installation.

An overview of the various types of network topographies is given in the following sections, and their relative merits are reviewed.

Linear Topographies

A linear topography is usually a straight-line network with each station wired directly to the next station in line. Exhibit III-2-2 illustrates this type of network. When a small number of stations are distributed over a wide geographic area this type of topography results in the minimum amount of cabling. It is often used with media that lend themselves to operation in a communications

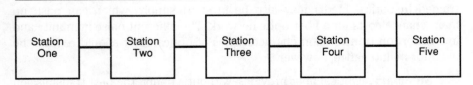

Exhibit III-2-2. Linear Network Topography

bus, such as coaxial cable. One disadvantage with this type of approach is that there is no central location at which network failures can be isolated. For this reason, the probability of prolonged network outage due to media failure is higher with this type of topography than in other topographies.

Star Topographies

When stations tend to be clustered together, a star topography is often used. Exhibit III-2-3 illustrates a star topography. This type of network is typical of that currently found in telephone wiring. All of the individual telephone locations are wired into a centralized wiring closet. A star topography may require more cable because each station must be wired to a central location, but the availability of a central location at which all cables can be accessed allows reconfiguration of the network should an individual portion fail. This greatly reduces the chance that media problems will cause prolonged periods of network failure.

Hybrid Topographies

In a real-world network the station density varies. Stations associated with individual work groups (e.g., the engineering or the accounting departments) may be very close to each other but distant from the stations of other work groups. It is also typical for the highest priority to be on communications within the work group; network failures that might interrupt communications with

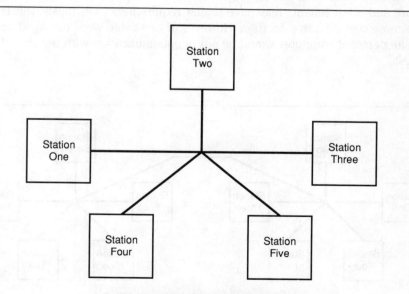

Exhibit III-2-3. Star Network Topography

stations outside the group are less serious.

In such a case, a hybrid topography, consisting of linear and star topographies, is particularly effective. Exhibit III-2-4 illustrates this type of network. The linear topography is used between work areas to minimize cable requirements, and the enhanced reliability of the star topography is used for connections within the individual work cluster.

A TYPICAL NETWORK

XYZ Co has 60 personal computers and shares a mainframe system with other tenants in its building. The personal computers are distributed throughout three floors of a high-rise office building. There are 20 personal computers in the accounting department on one floor, 20 personal computers in the engineering department on a second floor, and on the third floor, 10 personal computers in the marketing department, 2 personal computers in personnel, and 8 personal computers in the executive area. The mainframe is in the basement. XYZ Co wishes to give all of the personal computers access to the mainframe and allow each of the individual areas to exchange data files and other information. Each building floor is 200 ft by 200 ft, and the vertical distance to the basement is 400 ft.

To hardwire all the personal computers to the mainframe in the basement with a star topography would involve 60 cables, probably coaxial cables, considering the distances involved. All these cables running down the elevator shaft with an average length of 500 ft each would total altogether 30,000 ft of cable. This cable would occupy a substantial amount of space in the elevator shaft, and other tenants may have similar requirements. Obviously, this is not the most cost-effective solution. However, if one cable were damaged only a single personal computer would be out of communication with the rest of the LAN.

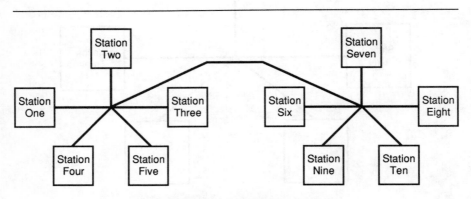

Exhibit III-2-4. Hybrid Network Topography

An alternative would be to snake a single piece of coaxial cable through the floors of the office and down the elevator shaft. This would involve approximately 400 ft of cable per floor plus the 400 ft to descend the elevator shaft, or 1,600 ft of cable. This would constitute a significant saving in cable, but any failure, anywhere in the network, could result in total loss of network communications.

A reasonable solution is to use a hybrid topography for this situation. Because the individual floors are only 200 ft by 200 ft, by placing a wiring closet at a central location on each floor, all the personal computers on a floor could be accessed by cables less than 300 ft in length. This would allow the use of unshielded twisted-pair cable. Star wiring each floor would require approximately 20 ft by 100 ft of unshielded twisted-pair cable per floor, or a total of 6,000 ft of unshielded twisted-pair cable. The 400-ft run to the basement through the elevator shaft could be accomplished using coaxial or fiber-optic cable. Because the amount of this more expensive cable is so small, a decision to use optical fiber would allow for future expansion without serious impact on the current cost. Fiber-optic cable also prevents any ground loops over the relatively long run down the elevator shaft. The total cable requirement is now 6,000 ft of unshielded twisted-pair cable and 400 ft of optical fiber. With this arrangement, any failure in a cable from a station can be isolated at the wiring closet. Stations on each floor could communicate with each other despite a failure in the optical fiber, although this could interfere with communications to the mainframe. Because the critical run of cable to the mainframe is so short, it might be advisable to install redundant optical fiber. This would minimize the risk of network failure causing mainframe unavailability. Overall, the hybrid topography is an attractive compromise between initial installation expense and long-term network life cycle costs.

SUMMARY

As with any engineering problem, every network situation must be examined and trade-offs made to arrive at an installation solution that meets the needs of the network users and administrators. Many of these issues, such as media access control techniques and certain types of network hardware (i.e., bridges, routers, and gateways), have not been covered in this chapter. Operational issues such as use patterns also must be considered. In the end, however, the media must move the data from place to place. For this reason, proper choice of media and media topography are critical to the long-term success of a network.

III-3
Fiber-Optic and Copper LANs

RICHARD A. CERNY

The most basic of LAN issues to be considered is that of cabling. At the bottom of the OSI model is the physical layer, which provides the interconnections to be used in the LAN. Strictly a hardware concern, the physical layer decision has to do only with the transmission of information signals in an efficient manner and the connections provided to and between devices.

A wide variety of transmission means, including microwave and infrared transmission, could be discussed, but in this chapter the focus is on the more pervasive medium: the cabling plant. Three important categories of cables are discussed: twisted-pair wire, coaxial copper, and fiber-optic cable. As the capabilities of twisted-pair cable are expanded and the cost-effectiveness of fiber-optic cable is improved, the outlook for coaxial cable will become increasingly bleak.

TWISTED-PAIR CABLE

Long used for telephone service, twisted-pair cabling is proving to be an excellent, low-cost medium for moderate-speed data transmission. This phone-wire approach to data cabling is often referred to as unshielded twisted-pair wire. Usually consisting of four pairs of 24-gauge, color-coded wires, it is the basis for new cabling provided to offices in today's voice-and-data wiring systems. It can be contrasted to such shielded data cables as the IBM type 1 used in the IBM cabling system. Use of the unshielded twisted-pair wire approach clearly has gained momentum, and in many respects it outperforms large, expensive shielded-pair cables, which are dedicated to data use.

Twisted-pair cables are available in a number of sizes, or gauges, and in a number of configurations. Each parameter affects the transmission properties of the cable, as do such other factors as geometric tolerances, lay length or twist rate, and shielding and insulation materials. In some copper-paired cables, the wires are not actually twisted, and this adversely affects transmission rates.

Twisted-pair cables are more prone to noise than other types of cables.

Therefore, shielding can be provided to minimize induced noise pickup or outgoing radiation of high-frequency signals. In some cable designs, every pair is shielded; in others, only the overall core is shielded. The shielding may increase the attenuation of high-frequency signals passing within the cable and thereby lower the effective information-carrying capacity, or bandwidth, of the cable.

Unshielded twisted-pair wire is attractive not only because it is relatively effective in carrying high-speed signals over short distances but also because it is economical and manageable. Using it for short-distance network traffic (e.g., to 100 m) has three advantages:

- Only one type of wire is needed for both voice and data.
- Much the same hardware is used for both voice and data.
- In most applications, the wire is already installed.

Unshielded twisted-pair cabling is now widely used for point-to-point data transmission, including asynchronous RS-232 data at rates of 19,200 bps. It is necessary to use balanced-to-unbalanced adapters (baluns) as terminal inter-connections for IBM 3270 and Wang systems. It is estimated that over 90% of the currently installed telephone twisted-pair wiring is adequate for 10M-bps Ethernet transmission. Further enhancing its application is the wire's demon-strated capacity for 16M-bps token network traffic over limited distances.

COAXIAL CABLE

Coaxial cable offers better signal bandwidth than does twisted-pair cable, and it is commonly used for video transmission as well as moderate-speed data communications. In a coaxial cable, a single metallic conductor is surrounded by a concentric metallic shield and the two are separated by a dielectric layer of plastic that serves to insulate them. The shield, which may be a solid tube or braided strands, acts both as an electrical shield and as a ground. Similarly, the center conductor may be of solid or stranded design; it acts as the signal conductor. Other applications of the coaxial concept include cables with dual center conductors (i.e., twinaxial) for balanced transmission and cables with multiple layers of shielding as in RG8, or IEEE 802.3, yellow Ethernet cable (see Exhibit III-3-1).

Ethernet coaxial cable was originally specified for IEEE 802.3 or 10BASE5 applications: transmission at 10M-bps baseband signaling rates over a maxi-mum segment distance of 500 m. Configured as a bus topology, each device attaches to the cable by means of a transceiver. Because Ethernet cable is bulky and expensive, a lower-cost alternative was developed. Called ThinWire by Digital Equipment Corp (DEC), the 10BASE2 bus topology uses smaller, lower-cost cables with T connectors and has a maximum segment length of 200 m. Usually, the transceivers are built into the station device and have a BNC output.

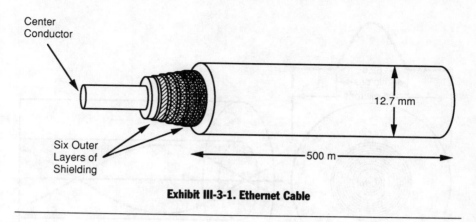

Center
Conductor

12.7 mm

Six Outer
Layers of
Shielding

500 m

Exhibit III-3-1. Ethernet Cable

Coaxial cable was primarily designed to have waveguide properties that would keep high-frequency radar and video signals within the cable. As computer manufacturers with high-speed data applications turned to coaxial cable, their primary purpose was to insulate the cable against noise, and cable types began to proliferate. Today there are many types of coaxial cable to choose from, and often each type is compatible with only a single computer system.

OPTICAL FIBER

The third and most promising communications medium is fiber-optic cabling. The term *fiber optics* is used to designate the technology of transporting information by guided light waves in optical fibers in contrast to the conventional transmission of electrical signal energy in copper wire. Through the phenomenon of total internal reflection, the glass fiber traps an entering beam of light from an optical source—for example, a light-emitting diode (LED) or semiconductor laser diode—and guides it to a detector at the far end (see Exhibit III-3-2). The fiber acts as an optical waveguide and thereby permits the light to travel over very long distances and even around corners and bends.

The light signal travels only in the center portion, or core, of the multilayer glass fiber, and the core is surrounded by an outer layer, or cladding. The throughput depends on the power of the source, the efficiency of input coupling, the size of the fiber, the leakage at connectors and splices, the physical condition of the flow path, the lack of constrictions at the bends, and the output coupling efficiency. In fact, fiber-optic cable has long been used for guiding light in other than communications applications—for example, in medical illumination and image transmission. (The light guides are often referred to as light pipes.) Unlike twisted-pair and coaxial cable, however, fiber-optic cable requires electrooptic interface adapters, and it should be thought of in the context of a fiber-optic system.

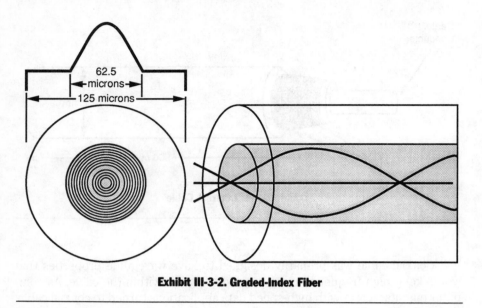

Exhibit III-3-2. Graded-Index Fiber

FIBER-OPTIC SYSTEM ELEMENTS

The basic fiber-optic system consists of three elements: the transmitting source or transmitter, the receiving detector or receiver, and the interconnecting fiber-optic cable (see Exhibit III-3-3). The transmitter converts electrical communications signals to light signals through intensity (brightness) modulation of the LED or laser diode source and launches the resultant signal into the end of the optical fiber. The fiber, perhaps one of several optical conductors in the

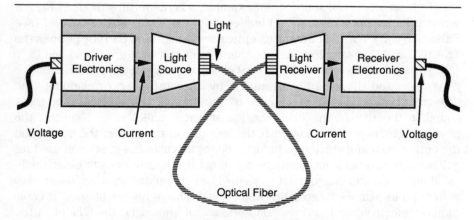

Exhibit III-3-3. Basic Fiber-Optic System Elements

cable, guides the light signal to the other end of the cable, which may be only a few feet or several miles away. At the far end, the receiver detects the optical signal and reconverts it to a replica of the original electrical signal.

Because both the transmitter and receiver are active electrooptical devices, they often include other electronic capabilities (e.g., self-testing, alarm indicating, signal processing, and electrical multiplexing). Bidirectional sets of digital data transmitters and receivers are commonly referred to as fiber-optic modems because both devices modulate and demodulate the signal from electrical to optical and back. Acting as a closed system, an optical modem set performs similarly to a conventional limited-distance wire modem. Only the performance capabilities differ.

Fiber Types

Optical fibers are usually classified by the type of refractive index profile their many layers of glass make up. The two profile types in common use today are single-mode and multimode. As previously noted, the core carries the light signal and the cladding acts like an optical pipe wall. In most fiber types the outside cladding diameter is approximately 125 microns but the diameter of the transmitting core varies greatly. Single-mode fibers are distinguished by their very small core diameters (only 8 microns), whereas multimode fiber cores range from 50 to 100 microns in diameter (see Exhibit III-3-4).

Mode is a term used in optics that relates to the number of wave fronts, each characterized by a ray angle that a fiber is capable of supporting or transmitting. The more modes a fiber supports, the more optical power the fiber can carry. However, because rays traveling at different angles arrive at the far cable end at slightly different times, time dispersion of light pulses occurs. Short pulses of light therefore become longer, spread-out pulses. Bandwidth suffers as a result.

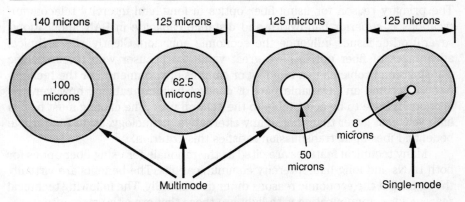

Exhibit III-3-4. Optical Fiber Types and Sizes

Because there is only one mode, the single-mode fiber suffers virtually no pulse broadening caused by mode time delays. The obvious drawback, however, is very small core size, which makes connector and splice alignment extremely critical and therefore expensive. Also, because its core is so small, a single-mode fiber requires a very small, high-radiance-emitting source—for example, a laser diode or special LED—to launch sufficient power into the core. For that reason, the primary application of single-mode fibers has been in long-distance telecommunications. Although their use in high-speed LANs will become prevalent, single-mode fibers have so far found little application in the LAN market.

The multimode fiber is currently the workhorse of the short-distance communications market. Its relatively large core makes interconnection simple and inexpensive. This is an important consideration in building cabling, which is connector-intensive. Inexpensive LED sources are used in multimode fiber modems, and the intermodal dispersion of the fibers is of little consequence over the short spans encountered on customer premises.

Multimode fibers can be subdivided into the graded-index and step-index types. For all practical purposes, however, step-index fibers are irrelevant because of their overwhelming bandwidth limitations. Virtually all multimode fibers now advocated by the large systems suppliers are of the graded-index type.

Two types of multimode fiber are currently promoted for use in LAN cabling systems; each is defined by the diameter of the optical core. AT&T supports the smaller but more easily installed 62.5-micron fiber; IBM supports the 100-micron fiber, which has higher coupling efficiency. IBM now acknowledges the 62.5-micron fiber, however, and that fiber has become the de facto standard and is specified by virtually all fiber-optic LAN standards organizations. The 100-micron fiber has been dismissed by standards organizations as being overpriced and technologically obsolete.

Advantages of Optical Fiber

The primary reason for using fiber optics in long-haul intercity telecommunications is superior bandwidth and distance capacity; in LAN applications, several other issues influence the economic equation. Clearly, the technical advantages of fiber optics have great value to the user who faces specific transmission problems in a building or campus environment. For the technology to become an invariable part of general building cabling, however, the economics have to be acceptable to the general user. The cabling must have a life-cycle cost lower than that of any alternative technology, aside from fringe benefits. Fiber-optic transmission satisfies this criterion.

Many technical features are cited as the rationale for using fiber optics for both LANs and long-haul intercity communications. The benefits are virtually the same, but the economic reasons differ dramatically. The following technical reasons for communicating with light are those that are cited most often:

- Greater distance capability—Optical signals can travel hundreds of miles without intermediate repeaters or signal boosting.
- Wider bandwidth—Optical fiber can be virtually unlimited in its digital information-carrying capacity. New laser transmission systems are transporting in excess of 1.5G bps over long-distance telecommunications trunks.
- Immunity to interference—Fiber-optic cables are noninductive. They are not susceptible to electromagnetic interference (EMI), radio frequency interference (RFI), electromagnetic pulses (EMP), or crosstalk from adjacent power or communication lines. Not even intentional jamming can disrupt the signals.
- Security and nonradiation—Fiber-optic cables do not produce electromagnetic fields at any frequency. They offer secure communications for the military or any other organization with high-security requirements because they are difficult to tap covertly. Stringent Federal Communications Commission (FCC) regulation of cable radiation makes fiber-optic technology attractive, especially at signal data rates higher than 1 MHz.
- Small size and low weight—Fiber-optic cables are much smaller than equivalent copper cables; the reduction in size and weight is as much as 100 to 1. A nonmetallic cable only 12.7 mm in diameter can contain up to 144 fibers. Transportation, storage, and installation costs can be lower. The substantial savings in or recapture of valuable conduit space can be greater than the first cost of the fiber cabling.
- Nonconductivity—Fiber-optic cables do not conduct electricity, so they are often used to solve troublesome ground loop problems. As data rates increase, nonconductivity becomes an increasingly important consideration. In addition, the use of fiber optics can limit damage from lightning strikes.
- Intrinsic safety—Fiber-optic cables do not shock, short, or spark. They do not cause fires, and they can be routed through explosive atmospheres in which conventional electrical cables cannot be allowed.
- Noncorrodibility—Fiber-optic cables do not corrode even when installed directly in water. Whereas corrosion causes outside-plant wideband copper cables to deteriorate over time, properly installed fiber cables maintain their transmission capacity indefinitely.

Signal Transparency

Although fiber optics have most of the advantages of the ideal communications medium—small size, lightweight, cleanness, wide bandwidth, low loss, electrical isolation, safety, and nonradiation—their real advantage is that they are universally transparent to any communications signal regardless of type, speed, or electromagnetic environment. Once a building or campus has been provided with a fiber-optic backbone, changes are made in the optical patch panels and terminal converters (fiber-optic modems). No new cables have to be pulled.

In contrast, a different type of copper cable is used in nearly every data communications application. As an example, RS-232 wire-pair cables are not compatible with the 93-ohm RG62 coaxial cables used in the IBM 3270 system. Neither of the two is compatible with the 75-ohm RG6 CAD/CAM cables or 50-ohm RG58 or RG8 Ethernet cables. An optical fiber with the appropriate transmitter-receiver, or modem, combination is capable of handling virtually any of the preceding communications signal interfaces and others as well. This is the driving force behind the use of fiber optics in the LAN environment.

STRUCTURED CABLING SYSTEMS

Within the last few years both AT&T and IBM have taken aim at coaxial cable and dealt it crippling blows. As LAN technologies continued to evolve, the two corporations were creating structured cabling systems that rely solely on the use of fiber-optic and twisted-pair cabling. AT&T and IBM are eliminating coaxial cable from their product offerings for virtually all premises communications distribution (i.e., voice, data, or video).

Many other companies are adapting their products to conform to AT&T's Premises Distribution System with its simple mix of standard fiber optics and ordinary unshielded twisted-pair cables. IBM's Cabling System appears to be meeting significantly more user resistance because of its use of several different types of larger and more expensive shielded cables, a more expensive, nonstandard fiber type, and large wire distribution frames for its shielded data wire cables. Not surprisingly, IBM has begun to acknowledge the AT&T claim for the suitability of unshielded twisted-pair cable by introducing IBM type 3 unshielded twisted-pair cable, which can be used in the 4M- and 16M-bps IBM Token Ring Network. Digital Equipment Corp has its own version of a cabling system, which is unique in that it also employs 50-ohm ThinWire coaxial cable.

Neither optical fiber nor twisted-pair cable alone could displace coaxial cable; applications of coaxial cable in LANs are threatened by the marriage of the two. Coaxial cable is not expected to be completely replaced, but the cost advantages of twisted-pair cable on the low end and the performance advantages of optical fiber at the high end leave coaxial cable with a much smaller role in networking applications.

Advantages of Structured Cabling

The problem of communications cabling management became much greater with the AT&T divestiture. No longer can the end user or building owner rely on the telephone company to specify, install, and maintain the wiring within a facility. Rather than treat the cabling as a service or hidden rental item, the network manager must now accept it as a large capital investment, one that must be planned for and managed wisely.

Without a structured cabling system, cable costs soar with relocations and service upgrades. Personnel moves to different offices are estimated to be 50% per year in most organizations, and new cable often has to be pulled to hook up a terminal, personal computer, or workstation at a new location. The old cable is destined to corrode in the ceiling. One computer company estimates the cost of moving a terminal, including rewiring, at about $3,000. The cost of reconfiguring a structured cabling system in which fiber-optic or wire crossconnections are used is about $750.

The Distribution Layout

The entire structured cabling system is made up of a system of cable types and administrative hardware (see Exhibit III-3-5). By using a modular approach, the end user can synthesize a wiring plan that will meet communications needs for many years to come. Virtually all structured building cabling systems employ the star-wire physical topology between buildings, between floors, and within floors. This approach offers the greatest flexibility in administration and troubleshooting. In a star-wired network, with the distribution frame or patch panel location acting as the hub, the cabling system can be used to serve all logical data topologies simultaneously, including bus, tree, ring, star, and simple point-to-point links.

Cables are made for specific installation environments. All fiber-optic ca-

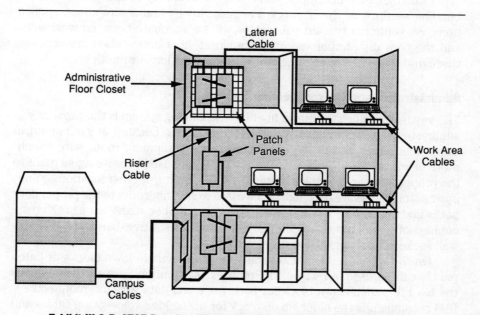

Exhibit III-3-5. AT&T Premises Distribution System Structured Cabling Concept

bles within a system will have the same optical specifications, but mechanical specifications (e.g., size and number of fiber conductors, jacketing material) may change, depending on the location of the cable. Twisted-pair cables for local distribution may have identical electrical properties but different construction, again depending on location.

Cables are classified by use as follows:

- Riser cables run vertically through the building core and connect the main optical distribution frame with designated administrative distribution closets on each floor—From 2 to 20 fiber cables are typically dropped off at each floor.
- Lateral feeder cables run horizontally on each floor between floor distribution closets and individual work area wall or floor sockets—The Underwriters Laboratories–approved flame-retardant cables are generally run in air plenums, and typically contain four wire pairs or from two to six fibers or both.
- Work area cables run from wall or floor sockets to the user terminals or devices—Usually, a two-pair or two-fiber (duplex) design, work area cable may resemble ordinary lamp cord, or it may be a flat cable designed for placement under carpeting.
- Campus cables are outside-plant designs; they are direct-buried, conduit, or aerial—They connect the buildings within a campus environment or serve in the user's other telecommunications bypass activities.

In many cases, fiber-optic cable will be used only in the riser and interbuilding sections of the network. For most low- to moderate-speed applications, conventional twisted-pair cables will be adequate between work areas and the floor distribution closets. At a closet, fiber-optic cables are accessed through the use of a fiber-optic concentrator, star hub, or multiplexer.

Administrative and Interconnecting Hardware

The key feature of a structured fiber or wire cabling system is the capability to administer signals through a system of patch panels. Located, at a minimum, in every floor closet and in the building's central equipment room, wire punchdown blocks and fiber-optic distribution panels are used to route signal paths to the proper work area terminal equipment, CPU ports, or other locations. Fiberoptic patch panels are used like splice cases to split fibers out to the proper floor paths and, when they are intermediate points of fiber spans, act as full crossconnections and interconnections. Other administrative hardware includes wall sockets, floor sockets, and splice cases.

On the wire side, any of several versions of punch-down blocks or patch panels can be used. AT&T, in its Premises Distribution System, recommends the No 110 punch-down block for both voice and data wire interconnections. IBM recommends the older No 66 block for unshielded voice-grade cables and the large rack-mounted distribution panel for its shielded data cables and data connectors.

Fiber-Optic Connector Standards

The fiber-optics industry is now in its third generation of optical connectors. The evolution was from the Amphenol SMA type to the AT&T biconic connector to today's AT&T ST connector (see Exhibit III-3-6). The ST has become the standard for fiber-optic building distribution cables. It is especially attractive because of its low-cost, power-coupling efficiency and repeatability. AT&T specifies it in its Premises Distribution System. Several other sources, including 3M/Dorran, also supply this type of connector.

When IBM announced the use of fiber-optic transmission in its Token Ring LAN as a means of extending wiring closet separation, it based the cable design on the 100-micron fiber. The cable is currently available only in a two-fiber version (type 5). IBM recommends that a combination of AT&T biconic connectors and Sumitomo mini-BNC equipment connectors be used for this network.

FIBER AND WIRE LOCAL AREA NETWORKS

Most LAN equipment suppliers now have or will soon offer both twisted-pair and fiber-optic options. With those options, LANs can connect directly to a structured building cabling system with no need for new coaxial cable installation. A simple point-to-point application of unshielded twisted-pair cable is the short-distance transmission of Ethernet signals, primarily as a thin Ethernet segment using devices similar to baluns. The Pair Tamer device by 3Com permits transmission over distances to 70 m using unshielded twisted-pair cable (see Exhibit III-3-7).

In their initial LAN applications, fiber-optic systems were also used in point-to-point configurations to link remote repeaters or bridges between network segments (see Exhibit III-3-8). Both DEC and IBM offer such fiber-optic

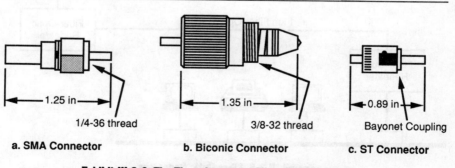

1.25 in	1.35 in	0.89 in
1/4-36 thread	3/8-32 thread	Bayonet Coupling
a. SMA Connector	**b. Biconic Connector**	**c. ST Connector**

Exhibit III-3-6. The Three Important Fiber-Optic Connectors

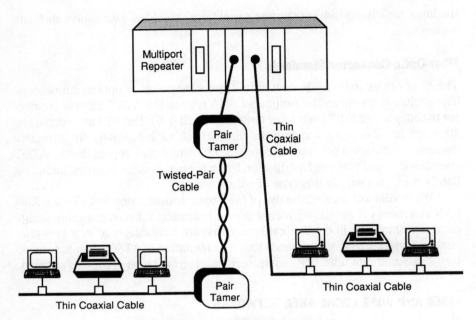

Exhibit III-3-7. Twisted-Pair Ethernet Section

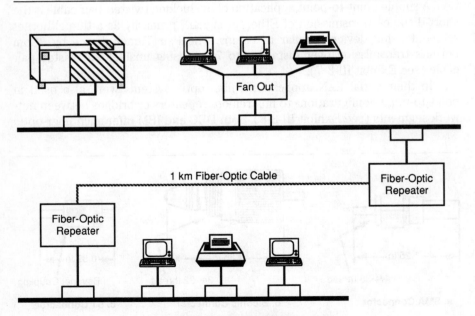

Exhibit III-3-8. Fiber-Optic Repeaters

repeaters for their networks. Wang Laboratories offers a fiber-optic option for extending the distances between its control units and terminal cluster switches.

Recently, both fiber-optic and unshielded twisted-pair cables have begun to emerge as primary network media. These star-topology networks use fiber-optic or twisted-pair transceivers to connect devices or repeaters to active star hubs. A hybrid approach is used in the SynOptics Communications LattisNet, which links user devices to hubs with twisted-pair cable and links hubs together with fiber-optic cable. Other modules link distant devices to hubs by using fiber-optic cables in conjunction with fiber-optic transceivers.

Fiber-only star networks also are becoming common, and may be constructed in either a hierarchical or lateral topology. In a hierarchical fiber-optic star network, active star hubs are used as repeaters at each layer of the hierarchy. Alternatively, the use of synchronous transmission can permit the lateral connection of star hubs (which act as concentrators), eliminating the use of multiple hierarchical layers, as illustrated in Exhibit III-3-9. ChipCom and BICC Networks are prominent suppliers of fiber-based networks.

10BASE-T and 10BASE-F Standards

Ethernet LAN standards for both fiber and wire systems are emerging and are compatible with structured cabling systems. The IEEE 802.3 committee has study groups for both media, 10BASE-T (twisted-pair) and 10BASE-F (fiber-

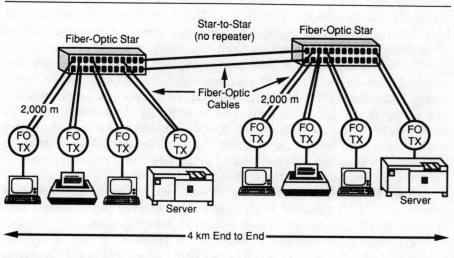

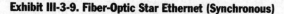

Note:
FO TX   Fiber-optic transceiver

Exhibit III-3-9. Fiber-Optic Star Ethernet (Synchronous)

optic). The standards are intended to assure interoperability of various manufacturers' components within a common network as contrasted to proprietary schemes that have evolved.

The 10BASE-T standard is an outgrowth of earlier attempts to use twisted-pair phone wire for networking [e.g., the 1M-bps, 500-m (1BASE5) StarLAN] and the success of the proprietary SynOptics and 3Com 10M-bps approaches. The new 10BASE-T standard permits the use of unshielded twisted-pair wire at 10M bps over distances to 100 m. 10BASE-T employs a star configuration with unshielded twisted-pair transceivers at each station end and a central multiport repeater at the wiring closet.

The 10BASE-F standard defines the fiber-optic passive and active star hubs, as well as fiber-optic interrepeater links (FOIRL) for IEEE 802.3 transmission. The outlook is for the active star to be of a synchronous nature with two basic components: the synchronous active star hub and the medium attachment unit (MAU). The MAU has a synchronous optical transmitter and an asynchronous optical receiver. It will be interoperable with the asynchronous FOIRL MAUs as well as the synchronous hub ports. The primary advantage of the synchronous transmission approach is that the number of repeaters is minimized. That makes possible a hierarchy of more than 20 cascaded stars in a network as opposed to the limit of three stars in an asynchronous hierarchy. The current distance limit for snychronous fiber-optic networks is 4 km.

Fiber Distributed Data Interface and Other Advanced Networks

The large bandwidth of optical fiber has led to its becoming the medium of choice for campus backbone networks. These networks are configured as logical rings, but they may be physically cabled as star-wired rings in the format of structured cabling systems (see Exhibit III-3-10).

The fiber distributed data interface (FDDI) is an impending recommended standard from the American National Standards Institute (ANSI) X3T9.5 committee. It specifies a 100M-bps transmission speed, using a dual counterrotating ring configuration. Based on token-ring standards, FDDI employs two fiber paths that for the sake of redundancy operate in reverse directions as primary and secondary waveguides (see Exhibit III-3-11). The network's software and hardware are designed with self-healing properties that allow operation over the secondary signal path in the event of a cable break.

Originally an effort to define high-speed back-end networks for storage devices and mainframes, the FDDI standard has evolved to encompass such other backbone applications as high-performance workstations. FDDI consists of four layered standards, one of which is the physical medium–dependent (PMD) sublayer of layer 1 of the OSI model. PMD defines the optical signals and waveforms as well as connectors and the cable plant.

FDDI specifies 1300-nm-wavelength LED transmitters and multimode optical fiber. When those components are used, signal dispersion within the fiber

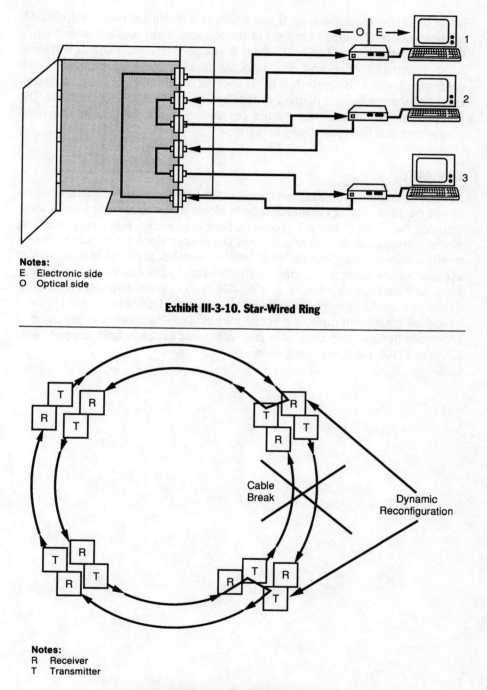

Notes:
E   Electronic side
O   Optical side

Exhibit III-3-10. Star-Wired Ring

Notes:
R   Receiver
T   Transmitter

Exhibit III-3-11. Dual Counterrotating Ring

limits links distances to about 2 km, which is suitable for most campus LAN applications. Single-mode versions of the standards also are being developed for longer distances, and an additionally developed standard, FDDI-II, will serve as an integrated voice and data LAN. Although there was originally much controversy about the preferred FDDI fiber, 62.5/125-micron (i.e., 62.5-micron core, 125-micron outside diameter) fiber has clearly become the standard. The FDDI connector is a keyed duplex connector at the station. Intermediate connectors at a path panel may be ST type.

SUMMARY

Several companies are taking advantage of the very high bandwidth capabilities of optical fiber. Certain commercially available systems already have a large installed base; they include Proteon's fiber-augmented token-ring network, which transmits at 80M bps, and Artel Communications Corp's time division multiple-access FiberWay network, which operates at 100M bps. FiberWay accommodates several simultaneous accelerated collision-free Ethernet circuits and high-speed bridging to T3 (45M-bps) telecommunications circuits. These two products were the basis for the original FDDI definition in the form of a dual counterrotating ring configuration. Together with the products of other companies, they provide a graceful transition path from copper cable LANs to FDDI if and when required.

III-4
ISDN Standards and Premises Wiring

ROBERT E. BLACKSHAW

O ne of the decisions that must be made regarding premises wiring is choosing whether to select different forms of wiring—twisted-pair, thin coaxial, thick coaxial—or to leave the wiring that is already installed. Much has been written promoting each form of wiring, but each proposal necessarily excludes all the others. A simple solution is to install all types of wiring, but this is unrealistic. Investigation of emerging standards reveals that:

- Some LANs operate over twisted-pair wires.
- ISDN uses twisted-pair wire.
- ISDN over PABX or centrex can offer LAN-like functions.
- Some voice and data PABXs are available.
- Some voice and data centrex services are available.
- ISDN is just around the corner.

Plans for reasonable growth must address the following questions:

- What current standards meet the needs?
- How long will they continue to meet these needs?
- Will unexpected growth require replanning and rewiring?
- What emerging standards offer alternatives?
- Does the problem defy solution?

STANDARDS ORGANIZATIONS

Most communications professionals are aware of the major standards-making bodies: the International Standards Organization (ISO), a voluntary body representing manufacturers and users of information systems and communications equipment, and the International Telephone and Telegraph Consultative Committee (CCITT), a United Nations treaty organization concerned mainly with standards for the communications area. In the area of physical interfaces, however, organizations of equal importance are the Institute of Electrical and Electronics Engineers (IEEE), which produced the major LAN standards, and the Electronics Industries Association (EIA), which creates such physical interface standards as RS-232C (now replaced by RS-232D), RS-422, and RS-423.

The International Electrotechnical Committee (IEC), which produces standards for electrical equipment and protection, has a say in the electrical characteristics of the ISDN plug and jack. The US formed the ANSI committee T1 to establish standards for the US communications field to replace the AT&T internal standards that became unacceptable to other vendors after the breakup of AT&T.

IEEE, ANSI-T1, and the IEC are defining new physical interfaces that will affect types of wiring, jacks, and plugs. New OSI protocols are continually emerging and must be carefully considered, but they all eventually end in a physical interface. Somewhere the system must all be wired together, and this is not a trivial problem.

All architectural models have as a base the physical medium that interconnects the systems. All models defer the physical interconnection problem to other standards makers or at least to other committees in their own organization. Several physical interfaces have been standardized in recent years that were supposed to be the standard physical interface (e.g., RS-449 and X.21). A new interface is now emerging as a general-purpose terminal interface—the ISDN 2B + D basic interface. This interface is designed to operate over two twisted-pair wires at a minimum, with four twisted-pair wires as the maximum requirement. EIA is working on a version of this interface, known as the general data communications interface, which is compatible with the ISDN basic interface except that it may be used with wiring arrangements for data terminal equipment–data communications equipment or data terminal equipment–data terminal equipment interfaces. It should be considered with other options for the premises wiring of any new plan.

THE ISDN BASIC INTERFACE

The basic 2B + D interface offers two 64K-bps clear end-to-end (B [bearer]) channels and a 16K-bps signaling (D [data]) channel. The term *clear* refers to the physical interface. Once these two B-channels get into the network, they may or may not be clear, depending on the services offered by the network (network service offerings are outside the scope of this chapter). The three channels of the basic interface are multiplexed onto a single pair of wires from the serving ISDN switch to the user. The network teminating device performs more functions than previous network terminating devices and produces a different protocol form of the 2B + D interface on the user side. This interface terminates in the simple and inexpensive RJ-45 plastic jack and plug—the eight-pin version of the familiar four-pin RJ-11 telephone jack and plug.

A review of some sections of the ISDN standards is helpful to understand the potential common wiring system proposed in this chapter. Exhibit III-4-1 illustrates a reference configuration for ISDN that was produced by the CCITT.

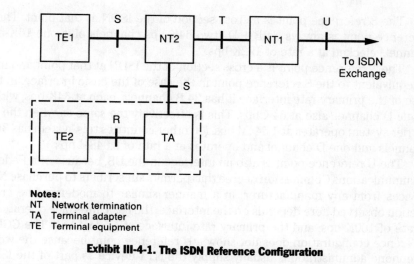

Notes:
NT Network termination
TA Terminal adapter
TE Terminal equipment

Exhibit III-4-1. The ISDN Reference Configuration

It is important to understand that this reference configuration is an abstract depiction of a typical customer premises; the boxes and points shown in the exhibit are not necessarily equated to real physical devices or components but rather illustrate all the possibilities. The R, S, T, and U reference points depict cross sections of ISDN at the points indicated; they are not interfaces, except perhaps in the case of reference point U.

Network termination 1 (NT1) represents a single-layer device (OSI layer 1) that terminates the local loop from the ISDN switch. This device also provides conversion between the loop protocol technology and the premises protocol technology. Network termination 2 (NT2) represents a three-layer device (OSI layers 1 to 3) that may support multiple terminal devices. This termination could be a PABX, cluster controller, or call distributor. It performs functions similar to the ISDN itself (e.g., switching between terminal devices). NT1 may be combined with NT2 in real physical components.

Several terminal devices are represented in Exhibit III-4-1. Terminal equipment 1 (TE1) is an ISDN-era terminal device that both recognizes and is capable of terminating all ISDN protocols. Terminal equipment 2 (TE2) is a pre-ISDN-era terminal device that does not recognize and is not capable of terminating ISDN protocols. The terminal adapter (TA) is a device that performs the necessary functions to adapt a terminal equipment 2 device to an ISDN. On the S reference point side, it recognizes and terminates the ISDN protocols. On the R reference point side, it recognizes and terminates such existing protocols as X.25, RS-232C, X.21, and V.24. The combination of a TA and TE2 device is equivalent to a TE1 device.

The R reference point is a cross section of the ISDN at the indicated point and equates to such standards as X.21, X.25, RS-232C, and V.24.

The S reference point is a cross section of the ISDN at that point. The S reference point is always a 2B + D (two 64K-bps channels plus one 16K-bps channel) clocked at a rate of 192K bps.

The T reference point is a cross section of the ISDN at that point and may be equivalent to the S reference point in the case of the basic interface. In the case of the primary rate interface it has 24 B channels, each at 64K bps, with a single D channel, also at 64K bps. This is effectively the same as when the T1 carrier system operates at 1.544M bps. (In other countries this system has 30 B channels and one D channel and operates at a rate of 2.048M bps.)

The U reference point is also an interface in the US, because of a Federal Communications Commission decree that permits subscribers to purchase NT1 devices from any manufacturer, in a manner similar to modems. The cross section observed here depends on the interface: the basic interface operates at a rate of 160K bps, and the primary rate interface at 1.544M bps. The CCITT reference configuration does not show a U reference point because the world telephone administrations usually supply the NT1 device as part of the ISDN service.

A PABX manufacturer may honestly claim ISDN compatibility by supplying only T and R reference-point types of interfaces. As long as the PABX is capable of interfacing with the network, providing R reference point interfaces (i.e., proprietary interfaces) is legitimate.

ISDN LOOP TECHNOLOGY

The ISDN subscriber connection—including the premises wiring, the loop, and the ISDN switch machine—comprises three different technologies, as illustrated in Exhibit III-4-2. At the subscriber premises, in the case of the basic rate interface, there are two 64K-bps B channels and one 16K-bps D channel. There

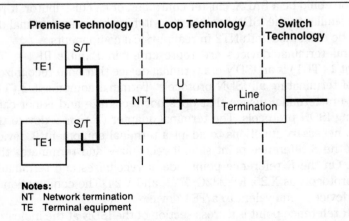

Notes:
NT   Network termination
TE   Terminal equipment

Exhibit III-4-2. Physical Layer Technologies

is also a point-multipoint configuration, in which as many as eight terminal devices can be attached to a single NT1, and the terminal devices must contend for the use of the D channel. The B channels do not contend with each other but are assigned to a given terminal device after a call with the ISDN switch machine is negotiated. Contention for the D channel and the resolution of the contention require significant overhead—16K bps of the 48K bps of overhead. The balance of the 48K bps is used for framing, synchronization, and a small embedded operations channel used for such tasks as setting loopbacks. The rate at which the basic rate interface operates, 192K bps, is the sum of 64 + 64 + 16 + 48. Exhibit III-4-2 refers to this premises wiring as the premise technology.

The actual two-wire loop from subscriber to switch is a point-to-point connection with no contention. Because there are only 144K bps of subscriber information to be carried (i.e., 64 + 64 + 16) and little overhead needed for framing, synchronization, cyclic redundancy checking, or the operations channel, this loop operates at a 160K-bps rate (144K bps of information + 16K bps of overhead). Because of the line code used, each line symbol conveys two bits of information, so the real line rate is 80K baud.

Once past the line termination of the ISDN switch, whatever technology fits best for each ISDN switch manufacturer takes over. This subscriber connection is a significant departure from the loop-start, direct current, two-wire loop technology of today. Communications professionals must be mainly concerned, however, with the premise technology.

PREMISES WIRING

ISDN provides four premises-wiring scenarios in the CCITT recommendations. One is a point-to-point arrangement with a single TE or NT2 wired to a NT1. The latest scenario is an NT1 star, in which the NT1 supports as many as eight terminal equipment devices in a star wiring arrangement. Exhibit III-4-3 shows the scenarios of most interest, termed passive bus arrangements. A short passive bus has an overall length of 250 m (820 ft); an extended passive bus has an overall length of 1,000 m (3,280 ft). In the extended form, the terminal equipment devices must be clustered in the last 50 m (164 feet). Each version supports a maximum of eight terminal equipment devices.

Passive bus scenarios are not depicting a simple residence wiring scheme with multiple jacks about the house; they are mainly designed for business applications in which the maximum of eight terminal equipment devices connected to the bus would be located in a single employee's office or work space. In an ISDN environment each office would have a telephone, a microcomputer, and such peripherals as a printer and a facsimile machine. The recommendation simply states that as many as eight terminal devices may be supported by one NT1 (or each NT2 port), which does not mean that each S reference point must have eight terminals.

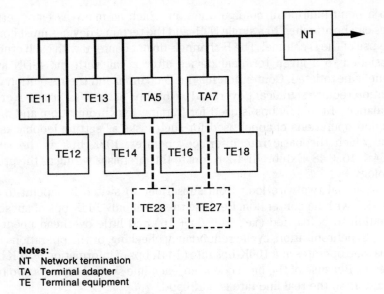

Notes:
NT   Network termination
TA   Terminal adapter
TE   Terminal equipment

Exhibit III-4-3. Passive Bus Arrangements

The Electrical Interface

Exhibit III-4-4 illustrates the electrical interface of ISDN at the S reference point and the T reference point in the case of a basic interface. The transmit and receive pairs (3 and 6, 4 and 5) are transformer coupled, eliminating the need for any network protection devices. There are three possible power sources: power source 1 is supplied over the transmit and receive pairs through center taps on the transformer windings; power source 2 is optional and is always provided locally; and power source 3, also optional and not used by ISDN, provides a form of LAN with one TE device providing power. Power source 3 is used and specified only in the general data communications interface draft standard.

This electrical configuration does not require that the network provide any power according to the standards—a distinct departure from current telephone networks. There are two reasons for this: ISDN terminal equipment would usually draw more power than analog telephones, and the copper wire loop may be replaced with optical fiber as optical-fiber technology advances and becomes cost-competitive with metallic pairs. Some networks may provide power, but if a TE device is to be truly portable, it should not be designed to require power from the network.

Only the four wires needed for transmission and reception (3, 4, 5, and 6) are mandatory; wires 1, 2, 7, and 8 may be omitted. Any premises-wiring scheme, however, should incorporate all eight wires.

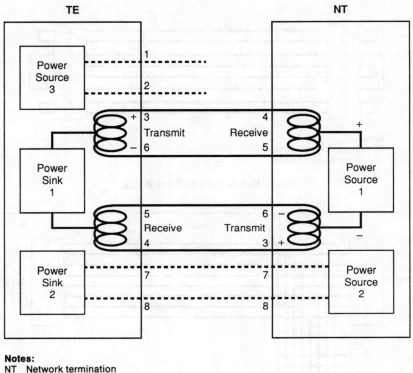

Notes:
NT Network termination
TE Terminal equipment

Exhibit III-4-4. Electrical Configuration

Actual Wiring

Exhibit III-4-5 shows a point-to-point wiring arrangement that is not very likely or useful. Exhibit III-4-6 shows a much more useful passive bus wiring arrangement. Although the electrical configuration in Exhibit III-4-4 shows different pin-to-pole assignments for the transmit and receive pairs at the TE and NT, the jacks are wired straight pin-to-pin. The pair swapping in a passive bus arrangement is done in the NT connecting cord to achieve the electrical configuration arrangement. This simplifies the actual wiring because there is no need to designate one of the connectors as the NT end. RJ-45 wall plates that have two jacks per plate are available; four jacks per office will probably be adequate.

The jacks are wired in a daisy-chain arrangement; terminating resistors, required for real ISDN use, can be added when needed. Almost any quality 24- or 22-gauge paired wire is adequate for ISDN use; the recommendation specifies the type of wire that should be used in testing arrangements but does not specify any for typical installations. The connecting cords at either device are

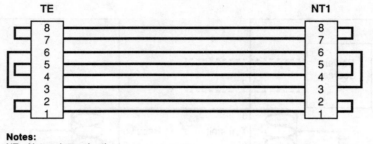

Notes:
NT   Network termination
TE   Terminal equipment

Exhibit III-4-5. Point-to-Point Wiring

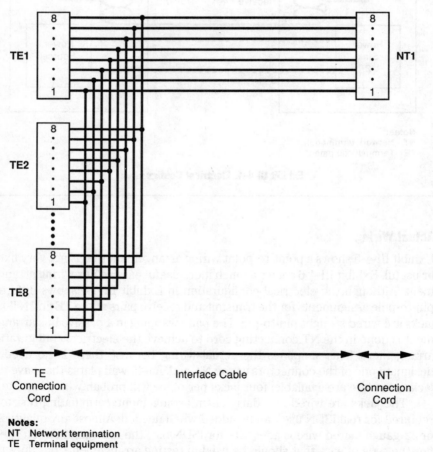

Notes:
NT   Network termination
TE   Terminal equipment

Exhibit III-4-6. Passive Bus Wiring

permitted to be 5 m (and in some cases even 10 m) in length, certainly much longer than necessary. Communications departments should consult both the ANSI-T1 standard and the local regional Bell operating company before any actual installation is undertaken.

ISDN Connectors

Exhibit III-4-7 shows typical pair assignments for four-, six-, and eight-pole RJ-series connectors, although some companies may deviate from these arrangements. The four- and eight-pole pair assignments shown are the current standard telephone wiring and ISDN wiring, respectively. The inner four poles of the eight-pole ISDN connector match the four poles of the standard telephone connector exactly. This arrangement was chosen deliberately because the RJ-series connectors have an interesting quality inherent in their design. If a four-pole plug, aligned in the jack by the centered latching piece, is inserted into an eight-pole jack, it will make contact on the four center poles (i.e., pole 1 of the four-pole plug mates with pole 3 of the eight-pole jack and pole 2 with pole 4). Therefore, if an office is wired for ISDN and the pair assignment shown is followed, existing equipment (e.g., telephones and microcomputer modems) can be used with the ISDN wiring. This means that communications departments can wire for ISDN now but use the wiring for current technology until the ISDN service is locally available.

Recent developments in LAN technology make this wiring suitable for LAN use as well. Several of the leading LAN providers have developed systems that run their LANs over twisted pairs at the usual 10M-bps rates. Various adapter

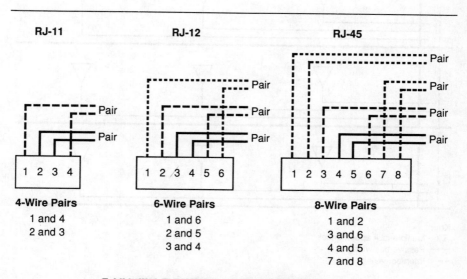

Exhibit III-4-7. RJ Series—Pair-to-Pole Assignments

techniques are used to convert the twisted-pair connection to the coaxial terminal boards used in the workstations. A typical adapter is a balun—a matching device that converts twisted-pair cable impedance into coaxial cable impedance. (Many cable television subscribers have one of these; it is the small, sometimes tubular, plastic device about 2 in long and ¾ in in diameter that has the cable connected to one end and the two wires from the other end connected to the antenna terminals of the television set.)

The significance of this wiring scheme is that any office can be wired for ISDN now and use this wiring for the regular telephone or data network or even LAN connections. Even if it is not likely that the organization will implement ISDN in the near future, it is still a sensible option because it is more economical than running separate telephone, data, and LAN wiring throughout the building.

A TYPICAL WIRING ARRANGEMENT

Exhibit III-4-8 illustrates a typical wiring arrangement for a multistoried corporate building. Most buildings today have a telephone room or cabinet on each floor, and cabling may be either built in or wired after completion through false ceilings and down interior walls. Wiring on each floor is in a star pattern, with each office cabled back to the telephone room or cabinet; regular telephone

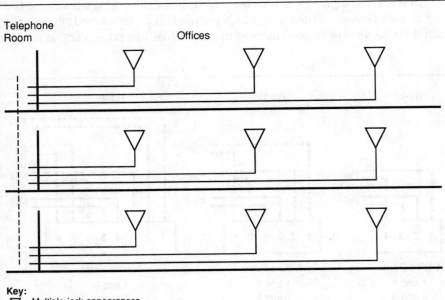

Telephone
Room   Offices

Key:
▽ Multiple-jack appearances
— Passive bus wiring
--- Interfloor wiring

Exhibit III-4-8. A Sample Wiring Method

terminal blocks can be used in the telephone room or cabinet to terminate these cables.

When there are multiple floors, the telephone room or cabinets require interfloor cabling on separate terminal blocks so that the appropriate cross-connections can be made on each floor. Some of the new twisted-pair LAN systems may require the use of coaxial cables here.

At the office ends, the multiple jack appearances are connected in daisy-chain fashion for ISDN use. If for some reason two pairs of jacks are not adequate in a single office, the jacks can temporarily be wired with the center poles (3 through 6) connected to two separate pairs on separate jack plates. This would allow four line (pair) appearances in a single office; these can be rewired into the ISDN configuration later simply by removing the jack plates. As an alternative, because of the relatively low cost of twisted-pair wiring, a single office can be double-wired for ISDN.

SUMMARY

Communications departments that are considering new wiring configurations should become familiar with the various RJ-45 wiring devices available in the marketplace. They should also investigate the new twisted-pair LAN systems available. It is always sensible to stay up to date with the current vendor offerings in the market because vendor marketing representatives are not always advised of new technology until it is actually in place and so may be of little assistance when organizations are making decisions about ISDN. Another possible source of wiring documentation leads is suppliers' catalogs.

ISDN premises wiring may not be the right choice for every corporation, but it does merit thoughtful consideration. Corporations involved in field trials for ISDN have estimated that their savings on wiring rearrangements would run in the thousands of dollars per year. This is partially because of ISDN's dynamic terminal address assignment capabilities; moving a terminal does not require any telephone room wiring rearrangement. It is also certain, however, that a significant part of the savings results from the universality and simplicity of ISDN premises wiring.

III-5
Encoding Techniques in Local Area Networks

WILLIAM STALLINGS

The emergence of local area networks (LANs) and the ongoing migration of public telecommunications networks to digital service have led to an increased interest in digital signaling techniques. An increasing reliance on digital communications requires a variety of solutions to the problems associated with digital signaling to accommodate all the networking applications being developed.

DIGITAL SIGNALING

Digital data is generated by a source—usually computing equipment or a voice digitizer. Whatever the source, the data is represented as discrete voltage pulses. The traditional digital encoding technique called non-return-to-zero-level (NRZ-L) uses one voltage level for binary 0 and another for binary 1. This technique is common in physical interfaces such as RS-232.

The usual way of transmitting digital data is to pass it through a modem to be transmitted as analog signals. This is not done, however, for the following:

- Baseband LANs, such as Ethernet and token ring.
- Digital PBX connections for terminals, hosts, and digital telephones.
- Digital access to public telecommunications networks over a digital local loop.

In each of these cases, digital signaling is used from end to end. Although it is possible to use NRZ-L encoding in these cases, the high data rates and long distances commonly associated with LANs and digital long-haul networks (including ISDN) make it an unattractive choice. For these cases the NRZ-L signal is therefore encoded in such a way as to improve performance.

Terminology

A *digital signal* is a sequence of discrete, discontinuous voltage pulses; each pulse is a *signal element*. Binary data is transmitted by encoding each data bit into signal elements. If the signal elements all have the same algebraic sign—all positive or all negative—then the signal is considered *unipolar.* In *polar* signaling, one logic state is represented by a positive voltage level and the other by a negative voltage level. The *data-signaling rate* (or data rate) of a signal is the rate, in bits per second (bps), at which data is transmitted. The *duration* or length of a bit is the amount of time it takes for the transmitter to emit the bit; for a data rate R, the bit duration is $1/R$. The *modulation rate,* in contrast, is the rate at which the signal level is changed; this rate depends on the nature of the digital encoding technique used. The modulation rate is expressed in *baud*— signal elements per second. Finally, the terms *mark* and *space,* for historical reasons, refer to the binary digits 1 and 0, respectively.

Evaluation Criteria

Interpreting digital signals at the receiver involves two important tasks. First, the receiver must know the timing of the signal so that the receiver can sample the incoming signal during each bit time to recognize the value of each bit. In other words, the receiver must know with some accuracy when a bit begins and ends. Second, the receiver must determine whether the signal level for each voltage pulse is high or low.

Several factors determine how successful the receiver will be in interpreting the incoming signal, including the signal-to-noise ratio (S/N), the data rate, and the bandwidth of the signal. When other factors, such as type and length of transmission medium, are held constant, the following statements are true:

- An increase in data rate increases bit-error rate (i.e., the probability that a bit is received in error).
- An increase in the signal-to-noise ratio decreases bit-error rate.
- Increased bandwidth allows an increased data rate.

The encoding scheme—another factor that can be used to improve performance—is simply the mapping from data bits to signal elements. A variety of schemes have been tried. Several factors are essential for evaluating or comparing them, including:

- Signal spectrum.
- Signal-synchronization capability.
- Error-detection capability.
- Cost and complexity.

Several aspects of the signal spectrum are important. When high-frequency components are absent, less bandwidth is required for transmission. (High frequency here is relative to the data rate—at a data rate of 1M bps, a frequency component of 10 MHz is high). The absence of a direct-current (dc) component is also desirable. A dc component requires a direct physical attachment of the transmission components; without it, alternating-current (ac) coupling by means of a transformer is possible, which provides excellent electrical isolation and reduces interference. Finally, the magnitude of the effects of signal distortion and interference depends on the spectral properties of the transmitted signal. In practice, because the transmission fidelity of a channel is worse near the band edges, a good signal design should concentrate the transmitted power in the middle of the transmission bandwidth. To minimize the amount of distortion present in the received signal, an encoding scheme should be designed with the goal of shaping the spectrum of the transmitted signal.

Successful transmission of digital data requires some signal synchronization between the transmitter and the receiver. Because some drift between the clocks of the transmitter and reciever is inevitable, a separate synchronization mechanism is needed. One solution is to provide a separate clock lead to synchronize the transmitter and receiver, but this is rather expensive because it requires an extra line, an extra transmitter, and an extra receiver. An alternative approach—providing some synchronization mechanism based on the transmitted signal—can be achieved with suitable encoding.

Although error detection is the responsibility of a data-link protocol that is executed on top of the physical signaling level, it is useful to have some error-detection capability built into the physical signaling scheme. This capability can increase the speed of error detection. Many signaling schemes have an inherent error-detection capability.

Finally, although digital logic continues to drop in price, the cost and complexity of the signaling scheme is a factor that must be considered when designing an encoding scheme.

NRZ-L and NRZI

In all NRZ codes, the voltage level is constant during a bit interval; they require no transition (i.e., no return to a zero voltage level). NRZ codes are the simplest codes to implement, and the simplest of them is NRZ-L, which uses a negative voltage to represent one binary value and a positive voltage to represent the other, as shown in Exhibit III-5-1. NRZ-L is the code generally used by terminals and other DP devices to generate or interpret digital data. If a different code is to be used for the transmission, it is usually generated from an NRZ-L signal by an interface device between the terminal or computer and the transmission system.

A variation of NRZ, known as NRZI (non-return-to-zero, invert-on-ones), also maintains a constant voltage pulse for the duration of a bit interval. The data itself is encoded as the presence or absence of a signal transition at the beginning of the bit time. A transition (i.e., low-to-high or high-to-low) at the beginning of a bit time denotes a binary 1 for that bit interval; no transition indicates a binary 0.

NRZI is an example of differential encoding, in which the signal is decoded by comparing its polarity to that of adjacent signal elements rather than determining its absolute value. One benefit of this scheme is that, in the presence of noise, detecting a transition may be more reliable than comparing a value to a threshold. Another benefit involves complex transmission layouts, in which it is

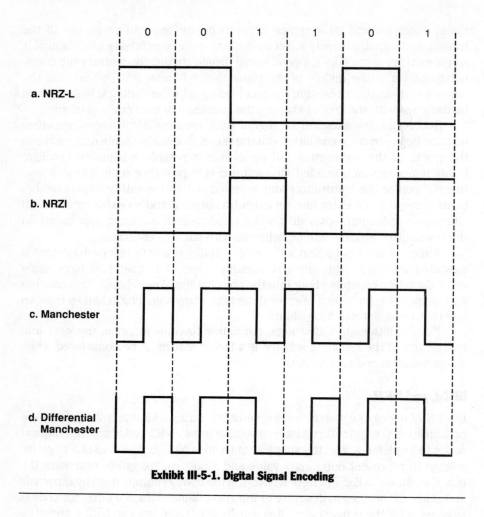

Exhibit III-5-1. Digital Signal Encoding

easy to lose the sense of the polarity of the signal. With NRZ-L on a multidrop twisted-pair line, for example, if the leads from an attached device to the twisted-pair were accidentally inverted, all 1s and 0s for NRZ-L would be inverted. This could not happen with differential encoding.

The NRZ codes are the easiest to engineer. As can be seen in Exhibit III-5-2, which compares the spectral density of various encoding schemes, they also make efficient use of bandwidth. (In the exhibit, frequency is normalized to the data rate.) Most of the energy in NRZ and NRZI signals is between dc and half the bit rate. If an NRZ code is used to generate a signal with a data rate of 9,600 bps, for example, most of the energy in the signal is concentrated between dc and 4,800 Hz.

The main limitations of NRZ signals are that they have a dc component and

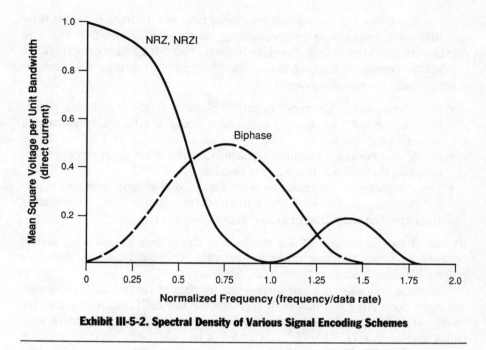

Exhibit III-5-2. Spectral Density of Various Signal Encoding Schemes

they lack a synchronization capability. If a long string of 1s or 0s (10 or more) were transmitted in NRZ-L or a long string of 0s in NRZI, the output would be a constant voltage over a long period of time (10 or more bit times). Under such circumstances, any drift between the timing of the transmitter and the receiver would result in the loss of synchronization between the two.

Because of their simplicity and their relatively low frequency-response characteristics, NRZ codes are commonly used for digital magnetic recording. However, their limitations make them unattractive for signal-transmission applications.

Biphase Codes

A set of alternative coding techniques, grouped under the term *biphase*, overcomes the limitations of NRZ codes. Two of these techniques, Manchester and differential Manchester (illustrated in Exhibit III-5-1), are in common use.

In the Manchester code, a transition at the middle of each bit period serves as both a clocking mechanism and as data. A low-to-high transition represents a 1 and a high-to-low transition represents a 0. In differential Manchester code, a mid-bit transition provides a clocking mechanism only. A 0 is represented by the presence of a transition at the beginning of a bit period, a 1 by the absence of a transition at the beginning of a bit period. Differential Manchester has the added advantage of employing differential encoding.

All of the biphase techniques require at least one transition per bit time and may have as many as two transitions, as shown in Exhibit III-5-3. The maximum modulation rate is therefore twice that for NRZ, making the required bandwidth correspondingly greater. To compensate for this, the biphase schemes have several advantages:

- Synchronization—The receiver can synchronize on the predictable transition during each bit time. The biphase codes are therefore known as self-clocking codes.
- No dc component—Because biphase codes have no dc component, ac-coupling through a transformer is possible.
- Error detection—The absence of an expected transition indicates an error. Noise on the line would have to invert the signal both before and after the expected transition to cause an undetected error.

As was shown in Exhibit III-5-2, the bulk of the energy in biphase codes is between one-half and one times the bit rate. The bandwidth is therefore reasonably narrow and contains no dc component.

Biphase codes are popular techniques for data transmission. Manchester, the more common code, has been specified for the IEEE 802.3 standard for baseband coaxial cable and twisted-pair carrier-sense multiple-access with collision-detection (CSMA/CD) bus LANs. It has also been used for military standard MIL-STD-1553B, a shielded twisted-pair bus LAN designed for high-noise environments. Differential Manchester has been specified for the IEEE 802.5 twisted-pair token-ring LAN.

Fiber Distributed Data Interface

The biphase codes are well suited to digital signaling on baseband IEEE 802 LANs. In principle, they could also be adapted for use on the most recent LAN standard, the fiber distributed data interface (FDDI), which specifies a 100M-bps optical-fiber ring. In Manchester coding, for example, a 0 would be represented by a pulse of light in the first half of the bit time and the absence of light in the second half, and a 1 would be represented by the absence of light in the first half and a pulse of light in the second half. The disadvantage of Manchester for fiber is that the efficiency achieved is only 50%. In other words, because

	Minimum	101010. . .	Maximum
NRZ-L	0 (all 0s or 1s)	1.0	1.0 (1010. . .)
NRZI	0 (all 0s)	0.5	1.0 (all 1s)
Manchester	1.0 (1010. . .)	1.0	2.0 (all 0s or 1s)
Differential Manchester	1.0 (all 1s)	1.5	2.0 (all 0s)

Exhibit III-5-3. Signal Transition Rate

Manchester can result in as many as two transitions per bit time, a signaling rate of 200 million signaling elements per second (200M baud) is needed to achieve a data rate of 100M bps. At the high data rate of FDDI, this represents an unnecessary cost.

To overcome this shortcoming, the FDDI standard specifies the use of a code referred to as 4B/5B. In this scheme, four bits are encoded at a time and each group of four bits is mapped into a 5-bit code. Each bit of the code is transmitted as a single signal element (i.e., the presence or absence of a light pulse). The efficiency of the code is thus raised to 80% and 100M bps is achieved with 125M baud. The resulting cost savings is substantial: A 200M-baud optical transmitter and receiver pair can cost 5 to 10 times that of a 125M-baud pair.

To achieve synchronization, FDDI calls for a second stage of encoding in which each element of the 4B/5B stream is treated as a binary value and encoded using NRZI. The use of NRZI, which is differential, aids in the ultimate decoding of the signal after it has been reconverted from optical to electrical.

Exhibit III-5-4 shows the symbol encoding used in FDDI. There are 32 5-bit codes; 16 of these are used to encode all of the possible 4-bit blocks of data. The codes selected to represent the 16 4-bit data groups contain a transition at least twice for each 5-cell pattern on the medium. Since NRZI is being used, this is equivalent to requiring that there be at least two 1s in each 5-bit code (in NRZI, a 1 is encoded by a transition). As can be seen, all 16 of the codes that represent data contain at least two 1s.

The reasoning behind the choice of an FDDI encoding scheme can be summarized as follows.

- A simple on-off encoding is rejected because it does not provide synchronization; a string of 1s or 0s would have no transitions with which to synchronize.
- The 4B/5B code is chosen over Manchester because it is more efficient.
- The 4B/5B code is further encoded using NRZI so that the resulting differential encoding will improve reception reliability.
- The specific codes chosen for encoding the 16 4-bit data groups guarantee at least two 1s and hence at least two transitions, thereby providing adequate synchronization.

Only 16 of the 32 possible code patterns are required to represent the input data. The remaining symbols are either invalid or have special meaning as control symbols. For example, two of the patterns always occur in pairs and act as start-delimiters for a frame.

ANALOG SIGNALING

Analog signaling techniques are used in broadband and carrierband LANs over a coaxial-cable medium.

Decimal	Code Group	Symbol	Assignment
Line State Symbols			
00	00000	Q	QUIET
31	11111	I	IDLE
04	00100	H	HALT
Starting Delimiter			
24	11000	J	1st of Sequential Starting Delimiter Pair
17	10001	K	2nd of Sequential Starting Delimiter Pair

Data Symbols			Hex	Binary
30	11110	0	0	0000
09	01001	1	1	0001
20	10100	2	2	0010
21	10101	3	3	0011
10	01010	4	4	0100
11	01011	5	5	0101
14	01110	6	6	0110
15	01111	7	7	0111
18	10010	8	8	1000
19	10011	9	9	1001
22	10110	A	A	1010
23	10111	B	B	1011
26	11010	C	C	1100
27	11011	D	D	1101
28	11100	E	E	1110
29	11101	F	F	1111

Ending Delimiter			
13	01101	T	Used to Terminate the Data Stream

Control Indicators			
07	00111	R	Denoting Logical ZERO (Reset)
25	11001	S	Denoting Logical ONE (Set)

Invalid Code Assignments			
01	00001	V or H	These code patterns shall
02	00010	V or H	not be transmitted
03	00011	V	because they violate
05	00101	V	consecutive code-bit
06	00110	V	zeros or duty cycle
08	01000	V or H	requirements. Codes 01,
12	01100	V	02, 08, and 16, however,
18	10000	V or H	will be interpreted as
			HALT when received.

(12345) = Sequential Order of Code-Bit Transmission

Exhibit III-5-4. 4B/5B Code

CSMA/CD Broadband

The IEEE 802.3 standard for CSMA/CD LANs includes a specification for a broadband coaxial-cable LAN operating at 10M bps. The modulation technique used is differential phase-shift keying (DPSK). In ordinary PSK, a binary 0 is represented by a carrier with a particular phase, and a binary 1 is represented by a carrier with the opposite phase (i.e., 180° difference). DPSK makes use of differential encoding in which a change of phase corresponds to a 0 and no change of phase corresponds to a 1. The advantage of differential encoding is that the receiver can more easily detect the presence or absence of a change of phase than determine the phase itself.

Token-Bus Broadband

The IEEE 802.4 standard for token-bus LANs includes a specification for a broadband coaxial-cable LAN operating at 1M, 5M or 10M bps. The modulation scheme used for this specification is known as duobinary AM/PSK (amplitude modulation/phase-shift-keying modulation). In this scheme, data is precoded and transmitted in signal pulses in which both the amplitude and the phase may vary. The nature of the precoding is such that receivers can demodulate the modulated signal without having to recover the phase of the signal. In essence, the PSK component of the modulation is used to reduce the signal bandwidth, not to carry data.

In duobinary AM/PSK, a special narrow-bandwidth pulse is created that is used for amplitude modulation of a radio frequency carrier. Exhibit III-5-5 illustrates such a pulse for a 10M-bps data rate. The pulse of opposite polarity is also used. Because the pulse spreads over a number of bit times, pulses that are generated in nearby bit slots overlap. The overlap is highly predictable,

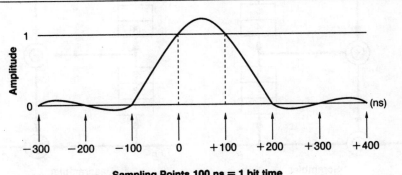

Sampling Points 100 ns = 1 bit time

Note:
AM/PSK   Amplitude modulation and phase-shift-keying modulation

Exhibit III-5-5. Input Pulse for Duobinary AM/PSK at 10M bps

however. At each sample point, a pulse has a value of 0 or 1. At any sample point, therefore, a 0, 1, or 2 can be detected. Two pulses—one bit-time apart—are used to encode digital data. A binary 1 is represented by two consecutive pulses of the same polarity, which will produce a sample of +2 or −2, and a binary 0 is represented by two consecutive pulses of opposite polarity, which produces a sample of 0. Each pulse participates in two bits; that is, each pulse is both the second pulse of one bit and the first pulse of the next bit.

Scrambling

A characteristic common to virtually all broadband-LAN modems is the use of scrambling, which gives data a pseudorandom nature that helps the receiver extract bit-timing information. It also improves the spectral characteristics of the signal, giving it a more uniform power distribution, in contrast to the potentially strong discrete spectral lines characteristic of nonscrambled data. A uniform distribution gives the signal better noise resistance.

The benefit of scrambling can be seen in relation to the fact that a long string of binary 0s or 1s in a transmission can degrade system performance. For example, in the DPSK scheme used in broadband-LAN modems, a phase shift occurs only when the input is a 0 bit. If the input is a long string of 1s, the receiver has difficulty maintaining synchronization with the transmitter. A similar problem arises with duobinary AM/PSK. The scrambling process helps correct this problem because it tends to make data appear more random.

Scrambling is accomplished through a feedback shift register and the corresponding descrambling through a feed-forward shift register. An example of a scrambler/descrambler pair is shown in Exhibit III-5-6. The scrambled data

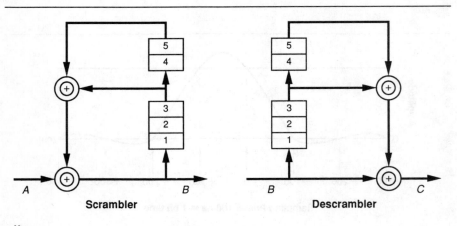

Key:
⊕ Exclusive-OR operation

Exhibit III-5-6. A Scrambler and a Descrambler

sequence the scrambler produces can be expressed as follows:

$$B_m = A_m \oplus B_{m-3} \approx B_{m-5}$$

where $\oplus$ indicates the exclusive-OR operation. The descrambled sequence can be expressed as:

$$
\begin{aligned}
C_m &= B_m \oplus B_{m-3} \oplus B_{m-5} \\
&= (A_m \oplus B_{m-3} \oplus B_{m-5}) \oplus B_{m-3} \oplus B_{m-5} \\
&= A_m
\end{aligned}
$$

The descrambled output is the original sequence.

This process can be represented using polynomials as follows:

$$P = 1 + X^{-3} + X^{-5}$$

The input is divided by this polynomial to produce the scrambled sequence. The receiver multiplies this scrambled signal by the same polynomial to re-produce the original input. Exhibit III-5-7 is an example of this process using the polynomial P and an input of 101010100000111. The scrambled transmission, produced by dividing by P (100101), is 101110001101001. Multiplying this number by P produces the original input. Note that the input includes the

```
                                101110001101001←B
       P→100101)101010100000111-----←A
                100101
                 111110
                 100101
                  110110
                  100101
                   100110
                   100101
                    110011
                    100101
                     101101
                     100101
                      100000
                      100101
                       101000
```

a. Scrambling

```
             101110001101001←B
                    100101←P
             ─────────────────
             101110001101001
            101110001101001
           101110001101001
           ─────────────────────
    C=A→101010100000111-----
```

b. Descrambling

Exhibit III-5-7. Example of the Scrambling Process with $P(X) = 1 + X^{-3} + X^{-5}$

periodic sequence 10101010 as well as a long string of 0s. The scrambler effectively removes both patterns.

Carrier-Band Modulation Techniques

Another application of analog signaling on a LAN is known as carrier-band or single-channel broadband coding. In this case, the entire spectrum of the cable is devoted to a single transmission path for the analog signals; no frequency-division multiplexing is possible. Although the entire spectrum is used, most of the signal energy is concentrated at relatively low frequencies—an advantage because attenuation is less at lower frequencies.

Because the cable is dedicated to a single task, modem output need not be confined to a narrow bandwidth; energy can spread over the entire spectrum. As a result, carrier-band electronics are simple and relatively inexpensive. The technique usually uses some form of frequency-shift keying (FSK), with two different frequencies representing two different signaling elements.

The IEEE 802.4 token-bus standard specifies two options for carrier-band systems: a 1M-bps phase-continuous FSK LAN, and a 5M-bps and 10M-bps phase-coherent FSK LAN. Phase-continuous FSK is a form of FSK in which the transition between signaling frequencies is accomplished by a continuous change of frequency rather than the discontinuous replacement of one frequency by another, as is accomplished by a switch. This implementation of FSK results in a tighter bandwidth and improved transmission and reception efficiency.

For this encoding scheme two frequencies are defined: H = 6.25 MHz and L = 3.75 MHz. The signal on the line can be viewed as a carrier of 5 MHz that varies continuously between the two frequencies H and L. Each 0 bit is encoded as H L and each 1 bit as L H. Because the data rate is only 1M bps, multiple periods of each signal will occur in one bit time. The encoding of the 0s and 1s effectively follows the Manchester encoding rules, translated into the analog realm.

Phase-coherent FSK is a form of FSK in which the two signaling frequencies are integrally related to the data rate. This scheme is called phase-coherent because the 0 crossing points are in phase at the beginning and end of each bit time. Proponents of this form of modulation, as opposed to those of phase-continuous FSK, contend that it is easier to implement digitally and can therefore permit a low-cost single-chip solution.

For phase-coherent FSK, as for phase-continuous FSK, two frequencies are defined, one with a frequency equal to twice the data rate and one with a frequency equal to the data rate. Therefore, for the 5M-bps specification, the higher frequency is 10 MHz and the lower frequency is 5 MHz. For the 10M-bps specification, the higher frequency is 20 MHz and the lower frequency is 10 MHz. A binary 1 is represented by a full cycle of the lower signaling frequency in one bit time, and a binary 0 is represented by two full cycles of the higher signaling frequency.

SUMMARY

The encoding technique used on a LAN has an effect on the cost of the transmission system and the quality of the signal as reflected in the error rate. This chapter has provided an overview of the advantages and disadvantages of the most common encoding techniques for both digital and analog signaling.

III-6
LAN Access Protocols

ROBERT A. PRICHARD, JR

Local area networks provide the means for sharing expensive resources and performing file transfers in office or campus environments. To accomplish these networking functions economically, the same transmission medium must be used by multiple stations. The specification of a common transmission medium poses various questions with regard to network use and operation; in particular, the following networking requirements must be addressed:

- Choosing the station that has permission to transmit.
- Informing the stations when they have permission to transmit.
- Informing stations when the network is available for transmission.
- Moving data in binary form onto the transmission medium.
- Establishing procedures to follow if the network crashes.

The techniques and rules developed to answer these and many other related requirements are known as access methods. This chapter provides an overview of the access methods used in communications networks in general, with a specific focus on those used in LANs.

In its most basic form, an access method accomplishes three fundamental tasks:

- It defines how data terminal equipment attached to networks gains access to the physical transmission medium connecting network nodes.
- It specifies the order in which the data terminal equipment uses the transmission medium.
- It governs the flow of traffic on the network.

The name given to an access method distinguishes various network types and, in many cases, becomes the primary way to discriminate between networks and vendor products. For example, a LAN may be identified as a token-ring network. This network descriptor identifies an access method (token passing), a logical topology (ring), and implicitly identifies the hardware supplied by a specific vendor.

A protocol is the set of rules by which two devices interpret the electrical signals (i.e., bits) containing the information passed between the devices. An access protocol, therefore, provides the set of communications rules to implement the access method.

All communications networks use some form of access method, but not all access methods are used with LAN technology. Access methods have two distinguishing characteristics: the location of the network control point and the method used to gain access to the transmission medium.

THE NETWORK CONTROL POINT

The network control point is the node in the system that controls the flow of traffic in the network. Traffic flow includes such items as which station is authorized to transmit on the network, the length of time each station can transmit, the sequence of station transmission, how a station may identify permission to transmit, and how the station knows that a previous transmission has ended. Networks are controlled by one of two basic methods: centralized or distributed control.

Centralized Control

Centralized control, depicted in Exhibit III-6-1, implies a master-slave relationship between the central control and remote stations. Most of the intelligence resides within the central unit, which is a host computer or front-end processor with individual workstation remotes (e.g., a personal computer or a cluster controller for a number of terminals). The central control unit issues inquiries or commands in the form of polls, and the remote units may not use the network until polled by the host.

Communication between the central unit and the remote units may be synchronous or asynchronous, half- or full-duplex, and bit- or byte-oriented, depending on the hardware and the protocol being used. The buffering and local intelligence requirements of the remote stations are minimal. Direct communication from remote unit to remote unit is generally not permitted; such communication is controlled by the central unit. Today, certain versions of hardware and software allow remote-to-remote communications with minimum central control unit intervention, but the primary network control still remains with the central unit.

Distributed Control

With distributed control (see Exhibit III-6-2) there is no central control unit; control is distributed to each station attached to the network. The network elements function as peers (i.e., no master-slave relationship exists). Distributed control, however, places different requirements on the network elements; specifically, each network element must have the intelligence to perform the following functions:

- Maintain the status of permissions to transmit.
- Know the state of the network.
- Identify network message addresses.

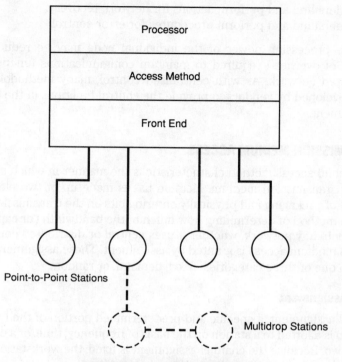

Point-to-Point Stations

Multidrop Stations

Exhibit III-6-1. Centralized Control

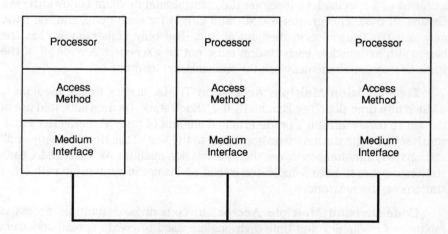

Exhibit III-6-2. Distributed Control

- Understand and perform actions for network recovery.
- Understand and perform procedures for error control.

The processing power of the individual node may be reduced by the amount of overhead required to maintain communications functions on the distributed network. As with centralized control, many methodologies have been developed by vendors to provide the control functions in the distributed environment.

TRANSMISSION MEDIUM ACCESS

The second access method characteristic is the manner in which stations can use the transmission medium. Medium use is made up of two elements: the method of packaging and physically entering bits on the transmission medium, and the method of determining how much of the bandwidth (or capacity) may be used. In any network, whether it uses central or distributed control, transmission medium access is granted by assignment. These assignments typically fall into one of three categories: fixed, demand, or random.

Fixed Assignment

In fixed assignment, a specific and predetermined portion of the transmission medium is allotted to a station on the basis of frequency, time, or a combination of the two. Because the channel assignment is fixed, the workstation views the assigned bandwidth as a dedicated circuit. Multiplexing occurs, but the individual station is unaware of contention for the channel. The three methods of fixed assignment are frequency-division multiple access (FDMA), time-division multiple access (TDMA), and code-division multiple access (CDMA).

Frequency-Division Multiple Access. In FDMA, each network node is assigned to a specific frequency on the transmission medium bandwidth (see Exhibit III-6-3). This creates a dedicated circuit for each node, and the node may use the transmission medium at will. The only constraint is that the bandwidth assigned to each station must not be exceeded. Any or all of the stations may simultaneously use the transmission medium.

Time-Division Multiple Access. In TDMA, access to the medium is divided into time slots (see Exhibit III-6-4). Each station is then allocated use of the entire bandwidth for a predetermined amount of time. The effective bandwidth seen by the station varies according to the size of the time slot. Any or all stations may simultaneously use the transmission medium. As with FDMA, each station appears to have a dedicated circuit and is not in contention with other stations on the network.

Code-Division Multiple Access. In code-division multiple access, a mixture of frequency and time divisions are used to create spread spectrum signals. This method simultaneously transmits station time slots on different

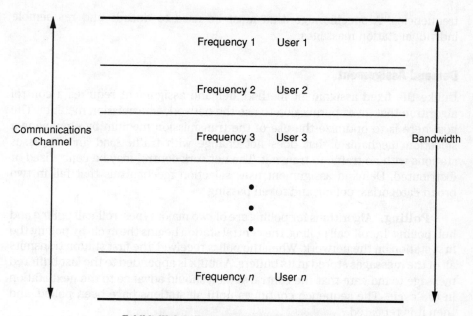

Exhibit III-6-3. Frequency-Division Multiplexing

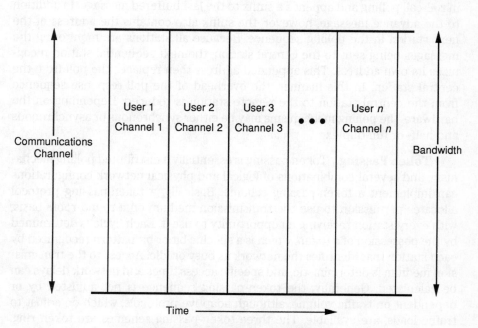

Exhibit III-6-4. Time-Division Multiplexing

frequencies. A specific algorithm must be used to decode and reassemble individual station messages.

Demand Assignment

Unlike the fixed assignment method, demand assignment requires a control algorithm that gives permission to use the network transmission medium. The goal here is to optimize the use of the transmission medium by employing a selection mechanism that does not change with traffic load and bypasses stations with no traffic to transmit. The network control may be centralized or distributed. Demand assignment uses selection mechanisms that fall in two broad categories: polling and token passing.

Polling. Algorithms for polling are of two major types: roll-call polling and hub polling. In roll-call polling, the central station begins the cycle by polling the first station on the network. When the poll is received, the first station transmits all of the messages stored in its buffers. A suffix is appended to the last buffered message to indicate that the central station should advance to the next station in the cycle. The sequence continues until all stations have been polled, and then it is repeated.

Hub polling works in a similar manner but requires the use of additional hardware to perform active monitoring of the messages being sent from each station to the central station. The central station begins the polling sequence as in roll-call polling and appends a suffix to the last buffered message. In addition to the advance message, however, the suffix also contains the address of the next station in the polling sequence. Because all stations are monitoring the messages being sent to the central station, the next sequential station recognizes its own address. This appended address then replaces the poll from the central station. In this manner, the overhead of the poll-response sequence from the central station to the remote station is reduced. Depending on the hardware, the polling mechanisms may be either synchronous or asynchronous and half- or full-duplex.

Token Passing. Token passing is essentially a distributed polling mechanism, and several combinations of logical and physical network configurations can implement a token-passing scheme. Basically, a token-passing protocol allocates permission to use the transmission medium on a round-robin basis, with every station receiving an opportunity to use it. Each cycle is determined by the possession of a token, which is a specific bit or bit pattern recognized by each station that identifies the network as busy or idle. Access to the transmission medium is deterministic, and specific access times and network delays can be calculated. Generally, the token-passing sequence is not adjusted by or dependent on traffic volume, although adaptive protocols, which do adjust to traffic loads, are available. The three token-passing schemes are token ring, token bus, and implicit token.

The Token Ring. The token ring is a series of point-to-point links closed up to form a logical ring that connects the stations (see Exhibit III-6-5). The term *logical ring* is used because several physical configurations may be used, but the network operates as if the stations were connected in a ring. A station consists of a terminal device (usually a personal computer or engineering workstation) and a ring interface unit. Each station is connected to the ring by a repeater, which is an active device that regenerates all the data flowing on the ring regardless of whether the station is in the transmit or receive mode.

When a station receives an idle token and has no data to transmit, the token is passed to the next station on the ring. If the station does have traffic to transmit, the idle token is modified and the information is sent on the network. The destination station then copies the information and forwards the information packet. All other stations simply regenerate and pass the message. When the message returns to the originating station, it is removed from the ring and the token is modified to indicate an idle condition and forwarded to the next station on the ring.

The Token Bus. The operation of a token bus is similar to that of the token ring, but the stations are physically attached in a bus configuration. The network operates as a logical ring, with the token being passed between stations in a predetermined sequence. The sequence of stations does not necessarily follow the order of attachment, however, as in the ring configuration. Stations, which are all passive rather than active, may appear at any single point in the sequence, have multiple appearances, or be omitted altogether. Because they are connected in a bus topology, the token bus is a passive broadcast network. Individual network stations do not regenerate the received signals from the

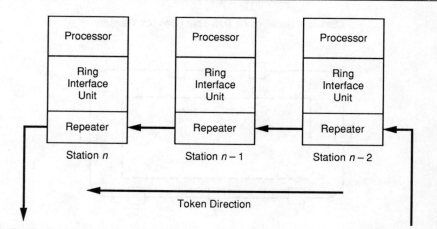

Exhibit III-6-5. Token Ring

network. This improves reliability because no single station failure stops all signal flow, but signal quality can degrade because of the absence of the regeneration function.

Another difference is the possibility of having a receive-only station that is not permitted to transmit (see Exhibit III-6-6). Because the station sequence is configurable and each station is passive, a station can be omitted from the ring sequence. The station is still attached to the bus and will, because of the broadcast nature of the network, receive all signals transmitted on the bus. The token, however, which grants permission to use the transmission medium, will never be routed to the station.

Implicit Token. Tokens have varying lengths and amounts of information associated with them, based on the specific protocol used. The implicit token scheme is a derivative of the token bus protocol, in which, to reduce the

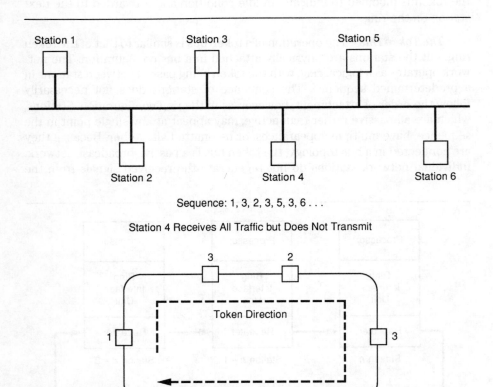

Sequence: 1, 3, 2, 3, 5, 3, 6 . . .

Station 4 Receives All Traffic but Does Not Transmit

Token Direction

Logical Configuration of Token Bus

Exhibit III-6-6. Token Bus

overhead associated with the token, the physical bit pattern can be replaced with an implicit token identified as an idle channel condition. When the idle channel condition is recognized, the next station in the sequence seizes the channel and begins to transmit. Each station constantly monitors the channel for the idle channel condition. Following a preset network timing algorithm, each station in the sequence must wait for a longer period of time to allow preceding stations to transmit. Because the idle channel carrier serves as the token, this method is also referred to as carrier-sense multiple access with collision avoidance (CSMA/CA).

Random Assignment

Random assignment networks are characterized by the absence of a central network control station and are classified as contention networks because all stations contend for the same transmission medium. Any station may attempt to transmit a packet at any time. Assurance that a second station will not interfere by attempting a simultaneous transmission is not given to the transmitting station. Although the most widely known random assignment LANs use the bus topology, these networks may be found in a variety of physical configurations. The three general categories of random assignment networks are the ALOHA network, the contention bus, and the contention ring.

ALOHA. Random assignment procedures were initially developed for radio and satellite links. Because a large portion of this research took place at the University of Hawaii, the result was named the ALOHA network and represents a contention network in that it allows a station to transmit a packet at any time with no channel monitoring. If a single station transmits a packet to a destination station (assuming an error-free medium and transmission procedure), the destination station receives the packet and returns an acknowledgment. The destination station may use a separate channel for the transmission of an acknowledgment.

If two stations attempt simultaneous transmission, the transmitted packets are garbled at the destination station and the destination station does not issue an acknowledgment. After a predetermined time-out period with no acknowledgment, the transmitting station assumes that a collision has occurred and queues the packet for retransmission. The retransmission times at each of the original transmitting stations are randomly set to avoid a second collision, and the entire procedure is repeated.

In an attempt to reduce the number of collisions and increase packet throughput, the ALOHA procedure has been refined. This method is called slotted ALOHA and offers several improvements over the pure ALOHA scheme. Slotted ALOHA requires the addition of a synchronizing element to the network and the division of the available time into time slots that are exactly the same size as the transmission packets. Each transmitting station is required to begin transmission at the beginning of a time slot, rather than on a random basis.

Although other reservation-type procedures have been developed and tested, this procedure essentially remains in use in radio and satellite networks. Very little application has been attempted in LANs because the propagation time is long compared with the size of the information packets.

The Contention Bus. Network use in limited geographic areas with short end-to-end propagation delay makes it possible to listen to the transmission medium before transmitting. If a carrier—which indicates a transmission is in progress—is sensed on the network, a station waiting to transmit defers until the medium is idle. When several stations are attached to a transmission medium and multiple access is required, the CSMA protocol is used. CSMA is characterized by a listen-before-transmit mode of operation and three classifications that implement this mode have been developed. These are nonpersistent, 1-persistent, and P-persistent CSMA.

Nonpersistent Carrier-Sense Multiple Access. With nonpersistent CSMA, a station waiting to transmit defers for a predetermined period of time (called back-off). The length of the back-off period is based on an exponential algorithm that makes the initial periods shorter. After the back-off period has expired, the station monitors the line again. If a busy condition is sensed, the station enters a second, slightly longer back-off period. When the transmission medium reverts to an idle condition, the station transmits as usual.

1-Persistent Carrier-Sense Multiple Access. In 1-persistent CSMA, the station waiting to transmit listens to the transmission medium. If a busy condition is detected, the station continues to monitor the line. The station then transmits the stored message immediately on detection of an idle channel.

P-Persistent Carrier-Sense Multiple Access. If several stations had messages waiting and all attempted transmission as soon as an idle channel condition occurred, collisions would naturally result. Therefore, a third method called P-persistent CSMA was developed. When a busy channel is sensed, the station waiting to transmit continues to monitor the channel. When an idle channel condition is sensed, the station, with a probability of P, transmits the stored message. If the channel is busy, the station persists in monitoring and the above sequence is repeated.

Carrier-Sense Multiple Access with Collision Detection. A refinement of the multiple access technique employs another type of operation, referred to as listen while transmitting. Using this technique, the station can rapidly detect collisions and promptly abort the transmission sequence. This provides a more efficient use of the transmission medium and increases throughput. The collision detection feature has resulted in this protocol dominating contention bus applications for LANs.

The Contention Ring. The third general category of random assignment networks is the contention ring. Contention rings share the same topological construction as the token rings, but the method of gaining access to the transmission medium is different. Two general types of contention rings—the slotted ring and the register insertion ring—are discussed.

The Slotted Ring. Slotted rings maintain the point-to-point link structure of the basic ring configuration. The ring operation differs in that a token is not used to indicate permission to access the transmission medium. Instead, the ring is divided into time slots that continually rotate around the ring. To transmit, a station must access an empty slot on the ring. The protocol does not provide a deterministic method for finding an empty slot, rather all stations on the network contend for the slots. An operational analogy is that of a conveyor belt. If a station cannot find immediate access to a time slot on the ring, it must monitor the medium until one becomes available.

The Register Insertion Ring. The register insertion ring functions like the slotted ring. Actually, it is a refinement of the slotted ring designed to increase the amount of data that may be transmitted on the ring. This is accomplished by using shift registers to create delay in the ring and increase the capacity, or the number of bits, that can reside on the ring at a given time. The contention is still for time slots, but the access methodology is different.

Three shift registers are used in each station on the register insertion ring: a receive register, a transmit register, and an insertion register. The receive switch is activated by the destination address of the incoming data packet. If the packet is addressed to the station on which it has arrived, it is routed to the receive register and removed from the ring. If not, it is placed in the insertion register and serially reentered onto the ring. If the station needs to transmit data, it enters the data in its transmit register. If the bits circulating on the ring can be buffered in the insertion register while the ring is broken and the bits to be transmitted are serially entered onto the ring from the transmission register, the transmission is completed. If the insertion register cannot meet this condition, the transmit function must defer. In this way, the ring capacity is increased by the bit capacity of the insertion register.

A visual summary of medium use schemes is shown in Exhibit III-6-7.

IEEE ACCESS PROTOCOLS

The OSI seven-layer model was selected by the IEEE as the basic framework for the development of LAN standards because it provided a global, relatively straightforward approach to systems design. To maintain consistency with the OSI model, a slightly modified approach was taken to meet the technical criteria specific to LANs in level two, the data link layer.

Initial solutions to LAN requirements were developed by vendors to meet the needs of commercial users. Because standards had not been established, the approaches were bottom-up, or application driven. A technical evaluation of the various vendor solutions to locally based, relatively high-speed networking

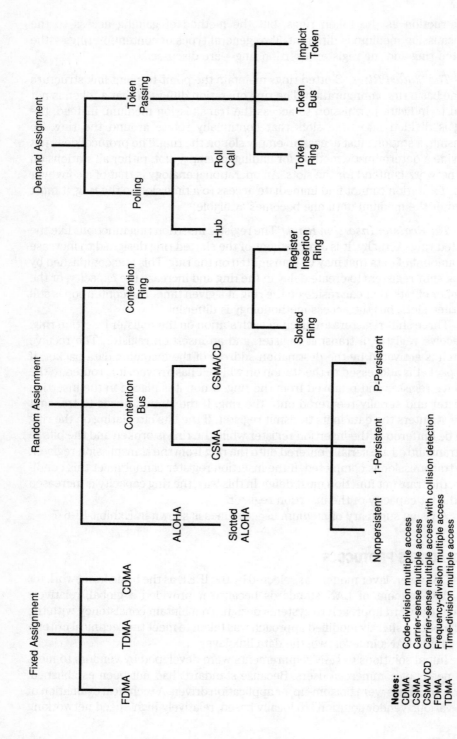

Exhibit III-6-7. Medium Use Summary

Notes:

CDMA	Code-division multiple access
CSMA	Carrier-sense multiple access
CSMA/CD	Carrier-sense multiple access with collision detection
FDMA	Frequency-division multiple access
TDMA	Time-division multiple access

indicated that a single data link protocol that would meet the requirements for all users could not be identified. The final determination of the IEEE provided an upper-level interface that supported multiple access methods and physical media. This was called the logical link control (defined as IEEE 802.2). Below the logical link control were multiple access methods, and the service sublayer designated to support these functions was named the media access control. The combination of the logical link control and the media access control defined the data link level for LANs. Layer one, the physical layer, retained the original function set defined in the OSI model.

Logical Link Control Sublayer

The logical link control provides an interface between layers two (data link layer) and three (network layer) in the OSI model. The service access point provides access to the following three services:

- Type 1—Connectionless services.
- Type 2—Connection-oriented services.
- Type 3—Acknowledged connectionless services.

Type 1 services (also called datagram services) do not provide a dedicated logical connection between the sending and receiving units. Individual or group addresses may be used. Each data unit is sent independently with no sequence checking, and the receiving station does not acknowledge received data packets. Flow control and error recovery are not provided by the service.

Type 2 services establish a logical connection between the sending and receiving stations. This logical connection must be set up before the transmission sequence, maintained during this sequence, and terminated at the end of it. The service provides packet sequence checking, error control, and flow control, and only individual addresses may be used.

Type 3 services are of two independent but related types. The first type is a guaranteed delivery service. This means that the datagram service described in type 1 is used, but the receiving station acknowledges receipt. The second service offered is a poll with a guaranteed response, which allows previously prepared packets to be exchanged among users.

Media Access Control Sublayer

After a logical link control service is invoked from the upper layers by a service access point, the protocol data unit passes to the media access control. The sublayer performs several functions to ensure that network management takes place during operation and that recovery occurs in the event of a network failure. The media access control sublayer passes the protocol data unit to the physical layer to enter the bits on the physical medium that connects the nodes of the network.

221

IEEE 802.3. The IEEE 802.3 standard is a random assignment contention bus with decentralized control. The following are medium-dependent physical layer standards incorporated into IEEE 802.3:

- 10BASE5—10M-bps baseband system using 50-ohm coaxial cable with a maximum segment length of 500 m.
- 10BASE2—10M-bps baseband system using a smaller-diameter 50-ohm coaxial cable with a maximum segment length of 200 m.
- 10BROAD36—10M-bps broadband system using 75-ohm coaxial cable with a maximum segment length of 3,600 m (two 1,800-m segments from a head end).
- 1BASE5—1M-bps baseband system using twisted-pair cable with a maximum segment length of 500 m.
- 10BASE-T—10M-bps baseband system using twisted-pair cable—This standard has not been fully defined to date.

IEEE 802.4. The IEEE 802.4 standard is a demand assignment (token passing) bus scheme. This media access control is primarily used in factory-automated applications requiring deterministic access to specific nodes. The primary proponent of this method is General Motors Corp, which pioneered the use of the token bus to implement the Manufacturing Automation Protocol. The physical medium specification that supports this standard has three alternatives, two of which are based on carrier band transmission (single-channel broadband) while the third is a full-broadband system.

IEEE 802.5. The IEEE 802.5 standard is a token-passing ring media access control. The supporting physical layer standards include a 4M-bps twisted-pair standard sponsored by the IEEE and a 4M-bps and 16M-bps twisted-pair standard proposed by IBM. IBM is also developing a 16M-bps standard for use on fiber-optic cable. IBM has adopted the token ring as the primary media access control to support the local and campus networking requirements of its distributed computing products.

Fiber Distributed Data Interface. Another standard gaining momentum is the fiber distributed data interface (FDDI), which is being promoted by the American National Standards Institute (ANSI). The media access control format is a derivative of the IEEE 802.5 token-passing ring and specifies a physical interface supporting optical fiber cabling at a data rate of 100M bps. FDDI assumes the IEEE 802.2 logical link control for interfacing with the upper layers of the OSI model.

SUMMARY

To provide the best possible selection and implementation of LANs and access methods, the network manager should understand the basic purposes of LAN technology; the various access methods and their applications; the requirements of the company or groups within the company that will use the LAN; and the effects of ancillary issues (e.g., cable plant management, maintenance, moves, adds, and changes). If all of these factors are understood, the manager will be able to evaluate effectively all proposed access methods and the associated LAN solutions.

III-7
IEEE 802 Standards

ASGHAR I. NOOR

Most networks are designed and constructed in functional layers, with the quantity, designation, and functions of the layers differing from network to network. Each layer offers certain services to the layers above it, and shields those layers from the implementation of its services. These layers constitute the network protocol architecture, the structure of rules that govern the exchange of information and services through the layers of one system and between two or more distinct systems.

The International Standards Organization (ISO) has defined a seven-layer network architecture that is known as the open systems interconnection (OSI) reference model. In OSI, corresponding layers, or peer processes, on different systems communicate only through the protocol hierarchy (see Exhibit III-7-1). No data is passed directly from layer N of system A to layer N of system B. Instead, each layer passes data and control information to the layer immediately below it, until the lowest layer of the system is reached. The lowest layer of system A then transmits the data to its peer layer on system B by way of the transmission medium.

The OSI model is composed of seven layers: the physical layer, data link layer, network layer, transport layer, session layer, presentation layer, and application layer. These layers are self-contained and isolated from each other. As a result, a given layer can be replaced and implementation can be changed without affecting the other six layers. Such a layered design is important in accommodating innovations in hardware and firmware technology.

IEEE 802 STANDARDS

Efforts to create standard LAN frameworks have been under way for some time, and recently the complete IEEE specifications have received the endorsements of several government, industry, and international organizations. Many of these groups are actively working to create a standard framework for LANs. The consensus decision has been to confine LAN protocols defined by the IEEE to the lowest two layers (i.e., physical and link layers) of the OSI reference model.

The IEEE 802 working groups were chartered to create standards by which devices could communicate over LANs. The committees' objectives were to define a LAN standard that ensures compatibility of multivendor equipment

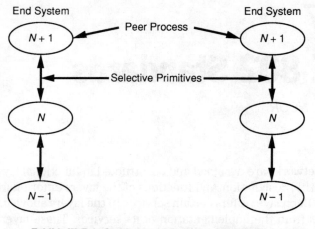

Exhibit III-7-1. Architectural Framework for Protocol

such that efficient data communications between devices and systems require minimal effort on the part of end users, equipment users, and network designers.

The IEEE 802 committee established two important premises. First, the task of communication across the LAN is complex and thus needs to be broken down into more manageable subtasks. Second, a single technical solution cannot meet the requirements of various applications.

The result of the first decision is the creation of the following flexible framework for LANs spanning the lower two OSI levels as well as network management of those layers (see Exhibit III-7-2):

- Physical layer.
- Media access control sublayer of the data link layer.
- Logical link control sublayer of the data link layer.
- Network management.

The second conclusion resulted in the formation of the following subcommittees to look into various alternatives:

- IEEE 802.1: Higher-layer interface—Chartered to make recommendations regarding internetworking and higher-layer interfaces and several network management functions.
- IEEE 802.2: Logical link control—Concerned with establishing, maintaining, and terminating a logical link between communicating stations.
- IEEE 802.3: Carrier-sense multiple access with collision detection (CSMA/CD)—Standard based on bus topology with a decentralized control structure.
- IEEE 802.4: Token bus—Standard based on token passing technology over a bus topology.

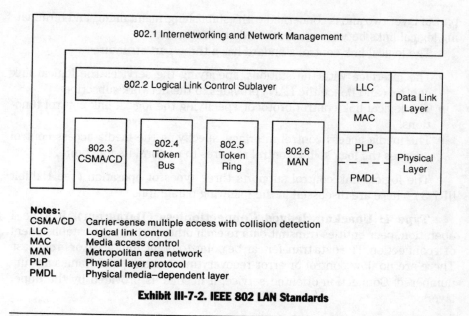

Notes:

CSMA/CD	Carrier-sense multiple access with collision detection
LLC	Logical link control
MAC	Media access control
MAN	Metropolitan area network
PLP	Physical layer protocol
PMDL	Physical media–dependent layer

Exhibit III-7-2. IEEE 802 LAN Standards

- IEEE 802.5: Token ring—Standard also based on the token passing access method, but over a ring topology.
- IEEE 802.6: Metropolitan area network (MAN)—Capable of providing high-speed switched connection over distances of at least 50 km.

In addition, three technical advisory groups were established—802.7, 802.8, and 802.9—to study and make recommendations about, respectively, broadband networks (e.g., techniques for broadband LAN frequency allocation), optical fiber technology (e.g., development of FDDI), and integrated voice and data applications (e.g., ISDN). These topics are not within the scope of this chapter.

The IEEE has also established Committee 802.10, with a charter to develop standards for interoperable LAN security. This subject is covered in the section of this handbook that treats security issues.

The remainder of this chapter is divided into two major sections. First, each of the IEEE 802 standards that defines services and protocols for operating within a LAN or MAN (i.e., 802.2 through 802.6) is described in depth. This section is followed by a discussion of standards and technologies for interconnecting multiple 802 LANs.

IEEE 802.2 LOGICAL LINK CONTROL SUBLAYER

The logical link control is a sublayer of the OSI data link layer and is designed to support a common set of services to the network layer. It resides at the upper part of layer two and is concerned with establishing, maintaining, and terminating logical links between communicating stations.

The logical link control standard has a three-part structure:

- The interface with the stations, specifying the services the logical link control (and hence the LAN) provides to the network subscriber.
- The logical link control protocol, specifying the logical link control functions.
- The media access control interface, specifying the media access control services the logical link control requires to perform its function.

The logical link control supports three types of operation (see Exhibit III-7-3). These are discussed in the following paragraphs.

Type 1: Unacknowledged Connectionless (Datagram). In type 1 operation, peer entities transmit data to each other without the establishment of a connection. The data transfer can be point-to-point, multicast, or broadcast. There are no flow control or error-recovery mechanisms, and frames are unnumbered. Connection-oriented service, if needed, is provided by the upper layers.

Type 2: Connection Oriented. Type 2 operation permits peer entities to establish, use, reset, and terminate connection services at the data link layer to exchange information. It provides data flow control at the network layer–data link layer interface. The connection establishment mechanism allows a network entity to request or be notified of the establishment of a data link layer connection.

Data transfer is the means by which a network entity can send or receive link service data units over a data link layer connection. This service also provides sequencing, flow control, and error recovery at the data link layer.

Connection reset is the means by which established connections can be returned to the initial state. Connection termination is the means by which a

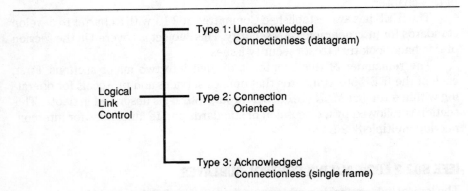

Exhibit III-7-3. Logical Link Control Procedures and Standards

network entity can request or be notified of the termination of data link layer connections. Flow control is the mechanism that controls data movement associated with a specified connection, across the network layer–data link layer interface.

Type 3: Acknowledged Connectionless (Single Frame). This permits a peer entity to send data and requests to other peer entities and to receive acknowledgment and data.

High-Level Data Link Control

The logical link control protocol mimics the high-level data link control developed by ISO. The frame is composed of three parts—header, body, and trailer (see Exhibit III-7-4). An 8-bit flag sequence, 01111110, at the beginning of the header and at the end of the trailer indicates the frame boundaries; it establishes and maintains synchronization. The header identifies the source and destination, as well as the frame type. (The source and destination addresses are required because LAN links support multiple sources and destinations.) The trailer is used in transmission-error detection.

For LAN configurations, IEEE 802.2 establishes three types of frames for data communication between service access points. The control field identifies the frame type and the role it plays during information transfer and the management of that transfer. IEEE 802 recommended link access protocol–balanced (LAP-B) for these tasks. LAP-B allows only one logical link with bidirectional flow to exist across one interface.

The LAP-B frame format is shown in Exhibit III-7-5. The IEEE 802 recommendation calls for two 8-bit address fields—the destination service access point and the source service access point (see Exhibit III-7-6). These have the following features:

- The address fields are 8 bits long.
- The least-significant bit of the destination service access point is used in two ways—If it is 0, the address field represents an individual address; if it is 1, it indicates a group address. The least-significant bit of the source service access point identifies the logical link control protocol data unit as a command (0) or a response (1).
- When the destination service access point address field is all 1s, it is predefined as the global address.

Flag	Header	Body	Trailer	Flag

Exhibit III-7-4. Logical Structure of High-Level Data Link Control Frame

01111110	Address	Control	Data	Frame Check Sequence	01111110

Exhibit III-7-5. Link Access Protocol–Balanced Frame Format

- Addresses 01000000 and 11000000 are designated as the individual and the group address, respectively, for a logical link control management function at the station—All other addresses with the second lowest-order bit set to 1 are reserved for future definition by IEEE 802.

The control field can be either 8 or 16 bits long. It is used to facilitate the numbered information and supervisory transfer, including the unnumbered control and information transfer functions. The two least-significant bits of the control byte identify the frame format (see Exhibit III-7-7).

I Format. The information transfer command and response I-format protocol data unit is used to carry numbered information transfer in type 2

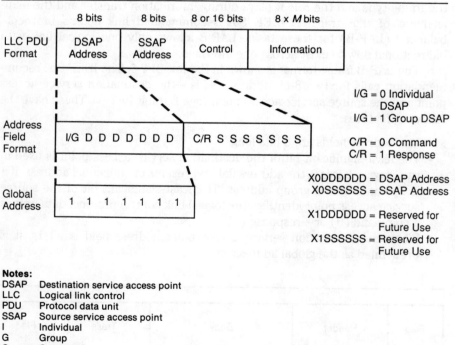

Notes:
DSAP Destination service access point
LLC   Logical link control
PDU   Protocol data unit
SSAP Source service access point
I   Individual
G   Group
C   Command
R   Response

Exhibit III-7-6. Protocol Data Unit and Address Field Format

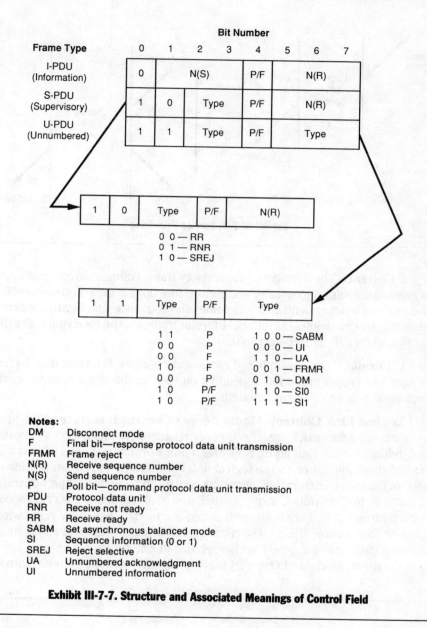

Bit Number

Frame Type	0	1	2	3	4	5	6	7
I-PDU (Information)	0	N(S)			P/F	N(R)		
S-PDU (Supervisory)	1	0	Type		P/F	N(R)		
U-PDU (Unnumbered)	1	1	Type		P/F	Type		

1	0	Type	P/F	N(R)

```
0 0 — RR
0 1 — RNR
1 0 — SREJ
```

1	1	Type	P/F	Type

```
1 1   P     1 0 0 — SABM
0 0   P     0 0 0 — UI
0 0   F     1 1 0 — UA
1 0   F     0 0 1 — FRMR
0 0   P     0 1 0 — DM
1 0   P/F   1 1 0 — SI0
1 0   P/F   1 1 1 — SI1
```

Notes:

DM	Disconnect mode
F	Final bit—response protocol data unit transmission
FRMR	Frame reject
N(R)	Receive sequence number
N(S)	Send sequence number
P	Poll bit—command protocol data unit transmission
PDU	Protocol data unit
RNR	Receive not ready
RR	Receive ready
SABM	Set asynchronous balanced mode
SI	Sequence information (0 or 1)
SREJ	Reject selective
UA	Unnumbered acknowledgment
UI	Unnumbered information

Exhibit III-7-7. Structure and Associated Meanings of Control Field

operation. The functions N(S), N(R), and P/F (poll/final) are independent entities and are required for each protocol data unit, where N(S) is the transmitter send sequence number and N(R) is the transmitter receive sequence number used to confirm or authorize transmission of additional I-format protocol data units. The poll/final bit is set to 1 or 0, on the basis of operation-type parameters.

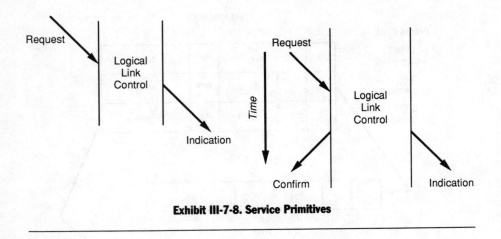

Exhibit III-7-8. Service Primitives

S Format. The S format or supervisory frame command/response is used to manage data link supervisory and control functions in type 2 operation. N(R) and P/F are independent; N(R) identifies the sequence number to confirm or authorize transmission of additional I-format frames at the receiving logical link control and a P/F bit to be set to 0 or 1.

U Format. The unnumbered command/response U format may be used in type 1 or type 2 operation depending on specific functions used to provide additional data link control functions.

Logical Link Control–Media Access Control Interface. Two primitives are used for unacknowledged connectionless (type 1) service—request and indication (see Exhibit III-7-8). The request primitive is used to pass a link service data unit frame to the logical link control. The indication primitive is used to pass a frame from the logical link control on reception. Type 1 operation is suitable for individual, group, global, and null destination-service-access-point addressing and applications that require no data link layer acknowledgment or flow control. IEEE 802.2 recommends a set of command and response protocol data units for type 1 service, shown in Exhibit III-7-9.

Connection-oriented (type 2) service supports a virtual circuit between

Commands	Responses
UI	
XID	XID
Test	Test

Notes:
UI   Unnumbered information
XID   Exchange ID

Exhibit III-7-9. Command and Response Protocol Data Units for Type 1 Operation

service access points. A set of service primitives supply the mechanism for a user to request or be notified of the establishment or termination of a data link connection. These primitives are shown in Exhibit III-7-10.

The sets of command and response protocol data units supported in type 2 operation are given in Exhibit III-7-11. Exhibit III-7-8 illustrates the operation of the request, indication, and confirm primitives. Exhibit III-7-12 illustrates the frame types, commands, and responses appropriate to each frame type, and their meanings.

MEDIA ACCESS CONTROL

The media access control sublayer allows network stations to share a single transmission facility. It provides the logic necessary to access the network for frame transmission and reception. Media access control capabilities can be grouped by function, into data link activities and media management activities. The data link activities consist of both transmit data encapsulation and receive data decapsulation functions. The media management activities consist of both transmit and receive media access management functions.

IEEE 802.3 Carrier-Sense Multiple Access with Collision Detection

The IEEE 802.3 CSMA/CD recommendation covers the lowest two layers of the OSI reference model and comprises the media access control layer frame format, physical layer, and media specification. It also includes the media access control–physical layer interface and the media access control–logical link control protocol interface. Together, the logical link control and media access control sublayer correspond to the OSI data link layer. The IEEE 802.3 domain is shown in Exhibit III-7-13.

DL__DATA__CONNECT.request
DL__DATA__CONNECT.indication
DL__DATA__CONNECT.confirm
DL__DATA__CONNECT.response
DL__DATA.request
DL__DATA.indication
DL__DATA.confirm
DL__DATA__DISCONNECT.request
DL__DATA__DISCONNECT.indication
DL__DATA__DISCONNECT.confirm
DL__RESET.request
DL__RESET.indication
DL__RESET.response
DL__RESET.confirm
DL__CONNECTION-FLOWCONTROL.request
DL__CONNECTION-FLOWCONTROL.indication
DL__CONNECTION-FLOWCONTROL.confirm

Exhibit III-7-10. Service Primitives for Type 2 Operation

Commands	Responses
I	I
RR	RR
RNR	RNR
REJ	REJ
SABME	UA
DISC	DM
	FRMR

Notes:

DISC	Disconnect
DM	Disconnect mode
FRMR	Frame reject
I	Information
REJ	Reject
RNR	Receiver not ready
RR	Receiver ready
SABME	Set asynchronous balanced mode
UA	Unnumbered acknowledgment

Exhibit III-7-11. Command and Response Protocol Data Units for Type 2 Operation

The interface between the logical link control and media access control layers is comparable to the LAP-B service request specification. It supports facilities required to transmit and receive frames, relay frame-processing parameters, and provide error and status information on an operation-by-operation basis to the network (and higher) layers.

IEEE 802.3 recommends a generic media access control frame format for use in data transmit and receive tasks. All frames are preceded by a preamble.

The media access control frame structure is flexible enough to accommodate baseband and broadband implementations. Both baseband and broadband implementations require addition of a preamble to the frame during transmission. In the broadband implementation, the frame is encapsulated with a preamble and postamble. The various frame fields defined in IEEE 802.3 are described in the following, and are shown in Exhibit III-7-14:

Frame Type	Command	Response	Meaning
Information (I)	I-frame		Contains data
Unnumbered (U)	SABM (E)		Set asynchronous balanced mode
	DISC		Disconnect
		UA	Unnumbered acknowledgment
		FRMR	Frame reject
		DM	Disconnect mode
	XID	XID	Exchange ID
	UI		Unnumbered information
Supervisory (S)	RR	RR	Receiver ready
	RNR	RNR	Receiver not ready
	REJ	REJ	Reject

Exhibit III-7-12. Type 2 Operator

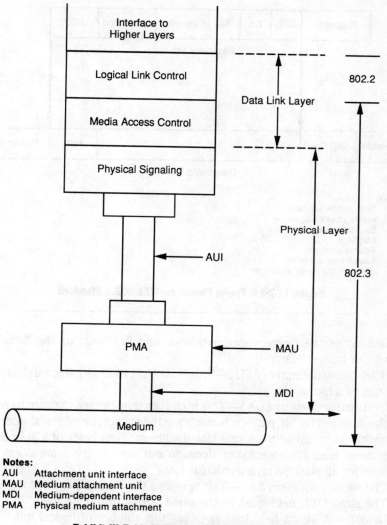

Notes:
AUI   Attachment unit interface
MAU   Medium attachment unit
MDI   Medium-dependent interface
PMA   Physical medium attachment

Exhibit III-7-13. IEEE 802.3 Service Specification

- Baseband preamble—A 56-bit pattern used by the physical layer signaling circuitry to establish bit synchronization and identify the first bit of the frame.
- Broadband preamble—The length of the preamble is 45 bits. The first 20 bits are used by the recipient to establish synchronization. These synch bits are followed by a 2-bit unscramble mode delimiter field. The final 23 bits of the preamble constitute the seed.
- Broadband postamble—The postamble is a 23-bit pattern that follows the

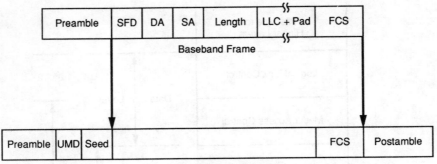

Preamble	SFD	DA	SA	Length	LLC + Pad	FCS

Baseband Frame

Preamble	UMD	Seed			FCS	Postamble

Broadband Frame

Notes:
DA   Destination address
FCS   Frame check sequence
LLC   Logical link control
Pad   Pad field
SA   Source address
SFD   Start frame delimiter
UMD Unscramble mode delimiter

Exhibit III-7-14. Frame Format for IEEE 802.3 Standard

---

last bit of the frame check sequence and functions as the broadband end-of-frame delimiter.

- Start frame delimiter (SFD)—This 8-bit 01111110 sequence indicates the start of a frame.
- Destination address (DA)—This identifies the stations that are to receive the frame. The bit pattern indicates either a unique physical address, a multicast-group address, or a global address. The choice of a 2- or 6-octet address is an implementation decision and must be the same at any given time for all stations on a particular LAN.
- The source address (SA)—This specifies the station that sent the frame. The size of this field must be the same as that of the DA field.
- Length—A 16-bit field that specifies the number of logical link control bytes that follow in the data field.
- The logical link control data—This field is prepared at the logical link control level, and its size must be in octet units.
- Pad field—Added if necessary; a sequence of bits is added to the logical link control data field to ensure that the frame is long enough for proper collision detection operation. The minimum and maximum sizes for the data field are a function of the maximum frame size and address size definitions for a given implementation.
- The frame check sequence (FCS)—Contains a 32-bit cyclic redundancy check value. This value is calculated based on the contents of all fields up to but not including the FCS.

The IEEE 802.3 standard specifies a CSMA/CD media access control operation at the media access control sublayer. On receiving a request for transmission, the transmit data encapsulation component constructs a protocol data unit frame using logical link control data. The transmit media access management samples the communication channel. When the medium becomes clear, transmission begins and the logical link control is informed. In the case of a collision, the transmit media access management transmits a jam signal to ensure that all transmitting stations have detected the collision. The transmission is terminated and retry begins after a back-off interval.

When a station enters the data receive mode, the physical layer signaling interface detects an incoming frame and discards the leading synch bits, the preamble, and the start frame delimiter. The physical layer signaling then forwards the data to the receive data decapsulation component. This process continues until the carrier-sense signal goes off. Then, the receive data decapsulation component evaluates the destination address and checks the data for transmission errors. If the address is valid and data is error free, the frame is forwarded to the logical link control; frames with invalid addresses or data transmission errors are discarded or passed to network management for further processing.

The transmit and receive media management activities are supported by the physical layer's three components: the physical layer signaling (PLS), attachment unit interface (AUI), and physical medium attachment (PMA).

The physical layer signaling shields the media access control layer from the intricacies of establishing, maintaining, and tearing down the serial communications pipe. This interface supports transmit-receive bit streams and channel-allocation and contention-resolution tasks. The physical signaling layer uses five primitives. Those can be grouped according to their functions as shown in Exhibit III-7-15.

The attachment unit interface includes specifications for cable connectors and transmission circuitry used to interconnect the physical layer signaling and media access unit in compliance with the following characteristics:

- The AUI must be capable of driving 50 m of cable.
- The AUI must permit data terminal equipment to test the AUI, AUI cable, medium attachment unit (MAU), and medium itself.
- The AUI must support the MAU for baseband coaxial cable, broadband coaxial cable, and baseband optical fiber.

Peer to Peer (Station to Station)	PLS__DATA__request
	PLS__DATA__confirm
	PLS__DATA__indication
Sublayer to Sublayer	PLS__CARRIER.indication
	PLS__SIGNAL.indication

Exhibit III-7-15. Physical Signaling Layer Primitives

The MAU is the portion of the physical layer between the medium-dependent interface and the AUI. It links the medium to the connector cable and contains the electronic circuitry that sends, receives, and manages the encoded signals impressed on and recovered from the trunk coaxial cable.

The medium-dependent interface is the mechanical and electrical interface between the trunk cable medium and the medium attachment unit.

The physical layer options for IEEE 802.3 are listed in Exhibit III-7-16. The recommendation calls for the media access control layer to use the parameter values shown in Exhibit III-7-17 and the typical specifications given in Exhibit III-7-18.

For baseband implementation the IEEE 802.3 standard uses a 10M-bps channel with a minimum frame of 512 bits. The network can use 500-m segments for coaxial cable and 1-km segments for optical fiber. The distance between the cable tap and the station should not exceed 50 m.

IEEE 802.3 broadband CSMA/CD allows a segment length of 3.75 km; however, 5.5 km is achievable. Historically, the major technological problem was the allocation of the frequency channels. Because no standard existed for frequency allocations, applications assigned to one channel by one vendor often overlapped with the frequencies of another, causing interference or cross talk on other channels. However, by adhering to the recommendations of the 802.7 technical advisory group, frequency overlap should not pose a serious threat.

In many implementations of CSMA/CD over cable television–type cable, two separate channels are used. A node that has packets to transmit listens for transmission activity on the downlink channel. If the downlink is idle, the station transmits its packet on the uplink channel while performing collision detection handling and enforcement. If the node senses that the downlink is busy, indicating a transmission in progress, the station waits before proceeding to transmit on the uplink channel. The station performs collision detection by comparing the received downlink transmission, bit by bit, with the data transmitted on the uplink. Collision detection is concurrent with packet transmission and is usually performed for an interval known as the collision window. When a transmitting station detects a bit mismatch at any time during the window, it knows that a collision has occurred. In accordance with the CSMA/CD algorithm, the sending node first initiates a collision enforcement, then retries the channel after the back-off interval.

Identifier	Signaling Rate	Typical Segment Length (m)	Medium
1BASE5	1M bps	500	Unshielded twisted-pair cable
10BASE2	10M bps	200	Thin coaxial cable
10BASE5	10M bps	500	High-grade coaxial cable
10BASE36	10M bps	3,750	Cable television cable
10BASE-T	10M bps	100	Unshielded twisted-pair cable

Exhibit III-7-16. IEEE 802.3 Physical Layer Options

Parameter	Value
Slot Time	512 bits
Interframe Gap	96 microseconds
Attempt Limit	16 tries
Back-off Limit	10 tries
Jam Size	32 bits
Maximum Frame Size	1,518 bytes
Minimum Frame Size	512 bits
Address Size	48 bits

Exhibit III-7-17. IEEE 802.3 Recommended Media Access Control Parameter Values

IEEE 802.4 Token Passing Bus Protocol

The development of the IEEE 802.4 token passing bus protocol has been spurred by General Motors Corp and the Manufacturing Automation Protocol (MAP) User Group. They felt that IEEE 802.3, which was intended for light industrial and commercial environment applications, failed to meet the timing constraints of real-time heavy industrial applications. IEEE 802.4 was designed to operate well with both broadband and carrier-band signaling. It covers a wide range of topics—electrical signaling methods, frame format, access methods, contention resolution, and the media access control–logical link control layer interface. It also specifies the physical and media layer requirements for single-channel, phase-continuous frequency shift keying bus, single-channel, phase-coherent frequency shift keying bus, and broadband bus.

Although the 802.4 standard uses a bus topology, it forms a logical ring during typical operation. Right-of-access to the communication medium is indicated by a token passed along the network from node to node. To become a member of the logical ring, a station must know three addresses—the predecessor's address, the next station address, and its transmit address. Steady-state operation is composed of two phases: token transfer and data transfer. Stations perform path initialization, token recovery, new station admission, and general housekeeping of the logical path.

Physical connectivity has little impact on node sequence within the logical ring. In addition, stations can receive information without being part of the logical ring. In Exhibit III-7-19, stations A, E, D, B, and C form the logical ring; they are not physically connected in sequence. Stations F and G, which are

Parameter	10BASE2	10BASE5
Data Rate	10M bps	10M bps
Maximum Segment Length	200 m	500 m
Network Span	1,000 m	2,500 m
Nodes per Segment	30	100
Node Spacing	0.5 m	2.5 m
Cable Diameter	0.25 in	0.4 in

Exhibit III-7-18. Typical Specifications for IEEE 802.3

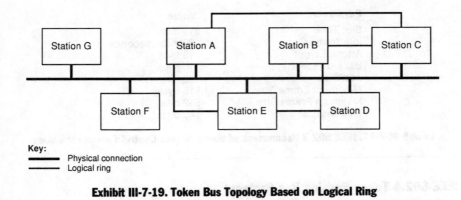

Key:
▬▬▬ Physical connection
───── Logical ring

Exhibit III-7-19. Token Bus Topology Based on Logical Ring

outside the ring, cannot initiate transmission but can receive all ongoing transmissions.

The IEEE 802.4 recommendation defines several functions as resident at the media access control sublayer. These general utilities are the lost token timer, distributed initialization, token holding timer, station address recognition, token preparation and frame encapsulation, frame check sequence generation and checking, valid token recognition, addition of new member to the ring, and station failure error recovery. These functions are assigned to and implemented as asynchronous logical machines (see Exhibit III-7-20)—an interface machine (IFM), an access control machine (ACM), a receive machine (RxM), a transmit machine (TxM), and an optional regenerative repeater machine (RRM).

Interface Machine. The IFM supports the logical link control to media access control sublayer and station management to media access control sublayer. This machine interprets all media-access-data and incoming-service primitives and generates appropriate responses. It maps the quality of service parameters from the logical link control to the media access control, manages service queueing and the address recognition function on received logical link control frames, and admits only those frames addressed to the station.

Access Control Machine. The ACM is the central nerve of the media access control sublayer. It cooperates with its peers on other stations in managing the token that controls transmission access. It also initializes and maintains the logical ring, including the admission of new nodes into the ring. Finally, the ACM performs fault or failure detection and error recovery, if needed in the network.

Receive Machine. The RxM accepts bits from the physical layer, reconstructs frames, and validates them before forwarding them to the IFM and ACM. Assembly and validation of frames are achieved through the detection of start delimiters, end delimiters, frame check sequence (FCS), and validating frame's

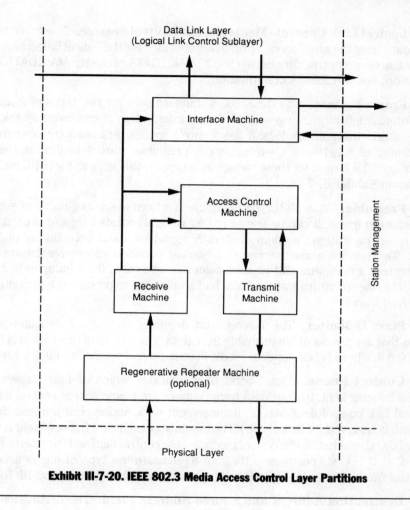

Exhibit III-7-20. IEEE 802.3 Media Access Control Layer Partitions

structural integrity. The RxM is also responsible for identification and reception of noise burst and bus quiet conditions.

Transmit Machine. The TxM accepts a data frame from the ACM and delivers it to the physical layer as a properly formatted frame. The TxM builds a media access control protocol data unit by adding the required preamble and start delimiters and by appending a frame check sequence and end delimiter to each frame. In the presence of a regenerative repeater machine, the TxM operates somewhat differently.

Regenerative Repeater Machine. The RRM is available as an option in special repeater stations (e.g., at a broadband or head-end remodulator). In such an operation both the RxM and the TxM cooperate with the RRM to repeat the bit stream coming in from the physical layer back to the physical layer.

Logical Link Control–Media Access Control Service. The token bus standard uses the same service primitives specified for the logical link control–media access control functions (802.3) MA_DATA.request, MA_DATA.indication, and MA_DATA.confirmation.

Frame Format. The IEEE 802.4 standard calls for two types of frames for information interchanges. The control information is conveyed by token frames and the data by logical link control frames. Frames may contain a maximum of 8,191 octets, excluding the preamble, start delimiter, and end delimiter. The format for these two generic types is the same as for IEEE 802.3, shown in Exhibit III-7-14.

Preamble. As in 802.3, the preamble is affixed to the beginning of every transmitted frame. It can be one or more (integral) octets long and is used by the receiving station's modem to identify signal level and detection of phase lock. The preamble also serves as a marker between successive frames. It guarantees a minimum end-to-start-delimiter interval of 2 ms independent of the data rate to ensure stations have had ample time to process the previously received frame.

Start Delimiter. The 1-octet start delimiter consists of signaling patterns that are always distinguishable from data. The format of this byte is N N 0 N N 0 0 0, where N is a nondata media access control symbol and 0 is a zero.

Control Frame. This 1-octet field indicates which of four classes of frame is being sent. Its four data frame classes are media access control data, logical link control data, station management data, and special-purpose data (which is reserved for future use). The media access control frame format is 0 0 C C C C C C, where C is the type of media access control field and 0 is a zero. The bits C C C C C C (positions 3 through 8) indicate the type of media access control frame. The meanings of the bit patterns are shown in Exhibit III-7-21.

Destination Address and Source Address Field. The destination or source address may be 16 or 48 bits in length. On a given LAN, the destination and the source address must be the same length.

```
C C C C C C
_____
0 0 0 0 0 0  = claim_token
0 0 0 0 0 1  = solicit_successor_1   (1 response window)
0 0 0 0 1 0  = solicit_successor_2   (2 response windows)
0 0 0 0 1 1  = who_follows           (3 response windows)
0 0 0 1 0 0  = resolve_contention    (4 response windows)
0 0 1 0 0 0  = token
0 0 1 1 0 0  = set_successor
```

Exhibit III-7-21. Media Access Control Frame Format

Data Frame. The data frame carries the actual information. The first byte indicates the priority and the action to be taken by the station. The format for the first byte is shown in Exhibit III-7-22.

Frame Check Sequence. The 32-bit frame check sequence is based on the standard generator 32-degree polynomial:

$$G(x) = X^{32} + X^{26} + X^{23} + X^{22} + X^{16} +$$
$$X^{12} + X^{11} + X^{10} + X^8 + X^7 + X^5 + X^4 + X^2 + X + 1$$

End Delimiter. The 1-byte end delimiter ends the frame and specifies the starting position of the frame check sequence. The signaling pattern of this field is always different from data. The format is N N 1 N N 1 I E, where N is the nondata media access control symbol, 1 is a one, I is the intermediate bit (1 means more to transmit, 0 means end of transmission), and E is the error bit (1 means error, 0 means no error).

Media Access Control Services. The services provided by the media access control sublayer of the token bus are more complex than the CSMA/CD protocol. Most of the complexities are pertinent to the management and maintenance of the token bus, and they include:

- Fault management:
  - —Multiple token.
  - —Lost token.
  - —Token pass failure.
  - —Deaf station.
  - —Duplicate station addresses.
- Classes of service and a priority algorithm.
- Addition of a station into the logical ring.

F F M M M P P P

F F = Frame type
0 1 = LLC_data_frame
1 0 = station_management_data_frame
1 1 = special_purpose_data_frame_reserved

M M M = MAC_action
0 0 0 = request_with_no_response
0 0 1 = request_with_response
0 1 0 = response

P P P = priority (maximum of 7)
1 1 1 = highest priority
. . .
. . .
. . .
0 0 0 = lowest priority

Exhibit III-7-22. Data Frame (First Byte)

- Deletion of a station.
- Ring initialization.

A station hands over the token to its successor using the media access control frame. The sending station then listens for evidence that the successor has received the frame. If there is no valid response frame, the sender repeats the token passing operation and performs the same monitoring as during the first attempt.

If the intended recipient, or successor, fails to respond, the sender assumes that its successor has malfunctioned and designates a new successor. The sender then broadcasts a who-follows frame using its address in the set-successor frame. This removes the failed station from the logical ring.

If the sending station fails to get a response to a who-follows frame, it retries. If the second trial is unsuccessful, the station initiates a new strategy by sending a solicit-successor-2 frame with its own address in the DA and SA fields and inviting any station in the network to respond.

An active station that hears the request and wants to join the logical ring may respond during the next response window. The sending station then transmits the remaining data frames and resumes the token passing process. At the end of its activity, the station switches to an idle state and waits for another station's transmission. If all attempts to solicit a successor fail, however, the station assumes the occurrence of one of the following events:

- All stations have failed.
- All stations have left the logical ring.
- The medium has broken.
- The station's own receiver has failed and cannot receive any frame.

The station then ceases its attempt and switches to an idle state.

Addition of Station. New stations are admitted to the logical ring through a response window–based controlled contention process. According to this scheme, a station waits a predetermined interval after the transmission of a media access control (e.g., solicit-successor) frame and listens for a response. If the station detects a response at any time during this response window, it continues to listen beyond the duration of the response window. Duration of response windows are identified by two solicit-successor frames; solicit-successor 1 indicates one response window, and solicit-successor 2 indicates two response windows. The solicit-successor frame indicates the range of station addresses between the frame source and destination address. Any station or stations whose addresses fall within this range may indicate desire to enter the logical ring. Three events can happen during the response window:

- No response—No station expressed an interest in joining the ring. The token holder then forwards the token to the successor.
- One response—Only one station issued a set-successor response frame. The token-holding station then designates the responding node as the

current successor and passes the token to the new successor. The responder then sets its linkages (i.e., predecessor and successor) accordingly and proceeds as usual.

- Multiple responses—The token holder detects a contention, indicating that more than one station intends to join the ring. The conflict is resolved by an address-based contention scheme using an algorithm wherein the sending node transmits a resolve-contention frame and waits for four response-window intervals. Each contender can respond during one of these windows, with responses based on the first 2 bits of its address. A contending station must refrain from transmission until the arrival of its window. If the token holder receives a valid set-successor frame, it passes the token to the appropriate station. If there is still a multiple response, the contention process is repeated. Only those stations that responded during the first window, however, are allowed to contend on the basis of the second pair of bits in their address. The algorithm continues until a valid set-successor frame is received. If there is no response or the maximum number of retries is reached, the sending node passes the token to the previously designated successor.

Deletion of Station. A station N must wait for a token before sending a set-successor frame to its predecessor $N - 1$ declaring its intention to drop out of the ring. Departing station N then passes the token to the successor $N + 1$ as usual. Receiving station $N + 1$ then automatically sets $N - 1$ (the predecessor address) as the source address of the token frame, indicating the token's path was from $N - 1$ to $N + 1$. This splices the departing station out of the logical ring.

Fault Management. The fault management routines of the IEEE 802.4 token passing standard are more complex than those of the CSMA/CD 802.3 standard. The 802.4 fault management must include contingencies illustrated in Exhibit III-7-23.

Multiple Token. The multiple token condition occurs when more than one station holds a token—for example, in the case of two stations having the same address. During the token holding mode, if station N detects a frame indicating that another station also holds a token, node N drops the token and enters into the listening mode.

Condition	Action
Multiple Token	Defer; drop to 1 or 0
Unacceptable Token	Retry
Station Failed	Who-follows determination
Failed Receiver	Drop out of the ring
No Token	Initialize after time-out

Exhibit III-7-23. IEEE 802.4 Fault Management Contingencies

Unacceptable Token. A sending station passes the token to its successor, then spends one time slot sampling the channel. A valid frame activity on the channel during the interval means that the would-be successor is alive, while invalid or no activity means that the successor is dead or the token was unacceptable. The station then reissues another token to the same successor and waits one time slot for a valid response. If no valid response is detected after the second try, the station assumes that the successor is dead and proceeds to find a new successor.

Who Follows. To find a new successor, a token holder issues a who-follows frame, asking the identity of the station that follows the failed station. In this case, the token holder should receive a set-successor frame from the second station down the ring. On receipt of a set-successor frame, the sending node forwards the token and updates the address of its successor.

If the sending station does not receive a valid (set-successor) response to its who-follows message, it retries. After two failures, the station issues a solicit-successor frame containing a full address range, thus inviting any station to become a successor. If a successor is found (i.e., if there is a response), the ring resumes usual operation.

Should there be no response to the solicit-successor frame, the token holder assumes that a major fault has occurred in the network or that all nodes have dropped out of the ring or its own receiver has failed. The station then sends any remaining data and attempts to pass the token again. It then refrains from transmission and enters into listening mode.

Ring Initialization. Initialization of the ring is triggered when a station's inactive timer expires (i.e., the token has been lost). This can be caused by startup of the station, crash of a token holder, and other network events. The initialization algorithm is triggered when a station issues a claim-token frame. This frame's information field length is a multiple of the system slot time and is calculated on the basis of the first 2 bits of the issuer's address. After transmission, a claimant listens for a valid response for one slot time from its own transmission and those of other stations that choose the same frame length. The station then samples the medium. In the event of a valid response, the station either drops its claim or tries again, using the second pair of its address bits. If all bits have been used and silence is still sensed, the station has succeeded in the initialization contest and becomes the token holder. The logical ring can now be created by using the response window process.

Priority Option. The token-passing-access method provides a priority option mechanism. This permits higher layers to assign priority (according to service class, rank, or order) to the frames destined for transmission. The priority option procedure allows the media acess control sublayer to support eight service classes (four are currently defined) for the logical link control sublayer and higher-layer protocols. The currently defined service classes are:

- Synchronous—Service class 6.
- Asynchronous urgent—Service class 4.
- Asynchronous urgent—Service class 2.
- Asynchronous time available—Service class 0.

The priority algorithm incorporates the maximum allowable time that a token can circulate for each access class. If the token hold timer has a remaining positive value, then the station can transmit frames at this access class until either the token hold timer value reaches 0 or this access class's queue becomes empty. When either event occurs, the station begins to service the next lower access class. At the completion of the lowest-level service request, the station performs any required logical ring maintenance and passes the token to its successor.

Physical Layer Specification. Exhibit III-7-24 illustrates the partitioning of the physical hardware for token bus networks. The standard specifies three bus media and corresponding physical layer entities for use with the token passing access method. Two of these, phase-continuous frequency shift

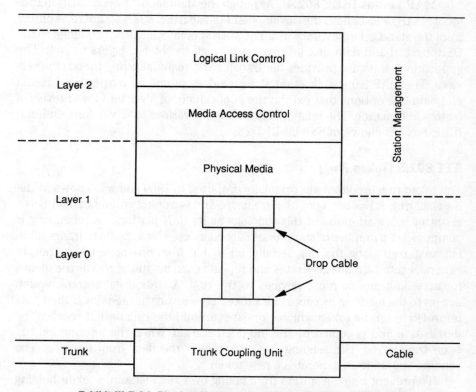

Exhibit III-7-24. Physical Hardware Partitioning for Token-Bus LAN

keying and phase-coherent frequency shift keying, use a nondirectional bus; the third, multilevel duobinary AM/PSK (a form of modulation where the radio frequency carrier is both amplitude-modulated and phase shift–keyed), uses a bidirectional bus with an active head-end repeater.

The physical layer also performs management services. IEEE 802.4 recommends that the physical layer be responsible for:

- Resetting the physical layer entity, determining the network topology, and determining its own role in that LAN.
- Determining the available and current operating modes of the physical layer entity and selecting the appropriate operating modes. The modes include such features as:
  —Transmit and receive channel assignment.
  —Transmitted power-level assignment (per drop cable).
  —Transmitter output enable and disable (per drop cable).
  —Receive signal source.
  —Signaling mode selection and reporting.
  —Received signal-level reporting.

MAP Versus IEEE 802.4. Although the Manufacturing Automation Protocol (MAP) was behind the development of the IEEE 802.4 standard, it differs from the standard in several ways. The MAP specification is not confined to the OSI physical and data link layers; it covers all the higher layers as well. The applications software provides file transfer and manufacturing messaging services. The MAP 3.0 specification also includes options for carrier band media and data link options that extend the applicability of MAP into lower levels of factory automation. The relationship among the various MAP versions, OSI, and IEEE 802.4 is shown in Exhibit III-7-25.

IEEE 802.5 (Token Ring)

The token ring topology was originally proposed in 1969 and was known as the Newhall ring. It has been popular in Europe and is gaining ground in the US as a result of IBM's adoption of this topology as its LAN platform. A token ring is composed of a number of stations serially connected by a medium. Information is transferred along the ring serially, bit by bit, from one node to another. In general, each station regenerates and repeats each bit and serves as the means for attaching one or more devices to the ring. A station gains transmission access to the medium by capturing a token passing on the medium. It then puts information on the token which circulates around the ring until it reaches the destination and is copied by the intended station. When the information has been transferred, the sending station removes the data from the ring. The sending station then generates a new token.

To prevent a single station from taking over the medium, a token-holding timer limits the length of time a station can occupy the medium before passing the token. The protocol also supports a multiple priority scheme.

ISO-OSI	MAP 2.1/2.2	MAP 3.0
Application Layer	Network Management	Network Management
	Manufacturing Messaging Format Specification	Manufacturing Messaging Services
	File Transfer, Access, and Management	File Transfer, Access, and Management
	Common Application Service Element	Associated Control Service Element
Presentation Layer	Null	Presentation Kernel
Session Layer	Session Kernel	Session Kernel
Transport Layer	Class 4 Transport	Class 4 Transport
Network Layer	Connectionless Network Protocol	Connectionless Network Protocol and End System Intermediate System Routing Protocol
Data Link Layer	IEEE 802.2 LLC-1/LLC-3 IEEE 802.4 MAC	IEEE 802.2 LLC-1/LLC-3 IEEE 802.4 MAC
Physical Layer	IEEE 802.4 Token Bus Broadband/Carrier Band	IEEE 802.4 Token Bus Broadband/Carrier Band

10M-bps Broadband

10M-bps Broadband
5M-bps Carrier Band

Exhibit III-7-25. Comparison of Various MAP and OSI Layers

Token and Frame Format. The 802.5 standard specifies two data formats, token and frames. The token, which is three octets long, is the means by which the right to use the medium is passed from one station to another. The frame carries the message between stations. Token and frame structures are shown in Exhibit III-7-26. The starting delimiter must contain the following bit pattern in order for a frame or token to be valid: J K 0 J K 0 0 0, where J is nondata J, K is nondata K, and 0 is binary zero.

The access control assigns special meaning to the token. Its bit pattern is P P P T M R R R, where PPP are priority bits, T is the token bit, M is the monitor bit, and RRR are reservation bits.

The priority bits, PPP, indicate the priority of the token. These bits identify

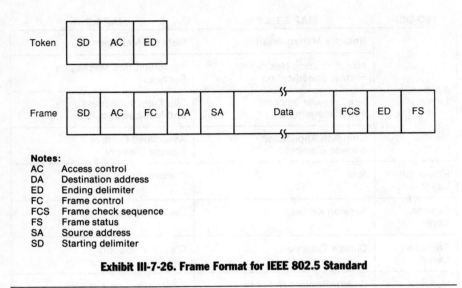

Notes:

AC   Access control
DA   Destination address
ED   Ending delimiter
FC   Frame control
FCS   Frame check sequence
FS   Frame status
SA   Source address
SD   Starting delimiter

Exhibit III-7-26. Frame Format for IEEE 802.5 Standard

---

eight priority levels, from 000 (the lowest) through 111 (the highest). In a multipriority system, stations use different priorities based on the priority of the protocol data unit to be transmitted.

The token bit, T, setting distinguishes a token from a frame. (T set to 1 is a frame; T set to 0 is a token.)

The monitor bit, M, is used to prevent a frame or token from continuously circulating on the ring and is normally set to 0 for all tokens or frames. Only the monitoring station can modify this bit; all other stations merely repeat it.

The reservation bits, RRR, allow stations with higher-priority protocol data units to request that the next token be issued at a given priority. As with the priority bits, eight levels of reservations are supported, from 000 (lowest) through 111 (highest).

The frame control field defines the type of the frame and includes certain media access control and information frame functions. The bits are F F Z Z Z Z Z Z, where FF are frame-type bits and ZZZZZZ are control bits.

The frame-type bits identify the type of frames as:

- 00—A media access control frame (contains a media access control protocol data unit).
- 01—A logical link control frame (contains a logical link control protocol data unit).
- 1X—Undefined format.

When the frame-type bits are 00 (i.e., the frame contains a media access control protocol data unit), the control bits ZZZZZZ are interpreted and acted on by all stations on the ring. In a logical link control frame (FF bits 01), the control bits are designated rrrYYY, where rrr has the value 000 during transmitted frames and is ignored on reception and YYY indicates the priority of the protocol data unit from the source logical link control entity to the destination logical link control entity or entities.

The end delimiter byte marks the end of transmission. The format is J K 1 J K 1 I E, where J is nondata J, K is nondata K, 1 is binary one, I is intermediate frame bit, and E is error-detection bit. The receiving station will interpret a valid ending delimiter if the first six symbols it receives are J K 1 J K 1.

The intermediate bit (I), if set to 1, indicates that this is a continuation frame of a multiple frame transmission. If I is set to 0, it is the last frame.

The error-detection bit (E) is used as an indicator by the stations during receive and repeating mode. Each station checks the passing frame for errors and if an error is detected, sets E to 1.

The frame status contains the address recognition and frame-copied bits. The bit pattern is A C r r A C r r, where A is address-recognized bits, C is frame-copied bits, and r is received bits.

The originating station transmits A and C as 0. The destination station sets A to 1 and if the receiving station is able to copy the frame then it sets C to 1. These bits help the originating station to identify the following three conditions after the transmission attempt:

- There is a nonexistent or nonactive station on the ring (A set to 0, C set to 0).
- The station exists but it failed to copy the frame.
- The frame was copied by the destination station.

A frame's information field may be empty or may contain one or more bytes of data. The values of this field are called vectors. The vector contains a length value, a function identifier, and zero or more subvectors as follows:

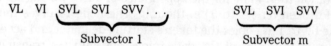

$$\text{VL} \quad \text{VI} \quad \underbrace{\text{SVL} \quad \text{SVI} \quad \text{SVV} \ldots}_{\text{Subvector 1}} \qquad \underbrace{\text{SVL} \quad \text{SVI} \quad \text{SVV}}_{\text{Subvector m}}$$

The vector length (VL) is a 16-bit number that specifies the length of the vector in octets and includes its subfield. The vector length range falls between 4 and 65,535 octets.

The vector identifier (VI) is a 16-bit field that identifies the vector itself. The valid VI codes (shown in hexadecimal form) and their meanings are:

- 0002—Beacon.
- 0003—Claim token.
- 0004—Purge MAC frame.
- 0005—Active monitor present.
- 0006—Standby monitor present.
- 0007—Duplicate address test.

Subvectors contain all data or modifiers. One subvector is required to contain each piece of data or modifier that is transported. A subvector is not position dependent within a vector; rather, each subvector must be identified by its subvector identifier.

The subvector length (SVL) is an 8-bit number that specifies the subvector length in octets, including the length of the field itself. A value of FF (hexadecimal) means that the length exceeds 254 octets and that the actual length value follows in the next two octets.

The subvector identifier (SVI), is also 8 bits long. An SVI value of FF (hexadecimal) indicates an expanded identifier, which is included in the next two octets.

Two types of subvectors exist. Subvectors having values between 00 and 7F (hexadecimal) designate specific, common, standardized strings of data. Subvector values (SVVs) from 80 through FE (hexadecimal) are used for specific definition within a particular vector by vector identifier.

The subvector values, variable in length, contain the actual data the station needs to transmit. It is important to understand that subvectors themselves may contain other subvectors and other types of vectors.

The frame check sequence is a 32-bit field calculated and appended to the frame as specified in the IEEE 802.3 and 802.4 standards.

The Media Access Control Sublayer Function. The IEEE 802.5 standard defines a set of services to be provided by the MAC sublayer of a token ring network. It includes frame transmission, token transmission, stripping, frame reception, priority operation, beaconing, and neighbor notification.

Frame Transmission. This is controlled by the access mechanism for the media. When a station receives a transmit request from a higher layer, the medium access layer prefixes the higher-layer protocol data unit with the appropriate header and puts it into the transmission queues.

The station then waits for the appearance of a free token (i.e., the access control field token bit set to 0) in the ring. The node reserves the token by altering the bit to 1. It copies the token's starting delimiter and access control, places them at the front of the data frame, and initiates transmission. The station continues to transmit until it has nothing to transmit or the token-holding timer expires. After the station receives the access control field of the last transmitted frame, it places a free token (T set to 0) into the ring and appends the appropriate bits to the end delimiter byte of the token.

Token Transmission. At the end of transmission token-holding time, the station checks to verify that its address has been returned in the source address field, as indicated by the MA_FLAG. In the event of a failure, the station transmits fill frames until the MA_FLAG is set. At the end the station places a token into the ring.

Stripping. After transmission of the frames, the station remains active until it has removed all transmitted frames from the ring. This simplifies the recovery mechanism that would be required if frames were allowed to circulate continuously on the ring.

Frame Reception. Stations, while repeating the incoming signal stream, check it for frames they should copy or act on. If the frame-type bits indicate a media access control frame, the control bits are interpreted by all stations on the ring. In addition, if the frame's DA field matches the station's individual address, relevant group address, or broadcast address, the FC, DA, SA, information, and FS fields are copied into a receive buffer and subsequently forwarded to the appropriate sublayer.

Priority Operation. The 802.5 specification supports a three-component priority scheme. The priority bits (PPP) and the reservation bits (RRR) contained in the access control field are utilized by the priority algorithm. The algorithm supports three types of priorities:

- Pm—Priority of the message to be transmitted by a station.
- Pr—Received priority.
- Rr—Received reservation.

The priority algorithm is a four-step process:

1. A ready-to-transmit station waits for a free token with received priority, Pr, less than or equal to the message priority, Pm.
2. During the waiting state, a station may receive an occupied token at its own priority level, Pm—However, if the station detects a free token, it sets the reservation field to its message priority (Rr equal to Pm) only if Rr is less than Pm and Pm is less than Pr. This is equivalent to preempting any lower-priority reservation. If the station detects a passing data frame, it sets the frames reservation field to priority Rr equal to Pm. It does that only if the priority of the reservation field is found to be less than its priority (Rr less than Pm).
3. When a station captures a token, it sets bits T to 1 and M to 0 and leaves the priority bits unchanged.
4. At the end of a successful transmission, a station issues a new token with the priority set to the maximum of Pr, Rr, and Pm and a reservation set to the maximum of Rr and Pm.

One possible drawback of the algorithm was the potential for a station to set the priority level at its highest value and maintain at that level. To avoid this situation, the 802.5 specification requires that each station maintain two stacks, one for reservation and the other for priority. Each station must ensure that no token circulates indefinitely because of its high priority. A station is able to detect this situation by remembering the priority of an earlier transmission. A station now can detect this condition and downgrade the priority to a lower priority or reservation.

Beaconing and Neighbor Notification. For proper token ring operation, hard failure must be detected and isolated. Failure can occur at the station reporting the failure (the beaconing station), at the station upstream of the beaconing station, or on the intervening ring medium.

To help identify the problem each station should know the identity of its upstream neighbor station. The process for obtaining this identity is known as neighbor notification. It is based on address-recognized and frame-copied bits of the frame status field that are transmitted as 0s. If a station recognizes the destination address of the passing frame as its own, and if it copies the frame, it sets the bit A equal to 1 and sets C equal to 1. In the event of a broadcast frame, the A and C bits are all set to 0. This means a broadcast frame's destination address will be recognized by all stations on the ring. Therefore, the first station downstream will set bit A equal to 1. Stations further downstream will therefore not reset the A and C bits to 0. As this process continues in a daisy-chain fashion, every station learns the identity of its upstream neighbor.

A monitor begins neighbor notification by broadcasting the active monitor present (AMP) media access control frame. On receiving this frame, a station immediately downstream takes the following actions:

1. It resets its timer, standby monitor (TSM), based on the active monitor current value obtained from the frame control field.
2. The downstream station copies the broadcast active monitor present media access control frame and stores the upstream station's identity in an upstream neighbor's address at the proper memory location.
3. If the frame is copied the station sets the A and C values to 1.
4. It broadcasts a similar monitor present media access control frame at a convenient time.

This process continues until each station has the opportunity to receive an A = 0, C = 0 similar monitor present frame, copy its upstream neighbor's address, and broadcast a similar monitor present frame itself.

The active monitor present frame must pass each station on a regular basis. In addition to the timer, active monitor (TAM) in the active monitor, each standby station has a TSM that is reset each time an AMP media access control frame passes. If the TSM expires, the standby monitor issues a claim-transmission frame; this initiates the recovery process.

Token Maintenance. The monitor station plays an active role in maintaining the integrity and stability of the network. It periodically issues an AMP status frame to inform other nodes that it is monitoring the ring. The monitor uses a watchdog valid frame timer with values initialized to a value greater than the time required for a token or frame to circulate around the ring. The timer is reset after every token or frame. The monitor issues a token only at the expiration of the valid frame timer. In order to detect a persistently circulating data frame, the monitor sets the monitor bit M to 1 the first time it sees a data frame. If it detects a data frame with the monitor bit already set to 1, it concludes that the transmitting station failed to remove the frame. The monitor removes the frame and issues a new token. The monitor follows the same algorithm to detect a priority failure and recovery mechanism that prohibits the circulation of a constantly nonzero priority-level token in the ring. If the monitor detects the presence of another monitor in the ring, it enters into standby monitoring mode. This, in turn, triggers the recovery mechanism.

Token-Ring Physical Layer Specification. The IEEE 802.5 standard specifies a baseband, shielded twisted-pair cable attachment to the trunk cable of the token ring (see Exhibit III-7-27). The communications medium consists of a set of trunk coupling units interconnected sequentially by the trunk cable links. Each trunk coupling unit is connected to the trunk cable/medium interface connector, where all transmitted and received signal specifications are met. Two balanced, 150-ohm shielded twisted-pair cables connect the station to the trunk cable medium. The standard defines a system with alternative data rates of 1M or 4M bps with a maximum capacity of about 250 stations per ring.

Physical Layer. The physical layer specification covers the data symbol timing, encoding and decoding, and reliability. The physical layer encodes and transmits four symbols passed down to it by the media access control layer. These symbols are binary 0, binary 1, nondata J, and nondata K.

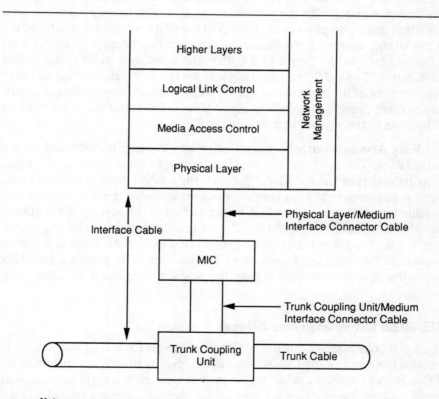

Note:
MIC   Medium interface connector

Exhibit III-7-27. IEEE 802.5 Connection System Hardware Separation

Differential Manchester encoding techniques are used to transmit the symbols. The nondata symbols J and K depart from the standard rules. A J symbol has the same polarity as the preceding symbol, whereas K has a polarity opposite to that of the preceding symbol. The nondata symbols must be transmitted as a pair (i.e., J and K) to avoid an accumulating dc component caused by the transmission of only one nondata symbol.

The physical layer recovers the symbol timing information encoded in the transmission between levels of the received signal. The timing information is required for internal use and for the transmission of symbols on the ring. During regular operation one station is designated as the active monitor, which acts as the timing source. All other stations on the ring are frequency and phase locked to the active station. A latency buffer is provided by the active monitor to ensure minimum latency and compensate for phase jitter.

A ring must maintain a latency equal to 24 bits (i.e., the number of bits in the token sequence) for the token to continuously circulate around the ring when all stations are in repeat mode. Because ring latency varies from one segment to another and no prior knowledge is available, a delay of at least 24 bits should be provided by the active monitor. If the ring latency is not constant, bits either will be dropped as the latency of the ring decreases or will be added as the latency increases. To maintain a constant ring latency, an elastic 6-bit buffer is added to the fixed 24-bit buffer. The result is a 30-bit buffer that is initialized to 27 bits. If the received signal at the monitor station is slightly faster than the clock of the monitor station, the buffer expands to avoid dropping bits. On the other hand, if the received signal is slow, the buffer contracts to avoid adding bits to the repeated bit stream.

Ring Access Control. Station entry into the ring is controlled by the station itself. The insertion and ring bypass mechanisms reside in the trunk coupling unit (see Exhibit III-7-27), which the media interface cable controls using a phantom-circuit technique. The circuit places a dc voltage on the medium interface connector which is transparent to the passage of the station transmitted symbol, or phantom. The technique is used within the trunk coupling unit to guide the switching action that causes the serial insertion of the station into the ring. Cessation of the phantom drive causes a switching action that removes the station from the ring and prepares it for offline self-testing.

IEEE 802.6 Metropolitan Area Network

The metropolitan area networking (MAN) group (IEEE 802.6) was formed to broaden the scope of the LAN standards and identify the major capabilities for MANs. Broadly speaking, a metropolitan area network is a network capable of providing high-speed switching connectivity across distances typically found within a metropolitan area. The committee recognized that a network spanning a metropolitan area may use multiple transmission media (e.g., copper, microwave, and optical fiber). Because MANs may be public offerings with multiple customers, the MAN must address such concerns as maintenance and billing and provide privacy and security. Because of the distance and the multiple media, the access methods for LANs were viewed as having serious deficiencies.

As a result, a new architectural framework and protocols are being developed for MANs. A consensus has emerged on the protocol. The distributed queue dual-bus, or QPSX, proposal from Telecom Australia received the working group's endorsement. The switch architecture of QPSX is based on two contradirectional buses, as shown in Exhibit III-7-28. It is configured as a physical ring but behaves as a logical bus to enable the generation of common frames. In case of a bus fault, the network can isolate the fault and close the data buses through the headpoint of the loop.

The protocol is based on time division multiple access (TDMA). It uses reservations, where the time is divided into continuous, discrete time segments (frames) of 125 ms (see Exhibit III-7-29). Each frame is subdivided into a number of cells, depending on the speed of the channel. A cell may be allocated to contain isochronous or nonisochronous traffic.

The operation of the protocol is based on two control bits: a BUSY bit that indicates whether a slot on the network is used, and a REQ, or request, bit that is sent whenever a station has a packet waiting for access. When a station wants to transmit downstream it sends a reservation upstream. Each station maintains a request/countdown for each transmission direction (see Exhibit III-7-30). When a reservation request passes along the upstream bus, the counter is incremented by one; it is decremented by one when an empty cell goes by on the downstream bus. A nonzero value in the counter means that there are unsatisfied requests for cells in the downstream direction. If the counter has a value of zero, then there are no outstanding requests and the station can transmit in the next vacant cell. By counting the number of requests it receives and nonbusy cells that pass it, each station can determine the number of cells queued ahead of it. This counting establishes a single, ordered queue across the

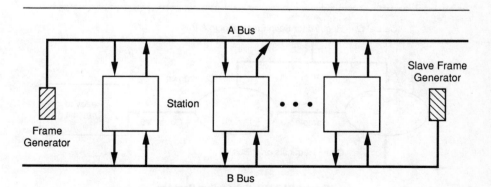

Exhibit III-7-28. QPSX Dual-Bus Architecture

Frame Header	Cell 0	Cell 1		Cell $n-1$	Cell n

Exhibit III-7-29. Frame Format for QPSX MAN

network for access to each bus. Thus, access priority levels can be established by operating a number of queues, one for each level.

The basic QPSX network is expected to operate at approximately 150M bps, with the streams divided into 53-byte cells (5 bytes overhead, 48 bytes payload) recurrently at the frame rate of 8K bps. A MAN may consist of many QPSX subnetworks interconnected in an approximately hierarchical manner using bridges or gateways.

IEEE 802.1 Media Access Control Bridge Standards

The IEEE proposed a number of standards for internetworking LANs. The IEEE 802.1 proposal calls for a media access control sublayer service common to all LANs and a network layer routing scheme for the more general case of LAN-to-any-subnetwork communications. The model identified three LAN interconnection topologies—LAN-to-LAN, LAN-to-X.25 wide area network (WAN), and LAN-to-X.25 WAN-to-LAN. The X.25 packet-level protocol is the basis of the network layer protocol designed to provide the connection-oriented network service.

The 802.1 working group's Internetworking Functional Requirements document serves as a framework for linking networks using a bridge architecture. This proposal identifies several important functions that bridge elements must perform. They are addressing, buffering, error handling, flow control, protocol conversion, segmentation and reassembly, and congestion control.

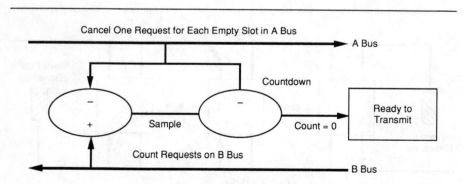

Exhibit III-7-30. Scheduling Counter

The primary architectures for LAN-to-LAN and LAN-to-WAN internet-working architectures can be categorized as one of two generic classes. The first is the use of transport protocol class 4, operating over the connectionless network protocol, based on logical link control 1. This configuration supports connectionless network service and connection-oriented transport service. The second is the use of transport protocol class 1 over the X.25 packet-level protocol, which operates over logical link controls 1 or 2 to create a connection-oriented transport service.

The X.25 packet-level protocol supports the following functions when implemented on a LAN:

- Addressing—The address field must be able to incorporate the network service access point information.
- Connection setup and release—These provide the data packet sequencing to facilitate the connection setup and release.
- Explicit flow control—Buffer overrun and loss of data are prevented by an explicit flow control.
- Transfer of expedited data—This allows up to 32 octets of high-priority data to be transferred in an interrupt packet that is not subject to flow control procedures.
- Error control—This provides for error detection and, optionally, recovery at the packet layer.
- Reset—This enables procedural error recovery.
- Q bit—This is used to qualify a packet as user data for a terminal or as control information for a packet assembler/dissassembler, which could support asynchronous, bisynchronous, or synchronous data link control terminals.
- Provision of OSI connection-oriented network service—This allows inter-networking with other OSI subnetworks.
- Error recovery at higher level—The proposed interconnection model is based on a number of assumptions, namely, that frames stayed in order on the links, that cyclic redundancy checks never experienced undetected errors, that the link remains functional, and that data link control modules never failed or malfunctioned.

In reality, transmission errors will go undetected, links will malfunction, and there will be hardware and software failures at the nodes. As a result, the higher-level protocol must compensate for the drawbacks of the low-level protocols.

One solution is to provide an adequate safeguard mechanism at the network layer so that it can provide error-free packet pipes from source to destination node. The advantages are that the error-recovery mechanism can take advantage of the mechanisms used in the network layer for routing and flow control.

Because a packet must travel through several subnets to reach its destination, the end-to-end recovery can be implemented at the transport layer within the external sites. However, if the subnetworks have to alter the size of the packet, it is preferable to provide end-to-end acknowledgment on a message rather than packet basis, making error recovery more appropriate at the transport layer.

Such applications as financial transactions, distributed data bases, and file transfers require lower error rates. In such cases, error-recovery mechanisms can be added at network, transport, or higher layers, or they can be combined to provide a complete structure.

Address translation can be performed by a bridge or a gateway. Both perform the interconnection function but at different levels of the OSI reference model. Bridges interconnect LANs at the data link layer, whereas the gateways achieve that at the network transport, or application layer. Gateways are more suitable for connecting heterogenous architectures.

INTERCONNECTION OF IEEE 802 LANs

The IEEE 802 standards committee has proposed two algorithms for interconnecting LANs through a bridge. The first, the spanning tree bridge, originated at Digital Equipment Corp and requires that the bridge maintain a data base of the addresses of stations on the LANs. The bridge monitors all frames that travel on the two LANs. It then learns the relative locations of the stations and puts this information into its data base. As each frame arrives at the bridge, it searches the data base for the destination address contained in the frame. The forwarding of the frame to the other LAN depends on the result of the search. The second algorithm, called the source-routing transparent bridge, was developed at IBM. It is based on routing information provided by the source station, which is used by the bridge to make the switching decision. As an example, a frame may contain an ordered list of addresses of the LAN segments through which the frame must pass before reaching its destination point. This algorithm makes the job of the bridge very simple, but each station must be aware of the network status.

Spanning Tree Bridge Algorithm

The spanning tree bridge algorithm consists of three processes: bridge forwarding, bridge learning, and formation of the spanning tree. In the bridge forwarding mode, the bridge intercepts all transmissions. It compares the destination address found in the frame header with the records contained in the forwarding data base. This data base contains addresses of the individuals and groups, along with the addresses of the bridge ports. The bridge discards a frame if it finds that the port identifier kept with the address is the same as the identifier of the bridge port on which the frame is received. In the event of an address mismatch, the port number is collected from the data base and the frame is forwarded to the appropriate port. However, if the destination address is not found in the forwarding data base, the frame is transmitted to all ports. This situation is illustrated in Exhibit III-7-31.

The bridge updates the forwarding data base every time it receives an error-free frame whose address it does not find in the data base. The data base entry is made of the source address along with the received-port identification number. The timer value, usually a few minutes, is also reset to indicate that this is a new entry in the data base. If the bridge detects a frame with a known source address from a different port number, it notes this change, updates the data base, and resets the timer for this record. Data is removed from the forwarding data base when the timer for an entry indicates that the data is stale (i.e., the timer value has been exceeded). The timer can be set by network management. When the spanning tree algorithm detects a change in the topology, a shorter time is used to ensure that bridges quickly age out potentially stale information.

The forwarding and learning algorithms assume a topology of bridges and LANs in which only one path exists between any two bridges in the entire constellation of LANs. However, fault tolerance parameters may dictate multiple paths between bridges. In such a case, the learning algorithm may break down if it confuses the direction in which end stations are found. As a result, a frame may circulate in a closed loop. The spanning tree algorithm is designed to prevent this by transforming any arbitrary mesh topology into a single spanning tree. The algorithm is based on the following assumptions:

- Each bridge must have a unique identifier—This identifier consists of two components, a priority field and a unique bridge station address, which is administered globally.
- A unique group address must be set aside for all bridges of the LAN—This is implemented in LAN architecture and therefore does not need to be assigned by the network manager.
- Each bridge port exists as a unique identity—The spanning tree is formed by selecting a unique root bridge that has the best priority. This priority could be the default assigned at the factory or set by the bridge administrator. Each bridge decides which bridge port lies in the direction of the root. This is the bridge port through which the least-cost path to the root is found and that is called the root port. A unique destination bridge is selected for each LAN. This is now the bridge that offers the least-cost path to the root from that LAN. Performance can be adjusted by tuning the parameters. For backbone topologies, it is advisable to assign higher root priorities to bridges that are directly connected to the backbone. Path cost can also be adjusted to accommodate variable link speeds. Lower-speed links can be assigned a higher cost in that they are placed into the spanning tree only in the absence of a higher-speed primary link.

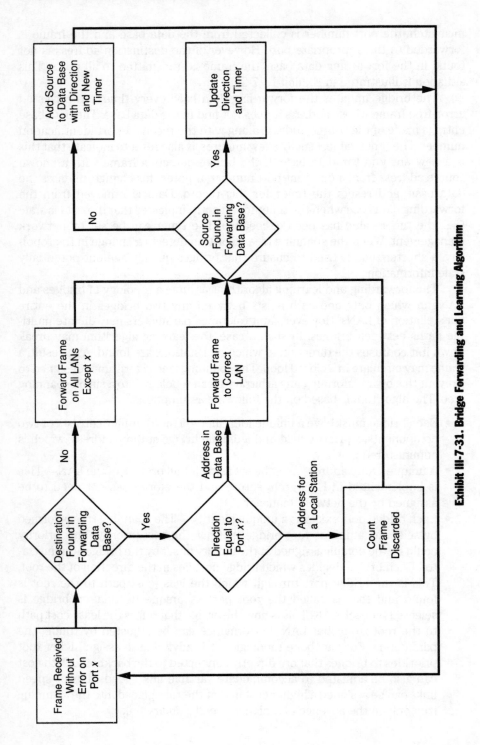

Exhibit III-7-31. Bridge Forwarding and Learning Algorithm

Source-Routing Transparent Bridge Algorithm

The source-routing algorithm was recommended by the IEEE 802.5 standards committee to allow stations to communicate across multiple rings. The primary issue in this algorithm is how to discover the route to the destination. The originating station identifies the message route and the recovery process in each frame. The node launches a query packet, which is broadcast over the entire bridged LAN. The query packet travels along all possible paths between the originating and recipient stations and records the various path descriptions as it travels. The originator then selects the most appropriate path, inserts that information into the header, and sets the group address or multicast bit within a frame to indicate the presence of routing information for all packets transmitted to that destination.

Because the routes are selected by the originator, the bridge can be simpler. On receiving a packet, a bridge scans the route information to determine whether an adjacent pair of LAN numbers matches any two of its attached LANs. The bridge forwards the packet if the result is found to be true; otherwise, it discards the packet. To avoid duplication, the algorithm divides the routing information into two logical parts, the route control field and the route descriptor field (see Exhibit III-7-32).

Each route descriptor is composed of a ring number and the bridge number and is administered by the LAN manager. The current recommendation uses a 12-bit field as the ring number. Each bridge number is 4 bits long and must be unique throughout the bridge LAN. These numbers are assigned manually to ensure their uniqueness.

The route control field allows for a maximum of 14 hops through the bridges. (The number of hops, however, can be extended to 28.) The route

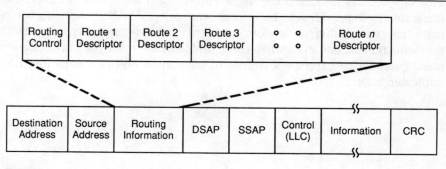

Notes:
CRC   Cyclic redundancy check
DSAP   Destination service access port
LLC   Logical link control
SSAP   Source service access port

Exhibit III-7-32. Frame Format for Source Routing

control field also includes information concerning the largest frame that could traverse the route. The receiving bridge continuously updates this field before forwarding it to the frame.

The recommendation also calls for source routing that allows for single-route broadcasting. In source routing, the selected frame travels across a spanning tree made up of source-routing bridges, thus ensuring that the frame will visit each ring at least once.

The cost of running this algorithm consists of the costs of route discovery, monitoring the routes, and carrying complete path information in every packet.

Interoperability Between the Two Algorithms

The main interoperability issues of importance to network integrators are the following:

- If the peer entities use logical link control type 1 service, how should the routes be maintained?
- What type or types of frame will be needed to determine the route?
- How can it be guaranteed that all media access control layers support the discovery frames and that they are replicated across the border?
- How is a broadcast frame propagated in a multiring source-routing network?
- How will an end station be notified that the source station is using a source-routing or spanning tree algorithm?
- Will there be support for configurations that place spanning tree bridges in parallel with source-routing bridges?

SUMMARY

This chapter has discussed the major current LAN standards. Adherence to these standards provides the basis for the formation of LANs comprising equipment from many different vendors. Standards, however, are not perfect. Some problems remain, and even when these problems are resolved, LAN designers must continue to exercise a degree of caution to ensure compatible LAN implementations.

III-8
The Fiber Distributed Data Interface

FLOYD E. ROSS

The basic fiber distributed data interface (FDDI) uses multimode optical fiber with light-emitting diodes (LEDs) transmitting at a nominal wavelength of 1,325 nm. A dual-fiber cable employing a polarized duplex connector connects stations. A single-mode fiber (SMF) version of the physical medium–dependent (PMD) layer, known as SMF-PMD, uses laser diode transmitters with two power-level categories specified; the lower level retains the same receivers as the basic physical medium–dependent layer. SMF-PMD allows individual links to be extended to 60 km or even 100 km.

The peak data transmission rate is 100M bps, and the effective sustained data rate at the data link layer can be more than 95% of this peak rate. The four-out-of-five code used on the optical fiber medium requires a 125M-baud transmission rate. The clocking, which adjusts for accumulated jitter between frames, limits frames to a maximum of 4,500 octets. Multiple frames may, however, be transmitted during the same access opportunity.

Frames use the 48-bit address structure defined by IEEE 802. The assignment of addresses to stations is administered by the IEEE standards office; IEEE 802 stations and FDDI stations share a common address space.

Calculation of the default values of the recovery timers is based on 1,000 physical connections and a fiber path of 200 km. These choices allow for a configuration of 500 stations (each station represents two physical connections) linked by 100 km of duplex cable. For the recovery timers, if longer times than the default values are chosen, larger networks can be configured. For smaller networks, performance can be optimized by choosing shorter times for the recovery timers. There is no minimum configuration requirement.

FDDI BENEFITS

There are several reasons for the widespread acceptance of FDDI. By providing several medium-speed (1M- to 20M-bps) LANs, the IEEE 802 effort in effect popularized the LAN. It thus created a market for a higher-speed LAN, both to perform the backbone function for the lower-speed IEEE 802 LANs and to satisfy applications that require a higher-performance LAN.

265

The dramatic improvement in the price and performance of optical fiber and such related components as optical transmitters and receivers has contributed measurably to the acceptance of FDDI. Considering the many advantages that optical fiber offers (i.e., high data bandwidth, security, safety, immunity to electromagnetic interference, and reduced weight and size), the concept of an all-fiber LAN is attractive to network designers. Because the FDDI design has been optimized for the use of optical fiber, it has successfully led in the development of optical fiber LAN technology.

FDDI focuses on standardization and conforms to the ISO model. The functions integrated into FDDI to meet the needs of different applications allow it to satisfy the requirements of the broad, high-speed LAN marketplace.

ORGANIZATION OF FDDI STANDARDS

FDDI is best described in terms of the standards that it comprises. The basic FDDI, when completed, will consist of the following four standards:

- A PMD-layer standard—Specifies the optical fiber link and related optical components.
- A physical-layer protocol standard—Specifies encoding and decoding, clocking, and data framing.
- A media access control standard—Specifies access to the medium, addressing, data checking, and frame generation and reception.
- A station management standard—Specifies the FDDI station and ring configurations and the control required for proper operation of stations in an FDDI ring.

The following two standard entities are being developed as extensions of the basic FDDI:

- SMF-PMD—A single-mode fiber version of the physical medium–dependent layer, which provides an alternative to the basic PMD layer, increasing the permissible fiber link length from 2 km to 60 km.
- A hybrid ring control standard—This specifies an enhanced version of FDDI, known as FDDI-II, which creates an integrated-services LAN by adding the capability for circuit switching to the packet switching of the basic FDDI.

Subsequent sections of this article address each standard in detail. Exhibit III-8-1 provides an overview of the basic FDDI standard as it relates to the OSI reference model (see also Exhibit III-8-11 for the relationship of FDDI-II to the OSI model). The FDDI media access control provides a superset of the services required by the logical link control protocol developed by IEEE 802.2. Exhibit III-8-1 depicts the use of the IEEE 802.2 logical link control as the upper sublayer of the data link layer. Any other appropriate logical link control may be used.

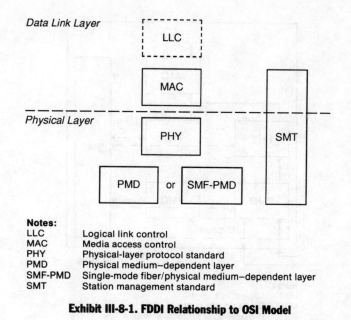

Data Link Layer

Physical Layer

Notes:

LLC	Logical link control
MAC	Media access control
PHY	Physical-layer protocol standard
PMD	Physical medium–dependent layer
SMF-PMD	Single-mode fiber/physical medium–dependent layer
SMT	Station management standard

Exhibit III-8-1. FDDI Relationship to OSI Model

STATION AND FDDI NETWORK CONFIGURATIONS

Each FDDI station is composed of logical entities that conform to the FDDI standards. The function of a given station depends on the number of entities it has. Networks with different physical topologies may be constructed, depending on the types of stations used.

Station Types

Two main classes of stations are specified, with the designation depending on whether the stations are allowed to attach directly to the trunk ring. A dual-attachment station may attach directly to the trunk ring. It has two pairs of physical-layer protocol and physical medium–dependent entities and one or more media access control entities. When there are two media access control entities, one may be in each of the counterrotating rings or both may be in the same ring. A dual-attachment station can have an optical bypass switch to remove it from both rings if the station is powered down or disabled by station management. Exhibits III-8-2 and III-8-3 provide examples of dual-attachment stations; Exhibit III-8-2 has a single media access control, and Exhibit III-8-3 has dual media access control.

Exhibit III-8-4 depicts another dual-attachment station. In this case, the station is a concentrator referred to as a dual-attachment concentrator. A concentrator has additional physical-layer protocol and physical medium–

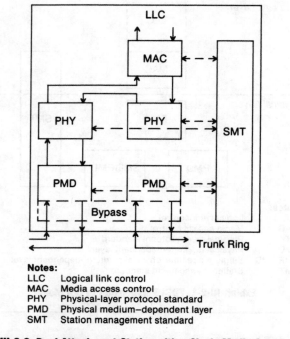

Notes:
LLC   Logical link control
MAC   Media access control
PHY   Physical-layer protocol standard
PMD   Physical medium–dependent layer
SMT   Station management standard

Exhibit III-8-2. Dual-Attachment Station with a Single Media Access Control

dependent entities beyond those required for attachment to the FDDI ring. The additional pairs permit attachment of additional stations. The additional stations, though logically part of the ring, are physically isolated from the trunk ring by the concentrator. Varying functions, including multiple media access controls, are permitted in concentrators. A more complex concentrator might attach its connected stations into either or both of the counterrotating rings of the trunk ring. A concentrator has its media access controls at the output ports following the stations it may insert into the trunk ring.

Exhibit III-8-5 depicts a single-attachment station. A single-attachment station has one physical-layer protocol and one media access control and therefore cannot be attached directly into the main FDDI ring. Instead, it must be attached to the ring by a concentrator.

Additional station types are possible beyond these examples. For example, a single-attachment concentrator is a concentrator that can attach to the trunk ring only through another concentrator.

The physical-layer protocol/physical medium–dependent pairs are divided into four types, depending on their intended connection into a ring. The pairs for direct attachment to the counterrotating trunk ring are designated as

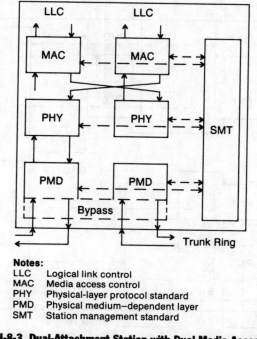

Notes:

LLC	Logical link control
MAC	Media access control
PHY	Physical-layer protocol standard
PMD	Physical medium–dependent layer
SMT	Station management standard

Exhibit III-8-3. Dual-Attachment Station with Dual Media Access Control

---

A and B ports. In a trunk ring configuration, each fiber-optic link is intended to have an A pair at one end and a B pair at the other end.

The physical-layer protocol/physical medium–dependent pairs supplied by a concentrator for the attachment of the additional stations are designated as master ports. The single pair in a single-attachment station intended to connect to the master port of a concentrator is designated as a slave port.

Network Topologies

The FDDI topology is a ring of trees. This corresponds to one counterrotating trunk ring with trees of cascaded concentrators. Exhibit III-8-6 depicts a ring-of-trees topology in which each square is a station or concentrator. Only one dual ring is allowed; multiple trees of varying depths may be attached to it. All subsets of this topology are allowed as well.

Exhibit III-8-7 depicts a portion of a sample ring in greater detail. Stations 1, 2, and 4 are dual-attachment stations. The two media access controls in station 1, a dual-attachment/dual–media access control station, are shown in the opposite paths of the counterrotating trunk ring. Direct communication is not possible unless the ring has been reconfigured to the wrap state because of

269

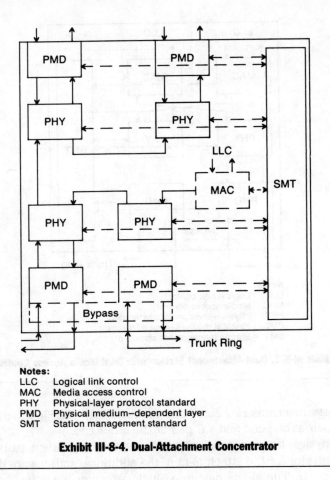

Notes:
LLC   Logical link control
MAC Media access control
PHY   Physical-layer protocol standard
PMD Physical medium–dependent layer
SMT Station management standard

Exhibit III-8-4. Dual-Attachment Concentrator

---

a fault. Therefore, both media access controls have independent access to a full 100M-bps data capability.

Station 3 is a concentrator connecting stations 4, 5, and 6 into the FDDI ring. Stations 5 and 6 are single-attachment stations. Station 4, although it is a dual-attachment station, performs as a single-attachment station as far as its attachment to the ring through the concentrator is concerned. Operation of the second physical-layer protocol/physical medium–dependent pair of station 4 on another ring is allowed, but there is no interconnection of the two rings within the station at a level visible to the media access control or physical-layer protocol.

Reliability Considerations

Ring topologies allow for the isolation of failed attachments through several mechanisms. Counterrotating rings, as shown in Exhibit III-8-8, are basic to the

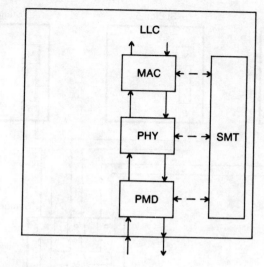

Notes:

LLC	Logical link control
MAC	Media access control
PHY	Physical-layer protocol standard
PMD	Physical medium–dependent layer
SMT	Station management standard

Exhibit III-8-5. Single-Attachment Station

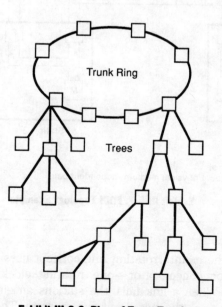

Exhibit III-8-6. Ring-of-Trees Topology

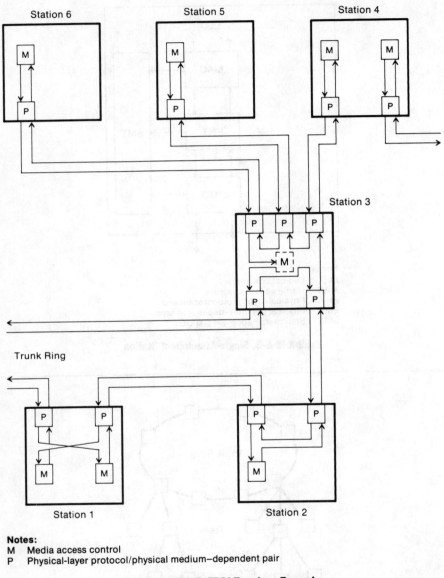

Notes:
M Media access control
P Physical-layer protocol/physical medium–dependent pair

Exhibit III-8-7. FDDI Topology Example

FDDI structure. The counterrotating ring concept uses two rings connected to each station or concentrator—one rotating clockwise and the other counterclockwise. When a link fails, the stations on either side reconfigure internally, as shown in the middle of the diagram. The functional stations adjacent to the break make use of the connection in the reverse direction to

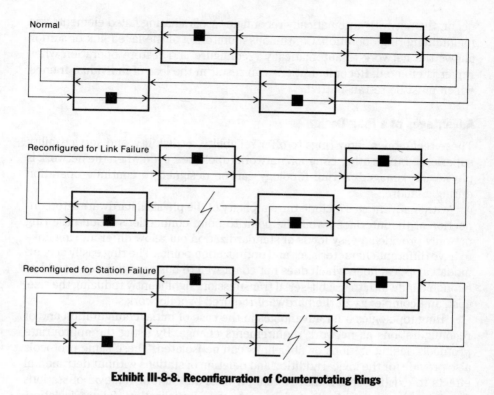

Normal

Reconfigured for Link Failure

Reconfigured for Station Failure

Exhibit III-8-8. Reconfiguration of Counterrotating Rings

close the ring, eliminating the failed link. In this exhibit, the dark squares represent the logical media access control attachment within the stations. If a station itself fails, as shown in the bottom of the diagram, the stations on either side reconfigure to eliminate the failed station and both of the links to it.

As shown in Exhibits III-8-2 through III-8-4, dual-attachment stations can offer a bypass capability in which an optical switch is used to bypass a station's receiver and transmitter connections so that the signal from the previous station is passed directly to the next station. Bypassing can be activated by a station itself, a neighboring station, or a human operator; automatically at the removal of power; or by an overall network-controlling function.

Another approach is the use of concentrators (as shown in Exhibit III-8-7). These attach directly to the trunk ring and provide drop connections for other stations or concentrators (in Exhibit III-8-7, stations 4, 5, and 6). This provides a level of isolation between the trunk ring and the attached stations. A concentrator monitors its slave stations and removes any faulty station that it detects. This isolation provides for efficient insertion and removal of stations from the ring.

The use of all three techniques allows FDDI networks to tolerate a variety of station or link failures without catastrophic consequences. When failures occur, the network automatically reconfigures, eliminating failed elements and maintaining ring operation. Continuous monitoring of the failed link or station allows the network to automatically reconfigure and restore operation when repair is effected. Reconfigurations can result in the loss of individual frames, which must be retransmitted.

Advantages of a Ring Design

These techniques allow rings to offer reliability, availability, and serviceability superior to or other common network topologies, even when the network is physically damaged. A ring topology can be designed to continue operation during a failure.

Other advantages include the simplicity of the physical hardware interconnection at the interface level. The point-to-point connections around the ring not only provide an easy focus of standardization but allow different ring links to have different characteristics and optimization points. The ring easily accommodates optical fiber, which does not adapt well to bus configurations, and has enough bandwidth to use bit-serial transmission, significantly reducing the size, cost, and complexity of the hardware required by a network.

Ring topologies offer advantages in the ease of initial configuration and of reconfigurations as network requirements change. By using the appropriate protocols, failing stations or fiber links can be isolated. These same protocols also provide for the logical addition and deletion of stations without detrimental effects to existing ring traffic. Actual physical addition or removal of stations from the network is facilitated because ring initialization, failure isolation, recovery, and reconfiguration mechanisms can provide for continued operation even when the cables are being rearranged.

Ring topologies do not impose a restrictive logical limit on the length of ring links, the number of stations, or the total extent of the network that can be accommodated.

Ring topologies and the protocols they support offer significant performance advantages. These include insensitivity to load distribution, easy and fair allocation of the available bandwidth, low arbitration times, bounded access delay, and no requirement for long preambles.

A ring topology best satisfies the requirements of large high-performance networks, offering high connectivity and operating speeds from 20M bps to more than 500M bps.

FRAME CHARACTERISTICS

Basic FDDI requires that all information transmitted on the fiber-optic medium be encoded into frames. The logical link control supplies the media access control with a service data unit, which is encapsulated into a frame for transmission by the physical-layer protocol/physical medium–dependent pair of the station. Data is transferred between the media access control and the physical-layer protocol and across the physical interface in terms of two kinds of symbols: data symbols and control symbols. A data symbol represents 4 bits of data. Control symbols may not occur within the body of the frame. Both kinds of symbol require 5 code bits for transfer on the fiber-optic medium.

Data Encoding

As shown in the 32-member symbol set in Exhibit III-8-9, seven symbols of the set cannot be transmitted. These violate code run length and direct current balance requirements. The QUIET symbol is necessary because it is used to indicate the absence of any functional signal. For line-state signaling, three symbols are used. These are recognized by the physical-layer hardware and are never transferred to the media access control.

Decimal	Code Group	Symbol	Name	Assignment	
00	00000	Q	QUIET	LINE STATE SYMBOL	
31	11111	I	IDLE	"	
04	00100	H	HALT	"	
24	11000	J		STARTING DELIMITER	
17	10001	K		"	
05	00101	L		"	
13	01101	T		ENDING DELIMITER	
07	00111	R	RESET	CONTROL INDICATOR	
25	11001	S	SET	"	
30	11110	O		DATA SYMBOL	0000
09	01001	1		"	0001
20	10100	2		"	0010
21	10101	3		"	0011
10	01010	4		"	0100
11	01011	5		"	0101
14	01110	6		"	0110
15	01111	7		"	0111
18	10010	8		"	1000
19	10011	9		"	1001
22	10110	A		"	1010
23	10111	B		"	1011
26	11010	C		"	1100
27	11011	D		"	1101
28	11100	E		"	1110
29	11101	F		"	1111
01	00001	V	VIOLATION	NOT TRANSMITTED	
02	00010	V	VIOLATION	"	
03	00011	V	VIOLATION	"	
06	00110	V	VIOLATION	"	
08	01000	V	VIOLATION	"	
12	01100	V	VIOLATION	"	
16	10000	V	VIOLATION	"	

Exhibit III-8-9. Symbol Coding

The remaining symbols, with the exception of L, are transferred across the interface between the media access control and the physical-layer protocol. Sixteen are data symbols, representing 4 bits of ordered binary data; 2 bits are used as control indicators, and 4 are used for starting and ending delimiters. One of the starting delimiters is not used in the basic FDDI. It is reserved for FDDI-II, in which it is used by the physical-layer protocol to create the regular starting delimiter for presentation to the media access control. In the basic FDDI, its code point is included with the seven violation symbols.

Line-State Sequences

A line state is generated by continuously transmitting the same or alternating line-state symbols. Line-state recognition at the receiving end is predicated on the receipt of 16 symbols of the required pattern and terminates on receipt of any other symbol.

Defined line states include QUIET, IDLE, and HALT. Each consists of a repeating pattern of the corresponding symbols. A MASTER line state is also defined. It consists of alternating HALT and QUIET symbols. These four line states (QUIET, IDLE, HALT, and MASTER) are used in the basic signaling sequences of station management.

Two other line states are defined. An ACTIVE line state is entered whenever the starting delimiter of a frame is recognized and is exited whenever the frame ends or an importer symbol is received. A NOISE line state, which is never intentionally transmitted, is entered according to certain defined noise criteria and events. If none of the criteria for the defined line state are met, the line state is UNKNOWN.

Frame and Token Formats

Information is transmitted on the FDDI ring in frames, which are variable in length. Short fixed-length frames, called tokens, are used to signify the right to transmit data. Exhibit III-8-10 shows the frame and token formats.

The preamble, consisting nominally of 16 IDLE symbols that establish and maintain clock synchronization, precedes every transmission. The starting delimiter field consists of a two-symbol sequence (JK) that is uniquely recognizable as a bit sequence independent of previously established symbol boundaries. The starting delimiter establishes the symbol boundaries for the content that follows.

The frame control is a two-symbol field that defines the type of frame and its characteristics. It distinguishes between synchronous and asynchronous frames, the length of the address field (16 bits or 48 bits), and the kinds of frames (e.g., logical link control or station management). One set of frame control values is reserved for implementer frames that have relaxed certain frame format requirements and are to be repeated unchanged by all conforming FDDI stations.

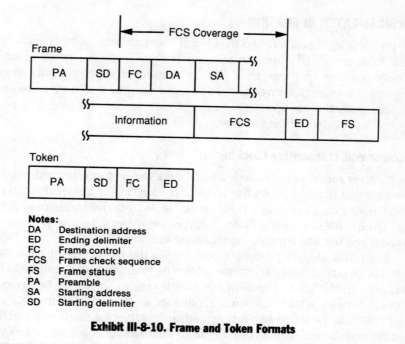

Notes:

DA   Destination address
ED   Ending delimiter
FC   Frame control
FCS Frame check sequence
FS   Frame status
PA   Preamble
SA   Starting address
SD   Starting delimiter

Exhibit III-8-10. Frame and Token Formats

The frame control field also distinguishes between a frame and a token. Separate code points provide for two kinds of tokens—restricted and nonrestricted. The latter is used in a special class of service that provides for extended dialogue among a limited set of cooperating stations. Two ending delimiter symbols (TT) complete a token.

The destination address and source address fields may be either 16 bits or 48 bits long, depending on the frame control value. The destination may be an individual or a group address; a group address can be recognized by more than one station.

The 32-bit frame check sequence field is a cyclic redundancy check using the standard polynomial of the IEEE 802 protocols. It is used to cover all the fields containing data symbols within a frame. The fields from the frame control through the frame check sequence field may consist of only the 16 data symbols. Data symbols are not used in the frame format requirements.

The ending delimiter field of a frame is one delimiter symbol (T). It is followed by the frame status field, which has a minimum of three control indicator symbols that are subject to modification by the station as it repeats the frame. When set, these indicate that an error has been detected in the frame by the station (E), that the addressed station has recognized its address (A), and that the frame has been copied by the station (C). They are transmitted in the ordered sequence—E, A, and C.

PHYSICAL-LAYER OPERATION

The physical-layer protocol and the optical fiber hardware components support a link from one FDDI station to another. The physical-layer protocol simultaneously receives and transmits. The transmitter accepts symbols from the media access control, converts them to non-return-to-zero 5-bit code groups, and transmits the encoded serial data stream on the medium. The reverse process is provided by the receiver.

Receiver and Transmitter Clocking

The receiver recovers the encoded serial data stream from the medium, establishes symbol boundaries on the basis of recognition of a start delimiter, and forwards decoded symbols to the media access control. Additional symbols (e.g., QUIET, IDLE, and HALT) are interpreted directly by the physical-layer protocol and used to support management functions.

The physical-layer protocol also provides the bit clocks for each station. From the perspective of each frame, each ring (including all stations and links) must remain the same apparent bit length (i.e., no bits may be created or deleted) during the transmission of a frame around the ring. Otherwise, an error is generated in the frame as it is repeated around the ring. Bit-length stability of the ring must be maintained despite jitter, fluctuations in voltage, temperature variations, and component aging effects. To accomplish this, the physical-layer protocol provides an elasticity buffer that is always inserted between the receiver and the transmitter.

A standard circuit, such as a phase-locked loop oscillator, is used to provide the receiver with a variable frequency clock. This variable clock is responsible for recovering from received data the clock signal of the previous transmitting station.

The transmitter, in contrast, uses a local fixed-frequency clock. The elasticity buffer in each station compensates for the difference in frequency between the local clock and that of the upstream station by adjusting the bit delay through the station. Because the stability of the transmitter clock is specified as 0.005%, an elasticity buffer of 10 bits allows transmission of frames 4,500 octets in length without overrunning or underrunning the limits of the buffer. The elasticity buffer in each station is reinitialized to its center position during the preamble that precedes each frame or token. This increases or decreases the length of the preamble, initially transmitted as 16 or more symbols, as it proceeds around the ring.

The Physical-Layer Protocol Smoother Function

Simulations of early FDDI designs showed that preambles, rather than maintaining a nominal 16-symbol length, tended in long rings to move toward a flat unbounded distribution. This causes a frame to creep in its position relative to other frames, creating longer and shorter preambles. Longer preambles posed no problem in themselves, but they caused shorter or even negative preambles. A negative preamble indicates that the preamble is so severely shortened that it has completely disappeared and that symbols are consequently lost off the end of a frame, resulting in the loss of the entire frame.

This problem was solved by means of a smoothing buffer function incorporated into the physical-layer protocol, which in effect recenters the frame between its neighboring frames. The smoother examines the preamble length between frames and either inserts or deletes preamble symbols (or bytes) to maintain the preamble near the nominal 16-symbol length. This ensures that the preamble never becomes shorter than 4 bytes. Simulation experiments have shown that the smoother algorithm chosen, even under worst-case conditions, reduced the probability of frame loss for the maximum-length frames to less than 10^{-12}. Extended testing of a large ring has confirmed this result.

PMD-Layer Signal Considerations

The optical signal transmitted by the physical medium–dependent layer is non-return-to-zero inverted, with 5 bits representing each symbol. A primary concern is the jitter introduced at the receiver that increases as the optical signal is reduced to the threshold level.

FDDI stations are required to receive an optical signal stream with an average power of -31 dBm and repeat it with a bit-error rate that does not exceed 2.5×10^{-10}. An increase of 2 dBm in the power of the input signal requires the bit-error rate to decrease to 10^{-12}. The data integrity goals for a full FDDI ring have been represented as a bit-error rate of 10^{-9} with a packet loss rate of 10^{-9}. The equipment offered by many vendors will typically exceed these requirements by several orders of magnitude.

Input signals with an average power as high as -14 dBm are permitted. Average output power levels are specified at -14 to -20 dBm. The difference between -20 and -31 dBm yields a maximum permitted cable plant loss of 11 dBm.

PMD-Layer Cable Plant Considerations

Choice of fiber size and the design of the duplex connector were the most difficult issues for the FDDI standards. Originally, a 100/140-micron (e.g., 100-micron core, 140-micron cladding outside diameter) fiber was chosen on the basis of the lower signal losses associated with connectors when used on larger fiber sizes. It was argued that FDDI should be optimized for a number of stations with the optical bypass switches activated. Smaller fiber sizes would result in greater losses at connectors even though the loss over a single long fiber link was less.

During the development of the PMD-layer standard, emphasis on the use of optical bypass relays decreased to some extent. As a result, a switch was made to 85/125-micron fiber, and eventually the more commonly available

62.5/125-micron fiber gained preference. The standard specifies the characteristics of the station and the cable plant on the basis of 62.5/125-micron fiber. This is important because it provides a single point of reference for conformance verification. Other fiber sizes may be used; data is available on the loss factors that must be taken into consideration for the other common fiber sizes. This data includes 100/140-, 82.5/125-, and several variations of 50/125-micron fiber.

FDDI requires a duplex optical connector. Because there were no satisfactory connectors in existence at the time, two new designs were proposed. The first used a fixed shroud to protect the tips of the optical fibers. The second had a spring-loaded retractable shroud. The retractable shroud provided less protection to the optical fiber tips but allowed more mounting flexibility, because active optical components could be placed directly in the receptacle. Although the design decision was a difficult one, the fixed-shroud duplex connector design was chosen.

The Link Error Monitor

Each physical link of an FDDI ring is monitored by a link error monitor. Whenever the estimated link error rate exceeds a threshold specified by station management, that link is excluded. The default value of the threshold is 10^{-7}, with 10^{-4} being the maximum permitted value.

It has been shown that the line-state signaling mechanisms used to bring up links function reliably when the physical-link bit error rate is 10^{-2} or better. It has also been shown that the media access control mechanisms, which rely on the transfer of short frames, function reliably when the network error rates are 10^{-3} to 10^{-4} or better. These conclusions are the basis for the choice of 10^{-4} as the lower link error monitor threshold.

FUNCTIONAL OPERATION OF TOKEN MEDIA ACCESS CONTROL

An important function of any station is deciding which station has control of the medium. The media access control schedules and performs all data transfers on the ring.

Frame Repetition and Reception

The basic concept of a ring is that each station repeats for its downstream neighbor the frame that it has received from its upstream neighbor. If the destination address of the frame matches the media access control's address and there is no error indicated, the frame is copied into a local buffer and the media access control notifies logical link control (or station management) of the frame's arrival. As the media access control repeats the frame, it modifies the trailing control indicator symbols in the frame status field to indicate the detection of an error in the frame, the recognition of its own address, and the copying of the frame.

The frame travels around the ring to the station that originally placed it on the ring. The transmitting station examines the indicator symbols in the frame status field to determine the success of the transmission. The media access control of this transmitting station is responsible for removing from the ring all of the frames that it has placed on the ring. This process is called stripping. The media access control recognizes these frames for stripping because the source address contained in them is its own. During stripping, IDLE symbols are placed on the medium.

Frame Removal

Stripping is an important aspect of FDDI ring operation. A station may initiate transmission after capturing a token, but an active long ring will at that moment contain several frames in transit that were placed on the ring by other stations.

Before these frames arrive for the second time at the current transmitting station's receiver, they are removed from the ring by the stations that originally transmitted them. Therefore, input to the current transmitting station's receiver consists of IDLE symbols and the remnants of stripped frames. Because the station is transmitting, it does not repeat on the ring anything that arrives at its receiver.

Remnants of stripped frames occur because a station's decision to strip a frame is based on recognition of its own address in the source address field. This cannot occur until after the initial part of the frame has been repeated. The remnants have no harmful effects because various criteria, including recognition of an ending delimiter, must be met before a frame is accepted as valid.

When the transmission is completed and a new token has been issued, the transmitting station continues to generate IDLE symbols until the starting delimiter of any frame (or fragment) is received. At this time, the media access control reinitiates the examination of all arriving frames, stripping those that it has originated and repeating all others.

Frame Validity Criteria

The media access control is responsible for recognizing frames that are addressed to it and ensuring that only intended frames are accepted. Furthermore, the media access control must ensure that they are valid frames and not the result of a burst of noise or a juxtaposition of two frame remnants caused by such events as configuration switching. The required reliability of frame reception is enforced by the valid frame criteria.

A valid frame must be correctly formed, including proper starting and ending delimiters, with its body composed entirely of the 16 data symbols. The frame control field must be one that is allowed for frames. In addition, all fields within the frame must conform to the proper length restrictions (e.g., the information field must contain an even number of symbols). The frame check sequence field must be correct, and the E indicator must be reset to indicate that no other station has detected any errors as the frame progressed around the ring.

One additional requirement is necessary to ensure the validity of frames repeated by media access controls: all media access controls must propagate the E indicator associated with a frame as set (i.e., indicating an error), unless the indicator was received in the reset condition.

Given these criteria, the probability that a media access control will accept an improper frame as valid (i.e., an undetected error) is on the order of 4×10^{-25} under worst-case conditions. Worst-case conditions exist when 1,000 physical links (a maximum default-sized ring in the wrap condition) have a worst-case bit error rate of 2.5×10^{-10} and all frames have the maximum length of 4,500 bytes.

Token Capture

If the media access control has a frame from the logical link control (or station management) to transmit, it may do so only after a token has been captured. A token is a special frame that indicates that the medium is available for use. Priority requirements, necessary to ensure proper handling of frames, are implemented in the rules of token recapture. Under these rules, if a given station is not allowed to capture the token, it must repeat it (or in certain cases reissue a token) to the next station in the ring. Only when the media access control has captured a token and stripped it from the ring can it transmit a frame or frames. When finished, it issues a new token to signify that the medium is available for use by another station.

The Timed Token-Rotation Protocol

The FDDI media access control uses a timed token-rotation protocol to control access to the medium. Under this protocol, the media access control in each station measures the time that has elapsed since a token was last received. The initialization procedures establish the target token-rotation time equal to the lowest value bid by any of the stations. This value is retained by each media access control and becomes the value used by the token-rotation timer.

Two classes of service are defined. Synchronous service permits the use of any token whenever the media access control has synchronous frames queued for transmission. Asynchronous service permits the use of a token only when the time since the receipt of the last token does not exceed the value of the token-rotation timer. Multiple levels of priority for asynchronous frames are provided within a station by specifying additional, more restrictive, time thresholds for token rotation.

The use of timed token rotation allows stations to request and establish (through station management procedures) guaranteed bandwidths and response times for synchronous frames. It establishes a guaranteed minimum response time for the ring because, in the worst case, the time between the arrival of two successive tokens never exceeds twice the value of the token-rotation time. It also provides a guaranteed level of ring use equal to:

$$\frac{TRT - RL}{TRT}$$

where:

TRT = token-rotation time

RL = physical ring latency

This represents the time that a token takes to propagate around the ring under a no-load condition.

Low values of target token-rotation time (e.g., 4 msec) may be used to establish an average token-rotation time of 4 msec and a guaranteed response time of more than 8 msec. This is useful in a time-critical application (e.g., packetized voice). Higher target token-rotation times allow very high ring use under heavy loads. For example, using a target token-rotation time of 50 msec and a ring latency of 0.25 msec (which is reasonable for a ring consisting of 75 stations and 30 km of fiber), the formula shows that 99.5% use can be achieved.

Ring Initialization

The media access control is responsible for ring initialization to ensure that only one token is generated at a time. This is accomplished through the claim process, which is started whenever the media access control is first activated. This process also establishes that the value for token-rotation time is the same in every station on the ring.

During this process, the media access control in each station generates a series of claim frames that contains that media access control's bid for the target token-rotation time value. The value in the frame control field is unique, allowing the stations to distinguish among themselves. When a claim frame is received, it is examined by each media access control. If the target token-rotation time value in the received frame is smaller than its own bid, the received claim frame is repeated and the media access control ceases to generate its own claim frames. Otherwise, the media access control generates its own claim frames and places them on the ring, stripping any incoming claim frames. In the event of equal target token-rotation time values, the media access control decides the precedence of claim frames on the basis of its address relative to the source address contained in the received claim frame. The highest address is given precedence.

This process continues until eventually the station with the lowest target token-rotation time bid that has the highest address is generating claim frames that are being repeated by all of the other stations. When a station receives its own claim frame, it knows that it has won the claim process and it then issues one token.

During the claim process, each station retains the most recent value of the target token-rotation time bid value received. When the token is received on its initial rotation, the retained value is activated as the operational value of the token-rotation timer. On the second rotation of the token, the ring becomes operational in each station in order, and synchronous frames can then be transmitted. The initialization process is now completed; on subsequent rotations of the token, either synchronous or asynchronous frames may be considered for transmission.

The Beacon Process

The beacon process is invoked when the initialization process fails to complete and when the operation of the ring is suspect. The beacon process is entered when the media access controls in one or more stations transmit a beacon frame. The source station of the beacon frame is identified by the value of the frame control field. During the beacon process, the media access control in each station yields to an incoming beacon frame and repeats it. Two conclusions to this process are possible.

In one case, the ring is healed. Eventually, the media access control in the station that beaconed originally recognizes the source address in a received beacon frame as its own. That media access control then enters the claim process, and when that process is completed, one token is generated and the ring is again made operational. Many of the faults that have the potential to cause the beacon state are detected by the link error monitor, and that monitor removes the faulty link. Given that, the stations at both ends of the fault domain are reconfigured to the wrap state. The beaconing media access control then receives its own beacon over the counterrotating ring.

In the other case, the fault persists. Eventually, a quasi-stable state is reached with the media access control in one station generating and transmitting beacon frames that are being repeated by all stations up to the fault domain. The media access control generating the beacon frames is not receiving any beacon frames and therefore follows the fault domain. This state continues except that the stations repeating the beacons insert occasional claim frames each time their token-rotation timers expire. Because the beacon frames contain the source address of the beaconing media access control, the location of the fault domain is apparent to a manager located at any of the stations. Alternatively, station management of the beaconing station may take the necessary corrective action, as discussed in the following sections, to restore the ring if the beaconing persists.

STATION MANAGEMENT OPERATION

Station management is the local portion of the network management application process, including the control required for proper operation of an FDDI station in an FDDI ring. It monitors ring activity and exercises overall control over station activity.

Each FDDI station has one station management entity. Its operation is divided into three broad categories: connection management, ring management, and operational management.

Connection Management

Connection management is primarily concerned with establishing and maintaining the point-to-point physical links between each of the adjacent physical-layer protocol/PMD-layer pairs. Primitive signaling sequences use the four defined line states to establish each physical link and to exchange a minimum of critical information between the pairs.

Information exchanged includes:

- Type of physical-layer protocol/PMD-layer pair (A, B, M, or S).
- Willingness to establish a link with a pair signaled.
- Duration of the link confidence test performed.
- Availability of a media access control for a link confidence test.
- Outcome of the link confidence test.
- Availability of the media access control for a local loop test.
- Intent to place a media access control in the connection if established.

An escape can also be signaled to provide for future expansion.

Using this information, each link can be established so as to be consistent with the physical-layer protocol/PMD-layer pairs detected, existing conditions, and the policy settings of the local station management. Examples of policy settings include whether an A-to-A link is permitted. Links that are always excluded from completion include an M-to-M connection.

With the links established according to the rules and policies of the FDDI networks, the next task of connection management is to establish the internal configuration of the station. The configuration must be consistent with the links already established, the capability of the station, and the policy in effect. Connection management establishes the internal connections of the FDDI station (including those of the various physical-layer protocol/PMD-layer pairs and media access controls) and controls the optional bypass relays.

The resultant internal configuration of a station is described as isolated, wrap A, wrap B, and through. Wrap A and wrap B refer to the internal configuration of a station. Its media access control has been connected to transfer input and output data by means of the indicated physical-layer protocol/PMD-layer pair (the other pair is deactivated). An isolated configuration means that the station's media access control is not connected to either ring. A through configuration means that the station's media access control is inserted in the usual way between the pairs, as shown in Exhibit III-8-2.

Other services performed by connection management include the trace function. The trace function is used to force stations or concentrators in the suspected fault domain (which extends from the first media access control upstream to the first one downstream) to leave the ring and enter self-testing in an effort to locate a fault.

Ring Management

Ring management provides a higher-level service to connection management, completing the configuration of the FDDI ring and delivering the ring in an operational state (i.e., with a usable token in circulation).

Ring management monitors the state of the media access control. This includes the detection of certain error conditions, such as the media access control of a station held in the beaconing state. Under appropriate conditions, ring management initiates the connection management trace function to attempt to locate the fault. Ring management may notify the nearest upstream neighbor of detected error conditions by transmitting a special directed beacon frame that is addressed to it. Ring management is also responsible for the detection of duplicate addresses on the ring that would otherwise prevent the ring from becoming operational.

Operational Management

The remaining functions of station management deal with the management of a station after the ring has achieved the operational state. An assortment of capabilities and protocols are provided. These services extend across multiple stations and therefore require a well-defined set of station management frames to achieve an interoperable implementation of the layer management protocol.

Station Management Frames

Specific station management frames are designated for a number of functions. The frames have fixed fields for limited basic information and self-defining fields for extended information.

Neighborhood information frames are one type of station management frame. These allow a station to transmit its address and a basic station descriptor. Some of the neighborhood information frames make use of a special frame control field format (next-station addressing) that allows a media access control to recognize that it immediately follows the transmitting media access control. One of these, an announcement frame, must be transmitted at regular time intervals. These frames allow the generation of physical ring maps that are useful for a number of management functions and in the detection and signaling of certain fault conditions.

Status information frames are used to request and supply status information about a station. An echo frame is defined for diagnostic purposes. A request-denied frame is specified for responding to an unsupported frame request or an unsupported version identification.

Also defined is a resource allocation frame, which is intended to support a variety of network policies for the allocation of resources. A typical use is for the allocation of the synchronous bandwidth to the stations within a ring.

Two optional additional station management frame types—parameter management frames and status reporting frames—provide the tools for the remote management of an FDDI station. Parameter management frames allow full access to all attributes within an FDDI station and provide the means to write all attributes that are writable. Status reporting frames allow for the reporting of condition and event information. Together, these frame types support a comprehensive remote management capability.

Finally, an extended service frame is specified to handle any new services that might be offered.

Station Management Services to Systems Management. The goal of station management is to provide the interface with open systems interconnection (OSI) systems management as well as all of the facilities required for management of FDDI in an OSI environment. Meeting this goal requires that attribute information be obtainable from any of the managed entities (e.g., media access control) and be suppliable to the management agent process. This information includes such items as current status, counter values, timer values, error information, addresses, and connection information. Also obtained from the managed entities and reported is event information, which includes such things as changes in availability of the managed entity and certain error events.

Station management standard services must also include the capability to provide control over the managed entities on the demand of OSI systems management. These include such capabilities as the disabling or enabling of a managed entity—for example, a media access control or a physical link—as well as the ability to modify the policy settings of the managed entities.

FDDI-II CONCEPTS

FDDI-II is an upward-compatible enhancement of the basic FDDI that adds a circuit-switched service to existing packet capability. A packet service is a service in which the elements of data to be transferred are placed in frames. Packets may vary in length and are self-defining in that each contains delimiters that mark its beginning and end. They also contain an address that specifies the target station. FDDI packets are called frames.

In contrast, a circuit-switched service provides a continuous connection between two or more stations. Instead of using addresses, the connection is established on the basis of a prior agreement, which may have been negotiated using packet messages or established by some other suitable convention known to the stations involved. This prior agreement typically takes the form of knowing the location of time slots that occur regularly relative to a readily recognizable timing marker.

A common timing marker used in North America is the basic systems reference frequency, a 125-microsecond clock used by the public networks. Use of this clock is assumed for FDDI-II. In local FDDI, it is referred to as the cycle clock and is signaled by the JK starting delimiter of the FDDI-II cycle format.

In FDDI-II, a circuit-switched connection is described as n bits beginning at byte M after the cycle clock marker in wideband channel number X. The last descriptor is necessary because FDDI-II has 16 wideband channels that may be independently assigned to either packet-switched or circuit-switched data. This definition allows connections at data rates of all multiples of 8K bps (i.e., $n = 1$) to the 6.144M-bps data rate of a wideband channel. If necessary, multiple wideband channels may be used to accommodate higher data rates.

The data transferred in circuit-switched mode is best described as a data stream. The data rate is appropriate to the service being provided—for example, 64K bps is used for a digital voice data stream. Other data stream rates, even as high as many millions of bits per second in the case of video, are used for other applications. Once a connection is established, the data rate remains constant.

The contrasting nature of packet-switched and circuit-switched data is of interest. Most packet traffic occurs in random quantities at random times; this is referred to as asynchronous traffic. Other packet traffic, occurring regularly in relatively predictable quantities, is referred to as synchronous packet traffic.

Circuit-switched traffic is usually isochronous data, a sequence of precisely numbered and timed digital samples from a sensor (e.g., voice or video). To ensure the accurate, undistorted regeneration of the signal, it is necessary to accurately regenerate the sampling clock information. This is accomplished by precisely calibrating isochronous data with the network cycle clock. The FDDI standard requires that one station (the cycle master) insert a delay for all isochronous data so that the length of the ring (as expressed by the time it takes for a signal to traverse the ring) appears to be an exact multiple of 125 microseconds (the cycle clock rate). FDDI incorporates this delay in the cycle master in such a way that it does not cause any delay in packet traffic. This is essential if an integrated services network is to provide acceptable packet service.

FDDI-II OPERATION

Exhibit III-8-11 shows how FDDI-II is implemented using one additional standard, the hybrid ring control (compare with Exhibit III-8-1). The hybrid ring control becomes the new lowest sublayer of the data link layer, taking its place between media access control and the physical layer. The hybrid ring control multiplexes data between the packet media access control and the isochronous media access control. This requires the packet media access control to be able to transmit and accept data on a noncontinuous basis because packet data is interleaved with isochronous data.

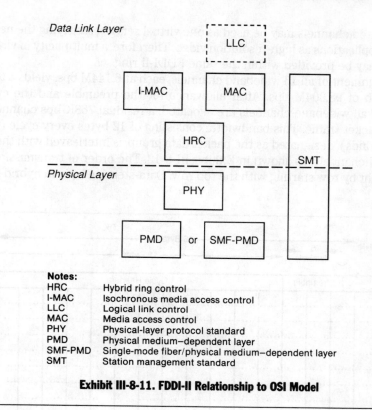

Data Link Layer

LLC

I-MAC   MAC

HRC

SMT

Physical Layer

PHY

PMD   or   SMF-PMD

Notes:
HRC   Hybrid ring control
I-MAC   Isochronous media access control
LLC   Logical link control
MAC   Media access control
PHY   Physical-layer protocol standard
PMD   Physical medium–dependent layer
SMF-PMD   Single-mode fiber/physical medium–dependent layer
SMT   Station management standard

Exhibit III-8-11. FDDI-II Relationship to OSI Model

FDDI-II is a network with 100M bps of bandwidth available. This bandwidth may be devoted entirely to operation as a packet network. Alternatively, portions of this bandwidth, in units of wideband channels, may be dynamically separated for use with circuit-switched data. As many as 16 wideband channels may be assigned. Each wideband channel is 6.144M bps, which is four times the North American and three times the European basic access rate to the telephone network. Wideband channels are full duplex and independently allocatable and deallocatable. In effect, a broadband circuit capability is provided with 16 available channels.

These channels provide a bandwidth division mechanism, which functions between the packet and isochronous traffic with a granularity of 6.144M bps. The allocation of virtual services within the isochronous traffic is allowed with an 8K-bps granularity. Once a station has been assigned a wideband channel (or several channels), it may suballocate the combined bandwidth of the wideband channels as required. This suballocation may be in terms of any multiple of 8K-bps subchannels, including the commonly used 16K-, 32K-, 64K- (B-channel), 384K-, 1,536K-, and 2048K-bps subchannels. Mixtures of these data rates in the same channel are allowed. In addition, the aggregate of any or all of the allocated channels may be used as one virtual service, satisfying the needs of such applications as high-resolution video. Therefore, a multiplicity of virtual circuits may be provided within the same FDDI-II ring.

Assignment of all 16 wideband channels, each at 6.144M bps, yields a total bandwidth of 98.304M bps. After allowance for the preamble and the cycle header, if all wideband channels are allocated, a residual 768K-bps channel is left for packet traffic. This bandwidth, consisting of 12 bytes every cycle (125 microseconds), designated as the packet data group, is interleaved with the 16 wideband channels, as shown in Exhibit III-8-12. The order of transmission is left to right by row starting with the top row. Data-steering logic in hybrid ring

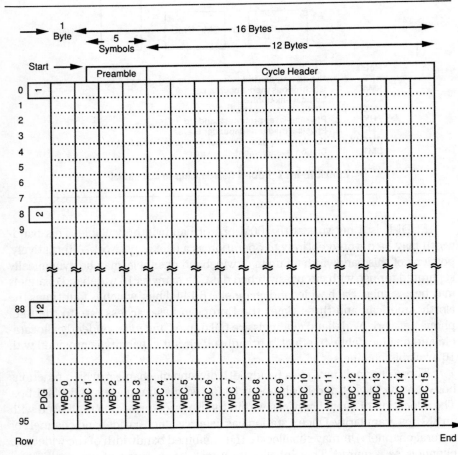

Notes:
PDG   Packet data group
WBC   Wideband channel

Exhibit III-8-12. FDDI-II Cycle Format

control augments the packet data group with the bandwidth of any wideband channels that are not assigned. Each channel is one of the columns in Exhibit III-8-12 and represents a bandwidth of 6.144M bps, or 96 bytes per cycle. This is an efficient system that allows the bandwidth of all unallocated wideband channels to be used by the packet channel. Therefore, with eight (i.e., half) of the wideband channels assigned to isochronous service, 49.92M bps of bandwidth is available for packet traffic.

It should be noted that the interleaved nature of the cycle format as shown in Exhibit III-8-12 results in a relatively uniform stream of data bytes for any of the assigned virtual services.

An FDDI-II ring is initialized in basic (i.e., token) mode and switched to a hybrid mode of operation, combining both packet-switched and circuit-switched data capabilities. This occurs only after a station has negotiated for and won the right to be cycle master and has the synchronous bandwidth allocation required to support it. The cycle master then generates cycles at an 8-kHz rate (every 125 microseconds) and inserts the latency required to maintain an integral number of cycles synchronously on the ring. Alternative designs may allow the ring to be initialized directly in hybrid mode.

The cycle header format is shown in Exhibit III-8-13. It follows the preamble, which is nominally five symbols long. The starting delimiter is the same symbol pair (JK) used as the starting delimiter for frames when FDDI is operating in basic mode. In hybrid mode, frames use an IL symbol as the starting delimiter. The C1 and C2 symbols are used for synchronization control in the transfer of this programming information to the other stations by the cycle master. The cycle-sequence byte provides a modulo 192-cycle sequence count and is used in the ranking process to establish the backup cycle master.

The 16 symbols of programming information (P0 through P15) determine whether the corresponding wideband channel is allocated to packet or isochronous traffic. Therefore, each Pn controls the multiplexing of one of the columns (WBC n) depicted in Exhibit III-8-12. The isochronous maintenance channel byte provides a 64K-bps voice channel for maintenance purposes.

Cycle Header

PA	SD	C1	C2	CS	P0	P1		P15	IMC

Notes:

C1, C2	Synchronization control symbols
CS	Cycle sequence
IMC	Isochronous maintenance channel
P0, P1, P15	Programming information symbols
PA	Preamble
SD	Starting delimiter

Exhibit III-8-13. Cycle Header Format

FDDI-II Priority Levels

Four kinds of traffic can coexist in an FDDI-II ring. Once any wideband channels have been allocated, the isochronous traffic within them has the highest priority.

The second-highest priority is given to synchronous packet traffic, which requires that predictable units of data be delivered at regular intervals. Delivery is guaranteed with a delay not exceeding twice the target token-rotation time. This data may be transmitted following the capture of either a restricted or nonrestricted token.

The bandwidth required for both isochronous and synchronous traffic is allocated from the available FDDI bandwidth. The allocation algorithm must ensure that the total allocation does not exceed 100%. Unallocated bandwidth is used on an as-available basis for asynchronous packet traffic.

The third-highest priority is given to asynchronous traffic operating in restricted token mode. Such traffic may be transmitted upon the capture of either a restricted or nonrestricted token. Cooperating stations may enter a restricted token mode of operation, which allows them to issue and use restricted tokens only after negotiating an agreement using nonrestricted tokens. Restricted token mode operation allows stations to vie for available asynchronous bandwidth on a dialogue basis.

The lowest priority is given to asynchronous traffic that is transmitted only by capturing a nonrestricted token. This mode of operation allows stations to vie for the available asynchronous bandwidth on a single-frame basis.

FDDI-II Applications

FDDI-II expands the range of applications that may be addressed by FDDI rings. An FDDI-II ring may connect high-performance processors, mass-storage systems, and high-performance workstations and perform the backbone function for a number of lower-performance LANs. The same ring may have some of its bandwidth allocated to isochronous services provided by the wideband channels. This isochronous bandwidth may in turn be suballocated into a variety of virtual circuit services (e.g., video, voice, and, possibly, control or sensor data streams). The division of bandwidth between packet and isochronous traffic may be adjusted on the basis of the time of day or other requirements. In practice, no single instance of FDDI-II connects to all the possible types of equipment and certainly not to all the equipment at a large site. Instead, multiple FDDI-II rings coexist with such high-traffic units as processors attaching to multiple FDDI networks.

In a packet-switched mode, FDDI can be a backbone for bridges to a variety of other lower-speed LANs—for example, the various IEEE 802 media access methods. It may also provide a backbone for gateways to the public data networks. In both cases, connections to processors and mass-storage subsystems can be provided.

FDDI-II implementations will most likely follow basic FDDI by one to two years. Committee X3T9.5's specifications require that FDDI-II operate in a basic mode, allowing full interconnectivity and interoperability with FDDI. When FDDI-II chip sets become available, they will provide both FDDI and FDDI-II.

Led by the ASC X3T9.5, this FDDI standards effort reflects the FDDI product implementations of its many supporters. These include many systems manufacturers as well as several semiconductor manufacturers working toward FDDI chip sets. FDDI chip sets available from several chip vendors promise cost-effective implementations of these FDDI standards.

SUMMARY

FDDI has developed as the high-speed LAN of choice. Its success has been the result of a high degree of cooperation between the many factions, each with its own interest, to complete the standard that best satisfies the common goals of all. When goals were radically different, flexibility was incorporated into the standards to allow local optimization of the FDDI ring to satisfy the different sets of goals. As a consequence, FDDI and its progeny (e.g., a version with possibly six times the current data rate) can be expected to dominate high-speed LANs into the 21st century.

Section IV
Interconnectivity Standards and Technologies

J ust as LANs themselves are evolutionary extensions of microcomputers and minicomputers, a similar extension occurs in the life cycle of a typical LAN. Sooner or later, it becomes inappropriate for the LAN to exist as an isolated entity. This section examines LAN interconnectivity, focusing on topics associated with standard interconnectivity architectures and concluding with an examination of gateways into proprietary environments, such as IBM's SNA.

By far the most widely discussed—and for the long term, probably the most important—architecture for interoperability among heterogeneous systems is the International Standards Organization's (ISO's) open systems interconnection (OSI) basic reference model. In fact, most LAN products today conform at least in part to the OSI model. Chapter IV-1, "Overview of OSI," introduces the OSI model and explores the structure, purpose, background, concepts, and principles of OSI. Commonly applied open system protocols are identified for reference.

Such architectures as the OSI model provide merely the framework for interconnection. To provide standardized interconnections, standard protocols and services must be implemented in hardware or software. The most commonly used devices for interconnecting LANs are bridges and routers, which operate at OSI layers 2 and 3 respectively. Another interconnection device, known as a gateway, provides interconnection between LANs and other systems or networks that may or may not use the same protocols as the LAN. Chapter IV-2, "Bridges, Routers, and Gateways—What Is the Difference?" examines these three devices, including their purpose and function as well as trade-offs to be considered in evaluating them for implementation.

Bridges, routers, and gateways represent a hardware implementer's perspective of providing connections between networks. A radically different approach has been developed by the IEEE 802.6 committee in the form of metropolitan area network (MAN) standards. The approach taken by this committee is to incorporate LAN-like functions into a higher-performance network design that is optimized for larger geographical coverage, thus providing a more seamless approach to interconnection and a clear migration path to the broadband Integrated Services Digital Network (ISDN). Chapter IV-3, "The IEEE 802.6 Metropolitan Area Network Distributed-Queue, Dual-Bus Protocol," discusses this approach in depth, detailing the various components of current MAN standards.

Although hardware- and network-oriented solutions perform the physical and logical functions necessary to allow devices on different networks to communicate, the usefulness of such connections is limited unless the upper layers of the OSI model are also implemented. Such implementations are usually found in end-system software and allow applications running in the end systems to communicate with one another, regardless of whether these end systems are on the same network or not. Chapter IV-4, "Higher-Level OSI Standards," discusses the role of layers 5 through 7 and expands this concept to include some standards beyond the scope of OSI. Most current standards and several emerging standards are discussed in considerable detail.

Another interconnection architecture is most commonly known as the TCP/IP (Transmission Control Protocol and Internet Protocol) family of protocols or simply (albeit inappropriately) TCP/IP. This set of protocols grew out of a research project originally funded by the US Department of Defense in 1969. Chapter IV-5, "An Introduction to the DARPA Internet Project and the TCP/IP Protocol Family," gives a brief history of the Internet project, then describes the architecture and each major protocol. Insight into the future of TCP/IP in relation to OSI is also provided.

The most likely scenario for at least the short and intermediate term is the coexistence of TCP/IP and OSI networks, with a gradual shift toward OSI over the long term. Accomplishing this transition with minimal user disruption is not a trivial task. Chapter IV-6, "TCP/IP and OSI," discusses similarities and differences between the two architectures and suggests several methods for accommodating their coexistence.

Many data communications managers face a more immediate problem: integrating personal computer LANs, or perhaps standalone personal computers, into a more global corporate networking environment (e.g., TCP/IP). Chapter IV-7, "Personal Computer Networking in a TCP/IP Environment," examines the issues to be considered. Several alternatives are presented, and the pros and cons of each are discussed.

Finally, a study of interconnectivity strategies in the vast majority of medium-sized to large organizations today cannot be considered complete without an examination of access to and from an IBM environment. Chapter IV-8, "Evaluating Gateways for Network Interconnection," takes an in-depth look at the subject of IBM–to–non-IBM gateways, with particular emphasis on application gateways for file transfer, electronic mail, and terminal access. The chapter provides considerable insight into the issues and trade-offs to be considered for each. Although written specifically about IBM networks, the principles and concepts apply to any gateway situation.

IV-1
Overview of OSI

JAMES W. CONARD

The phrase *open systems* refers to the ability of equipment supplied by different vendors to communicate. Such compatibility is possible if the connected systems conform to the standards of open systems architecture.

Interconnection, however, is not possible with most current network architectures. Because each vendor's network system has its own structure, it is usually impossible to directly connect systems supplied by different vendors. If this situation is left uncorrected, an overwhelming number of systems will be able to communicate only with their own type. Interconnectivity is a solution that benefits both users and vendors. Users are not tied to a particular vendor, and easier interconnection expands distributed processing and allows vendors to access a larger market. These potential benefits fueled the development, under the auspices of the International Standards Organization (ISO), of a standard network architecture model that would facilitate open systems interconnection (OSI). This model, identified as the reference model for open systems interconnection and promulgated as International Standard 7498, is significantly affecting the design of new systems and networks. The model has also been adopted by the International Telephone and Telegraph Consultative Committee (CCITT) as Recommendation X.200.

THE OPEN SYSTEMS ENVIRONMENT

Network managers should understand that the OSI reference model does not specify a particular network systems architecture. The OSI model is simply a framework or skeleton that permits standard connection procedures to be defined. These procedures, defined as protocols, enable diverse users to interconnect and exchange information regardless of the particular network system or vendor used.

Conformance with the reference model neither requires nor implies a particular implementation. It simply indicates that the behavior of a system as perceived by another system is predictable. Systems that agree to conform to the principles of the model and are thus able to exchange information with one another are open systems.

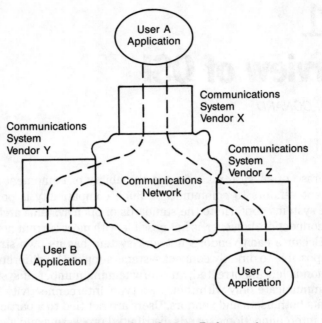

Exhibit IV-1-1. Open Systems Environment

Exhibit IV-1-1 is a simplified version of the open systems environment. A user may be a computer, a terminal, a process, a human operator, or any autonomous entity that has the intelligence required to process and communicate information. The interconnected systems may be but—most important—need not be products of the same vendor. The model requires only that the system be connected to a physical communications medium through which access can be gained to one or more other systems. The medium can be as simple as a point-to-point communications line or as complex as interconnected private, local, and packet-switched networks.

In this environment, the open systems reference model should:

- Serve as a globally accepted logical structure for communications requirements.
- Act as a framework and reference for the continued development of new services and protocols.
- Facilitate more extensive interconnection between users by encouraging the development of compatible communications features.
- Provide the flexibility needed to accommodate evolving technology and requirements.

The model currently is used worldwide as a framework for developing new communications services. Significant progress has been achieved in the availability of compatible protocols at all layers of the architecture; these are discussed in a later section of this chapter. Before the model is examined in detail, it is helpful to review the concepts on which open systems architecture was based.

Layered Architecture

The open systems model is based on the concept of a layered, or partitioned, architecture. The partitioning approach, which has long been used to develop structured solutions to complex problems, segments a problem into functional groupings that are easy to comprehend.

The partitioning approach to the communications problem resulted in seven distinct partitions, called layers. Each layer possesses a unique set of attributes and interacts with its adjacent layers. The seven layers are illustrated in Exhibit IV-1-2 as a vertical structure that exists in each connected system.

Basis of Development. Three principles governed the number of layers that were chosen:

- The creation of just enough layers to ensure that developers can easily understand and implement the structure without complicating the task.
- The minimization of the number of interactions across layer boundaries.
- The creation of a layer on the basis of a previous successful grouping.

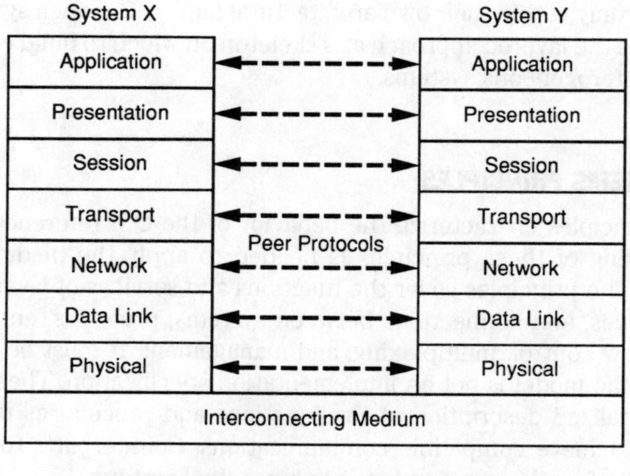

Exhibit IV-1-2. The Seven-Layer OSI Architecture

Layer Definitions. The major functions of each layer are defined as follows:

- Physical layer—Provides for the transparent transfer of a bit stream over a physical circuit.
- Data link layer—Is responsible for the reliable delivery of information over a point-to-point or multipoint link. The link layer supervises the interchange of both link control data and user information.
- Network layer—Selects and manages a route chosen from among the available data links arranged as a network.
- Transport layer—Ensures end-to-end information transfer. The transport layer isolates the user from any concern for the actual movement of the information.
- Session layer—Coordinates the communication between cooperating application processes.
- Presentation layer—Ensures compatible syntax among the communicating processes by adjusting data structures, formats, and codes.
- Application layer—Provides a window by which the user gains access to the communications services provided by the architecture.

The OSI layers are often referred to by their numerical position in the architecture—for example, the physical layer is level 1, and the application layer is level 7.

It should be noted that communications systems have been based on layered approaches for years. More recently, vendors have referred to their total solutions to the distributed processing problem as layered network architectures. Examples include IBM's SNA and Digital Equipment Corp's DECnet. These achitectures were basically homogeneous because they were totally compatible only within their own architectural family. The open systems architecture uses the layered approach as a skeleton on which to build compatibility between heterogeneous systems.

OPEN SYSTEMS PRINCIPLES

Various principles characterize the behavior of the OSI reference model. An understanding of these principles is needed to apply the model to specific situations. The principles cover the functions and services of layers, access to those services, and connections between systems, protocols, and such attributes as flow control, multiplexing, and management. It must be emphasized again that the model is not an implementation specification. These principles are a generalized description of the functions and procedures that must be present to achieve compatible communications. Counterparts to these principles can be found in varying forms in any actual system.

Layers and Entities

The reference model is based on the previously described concept of layered architecture. Each system comprises a logical series of successive layers. Each layer, as illustrated in Exhibit IV-1-3, consists of a group of functions designed to provide a set of services related to the mission of that layer. For example, the functions that perform data link control are referred to as the data link layer.

An entity is a group of functions for a particular task. An example is a bit-oriented control protocol within the data link layer. Entities can also be viewed as state-driven machines: they accept input and produce output.

Each layer is bounded by the layers above and below it. The entities in a layer provide a set of defined services to the layer above. In providing these services, a layer uses the services of the layer below. Each layer effectively isolates the layer above from details of the underlying layers; thus, a particular layer's characteristics can change without affecting the rest of the system, provided the services do not change. For example, a character-oriented link control can be replaced with a bit-oriented protocol. In general, a layer is called the N layer, the layer immediately above it is referred to as the $(N + 1)$ layer, and the layer immediately below it is the $(N - 1)$ layer (see Exhibit IV-1-3).

Services and Primitives

The services of the N layer are made available to the $(N + 1)$ layer at the upper boundary of the N layer. The entire structure can be viewed as a group of

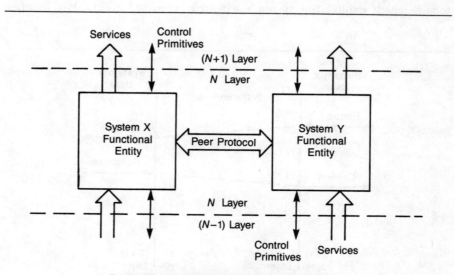

Exhibit IV-1-3. Concept of an Architectural Layer

value-added services, with each layer adding value to the services of the underlying layer until the total communications service is made available to the application process.

An N layer's services, including the movement of user information, are selected and controlled across the boundary of the $(N + 1)$ layer by control functions called primitives. A primitive is a request for a service or an indication that a request has or has not been executed; it represents the input command to an entity. Primitives may be accompanied by parameters; for example, a request to establish a link connection may be accompanied by parameters that specify the address and the quality of service desired. Four generic primitives have been defined:

- Request—This primitive is a command to perform a service, such as establishing a connection or delivering data.
- Indicate—This primitive informs the $(N + 1)$ layer that a significant event has occurred.
- Response—This primitive signifies that the indication has been accepted.
- Confirm—This primitive informs the $(N + 1)$ layer that the service requested has been executed.

Exhibit IV-1-4 illustrates the typical relationship between OSI primitives.

Peer Protocols

Peer layers are equally ranked layers in connected systems that communicate with one another by means of peer protocols (see Exhibit IV-1-3). Peer protocols, which exhibit the system's external behavior, are the key to open

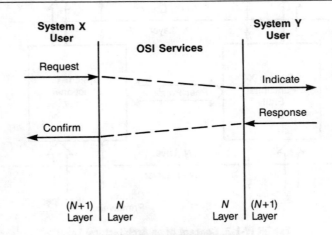

Exhibit IV-1-4. OSI Primitives

systems compatibility. Peer protocols are the subject of standardization within the framework of the reference model. Examples of peer protocols include high-level data link control (HDLC) at the data link layer, RS-232 at the physical layer, and the X.25 packet procedures at the network layer.

Service Access Points

The services of an entity within an N layer are available at a service access point, located at the boundary of the $(N + 1)$ layer. As illustrated in Exhibit IV-1-5, a service access point is the $(N + 1)$ layer's interface point to the peer layer in a connected system. Service access points are known by a name to the $(N + 1)$ layer and by an address to the N layer. To avoid the argument as to whether a name is also an address, the network manager should view the service access point as simply the point or location in a system at which a known service is available. Mapping of layer-by-layer addresses can be implemented with mapping tables or hierarchical address structures.

Connections

A connection is the link between the service access points of two communicating peer entities. Logically, the connection appears to behave as though the two peers were directly connected, but in actuality, the fact that the underlying layers are providing services to establish and support the connection is invisible to the layer using the connection. In other words, each functional layer views the entire underlying structure, including the communications facilities, as a black box that provides services and has input and output at the service access points. Exhibit IV-1-6 illustrates the black box from the transport layer's point of view. To the user, the entire architecture simply represents the set of

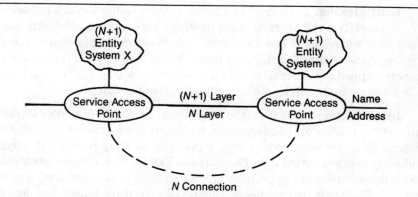

Exhibit IV-1-5. Service Access Points and Connections

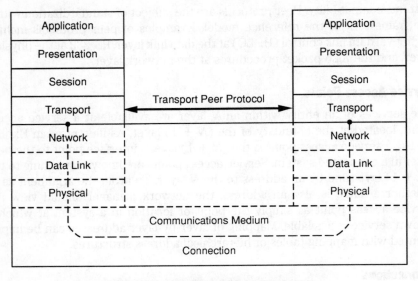

Exhibit IV-1-6. Black Box View of OSI Services

communications services that provides a path over which information may be moved between cooperating applications. The individual layers, intermediate systems, nodes, and facilities are invisible to these applications.

Other Attributes

In addition to the principles already discussed, the reference model recognizes additional functional capabilities that may be characteristic of a layered process.

Multiplexing. An N layer may provide multiplexing services between the $(N - 1)$ and $(N + 1)$ layers. Upward multiplexing can more efficiently use the lower layer's services or can distribute input to several higher-layer processes (i.e., resource sharing). In upward multiplexing, one $(N - 1)$ service access point is mapped into several $(N + 1)$ service access points. The reverse process, called downward multiplexing or splitting, is also possible.

Intermediate Nodes. In the OSI (or any) architectural model, systems can serve as originators of information, recipients of information, or both. Other systems (e.g., network nodes) may serve only as relay points, gateways, or bridges to another network. As illustrated in Exhibit IV-1-7, these intermediate nodes need implement only those layers required to perform their intended function. The layers that are needed are usually the three lowest: physical, link, and network. The network layer (i.e., an internet or gateway sublayer) would

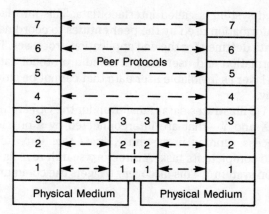

Exhibit IV-1-7. Intermediate Node or Relay

handle the routing and switching needed to provide an end-to-end connection between the transport peer layers in the cooperating systems. It is important to note that for the layers required in the node, the peer-to-peer protocols operate only between the originating, or destination, system and the nearest intermediate node. Higher-layer peer protocols operate end to end.

Management Aspects. Because the management of all these layered functions is system dependent, the reference model does not specify how such management is to be accomplished. The reference model does, however, recognize three kinds of management activities associated with the architecture. A system management function is responsible for activation, deactivation, monitoring, and resource control. This function is considered to reside at the application layer. An application management function is needed to interface with the system management process in dealing directly with user applications. Finally, there are layer management processes that reside at each layer and interact with the systems management process.

A layer that is not needed for a particular situation is neither present nor activated by the management function. The services of the next lower layer, however, must be mapped to the requirements of the service user.

OPEN SYSTEMS DATA TRANSFER

Several kinds of information and data units flow between layers and between connected systems in the OSI architectural model. To transfer data between systems, the N layer interacts with the $(N - 1)$ layer through the use of interface control information (i.e., the primitives and associated parameters). The information that is transferred across the layer boundary for transmission to the connected system is called interface data. This interface data may be peer protocol information used by the peer entities to coordinate their activity or actual user data destined for the end application processes. The combination of protocol information and user data is called a protocol data unit, which is treated by each layer as inviolable user data that cannot be altered or contaminated in any way.

Exhibit IV-1-8 illustrates data transfer under the OSI architecture through two systems—X and Y—that are interconnected by a physical medium. An application process running in system X finds that it requires access to a process or file to complete its task. A directory search reveals that the needed file is available on system Y. This discovery triggers the communication activity.

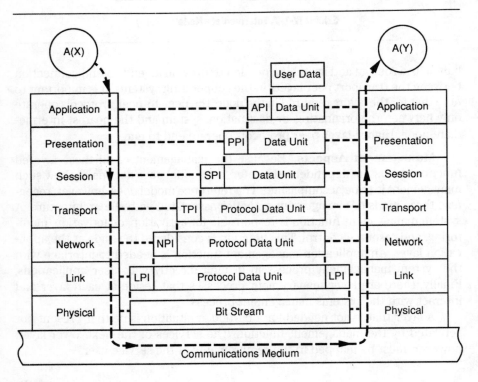

Notes:

API	Application protocol information
A(X)	Application X
A(Y)	Application Y
LPI	Link protocol information
NPI	Network protocol information
PPI	Presentation protocol information
SPI	Session protocol information
TPI	Transport protocol information

Exhibit IV-1-8. OSI Data Transfer

Communication activity under the OSI model usually occurs in phases. A connect phase establishes the connection. Once the connection is established, the data transfer phase allows user information to be exchanged. When the exchange is completed, a clearing phase takes down the logical connection.

In the example in Exhibit IV-1-8, the need for access to system Y triggered application layer activity in system X, in turn activating the presentation and session layers. Their services were requested by means of interface primitives. The transport layer accepts a **request connect System Y** primitive. The transport layer selects a network layer entity with the required capability (e.g., public data network access) and issues a **request connect** primitive accompanied by necessary parameters (e.g., the network address of the host associated with system Y). The network layer calls on the data link layer to establish a logical link to system Y or the nearest intermediate point. In turn, the link layer calls on the physical layer to provide a bit transport mechanism to system Y.

Because at this point the process is in the connect phase, the protocol data units consist entirely of peer protocol information. When the bit stream transits the communications facilities and arrives at system Y, the reverse process occurs, with each layer acting on the protocol information received from a peer layer in system X. The upward-flowing **indicate** primitives reach the application layer, and the required process or file is accessed. Given that access by system X is authorized, system Y responds; this response flows through the system, arriving at the requesting process in system X as a **confirm connect System Y** primitive.

Following the connect phase, the system enters the data transfer phase. The user application information logically flows across the layer boundaries. The data is usually moved in queues or buffers, directed by the **request send** primitives. In turn, each layer may add any required protocol information and pass the complete unit to the next lower layer. This process continues downward in the source system and upward in the destination system until the user data arrives at the required application process. When data transfer is complete, the clearing phase clears the connection.

LAYER DESCRIPTIONS AND PROTOCOLS

Although the specific layered structure of the reference model was chosen after much deliberation among industry experts, it is not necessarily the best, or the only possible, structure. The decisions concerning the number of layers, their placement, and their boundaries were based on a set of principles and experience.

Each layer, beginning with the lowest one and working up to layers with added value, is described in terms of the functions it implements and the services it provides. The existing protocols that provide these services and those that are planned or being developed are also identified.

The Physical Layer

The lowest layer of the OSI architecture is the physical layer, which provides the link layer with services associated with acquiring, maintaining, and disconnecting the physical circuits that form the connecting communication path. Physical layer protocols handle the electrical and mechanical interface as well as the procedural requirements of the interconnection medium. The physical layer is the rough equivalent of the traditional data terminal equipment–to–data communications equipment (DTE-DCE) interface. The physical layer is responsible for bit synchronization and the identification of a signal element as a 1 or a 0. A protocol data unit at this level is a bit.

Typical protocols at the physical layer include RS-232, the RS-449 family, CCITT X.25 and X.21 facility interfaces, other CCITT V and X series recommendations, and the physical aspects of the IEEE 802 media access control protocols for LANs.

The Data Link Layer

Excluding the physical layer, the link layer's protocols and services may be most familiar to those in the data communications industry. Data link control protocols include the character-oriented binary synchronous communications; ANSI X3.28; the more recent bit-oriented advanced data communications control procedure and its international counterpart, HDLC; X.25 link access protocol-B; ISDN link access protocol-D; and the IEEE 802 logical link control.

Link layer services relate to the reliable interchange of data across a point-to-point or multipoint data link, which has been established at the physical layer. Link layer protocols manage the establishment, control, and termination of logical link connections as well as control the flow of user data, supervise recovery from errors and abnormal conditions, and acquire and maintain character and block or frame synchronization.

The Network Layer

The network layer's services, which are associated with moving user data through a network with concatenated data links and multiple routes available between points, include routing, switching, sequencing of data, flow control, and error recovery. Although such functions as flow control and error recovery appear to duplicate those at the data link level, they are concerned with end-to-end network connections spanning multiple data links.

Network layer protocols isolate the transport layer from concern over routing and switching considerations. These protocols select and control logical paths and connections between user end points on a network. A virtual circuit through a public data network is an example.

Internet protocols control routing and recovery between network nodes and gateway protocols, which control data transfer between connected networks. These protocols constitute another important network layer role.

The CCITT X.25 packet layer is the best-known network layer protocol for packet-switched networks. The X.21 is used for circuit-switched networks. The Department of Defense (DoD) has developed an internet control protocol known as the Internet Protocol (IP). Other examples of network protocols include the CCITT Q.931 network layer protocol and the ISO 8473 connectionless internetwork protocol.

The Transport Layer

The transport layer is the highest layer directly associated with the movement of data through the network. It provides a universal transparent transfer mechanism for use by the higher layers, which represent the users of the communications service. The transport layer is expected to optimize the use of available resources while meeting the requirements of the users.

Transport protocols are responsible for the end-to-end integrity of data exchange. Because the transport layer must bridge the gap between services provided by the underlying network and those required by the higher layers, classes of transport protocols ranging from the very simple to the very complex have been developed. Simple transport layers can be used when the network provides a high-quality, reliable service; a complex transport protocol is used when the underlying service cannot provide the required level of service. In effect, the transport layer duplicates recovery mechanisms that should have been provided by the lower layers.

The ISO has promulgated international standard 8073 as a transport protocol. This standard defines five classes of protocol, ranging from a simple class 0 to a complex class 4. Another transport protocol is the transmission control protocol developed by the DoD and now finding wide application in commercial environments.

The Session Layer

A session occurs when two application processes are bound into a cooperative relationship for a period of time. The session layer provides two categories of services: administrative and dialogue. An administrative service handles the establishment (i.e., binding) and release (i.e., unbinding) of a connection between two presentation entities. Sessions are established when an application process requests access to another application process.

After a session is established, dialogue services are used to control and supervise the actual data exchange. A single session can span several transport connections, or several consecutive sessions can be held on a single transport connection.

Current session protocols include ISO 8327, CCITT X.225, European Computer Manufacturing Association (ECMA) 75, and CCITT T.62, which is intended for use in teletex services.

The Presentation Layer

Presentation layer services allow an application to properly interpret the information being transferred. They are concerned with the translation, transformation, formatting, and syntax of the information—functions that may be required to adapt the information handling characteristics of one application process to another application process. Examples include code translation, structuring of data for display on screens, format control for printers, and virtual terminal protocols.

Work on formal presentation protocols is well under way. ISO has a draft international standard presentation protocol identified as DIS 8823. The syntactical representation of data is being defined in DIS 8824 and 8825. CCITT has described the presentation protocol for message handling systems in X.409 and for teletex in T.61.

The Application Layer

Because it is the highest layer of the OSI architecture, the application layer provides its services to the application processes. Applications do not reside in the application layer; the layer is simply the window through which the applications gain access to the services provided by the communications architecture.

The application layer provides communications services most directly comprehensible to the user. These include identifying the cooperating processes, authenticating the communicant, verifying authority, determining availability of resource, and ensuring agreement on syntax.

Work on the formal definition of application-layer service descriptions and protocols is progressing rapidly. It is likely that many application layer protocols will meet the needs of a specific application and user. The application layer can be visualized as a user-specific element to the application process, as an application-specific element for such functions as file and job transfer, business data interchange, or virtual terminal operation, and as a common element consisting of generally useful functions.

Standardization efforts at the application layer include ISO's file transfer and management (DIS 8571), job transfer and manipulation (DIS 8832), and virtual terminal protocol (DIS 9040); these are called specific application service elements. Common elements are being defined by ISO as DIS 8649 and 8650. CCITT and ECMA are also active in the application layer work.

STATUS AND INDUSTRY ACCEPTANCE

Great progress has been made toward establishing an open systems architecture. The architectural model has become an international standard (ISO 7498). Because such standards bodies as ISO represent users, vendors, carriers, and national and international governments, consensus on a globally acceptable communications architecture is a highly significant event.

The reference model is already finding its way into vendor product lines. Many new architectures are designed to be compatible with the OSI model. Other vendors are developing systems under the OSI framework. As agreement is reached on the higher-layer protocols, products including or emulating these protocols can be expected.

Open systems compatibility is already widely available at the lower layers of the architecture. For example, the CCITT X.25 public data network interface spans the physical, link, and network layers.

The transport layer may be the most critical layer from a communications compatibility point of view. Compatibility ensures that data can be moved transparently and reliably between systems without regard for the vendor label on the systems. Standard transport protocols should soon find their way into available vendor products.

Some in the industry argue that true compatibility will never be achieved above the transport layer. Others believe that the entire set of communications services encompassing all seven layers can, and will, be executable. The truth probably lies somewhere in between. It is likely that no single protocol will evolve that will satisfy all of the diverse session, presentation, and application requirements. These higher layers will probably be sliced vertically into application-specific protocols (e.g., videotex and electronic mail). These application-specific protocols could then be transformed to silicon chips.

Functional open architectures, which can select a set of protocols from the open systems repertoire to meet a specific generic application, have been developed. Examples include the manufacturing automation protocol (MAP) and the technical office protocol (TOP). MAP and TOP are significant because they represent actual user acceptance and application of the principles of open systems interconnection.

SUMMARY

The ISO reference model provides the network manager with a powerful tool for planning, designing, procuring, and implementing communications networks. Its framework adds a much-needed discipline for controlling the proliferation of incompatible network architectures and protocols.

Network managers should be aware of the role that an open systems architecture can play in their environments. The reference model, however, is only a baseline reference and not a specific solution. Its value lies in identifying areas in which the industry can agree on standard interconnect and access procedures and in providing a commonly understood partitioned framework for discussion and planning that can be translated into a compatible and cohesive whole to satisfy user requirements.

IV-2
Bridges, Routers, and Gateways— What Is the Difference?

NATHAN J. MULLER

Initially, LANs were used to link common sets of hardware. With their increasing popularity among organizations, coupled with the widespread availability of the Transmission Control Protocol and Internet Protocol (TCP/IP), LANs began to be used for linking diverse hardware and operating systems. Repeaters, bridges, routers, and gateways facilitate networking; bridges, routers, and gateways relieve host computers of the processing-intensive tasks of protocol conversion and routing information to appropriate locations. Because these devices can be shared among many users, they contribute substantially to lowering the cost of networking.

BENEFITS

Each interconnection device is designed to operate in conjunction with a different layer of the open systems interconnection (OSI) reference model (see Exhibit IV-2-1), which provides specific levels of network functions. When properly integrated with the LAN, bridges, routers, and gateways offer the following advantages:

- Extended network reach.
- Simplified cabling.
- Improved overall performance.
- Additional configuration flexibility.
- Enhanced security and maintenance through partitioning.
- Simpler network management.
- Reduced operating costs.

INTERCONNECTION BASICS

The most basic interconnection device used with LANs is the repeater. A repeater regenerates a signal, allowing it to traverse a longer distance without

Layer	Function	Description	Interconnection Device
7	Application	Selects appropriate service for application	Gateway
6	Presentation	Provides code conversion data reformatting	Gateway
5	Session	Coordinates interaction between end-application processes	Gateway
4	Transport	Provides end-to-end data integrity and quality of service	Gateway
3	Network	Switches and routes information	Router
2	Data Link	Transfers units of information to the other end of the physical link	Bridge
1	Physical	Transmission onto the network	Repeater

Exhibit IV-2-1. Functional Abilities of Repeaters, Bridges, Routers, and Gateways in Relation to the OSI Reference Model

becoming distorted. For this reason, the repeater is most often used to inter-connect LANs that are close together, typically in the same building. The repeater operates at the lowest level of the OSI reference model—the physical layer—and can be used only to link LANs with the same protocols. It cannot control or route information, and it does not have management capabilities. In addition, repeaters are limited to connecting only two or three LAN segments, with the total bus length not to exceed 1,500 m. Beyond that, the delay becomes too long, which causes problems because most networking protocols require messages to be answered within a set time.

Bridges, which operate at the data link layer of the OSI model, interconnect LANs that have the same type of operating system. Therefore, the bridge does not have to perform protocol conversion. In this case, the bridge simply looks at the packet address to see where it is going and then forwards data packets destined for an address beyond the local network to other networks. For example, a bridge can interconnect DECnet, TCP/IP, or Xerox Network Ser-vices (XNS) networks but cannot ensure that users on one network can com-municate with users on another. That level of performance is provided by a router.

A router has more intelligence capabilities than a bridge because it can handle several levels of addressing. It keeps a map of the entire network, including all the devices operating at or below its own protocol level. Whereas a bridge only checks the packet address to see if it is bound for another network, a router refers to its internetwork map, examines the status of the different paths to the destination, and chooses the best method of getting the packet to the addressee. Routers are protocol dependent—that is, they can be used only to link LANs that have identical protocols.

A gateway operates at the highest levels of the OSI reference model. It interconnects networks or media with different architectures by processing protocols to allow a device on one type of LAN to communicate with a device on another type. Therefore, a Systems Network Architecture (SNA) gateway, for example, may be used to interconnect a microcomputer network to an IBM SNA mainframe. The gateway, then, acts both as a conduit over which computers communicate and as a translator among the various protocol layers.

Additional Interconnection Methods

Not all products fit neatly into these basic categories of LAN products. Many vendors have developed hybrid products that include functions traditionally associated with one or another of these categories. Therefore, an intelligent gateway device may include some attributes commonly associated with bridges and routers. Another device may operate as a gateway but default to operation as a bridge under certain circumstances.

Single-unit bridges and routers (i.e., brouters) are really bridges that include some router capabilities. Depending on the protocol or packet, the data is bridged or routed through the LAN. A combination router-terminal server is called a trouter. This device gives small work groups the ability to connect to LANs, wide area networks (WANs), modems, printers, and other microcomputers without purchasing both a terminal server and a router (see Exhibit IV-2-2).

To further complicate matters, the terms *gateway, bridge,* and *router* are rapidly falling into generic use; they no longer relate strictly to LANs. Some vendors of simple controllers and front-end processors are calling their prod-

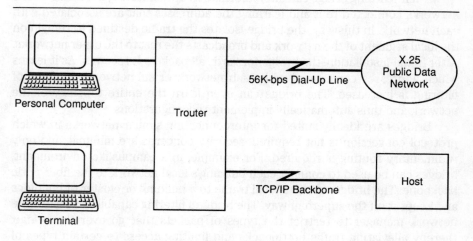

Note:
TCP/IP   Transmission Control Protocol and Internet Protocol

Exhibit IV-2-2. Trouters Combine Terminal Server and Routing Functions

ucts gateways or bridges. Interexchange carriers are referring to their digital access and cross-connect systems as gateways to public network services. Likewise, local exchange carriers are touting Centrex as a gateway, and multiplexer vendors are describing their equipment as bridges between public and private networks.

The confusion does not end there; what the Department of Defense calls a gateway on its Internet is merely a router in OSI terminology, whereas Novell's NetWare bridge is the equivalent of a router in OSI. Nonetheless, these specialized interconnection devices are necessary, both to prevent the host from becoming a throughput bottleneck and to off-load precious computing resources, which can then be devoted to applications processing.

BRIDGES

Although the terms *gateway* and *bridge* are often used interchangeably, there is a subtle difference: a gateway connects dissimilar networks, and a bridge connects similar networks. A bridge may connect two or more LANs in the same building or LANs that are farther apart. Local bridges can operate at 16M bps; remote bridges typically operate from 4.8K bps to 1.544M bps, depending on the type of leased line used (see Exhibit IV-2-3).

Bridges perform minor routing by using a hierarchical routing feature that filters local data traffic without affecting local network performance. The bridge receives packets of data, scans only to the network address, and passes the packets to the appropriate network, where they are ultimately routed to the intended addressee.

A self-learning bridge can filter information by monitoring the traffic on the networks connected to it and learning the addresses that are associated with each network. In this way, the bridge isolates the traffic destined to remain on the local segment of the network and broadcasts the rest to the other networks. After initial installation, the bridge forwards all packets it receives. As it learns which addresses correspond with each network or subnetwork, the level of filtering is increased. The bridge can even learn the entire topology of the network and thus automatically implement reconfigurations.

Bridges are ideally suited for interconnecting similar networks in which protocol conversion is not required, security concerns are minimal, and only rudimentary routing is required. For example, in a campuslike environment, bridges can be used to connect each building's local network to the fiber-optic backbone. The bridge restricts local traffic to a building or cluster of buildings and keeps it off the superhighway. The bridge's filtering capabilities enable the network manager to restrict the types of packets that go over the bridge, thereby alleviating traffic bottlenecks and limiting access to certain types of network resources.

Backbone traffic does not enter a building's local traffic unless it is addressed to a node there. The use of bridges at this level provides an effective

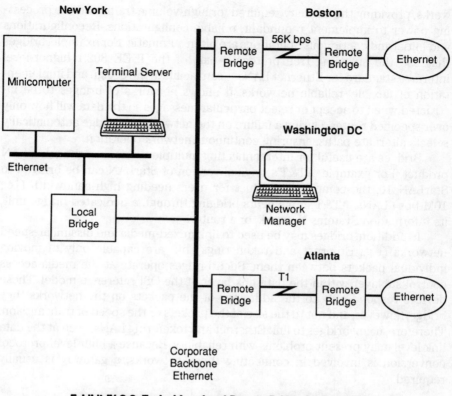

Exhibit IV-2-3. Typical Local and Remote Bridge Configurations

way of expanding the capacity and physical reach of computer resources while minimizing the performance interconnection costs at higher levels.

Subnetworks

Many organizations find bridges useful in dividing large LANs into discrete subnetworks that are easier to control and manage. Bridges can be used to group similar devices, protocols, and transmission media into communities of interest. Each community of interest constitutes a subnetwork. Such partitioning can yield many advantages—for example, the elimination of congestion and the improvement of response time for the entire network. In addition, partitioning can make adding, moving, and changing devices on the network much easier because only the effects of these activities on the subnetwork must be considered. Finally, partitioning facilitates diagnosis and isolation of problems and enhances overall security.

More sophisticated bridges support multiple bridging between two networks, providing the capacity required for high-volume traffic and the processing power to implement redundant, reliable configurations. Reconfigurations and initial and continuous operations are often automatic. For example, bridges that use the spanning tree protocol—part of the IEEE 802.1 higher-level interface standard for Ethernet LANs—can facilitate the design and implementation of flexible, reliable networks. It allows networks of bridges to be instructed when to accept or reject particular messages so the data will flow only over specified routes. During a failure on the network, the bridge automatically selects alternate paths, ensuring continuous network operation.

Bridges are useful for interconnecting multiple versions of the same LAN product. For example, AT&T's original version of StarLAN can be bridged to StarLAN 10, the company's product for users needing high-bandwidth (i.e., 10M-bps) LANs. AT&T implements bridging through a dedicated bridge unit, its Information Systems Network, or a router.

In addition, bridges may be used to link mixed-media and dissimilar-speed networks (e.g., Ethernet and token rings) but are capable only of moving individual packets between them. Such bridges operate at the media-access control sublayer within the data link layer of the OSI reference model. These devices respond only to the addresses of the packets on the networks they bridge, however, and not to the size of the packets or the speed of transmission. Therefore, using bridges to link Ethernet and token-ring LANs, even at the data link level, may present problems with reliability. Because a high-level protocol conversion is involved in connecting these networks, a gateway is usually required.

Hardware Configurations

Bridges are available in a variety of hardware configurations, including standalone bridges, plug-in bridges to multiplexers, and hybrid devices that include the functions of routers. One advantage of standalone products is portability; because they are complete, self-contained units, they can be moved wherever needed with minimal disruption to other network components. Disadvantages include bulkiness, the consumption of large quantities of power, and the use of a disproportionate share of available space in equipment rooms. In addition, standalone units usually are not expandable. To interconnect remote LANs, they require a dedicated connection to a remote bridge, by way of a leased line or a dedicated port on a multiplexer, regardless of how much the line is used.

In addition to the obvious advantages of reductions in cost, power consumption, and space, a bridge that is an integral part of a T1 multiplexer allows bandwidth allocation to either LAN-to-LAN communications or to voice or data communications. A T1 multiplexer with card-mounted bridges can allocate between 9.6K bps and 1.5M bps of bandwidth to the point-to-point LAN connection. Any remaining bandwidth may be allocated to voice and data.

The management systems of standalone bridges can graphically represent the network topology at a workstation, collect network performance statistics, receive alerts from other bridges and links, and allow the operator to remotely disable faulty network elements. It is also possible for network managers to control access, set priorities for passing data over the network, and segment the network for maintenance and expansion purposes.

There are advantages to integrating the bridge into the multiplexer in wide area networking environments. The multiplexer's existing management system can monitor and collect error and use statistics from the bridge, thereby simplifying overall network management. In addition, this arrangement eliminates unnecessary start-up costs, because a separate bridge management software package typically sells for $6,000 to $10,000.

The combination channel service–data service unit is used to link remote LANs at T1 speeds. Because T1 provides 1.544M bps of bandwidth throughput, users can break the traffic jam that inevitably results when high-speed (e.g., 10M-bps) LANs attempt to pass data to remote LANs over dial-up telephone lines equipped with relatively slow (e.g., 2.4K-bps to 19.2K-bps) modems (see Exhibit IV-2-4).

The channel service unit functions as the front end of a circuit to equalize the received signal, filter both the transmitted and received waveforms, and

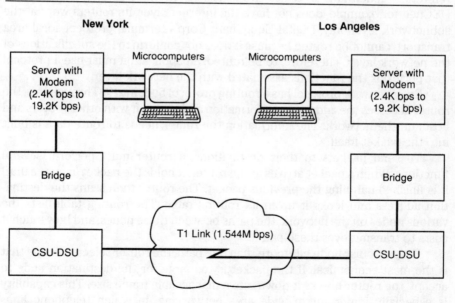

Note:
CSU-DSU   Channel service unit–data service unit

Exhibit IV-2-4. High-Speed Bridge Interconnection of a Wide Area Network Using T1

interact with the carrier's test facilities. The data service unit element transforms the encoded waveform from alternate mark inversion (AMI) to a standard required business equipment interface (e.g., RS-232 or V.35). In addition, it performs such functions as data regeneration, control signaling, synchronous sampling, and timing.

Depending on the complexity of the network and the protocols used, a hybrid bridge and router unit (i.e., a brouter) may be appropriate. Such devices typically house two main boards: one makes intelligent routing decisions, and the other performs the filtering function of a bridge. For example, if the user wants to select a pure bridging operation to achieve maximum packet throughput, the routing function of the hybrid device can be suppressed by sending the appropriate command.

ROUTERS

A router is similar to a bridge in that both provide filtering and bridging functions across the network. Routers, however, offer more sophisticated network management and traffic control capabilities. In terms of complexity, a router falls between a bridge and a gateway.

The function of a router is to join LANs at the network layer of the OSI reference model. This layer has two levels: internet and subnetwork. Because DECnet, for example, does not have the internet layer, its routers work at the subnetwork level only. Digital Equipment Corp's terminal protocol, local area transport, cannot be routed because it does not conform to the specifications of the network layer. Therefore, to be routed, an application must use a protocol that performs the functions associated with the network layer.

Each network protocol has a routing protocol built into it. Through this, the router accesses the addressing information and shares it with other routers and hosts on the network. The information the router needs to route data is built into the packet itself.

To send packets to their destinations, a router must perform several functions. When a packet arrives at the router, it holds the packet in queue until it is finished handling the previous packet. The router then scans the destination address and looks it up in its routing table. The routing table lists the various nodes on the network, the paths between those nodes, and how much it costs to transmit over these paths.

If a particular node has more than one path, the router selects the one that is the most economical. If the packet is too large for the destination node to accept, the router breaks it down into a manageable frame size. This capability is especially important in wide area networking, in which telephone lines provide the link between LANs. With smaller packets, there is less chance that the data will be corrupted by noise on the line. Even if that occurs and a retransmission is necessary, the smaller packet size reduces information delay.

Routing Types

There are two types of routing: static and dynamic. In static routing, the network manager must configure the routing table. Once set, the paths on the network never change. This might be acceptable for a LAN confined to a small geographic area, but it is not practical for wide area networking. Although a static router issues an alarm when it recognizes that a link has gone down, it does not automatically reconfigure the routing table to reroute traffic. A dynamic router, on the other hand, automatically reconfigures the routing table and recalculates the least expensive path. Some routers even rebalance the traffic load.

Because routers are protocol specific, more than one router may be needed to support all of an organization's networking needs. Some multiprotocol routers can route several protocols simultaneously, thereby approaching the function level of gateways.

Routers can link failures and congested nodes, which is critical for applications that cannot tolerate unnecessary delays or prolonged outages. Bypasses are facilitated by the ability of routers to share information with each other through the OSI network layer. Bridges cannot do this, because they do not have access to the network level through a routing protocol. Therefore, when one bridge gets overloaded, the others will never know about it.

GATEWAYS

Because organizations generally consist of specialized work groups, different networks may be needed to meet the requirements of different users. To link different networks (e.g., Ethernet and AppleTalk), a server is equipped with circuit cards for each network; the server then performs the necessary protocol conversion. When a device performs protocol conversions that allow information to be exchanged among different types of networks, it is called a gateway.

As organizations become more complex, the ability to share files and communicate information across diverse networks becomes necessary to improve efficiency and productivity. The need to connect dissimilar LANs may also result from corporate mergers or acquisitions, or it may stem from the desire to interconnect LANs with WANs (e.g., packet-switched networks) for economical data transport over long distances.

Before gateways became widely available during the early 1980s, users had to purchase one special board (e.g., IRMA, from Digital Communications Associates Inc in Alpharetta GA, or Tempus-Share, from Micro Tempus Inc in Montreal, Canada), for each microcomputer, to permit occasional access to the host. Such products permit micro-to-host connections but are a very expensive connectivity solution. Because a gateway connects several microcomputers to the WAN, it reduces operating costs and streamlines the network (see Exhibit IV-2-5).

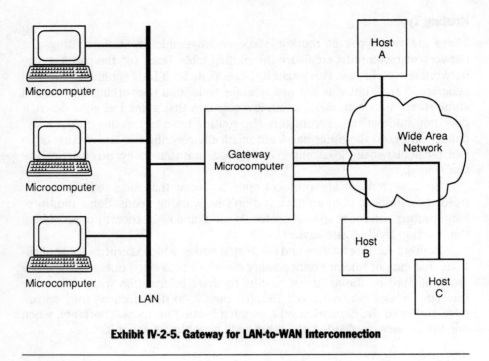

Exhibit IV-2-5. Gateway for LAN-to-WAN Interconnection

A gateway can physically consist of a two-port card that plugs into the expansion slots of the microcomputer that has been designated as the server. The two-port configuration allows gateways to perform speed conversion. For example, one port on the board might provide a 64K-bps connection, whereas the other might provide a 19.2K-bps connection. Together, the two ports can support 32 concurrent sessions. Some gateways even include a built-in packet assembler-disassembler to provide logical access, eliminating the need for separate units.

Access to the gateway is controlled by assigning specific ports to certain microcomputers. When a microcomputer requests access to the gateway, it is given the port reserved for it. Because no other microcomputer can access the port, security is enforced. In addition, each port may have access privileges associated with it. One port may provide access to all mainframe applications, for example, whereas another port may be limited to only one application. The problem with dedicated access is that idle ports may not be used, which means that efficiency is sacrificed for the sake of security.

When security is not an issue, a gateway can provide access to all ports on a contention basis, providing more opportunities for users to link with the mainframe or other network resources because users are not limited to specific gateway ports. Some gateways permit both shared and dedicated access, allowing some ports to be reserved for specific microcomputers and the rest pooled for general use.

Advantages

When a separate server is used as a gateway, cabling costs and installation time are reduced and moves and changes are easier to make. Users can change the physical location of their equipment and retain their logical address on the network. With communications functions off-loaded from the host, valuable processing resources are made available for more important tasks.

Another advantage of using gateways is simplified network management. Instead of monitoring the traffic of 100 microcomputers on the network, managers can monitor one gateway, which appears to the host as a single peripheral device. In this case, a separate cluster controller is unnecessary because the gateway replaces it.

Gateways extract detailed information about the data traffic that passes through them and about the status of the data links it interfaces with. The gateway ensures that the links are handling data reliably, without exceeding user-defined error rate thresholds. In addition, it monitors the various protocols being used, ensuring that enough protocol conversion processing power is available for any given application. The gateway's management system generates a variety of reports that can be output automatically at specified times or on demand. Network statistics can be archived for trend analysis to help in long-range planning.

In wide area networking environments, the gateway balances load levels, bypasses failed links, and finds the most economical route. With some gateways, these functions are performed automatically as the result of a single connection request from a user, regardless of the equipment location or the protocols involved. In this environment, the ability to detect, isolate, and diagnose problems becomes important. The network management tools that are available with today's sophisticated gateways allow the remote configuration of channels, links, and such network interconnection devices as bridges and routers. Through the network management system, gateway ports may be brought online or offline as required.

Because gateways perform protocol conversion at every layer of the OSI reference model, performance bottlenecks may become a problem. Every new connection, hop, and protocol that is added to the network not only intensifies the problem but invites new problems (e.g., higher system costs, limited growth and expansion, and nontransparent connections), which complicates network management. With so much networking overhead devoted to protocol translation, gateways have been relegated to such specific applications as electronic mail and batch file transfers.

Intelligent Gateways

Some vendors are developing so-called intelligent gateways that communicate with each other to determine the best way to route information, taking into consideration such factors as congestion, priority, performance (i.e., throughput, delay, and error rate), security, and even cost. Building such capabilities into intelligent gateways relieves users of having to make these decisions.

An inherent weakness of such schemes, however, is congestion, which may affect the performance of the entire network or of only one gateway of the network. An inefficient routing scheme can cause traffic to stay on the primary data link longer than necessary, slowing down the entire network. Alternatively, congestion may occur in the gateway itself, particularly when there are too many packets to filter.

Gateway protocols must perform flow control and respond to congestion indicators. When congestion is detected, the intelligent gateway assigns priority to the information that is to be routed (e.g., it determines whether local or internetwork traffic should be given preferential treatment). Ranking information is also important in the management of the network. Intelligent gateways allow diagnostic information to pass through or around congested areas, providing real-time status reports on each link.

If the entire network is congested, the packets can bypass the alternative gateways located on the other side of the network in favor of hopping through a different network. Hopping to another network may pose a threat to security, however. Intelligent gateways maintain security by distinguishing between routine and sensitive information during the routing decision.

SUMMARY

Bridges, routers, and gateways provide varying levels of connectivity, efficiency, and economy to corporate networking. The choice of interconnection device hinges largely on the topology of the network and the types of applications being run on the network. Such devices are increasingly appreciated not only for providing internetworking connectivity but for helping to unify the organization into an enterprisewide utility.

IV-3
The IEEE 802.6 Metropolitan Area Network Distributed-Queue, Dual-Bus Protocol

The proliferation of local computer networks has underscored the need for interconnecting these networks reliably and efficiently. The method of interconnection must satisfy requirements of distance, high speed, and standardized protocols and services. Interconnections must cover a large geographic area. They must be able to operate at greater than 20M bps to serve as backbones for the installed LANs, which are invariably heterogeneous. Therefore, a metropolitan area network (MAN) based on an international networking standard is a highly desirable method of providing the interworking element for multivendor LANs. In addition, because of the changing nature of network traffic from data only to a mixture of data, voice, and video traffic, these MANs must support multimedia services. Furthermore, as MANs are deployed in the public domain, support of voice services assists the integration of data and voice over a common set of equipment, thereby reducing maintenance and administrative costs.

Considerable work is under way in the standards groups to define the features of a broadband ISDN that provides a universal and seamless connectivity for multimedia services like the one that the public telephone network currently provides for voice services. There is, however, an immediate need to interconnect LANs and support other high-speed communications services across a metropolitan area, which demands an interim solution. This interim network must act as a migration path to a broadband ISDN and may, following large-scale deployment of broadband ISDN, act as an access method to these networks.

The IEEE project 802.6 committee is working on a MAN that attempts to address these issues. This chapter reviews the work that has been done by the committee and presents an overview of the technical aspects of the proposed standard.

THE DISTRIBUTED-QUEUE, DUAL-BUS PROTOCOL

A distributed-queue, dual-bus protocol is the access protocol specified in the 802.6 MAN standard. The protocol can support such traffic types as data, voice, and video. The distributed-queue, dual-bus subnetwork is used as a public network controlled by the operating companies or as a private backbone network within the customer premises. It also serves as a LAN.

The 802.6 MAN operates on a shared medium with two unidirectional buses that flow in opposite directions. Depending on the type of traffic, a node on the distributed-queue, dual-bus subnetwork can queue to gain access to the medium by using a distributed-queue, arbitrated access method or by requesting a fixed amount of bandwidth through a prearbitrated access method. Data is transmitted on the medium in fixed-size units called slots, which are 53 bytes long (i.e., a 52-byte data slot plus a 1-byte access control field).

Distributed-queue, dual-bus subnetworks are connected with a dual-port or multiport bridge. (The multiport bridge, which could be based on the fast packet-switching technology being developed for broadband ISDN, will be considered by the 802.6 committee in the future.) Distributed-queue, dual-bus private networks are connected to the public network by point-to-point links, which are distributed-queue, dual-bus subnetworks with two nodes (see Exhibit IV-3-1).

To support services across a metropolitan area, a single distributed-queue, dual-bus subnetwork may range from a few kilometers to more than 50 km in diameter. The subnetwork can be implemented to operate at a variety of speeds greater than 1M bps (a typical implementation of a distributed-queue, dual-bus subnetwork operates from 34M bps to 150M bps).

Network Topology

Nodes in a distributed-queue, dual-bus subnetwork are connected to a pair of buses flowing in opposite directions. The subnetwork operates in one of two topologies: open bus or looped bus. The node, or head, at the beginning of each bus generates empty slots to be used on the bus (see Exhibit IV-3-2). In the looped-bus topology, the two heads of buses are located at the same node (see Exhibit IV-3-3). The two topologies provide the same service, but the looped bus can reconfigure to provide full connectivity if a fault occurs (see Exhibits IV-3-4 and IV-3-5).

Data Types

All data on a distributed-queue, dual-bus subnetwork is carried in fixed-size data units called slots. The slot size and format align with the broadband ISDN cell size proposed by the CCITT SGXVIII committee. This was done to facilitate eventual migration to the broadband ISDN. The payload of each 52-byte slot is called a segment.

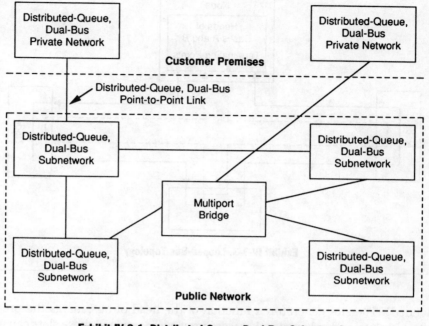

Exhibit IV-3-1. Distributed-Queue, Dual-Bus Subnetworks

The two types of slots generated in a distributed-queue, dual-bus subnetwork are queued arbitrated and prearbitrated. Nodes gain access to the queued arbitrated slots by using the distributed-queue access protocol. Nodes gain access to the prearbitrated slots by requesting and receiving bandwidth from a call/connection control entity (the functions of which have yet to be

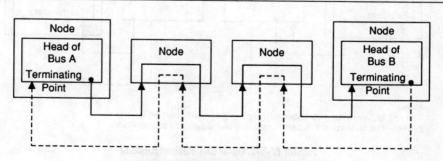

Exhibit IV-3-2. Open-Bus Topology

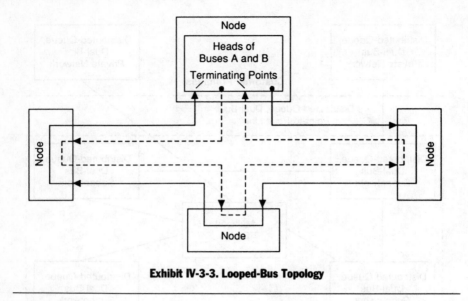

Exhibit IV-3-3. Looped-Bus Topology

---

defined). The slot generator, a function of the head of bus, marks the prearbitrated slots, and only nodes that were previously assigned these slots can use them.

Services

The distributed-queue, dual-bus layer is intended to provide a range of services, including connectionless data transfer, connection-oriented data transfer, and

---

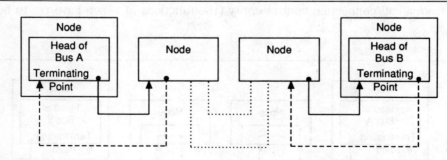

Note:
The link between the two nodes in the open-bus configuration is broken. The subnetwork is partitioned into two disjointed subnetworks.

Exhibit IV-3-4. Open-Bus Reconfiguration

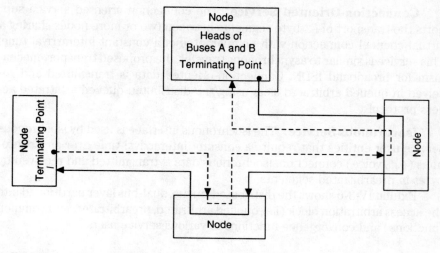

Note:
The link between the two nodes in the looped-bus configuration is broken. The subnetwork is reconfigured to an open-bus configuration. Connections along all nodes are maintained.

Exhibit IV-3-5. Looped-Bus Reconfiguration

isochronous data transfer. Convergence functions adapt the underlying medium access services to provide a specific service to a user. The standard specifies the convergence function, which provides connectionless media access control data service to the logical link control sublayer and offers guidelines for the provision of an isochronous service. The connection-oriented data service is under study. Additional convergence functions may be defined as future services are developed or defined.

Connectionless Media Access Control Service. The logical link control sublayer operating over the distributed-queue, dual-bus layer provides the service of the OSI data link layer, which supports link-level data communications between two open systems. The connectionless media access control service supports the transport of frames as long as 9,188 bytes. This frame size can encapsulate all types of 802 LAN packets except for the 18K-byte 802.5. The service is provided to the logical link control sublayer (802.2 LLC). It is the media access control service because it is compatible with the access control service provided by other 802 LAN standards. The function providing this service is called the convergence function. Connectionless media access control data is transmitted and received in queued arbitrated slots using the distributed queued arbitrated access protocol.

Connection-Oriented Service. The connection-oriented service supports the transport of 52-byte segments between two or more nodes sharing a virtual channel connection with no guarantee of a constant interarrival time. This service is similar to asynchronous transfer, the proposed transport mechanism for broadband ISDN. Connection-oriented data is transmitted and received in queued arbitrated slots using the distributed queued arbitrated access protocol.

Isochronous Service. The isochronous interface is used by isochronous service user entities that require a constant interarrival time over an isochronous (e.g., voice) connection. Isochronous data is transmitted and received by bytes in prearbitrated segments.

Exhibit IV-3-6 shows the distributed-queue, dual-bus layer partitioned into the access arbitration block (i.e., queued arbitrated, prearbitrated, and common functions) and convergence functions to various service users.

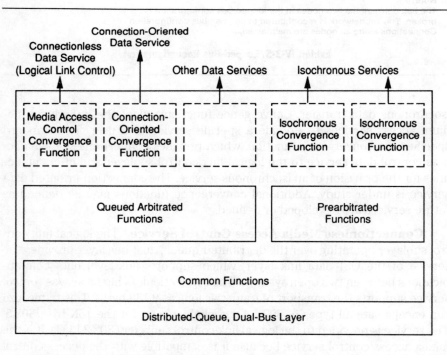

Exhibit IV-3-6. Distributed-Queue, Dual-Bus Services

PHYSICAL ATTRIBUTES

The distributed-queue, dual-bus access layer is independent of the physical layer. Therefore, a variety of distributed-queue, dual-bus networks can be built using the same access layer yet operating at different data rates, depending on the transmission systems selected.

Three transmission systems have been considered to date:

- The ANSI DS3—This system transmits data at 44.736M bps over 75-ohm coaxial cable or fiber.
- The ANSI SONET STS-3c—This system transmits data at 155.52M bps over single-mode fiber.
- The CCITT G.703—This system transmits data at 34.368M bps and 139.264M bps over a metallic medium.

The physical layer incorporates a convergence protocol that provides a consistent service to the distributed-queue, dual-bus layer, regardless of the transmission system used (see Exhibit IV-3-7). This protocol provides a mapping function, operation and maintenance parameters, and information to the distributed-queue, dual-bus layer. Each transmission system has a different physical layer convergence protocol.

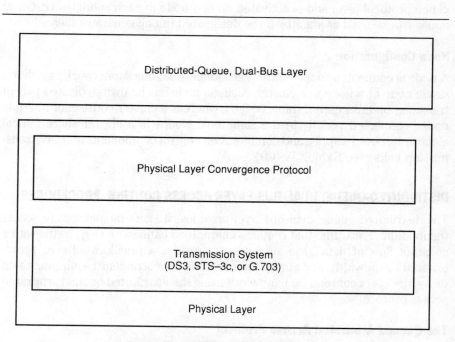

Distributed-Queue, Dual-Bus Layer

Physical Layer Convergence Protocol

Transmission System
(DS3, STS–3c, or G.703)

Physical Layer

Exhibit IV-3-7. Physical Layer Structure

Network Components

Several functions are associated with operating a distributed-queue, dual-bus subnetwork. A single node can perform one or more of these functions. Two major functions are described in this section: slot generation and timing generation.

Slot Generation. Every 125 μsec, a slot generator transmits multiple slots to the shared medium (the number of slots generated depends on the physical transmission rate). Nodes read and copy data from the slots; they also gain access to the subnetwork by writing to the slots.

In the open-bus topology, two slot generators serve as the head of bus A and head of bus B. In the looped-bus topology, only one default slot generator serves as the head of both bus A and bus B; any node on the subnetwork can become the slot generator if the designated slot generator fails.

Timing Generation. The distributed-queue, dual-bus subnetwork operation is based on a 125-μsec clock to allow for isochronous services (the 125-μsec interval reflects the 8-kHz public networking frequency required by voice services). The clock is either generated internally, within the subnetwork, or extracted from an external timing source (e.g., from the public network).

The timing generator function is performed at the physical layer convergence protocol level and is activated on one node in each subnetwork. Other nodes can be used as standby if the designated timing generator fails.

Node Configuration

A node is connected to the distributed-queue, dual-bus subnetwork as either a single node or a node in a cluster. A single node has its own dedicated pair of transmission links (see Exhibit IV-3-8), whereas a cluster consists of multiple nodes connected serially in the same box. Nodes in a cluster share optical electronic, power supply, and configuration control components and two transmission links (see Exhibit IV-3-9).

DISTRIBUTED-QUEUE, DUAL-BUS LAYER ACCESS CONTROL PROCEDURES

The distributed-queue, dual-bus layer provides two general methods to access the medium. For traffic that requires guaranteed bandwidth (e.g., traffic with a constant flow of data), the subnetwork provides a preallocated (i.e., prearbitrated) bandwidth. For bursty data that has less stringent requirements on delay, the users contend for bandwidth using the distributed queued arbitrated access protocol.

The Queued Arbitrated Access Protocol

A node gains access to transmit by putting itself in a queue. There are two queues, one for each bus. They are monitored and controlled by each node on

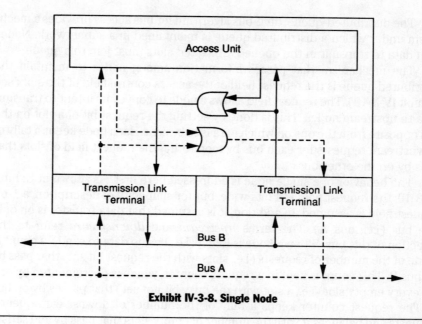

Exhibit IV-3-8. Single Node

the subnetwork. In each node, the distributed queue on bus A is maintained by counting requests passing on bus B and counting free slots passing on bus A. The difference between the two sums is the number of outstanding requests for slots on bus A. This value also indicates the position of the node in the queue to transmit on bus A. The distributed queue on bus B operates symmetrically.

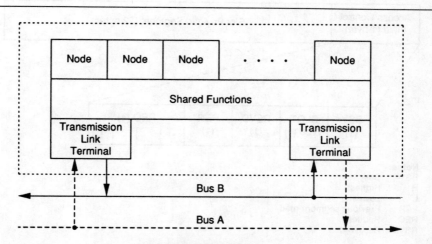

Exhibit IV-3-9. Cluster

The distributed-queue, dual-bus algorithm for bus access provides a mechanism under which a distributed queue is maintained in a subnetwork. Nodes with data to transmit in the queued arbitrated slots must join this queue.

The mechanism that passes information among nodes to maintain the distributed queue is the request field of the access control field of the slot (see Exhibit IV-3-10). The request field allows a node to convey its intent to transmit data to upstream nodes. This is done by setting the request bit of a slot on the bus opposite from the one on which data is to be sent. Each node keeps a tally of downstream requests for each bus by monitoring the request field of slots that pass by on the other bus.

The behavior of a single node is addressed here first. As shown in Exhibit IV-3-10, the request field is 4 bits wide, but for simplicity of description, a 1-bit request field is assumed. In addition, it is assumed that data transfer is on only one bus (i.e., bus A). The terms *upstream* and *downstream* refer to the direction of this bus. When a node is idling (i.e., has no data to send), a count is made of the number of requests (i.e., slots with the request bit set) that pass by on bus B. This count is kept in a request counter, which is decremented by one for every empty slot (i.e., a slot with the busy bit not set) that passes by on bus A. The request counter keeps a tally of the number of downstream queued requests and balances it with the number of empty slots that pass by and satisfy the requests (see Exhibit IV-3-11). The request counter is never allowed to become negative. If more empty slots pass by on one bus than request bits on the opposite bus, the counter remains at 0.

When the node wishes to transmit data, it joins the distributed queue by first putting its request on bus B (to inform upstream nodes) and waits for its

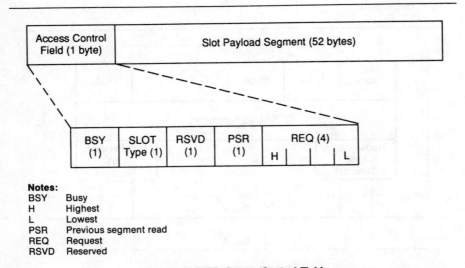

Notes:

BSY	Busy
H	Highest
L	Lowest
PSR	Previous segment read
REQ	Request
RSVD	Reserved

Exhibit IV-3-10. Access Control Field

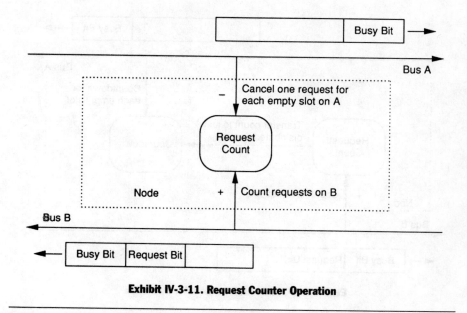

Exhibit IV-3-11. Request Counter Operation

turn in the queue. The node's position in the queue is determined by the value of the request counter. This value is transferred to the countdown counter, and the request counter is reset to 0. The countdown counter decrements for every empty slot that passes by on bus A; the node transmits its own data when this counter reaches 0. The request counter, on the other hand, no longer decrements for empty slots on bus A but simply counts the number of requests on bus B (see Exhibit IV-3-12). The dual bus is symmetric; a node with data to transmit on bus B goes through a process equivalent to the one described with a separate set of request and countdown counters. To send another slot of data, the node must repeat the process.

As shown in Exhibit IV-3-10, the request field is 4 bits wide, allowing for four access priority levels; 0 is the lowest priority, and 3 is the highest. Each node on the subnetwork has a request counter and a countdown counter for each priority level. When a node is idling, the request counter increments for requests of priorities equal to or greater than its own priority level. When a node is queuing, each request counter increments for the requests of its own priority level; the countdown counter increments for requests of a higher priority level. For example, when a node is idling, the request counter of priority level 1 counts the requests of priority levels 1, 2, and 3.

In summary, to gain access on a bus, a node:

- Sends a request to tell the upstream nodes that it wishes to transmit data.
- Puts itself in the distributed queue by using the countdown counter.
- Maintains the distributed queue with the request counter.

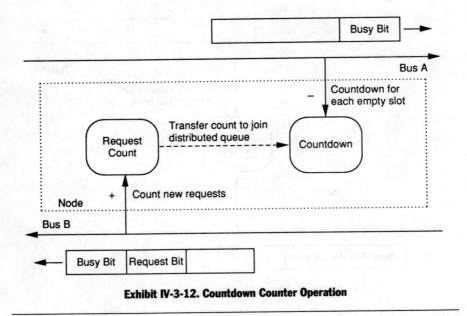

Exhibit IV-3-12. Countdown Counter Operation

- Allows enough empty slots through to satisfy the needs of nodes that are ahead in the distributed queue.
- Sends its own data when its turn comes.

Queued Arbitrated Access Operation. The following example demonstrates the operation of a distributed queue of a five-node, dual-bus network. Again, for simplicity, a 1-bit request field is assumed. It is also assumed that all request counters start with the value 0 and that all slots are busy (see Exhibit IV-3-13).

Node 5 wishes to transmit data on bus A. It sets the request bit in a slot on bus B. Every node that detects this request bit increments its request counter by one. Node 5 also transfers its request counter (with a value of 0) to its countdown counter. It clears its request counter to 0.

Node 2 wishes to transmit data on bus A. It sets the request bit in a slot on bus B. Only the upstream node, node 1, sees the request bit and increments its request counter. Node 1's request counter is incremented to 2. Node 2 copies its request counter value to its countdown counter and sets its request counter to 0.

Node 3 wishes to transmit data on bus A. It sets the request bit in a slot on bus B. Nodes 1 and 2 see this request bit and increment their request counters. The request counter of node 2 is incremented, but its countdown counter value is unchanged.

In the situation in Exhibit IV-3-14, the nodes have been placed on the

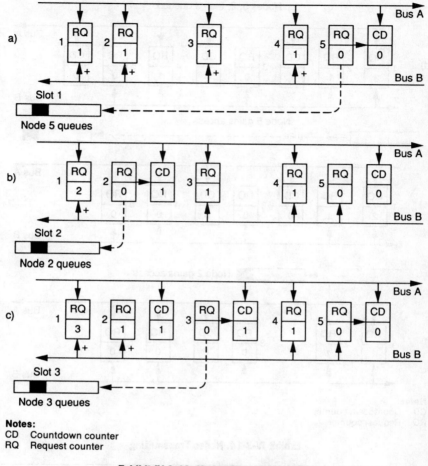

Notes:
CD   Countdown counter
RQ   Request counter

Exhibit IV-3-13. Nodes Queuing for Slots

distributed queue but no data has been transmitted. Node 5 is queued first, followed by nodes 2 and 3. The next empty slot passes by on bus A. All nodes decrement their request counters and countdown counters appropriately. Nodes 2 and 3 decrement their countdown counters but do not transmit because the value of their countdown counters is not 0 when the slot is received. Node 5 has a countdown counter value of 0 and uses this slot to transmit data. The countdown counters of nodes 2 and 3 are also 0. In such a case, the position of the nodes on this bus determines the order in which they are served (the most upstream node is served first).

The next empty slot causes the request counters and countdown counters

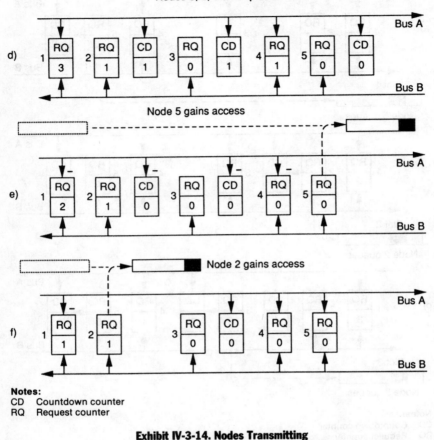

Notes:
CD   Countdown counter
RQ   Request counter

Exhibit IV-3-14. Nodes Transmitting

to be decremented. Node 2 gains access to the bus. Node 3 is able to send its data in the next empty slot.

The Prearbitrated Access Protocol

Access to the prearbitrated slot is based on a request-and-assign procedure. When a node needs to establish an isochronous connection with another node, it requests a connection from a call/connection control entity. These procedures are beyond the scope of the current 802.6 standard; they may be based on such a signaling scheme as Q.931.

The slot generator, or default slot generator, of the subnetwork is notified by the call/connection control entity to generate the appropriate prearbitrated slots. Nodes are assigned to write to 1 or more bytes in a prearbitrated slot. They are also assigned to read from 1 or more bytes in another prearbitrated slot.

THE INTERNAL STRUCTURE OF THE DISTRIBUTED-QUEUE, DUAL-BUS LAYER

The distributed-queue, dual-bus layer is divided into three functional blocks: convergence, media access control, and layer management entity (see Exhibit IV-3-15).

The Convergence Block. The convergence block provides the necessary translation between the service requirements of the users and the segment-based transport. Therefore, the convergence functions adapt data from the users to the formats required by the distributed-queue, dual-bus access layer. Conversely, they also extract data from the distributed-queue, dual-bus segments and present the information to the users.

The standard specifies the media access control convergence function, which provides the connectionless datagram service to the logical link control sublayer. It also provides guidelines for an isochronous convergence function. The connection-oriented convergence function is under study.

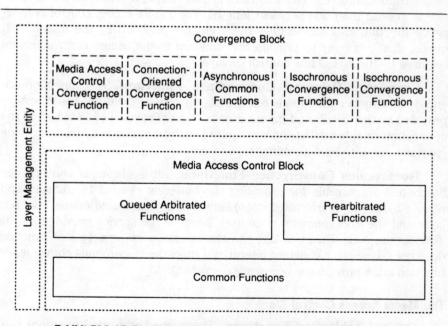

Exhibit IV-3-15. Distributed-Queue, Dual-Bus Layer Internal Structure

The Media Access Control Block. The media access control block is responsible for transmitting and receiving slots to and from the buses using the prearbitrated and queued arbitrated access procedures. The media access control block is divided into three subentities: common functions, queued arbitrated functions, and prearbitrated functions.

The Layer Management Entity Block. The layer management entity block is composed of two elements: a distributed-queue, dual-bus layer management and a layer management interface to network management interface.

The distributed-queue, dual-bus layer management entity handles the functions that are required to provide distributed-queue, dual-bus layer management when services to higher layers cannot be guaranteed to be fully operable (e.g., when the subnetwork is being initialized). Work in this area is currently in progress.

The interface protocol for layer and network management is reserved for future study while its primitives are being defined in the standard.

The Convergence Block

The Media Access Control Convergence Function. The media access control convergence function is responsible for segmenting the logical link control protocol data unit and appending the appropriate headers and trailers before transmitting data (data is transmitted in multiple segments if its overall size is greater than one segment length). The media access control convergence function also reassembles the segments provided by the distributed-queue, dual-bus layer to provide the standard media access control service required by the logical link control sublayer.

Connection-Oriented Convergence Functions. A connection-oriented convergence function is responsible for adapting the slot-based service provided by the distributed-queue, dual-bus layer (payload of 48 bytes) to the connection-oriented data services required by the asynchronous transfer mode (payload size is to be determined).

Isochronous Convergence Functions. An isochronous convergence function is responsible for providing the buffering needed to transmit and receive bytes (in prearbitrated slots) between the distributed-queue, dual-bus layer and the isochronous service user. Because the service provided by the distributed-queue, dual-bus layer to the isochronous convergence function does not guarantee a constant interarrival time, the isochronous convergence function must provide the necessary smoothing.

The Media Access Control Block

Queued Arbitrated Functions. The queued arbitrated functions provide service for the media access control convergence function and the connection-oriented convergence with the queued arbitrated segments.

The queued arbitrated functions provide a data transfer service of 48-byte payloads. The queued arbitrated functions accept the payload from a media access control or connection-oriented convergence function and add the appropriate header to the payload to create a queued arbitrated segment. Queued arbitrated segments received by queued arbitrated functions destined for the node are stripped of the header, and the payload is passed to the appropriate convergence function.

Prearbitrated Functions. The prearbitrated functions provide service for the isochronous convergence functions with the prearbitrated segments. The use of the prearbitrated segments by isochronous convergence functions requires the establishment of a connection. The prearbitrated functions can support the transfer of 1 or more bytes to provide variable service rates and the sharing of one segment by multiple isochronous users. The prearbitrated functions accept a byte from an isochronous convergence function and write it into the preallocated positions within the payload of the prearbitrated segment. To receive a byte, the prearbitrated functions copy the byte from the preallocated position within the payload of a prearbitrated segment and pass it to the isochronous convergence function.

Common Functions. After receiving a slot from the bus, the common functions process the slot header and relay the slot payload to queued arbitrated or prearbitrated functions, depending on the slot type. For transmission, the common functions include data from queued arbitrated and prearbitrated functions in the slot after modifying the slot header according to the access protocol.

The common functions also perform other functions to maintain the operation of the subnetwork. The functions that have been specified thus far are configuration control and reservation of message identifiers (used for the segmentation and reassembly process, which is described later in this chapter).

THE MEDIA ACCESS CONTROL SERVICE DATA UNIT

Structure

Project 802.6 is viewed as the mechanism to bridge lower-speed 802 LANs to the public network. Because of this, the subnetwork is required to provide necessary media access control service to the IEEE 802.2 logical link control sublayer.

As shown in Exhibit IV-3-16, the logical link control protocol data unit is enveloped in a header and trailer to form an initial media access control protocol data unit. The initial media access control protocol data unit is divided into 48-byte fragments to fit in the payload of a slot (although the payload of a slot is 52 bytes, header fields reduce the effective payload size to 48 bytes). If

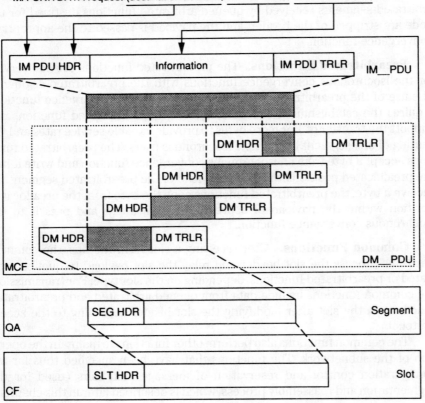

MA-UNITDATA request (destination address, service class, service data unit)

Notes:

CF	Common functions
DM	Derived media access control
HDR	Header
IM	Initial media access control
MCF	Media access control convergence function
PDU	Protocol data unit
QA	Queued arbitrated
SEG	Segment
SLT	Slot
TRLR	Trailer

Exhibit IV-3-16. Protocol Data Unit Structure

the initial media access control protocol data unit is larger than 20 bytes, it is divided into multiple fragments. Each fragment is enveloped in a 2-byte header and 2-byte trailer to form a derived media access control protocol data unit. The derived media access control protocol data unit is the fixed-size segment payload that is transmitted on the bus. The media access control convergence function is required to perform the segmentation process to divide one logical link control protocol data unit to one or more derived media access control protocol data units as described. The convergence function is also required to reassemble the received segments before presenting data to the logical link control sublayer.

Each derived media access control protocol data unit is enveloped into a segment by the queued arbitrated functions. Each segment is in turn enveloped into a slot in the common functions.

Segment Type. The segment type indicates the order in which the segments are divided and transmitted to provide a reliable scheme for reassembling the segments at the media access control convergence function of the receiving end.

There are four segment types:

- Beginning of message.
- Continuation of message.
- End of message.
- Single-segment message.

If the initial media access control protocol data unit has 20 bytes of data or less in the information field, the entire protocol data unit can be transmitted in one segment.

Destination and Source Addresses. Connectionless datagrams must contain addressing information, and in 802.6, the address field is fixed at 64 bits wide to accommodate 16-, 48-, and 60-bit addresses. The 60-bit address specified in 802.6 is based on the ISDN E.164 public addressing scheme with 15 binary coded decimal (BCD) digits. Each node on a distributed-queue, dual-bus subnetwork must have a 48-bit address because it is the required 802 address. Addresses of 16 and 60 bits are optional.

Nodes on a distributed-queue, dual-bus use the 48-bit addresses as do other 802 LANs. Nodes on a distributed-queue, dual-bus MAN are assigned 60-bit addresses within its subnetwork and are managed by the telephone operating companies. The destination and source addresses are parts of the initial media access control protocol data unit.

The Message Identifier. If the initial media access control protocol data unit is too long to fit into one slot and must be segmented, the source and destination addresses are transmitted in the beginning-of-message segment only. The message identifier field provides the labeling mechanism for the segments following the beginning-of-message segment. At the receiving end, the message identifier allows the node to reassemble the datagram from the incoming segments.

The message identifiers must be unique within the subnetwork to prevent segments from different sources with the same destination from being mixed up. A distributed page-allocation algorithm is defined to allow nodes to obtain pages of message identifiers for use. Each page contains four message identifiers—one for each priority level of the distributed-queue, dual-bus access protocol. The message identifier is part of the derived media access control protocol data unit header.

The Virtual Channel Identifier. The virtual channel identifier is used along with the message identifier to identify the convergence function to direct segment payload. Because there is no destination address or source address associated with an isochronous connection, the virtual channel identifier and the byte offset are used to identify the byte in a prearbitrated slot that has been preassigned to a node.

There is at least one virtual channel identifier for each convergence function. For the connectionless service, the media access control convergence function, the default virtual channel identifier that requires support is the hexadecimal value FFFFF. For the isochronous services, at least two virtual channel identifiers are associated with each connection. The virtual channel identifier is a part of the segment header.

Detailed Header Structure

The relationship between the different structures and fields that constitute a media access control protocol data unit is shown in Exhibit IV-3-17. The numbers in roman font denote the field size in bytes; those in italic denote the field size in bits.

Media Access Control Service Data Unit Transmission Flow

The slot generator generates multiple empty queued arbitrated slots within each 125-μsec interval. A node gains access to transmit the derived media access control protocol data units of a service data unit to the subnetwork in these queued arbitrated slots on the basis of the distributed-queue protocol. The node must queue up to transmit each derived media access control protocol data unit individually; therefore, derived media access control protocol data units from a media access control service data unit may not appear contiguously on the medium.

ISOCHRONOUS DATA UNIT STRUCTURE AND TRANSMISSION FLOW

Each isochronous data unit is represented as 1 or more bytes of data. They are transferred between the isochronous service user and the distributed-queue,

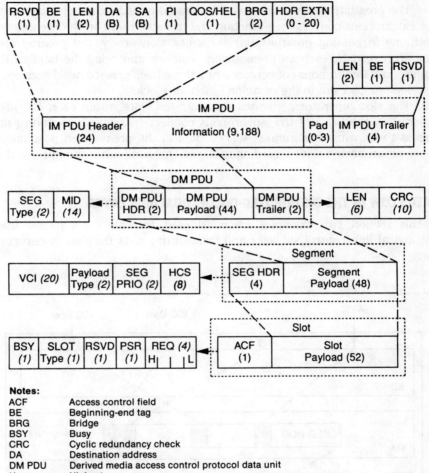

Notes:

ACF	Access control field
BE	Beginning-end tag
BRG	Bridge
BSY	Busy
CRC	Cyclic redundancy check
DA	Destination address
DM PDU	Derived media access control protocol data unit
H	Highest
HCS	Header check sequence
HDR EXTN	Header extension
IM PDU	Initial media access control protocol data unit
L	Lowest
LEN	Length
MID	Message identifier
PI	Protocol identification
PRIO	Priority
PSR	Previous segment read
QOS/HEL	Quality of service/header extension length
REQ	Request
RSVD	Reserved
SA	Source address
SEG	Segment
VCI	Virtual channel identifier

Exhibit IV-3-17. Media Access Control Protocol Data Unit Structure

dual-bus layer at fixed time intervals (see Exhibit IV-3-18).

The prearbitrated functions receive data from the isochronous users over the isochronous convergence function and transmit them on the preassigned positions in passing prearbitrated segments. Conversely, the prearbitrated functions read bytes from preassigned positions and relay the data to the appropriate isochronous convergence functions. Each prearbitrated segment is enveloped into a slot in the common functions block.

The slot generator generates prearbitrated slots within each 125-μsec interval on the basis of the isochronous connection requests. A node gains access to transmit isochronous service data in the preassigned positions in these prearbitrated slots according to the isochronous connection protocol.

DATA FLOW IN THE DISTRIBUTED-QUEUE, DUAL-BUS LAYER

In this section, two examples are considered: transmitting a packet from the logical link control sublayer and transmitting data from an isochronous user.

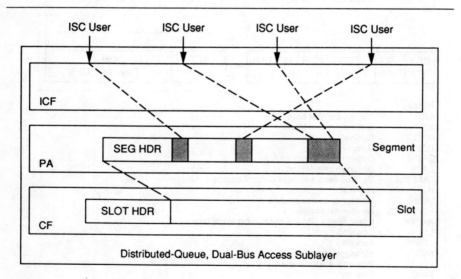

Notes:
CF   Common functions
HDR   Header
ICF   Isochronous convergence function
ISC   Isochronous
PA   Prearbitrated
SEG   Segment

Exhibit IV-3-18. Isochronous Data Unit Structure

Transmitting a Packet from the Logical Link Control Sublayer

A packet sent from the logical link control sublayer is processed in the following manner. In the media access control convergence function block, the packet is enveloped with the initial media access control protocol data unit header and trailer to form an initial media access control protocol data unit (see Exhibit IV-3-19). The initial media access control protocol data unit is then segmented into multiple units to fit the fixed-size slots. Each unit forms the payload of a derived media access control protocol data unit. Headers and trailers are then added (see Exhibit IV-3-20).

In the queued arbitrated functions block, the derived media access control protocol data unit is enveloped into a segment including a header field. For the current standard, these fields are set to predefined values, as shown in Exhibit IV-3-21.

In the common functions block, the queued arbitrated segment is envel-

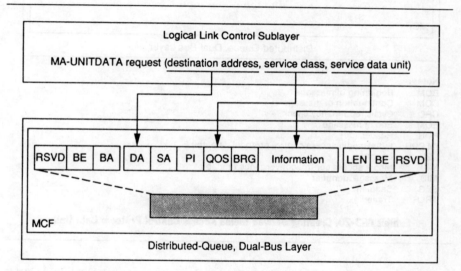

Notes:

BA	Buffer allocation size
BE	Beginning-end tag
BRG	Bridging
DA	Destination address
IM PDU	Initial media access control protocol data unit
LEN	Length
MCF	Media access control convergence function
PI	Protocol identification
QOS	Quality of service
RSVD	Reserved
SA	Source address

Exhibit IV-3-19. Processing a Packet in MCF: Creating an IM PDU

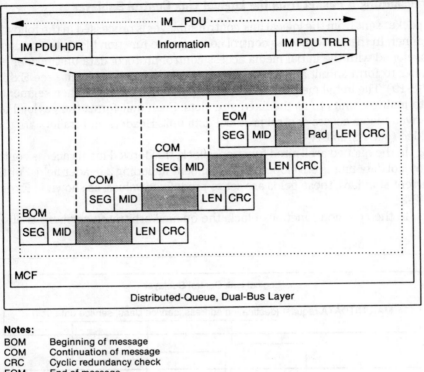

Notes:

BOM	Beginning of message
COM	Continuation of message
CRC	Cyclic redundancy check
EOM	End of message
HDR	Header
IM PDU	Initial media access control protocol data unit
LEN	Length
MCF	Media access control convergence function
MID	Message identifier
SEG	Segment
TRLR	Trailer

Exhibit IV-3-20. Creating Derived Media Access Control Protocol Data Units

oped into a slot. The busy bit of the slot header (the access control field) is set to 1 to mark the slot as used, and the slot type is set to 0 to denote a queued arbitrated slot. The previous-segment-read bit is set at 0, and the request field is left unchanged (see Exhibit IV-3-22). The slot is then transmitted to the shared medium according to the signals from the physical layer convergence protocol entity.

Transmitting Data from the Isochronous User

A byte or series of bytes sent from an isochronous user is processed as follows. Bytes are written on the basis of the information table set up in the isochronous

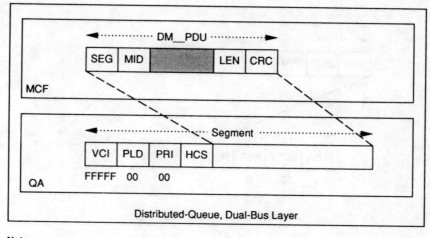

Notes:

CRC	Cyclic redundancy check
DM PDU	Derived media access control protocol data unit
HCS	Header check sequence
LEN	Length
MCF	Media access control convergence function
MID	Message identifier
PLD	Payload type
PRI	Priority
QA	Queued arbitrated
SEG	Segment
VCI	Virtual channel identifier

Exhibit IV-3-21. Processing a DM PDU in the Queued Arbitrated Functions Block: Creating a Segment

convergence functions after the isochronous connection has been established between the calling and called isochronous users. The transmitted bytes are buffered by the prearbitrated functions block and written to the appropriate positions in the preassigned segments as they arrive. In each prearbitrated segment, a particular byte is written to and from the segment on the basis of the offset value specified. (Exhibit IV-3-23 shows data transmitted in the fifth bytes of the prearbitrated segment with the virtual channel identifier of 00002 on bus A).

In the common functions block, the prearbitrated segments are enveloped in slots. The busy bit of the slot header (i.e., the access control field) is set to 1 to mark the slot as used, and the slot type (i.e., SLOT) is set to 1 to denote a queued arbitrated slot. The slot is then transmitted to the shared medium according to the signals from the physical layer convergence protocol entity.

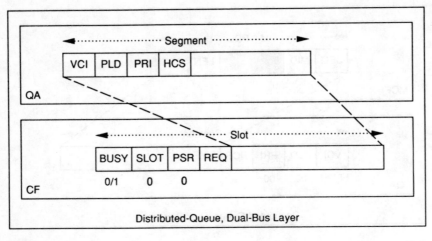

Notes:

CF	Common functions	PSR	Previous segment read
HCS	Header check sequence	QA	Queued arbitrated
PLD	Payload type	REQ	Request
PRI	Priority	VCI	Virtual channel identifier

Exhibit IV-3-22. Processing a Segment in the Common Functions Block: Creating a Slot

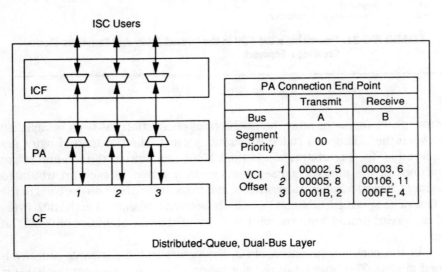

Notes:

CF	Common functions
ICF	Isochronous convergence function
ISC	Isochronous
PA	Prearbitrated
VCI	Virtual channel identifier

Exhibit IV-3-23. Transmitting Isochronous Data

SUMMARY

This chapter summarizes the features of the emerging MAN currently being defined by the IEEE 802.6 committee. The need for a fast, efficient, and transparent interconnection for information interchange across the public network is clear. The survival of most companies and corporations increasingly depends on maintaining up-to-date information and on transferring information in the most timely and efficient manner. Although broadband ISDN must be developed further before it becomes a feasible solution to this problem, 802.6 is an attempt to bridge the gap and offers an evolutionary route to a universally networked environment.

IV-4
Higher-Level OSI Standards

VINCENT C. JONES

B uilt on the basic bit-moving services provided by open systems interconnection (OSI) layers 1 through 4, the session, presentation, and application layers (i.e., five through seven) combine to provide the networking services
required by developers of network applications. The simple structure of the OSI
layering at this high level, shown in Exhibit IV-4-1, is deceptive. It is actually a
very complex structure, made necessary by the wide range of application needs
and the profusion of protocol standards required to meet those needs. Whereas
there is only one major standard for the OSI session layer, the application layer
has more than a dozen. Above the application layer are additional information
exchange standards that, though technically not part of the OSI reference
architecture, are critical to useful information exchange in the real world. Such
standards as office document architecture, initial graphics exchange standard,
and electronic data interchange enable users to share information between
applications in the same manner as the OSI protocol stack facilitates communications between different physical machines.

From the user's perspective, the logical layering of the upper layers is
closer to that shown in Exhibit IV-4-2. At the bottom is the bit movement facility
provided by the protocols making up the lower layers of the OSI model. The
data exchange layer upgrades the bit movement capability to handle data
movement, and the data exchange function performs data encoding functions
and bridges differences between the source and destination systems. Given the
ability to freely exchange data values, the distributed services layer can package those exchanges into useful services (e.g., electronic mail or file transfer).
Between the distributed services layer and the applications proper is the
domain of standards for information sharing. These standards extend the data
exchange provided by the OSI reference model protocols to include the meaning of the data. For example, whereas an electronic mail service can preserve
the value of a date, a business-oriented protocol for purchase order exchange
must also preserve its meaning as the desired delivery date for the item being
purchased.

The logical model does not demean the OSI reference model or imply that
it is defective. Rather, it recognizes that the OSI reference model is a model for
networking from the protocol definition viewpoint. The OSI model was never

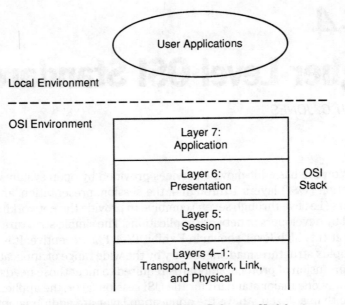

Exhibit IV-4-1. OSI Upper-Layer Reference Model

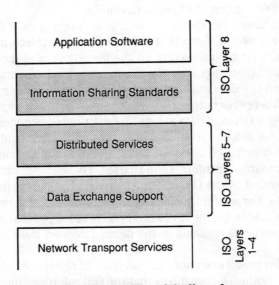

Exhibit IV-4-2. Logical View of the Upper Layers

intended to direct the implementation of networking or dictate the purpose or utility of the information flow provided; OSI is a framework for defining and comparing the protocols that work together to constitute a functioning network.

UNDERLYING SERVICES

The underlying services for OSI architecture networks consist of the International Standards Organization (ISO) connection-oriented session service, the ISO connection-oriented presentation service, and three services from the application layer (association control service elements, remote operation services, and concurrency, commitment and control). User applications generally do not access these services directly; rather, they are used by other application layer services to provide commonly required services—the network services equivalent of a subroutine library.

Session Services

The session services are defined by ISO standards 8326 (i.e., the connection-oriented session service) and 8327 (i.e., the connection-oriented session protocol). These standards are equivalent to CCITT X.215 and X.225 respectively. The session services add controls to the full-duplex, error-free communications channel provided by the transport service. The OSI reference model identifies the following session layer services:

- Session connection establishment.
- Session connection release.
- Normal data exchange.
- Expedited data exchange.
- Quarantine service.
- Interaction management.
- Session connection synchronization.
- Exception reporting.

All of these services, except the quarantine service, are provided by the ISO connection-oriented session standard and are managed by the definition of functional units. At the start of any session, the session layer entities at each end of the association negotiate the functional units to be active for the session. This is the function of the kernel functional unit, which must always be present. The kernel provides the ability to make and release session connections and to send and receive data. Use of the kernel functional unit is not negotiable, but all other functional units may be rejected by either session entity. Failure to accept session functional units required to support a particular application can result in rejection of the application association request.

In addition to the kernel, there are 11 other functional units:

- Half duplex—This unit provides a data token that allows only one side of the connection to transmit at a time, allowing emulation of a half-duplex connection over the ISO full-duplex transport.
- Duplex—This unit allows operation in full-duplex mode. A session connection must use either the duplex or the half-duplex functional unit but cannot use both.
- Typed data—This unit is used only with the half-duplex functional unit and provides a reverse channel for sending information against the prevailing flow of traffic.
- Minor synchronize—This unit defines minor synchronization points in the communication flow, which may be confirmed or unconfirmed. The sender can continue sending after setting a minor synchronization point without waiting for confirmation from the receiver.
- Major synchronize—This unit is similar to the minor synchronize functional unit except that major synchronization points must be confirmed, and the sender cannot send any data following a major synchronize until a confirmation is received.
- Resynchronize—This unit allows an application to issue resynchronization requests. These reset the connection to a defined state after an error or lack of response by the local application, remote application, or network service provider.
- Negotiated release—This unit ensures that a connection is not closed until both ends of the connection have agreed to the closure. Without this functional unit, orderly release is possible, but a release request cannot be refused.
- Expedited data—This unit provides a data path around the flow controls associated with normal data. Availability of this functional unit does not ensure availability of a true expedited data path, which depends on support at the transport and lower layers.
- Exceptions—This unit allows applications and the service provider to issue exception reports. The exceptions functional unit can be proposed only if the half-duplex functional unit is also proposed.
- Activity management—This unit permits applications to define logical pieces of work as activities and organizes the flow of communications accordingly. The only application service to use this functional unit is X.400 messaging.
- Capability data exchange—This unit permits the sending and receiving of data while activity management is in effect when no activity is in progress. It can be used only if the activity management functional unit has been negotiated.

The session layer makes extensive use of tokens. In the context of the OSI session layer, a token confers the exclusive right to perform a given function.

For example, in half-duplex mode, only the application holding the data token can send data. Before the peer application can send data, it must acquire the data token. No data token is used in full-duplex mode.

There are four session tokens, and each is associated with the individual functional units listed in Exhibit IV-4-3. If an OSI connection uses one or more of the functional units shown, the corresponding tokens are brought into play and are available on the connection. Any other tokens are unavailable.

Communication between OSI layers takes place through the use of primitives, of which there are four types: request, indication, response, and confirm. Information is sent to a remote system by invoking request or response primitives. Information is received from a remote system or the service provider by means of indication or confirm primitives. In general:

- A request primitive is invoked to initiate a session layer operation.
- An indication primitive denotes that a remote application or the service provider has initiated an operation.
- A response primitive carries the response to an indication primitive—Not all indications require a response.
- A confirm primitive completes the cycle by indicating the remote applications response to a locally initiated request—A confirm primitive can carry a negative or a positive reply.

Exhibit IV-4-4 illustrates the full sequence of the four primitives. The example used is the issue of a session activity-end request. If the local application has all the prerequisite tokens (i.e., the major activity token and, if half-duplex, the data token), the local application issues an activity-end request (1); the remote application receives the request as an activity-end indication primitive (2); and the remote application responds to the request with an activity-end response primitive (3) that is received by the local application as an activity-end confirm (4).

Not all session services require a response. For example, a transmission of normal data is illustrated in Exhibit IV-4-5. The remote application sends data with a session-data request primitive (1) and the local application receives it with a data-indication primitive (2). No response or confirm primitives are defined in the session for normal data transfer.

Session Token	Functional Unit
Data Token	Half Duplex
Synchronize-Minor Token	Minor Synchronize
Major Activity Token	Major Synchronize Activity Management
Release Token	Negotiated Release

Exhibit IV-4-3. Session Tokens and Functional Units

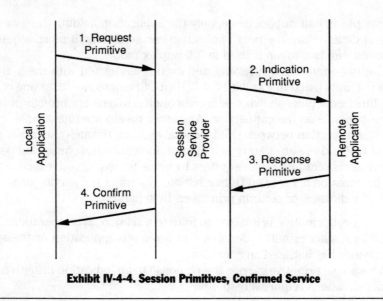

Exhibit IV-4-4. Session Primitives, Confirmed Service

Finally, a situation can arise in which the service provider independently initiates an indication request. Exhibit IV-4-6 diagrams a situation in which the network connection has been lost; the session service provider uses the provider-abort indication primitive to inform both local and remote applications.

Most session-layer services are propagated through the presentation layer up to the application layer. It is up to an application layer protocol to combine sequences of session service primitives into useful functions.

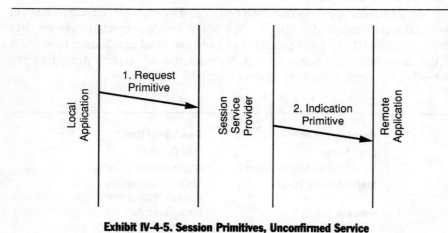

Exhibit IV-4-5. Session Primitives, Unconfirmed Service

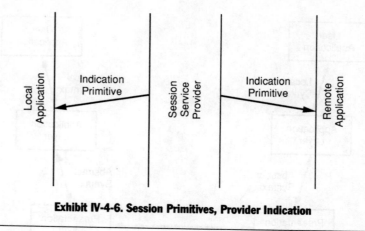

Exhibit IV-4-6. Session Primitives, Provider Indication

Presentation Services

Although the value and benefits of the ISO OSI session layer were debated in its early history, the role of the presentation layer has never been questioned. This was primarily because of the absence of anything resembling a session layer in contemporary network implementations, whereas all useful networks had a protocol function that was obviously a presentation layer.

The function of the presentation is conceptually simple. For two applications on arbitrary systems to communicate, they must speak a common language. The presentation layer serves as the required interpreter. However, the data bits passed across the network must have the same value to both sender and receiver, even if the representation of equivalent values differs. For example, July 4, 1776, would be represented as 7/4/1776 in the US but as 4-7-1776 in France.

The presentation layer functions by separating the data content of an item from its representation. The application layer communicates with the presentation layer by using an abstract description of the data (e.g., the integer 241, or the lowercase form of the 26th letter in the English alphabet, commonly called Z. The presentation entities at each end of the communication agree on an appropriate concrete transfer syntax to actually send the data. The application entities at each end can then convert the abstract representation into the local syntax used on their machine, whether it be EBCDIC character number 169_{10} on an IBM Corp mainframe or ASCII character number 122_{10} on a Digital Equipment Corp VAX.

The relationship of the various syntaxes in use is shown in Exhibit IV-4-7. Two key features of this model should be noted. First, the presentation layer is concerned only with the form, format, and syntax of the data and not with its meaning. Second, there is a one-to-one correspondence between presentation

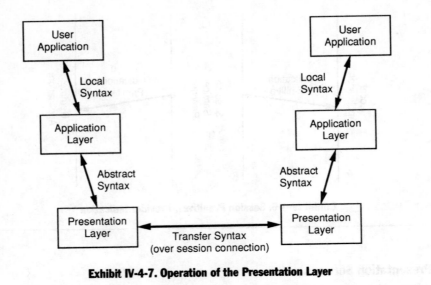

Exhibit IV-4-7. Operation of the Presentation Layer

connections and session connections. That is, the presentation layer performs no splitting, multiplexing, or other connection management.

The presentation layer service provided to the application layer includes:

- Session establishment, including transfer syntax negotiation.
- Renegotiation of transfer syntax as required (optional).
- Transfer of data.
- Session termination request.

Session services are passed directly through the presentation layer without intervention. Negotiation of the transfer syntax to be used is carried out by a dialogue between the presentation entities to determine the form that the data will have while in the OSI environment. These negotiations may be limited to the initiation phase, or they may be permitted at any time during a session if the appropriate function was negotiated at session initiation.

The negotiation process is typical of OSI protocol negotiations. One side requests certain connection states, and the other side responds with the requests that it can meet. The originator then decides whether the facilities offered in the response are adequate and either continues or closes the connection. In the example in Exhibit IV-4-8 of the negotiation of a transfer syntax for the exchange of text data, the local host starts out with a P-connect request, stating that it can handle ASCII, EBCDIC, and Intermediate encodings of text data. If the remote host can handle ASCII, Intermediate, and IBM PC character sets, it sends a P-connect response that represents the only two encodings

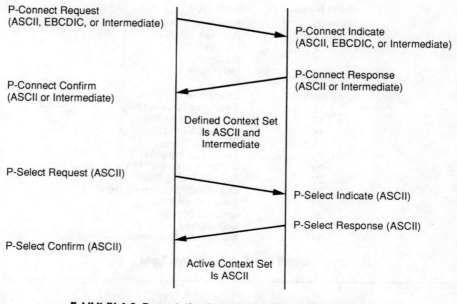

Exhibit IV-4-8. Presentation Layer Negotiation of Transfer Syntax

requested by the local host that it can support. This initial negotiation determines the defined context set, or the set of contexts—ASCII and Intermediate in this case—available for communication.

The active context set is then selected from the defined context set using the P-select exchange. This is the second exchange occurring in the illustration. The local host declares its preference for ASCII with a P-select request and the remote host confirms the selection.

Standard presentation layer syntax is defined by ISO Standard 8824, abstract syntax notation one (ASN.1). Nonstandard syntaxes may also be negotiated so that, for example, two machines can use a proprietary exchange syntax for higher performance. ISO 8824 is a superset of CCITT X.208 and X.209 and is used for more than just presentation layer data exchange. Because ASN.1 provides a notation for describing data structures independent of their physical implementation or encoding, it is widely used in the definition of many ISO data communications protocols. Programs are available to translate directly from ASN.1 to data structures for popular programming languages and vice versa.

Although ASN.1 can handle virtually any type of data, it also defines some universally accepted data types. The built-in types are listed in Exhibit IV-4-9 and include primitive types (e.g., Boolean and time representation) and constructors (e.g., set and sequence).

Class Number	Data Type
0	Reserved
1	Boolean
2	Integer
3	Bit String
4	Octet String
5	Null
6–15	Unassigned
16	Sequence (ordered list)
17	Set (unordered list)
18	Numeric String
19	Printable String
20	Teletex String (S61)
21	Videotex String (S100)
22	ISO 646 String (IA5)
23	Coordinated Universal Time
24	Generalized Time
25	Graphic String
26–30	Unassigned
31	Multioctet Identifier

Exhibit IV-4-9. ASN.1 Built-In Types

Equally important from the presentation services viewpoint are the encoding rules for ASN.1 defined by ISO 8825. These provide a universal means of converting ASN.1 abstract data into a physical encoding of bits and vice versa.

The representation of each data element comprises three components: the identifier, which determines the type of data; the length, which specifies the size of the representation of the contents; and the contents, which provide the value of the data element. These three components are referred to as the type-length-value of a data element.

The identifier uniquely distinguishes the data type by class, form, and class number. Bits 8 and 7 of the first octet are the class bits. If the bits are 00, the class is defined by ASN.1 and called a universal class. The application-specific class is denoted by 01 and defined by standards other than ISO 8824 (and CCITT X.208 and X.209). Class 10 is context specific, and class 11 (i.e., private use) is outside the scope of ASN.1. Bit 6, the form bit, can be either 0 (signifying a primitive form containing a simple value) or 1 (signifying a constructed form composed of multiple values). The remaining five bits of the first octet are either the class number or a multioctet identifier indicating that the class number follows in one or more identifier octets. The number of octets making up a multioctet identifier is determined dynamically. Bit 8 of each subsequent identifier octet is checked; if the value is 1, the other 7 bits and the next octet are part of the identifier. If the value is 0, bits 7 through 1 are the last 7 bits of the multioctet identifier.

The length component specifies the length of the contents in octets. This component can have three forms. The short form is 1 octet long and is identified by bit 8 having a value of 0; the low-order 7 bits then specify the length of the contents in octets. The long form is indicated by bit 8 having a value of 1; the low-order 7 bits of the first octet indicate the length of the length field in octets. Specifying the length of the length field to be 0 yields the indefinite form, in which the length of the contents must be determined from the contents itself (e.g., a null terminated string of ASCII characters).

Finally, the contents field contains the actual information to be communicated. This must be interpreted in accordance with the identifier and can be simple or constructed. Constructions can be nested without restriction, though finite machine resources can impose implementation limits.

Application Services

The application layer consists of a set of objects in each system. These objects, called service elements, accept and process requests for services from the OSI environment. Traditionally, there have been two distinct families of service elements: common application service elements and specific application service elements. The common application service elements provide capabilities required by other application service elements that are independent of any particular application (e.g., setting up a connection). The specific application service elements provide capabilities to satisfy the needs of specific information transfer processes of broad utility (e.g., transferring a file or accessing a data base). A third family of service elements, user application service elements, is considered outside the scope of ISO general-purpose standardization activity.

Common application service elements comprise three protocols: association control service elements, remote operations service elements, and commitment, concurrency, and recovery. All three are intended for use by other application service elements rather than by OSI users.

Association control service elements are used by most of the ISO-developed protocols (e.g., file transfer, access, and management (FTAM), virtual terminal, and manufacturing messaging specification). Association control service elements are defined by ISO Standards 8649 Part 2 and 8650 Part 2. They allow a communications association (i.e., a connection) to be set up between two application layer processes, independent of the location or implementation of either. Once the association is set up, the application protocol communicates directly with the presentation layer and the association control service elements are not used again until it is time to release, or abort, the association.

The protocol exchange required to set up an association is illustrated in Exhibit IV-4-10. A connection is established when an application entity using an association control service element issues an **A-ASSOCIATE** request to the service element. The remote application entity then receives an **A-ASSOCIATE** indication from the remote association control service element. On the basis of the application name requested, application name of the requester, capabilities,

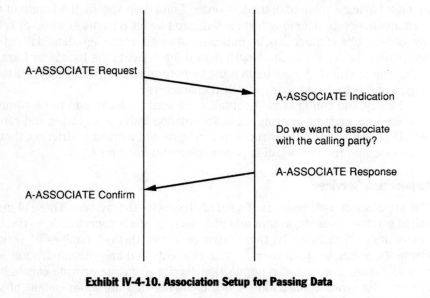

A-ASSOCIATE Request

A-ASSOCIATE Indication

Do we want to associate
with the calling party?

A-ASSOCIATE Response

A-ASSOCIATE Confirm

Exhibit IV-4-10. Association Setup for Passing Data

passwords, and other data provided by the initiator, the appropriate positive or negative **A-ASSOCIATE** response is issued to the remote association control service element implementation. The results of this negotiation are finally reported to the initiator through the **A-ASSOCIATE** confirm primitive.

A connection is released through a similar handshake. An abort does not require confirmation from the remote partner, so the service primitives are used only for request and indication. Two independent abort indications are defined to permit distinguishing between the two sources of aborts. The **A-ABORT** indication is used to signify an abort requested by the remote application entity using an association control service element. Aborts caused by internal networking failures are signaled with the **A-P-ABORT** indication.

The remote operations service elements protocol was developed to control the remote execution of simple commands. It establishes and releases associations and initiates remote operations. Defined by ISO 9072, this protocol is used as the underlying communications mechanism to support ISO directory service and network management.

Although the remote operations service elements protocol, like the association control service elements protocol, establishes and releases associations, its primary purpose is to control the remote execution of simple commands through the five primitives: **INVOKE, RESULT, ERROR, USER REJECT,** and **PROVIDER REJECT.** The **INVOKE** primitive is used to invoke an operation on a remote system. The results of the operation are returned by the **RESULT** primitive. Failure to invoke the requested operation is reported by the **ERROR, USER REJECT,** or **PROVIDER REJECT** primitive, depending on the cause of the failure.

The third common application service element is commitment, concurrency, and recovery. Originally defined along with association control service elements by ISO 8649 and 8650, work is under way to make ISO 8649 and 8650 exclusively association control service elements and to move commitment, concurrency, and recovery to its own standard designation.

The commitment, concurrency, and recovery protocol is the underlying protocol that allows a process to safely control the operation of multiple remote processes. The goal is to automate the task of synchronizing processes over unreliable communications links. For example, a bank that wishes to withdraw $5 million from one account and deposit it into another must be certain that no money is deposited until after the $5 million has been withdrawn. At the same time, the owner of the money is concerned that the money is not withdrawn until deposit is guaranteed. It must be recognized that at any stage of the transaction, a communications link could fail, leaving the bank unable to communicate with the managers of either the account being withdrawn from or the account being deposited to. Although this type of communication is needed by all applications in which data is distributed among multiple data bases that must be kept consistent, it is technically classified as difficult to attain. Mathematicians have shown that it is impossible for two entities communicating over an unreliable channel to have the same state of knowledge at the same time.

The goal of commitment, concurrency, and recovery is not to do the impossible but to minimize the risk by concentrating all efforts toward reaching an acceptable solution and to avoid the wasteful duplication of effort required if every application has to invent its own solution. The commitment, concurrency, and recovery protocol minimizes the exposure of each transaction to failure by creating a separate transaction phase in which each entity involved is asked to prepare for the transaction. Preparation has three aspects: all local resources required to complete the transaction are locked to guarantee the ability to complete the transaction, the ability to back out of the transaction is retained, and the desire to carry out the requested transaction is determined.

The protocol works in a master-subordinate fashion (see Exhibit IV-4-11). In phase 1, the master goes out to each of the subordinates involved and asks each subordinate to prepare its part of the transaction using the **BEGIN** primitive. Each subordinate responds with either **READY,** indicating ability and willingness to complete the requested action, or **REFUSE,** indicating that the transaction cannot be completed as requested (see Exhibit IV-4-12). When the master gets responses back from all the subordinates, it knows whether the overall transaction can be completed. When all responses are **READY,** the master can direct the subordinates to **COMMIT,** completing the transaction.

If any subordinate indicates an inability to complete the transaction,

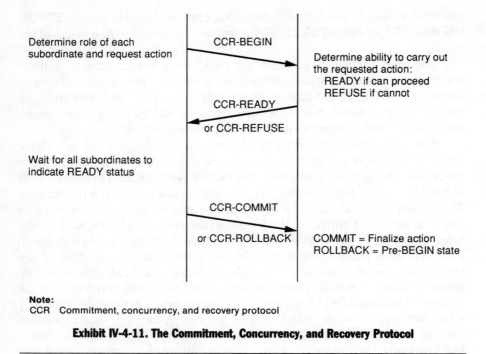

Determine role of each
subordinate and request action

CCR-BEGIN

Determine ability to carry out
the requested action:
READY if can proceed
REFUSE if cannot

CCR-READY
or CCR-REFUSE

Wait for all subordinates to
indicate READY status

CCR-COMMIT
or CCR-ROLLBACK

COMMIT = Finalize action
ROLLBACK = Pre-BEGIN state

Note:
CCR   Commitment, concurrency, and recovery protocol

Exhibit IV-4-11. The Commitment, Concurrency, and Recovery Protocol

however, the master can instead direct all the subordinates to **ROLLBACK** (see
Exhibit IV-4-13). Each subordinate then restores modified data base entries
and unlocks reserved resources. The result, aside from the rejection of any
transaction requests that are incompatible with the original lock, is as if nothing had happened. Thus, either all machines proceed ahead to completion or
none do.

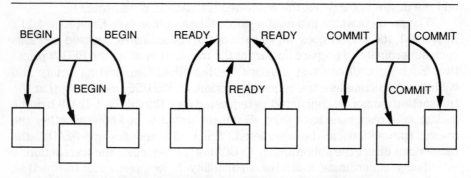

BEGIN   BEGIN   READY   READY   COMMIT   COMMIT

BEGIN   READY   COMMIT

Exhibit IV-4-12. Commitment, Concurrency, and Recovery in Operation

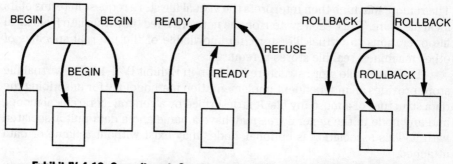

Exhibit IV-4-13. Commitment, Concurrency, and Recovery in Operation: Recovery

USER-ACCESSIBLE SERVICE ELEMENTS

Application service elements provide basic capabilities of general utility and may be employed directly by the utility programs of user applications or integrated into the native operating system. Only the services provided and the protocols to implement those services are defined by the OSI standards; the method of access is considered part of the local systems environment and is deliberately excluded from the current OSI standards.

Standards have been developed for several common needs (e.g., terminal access, file transfer, and electronic mail), and other standards (e.g., transaction processing and distributed data base) are being developed, but all share a key characteristic: they are relatively independent of any specific user application. For example, file transfer is required in applications as diverse as banking and factory automation. Whereas the contents of the files being transferred may be application specific, the tools required to implement the movement are not.

Some standards at this level (e.g., the manufacturing messaging specification) include application-specific extensions. In the case of the manufacturing messaging specification, the ISO standard defines a framework and general-purpose capabilities. Industry-specific semantics (e.g., robot control messages or programmable logic controller programming) are delegated to companion standards developed by industry groups. For example, development of the robot message specification is coordinated under the R15 Standards Committee of the Robot Industries Association.

File Transfer, Access, and Management

FTAM is defined by ISO IS 8571 and allows the transfer of data between any two systems in the form of files and a program on one system to manipulate files on another system. Interoperation between systems with incompatible file systems is made possible through the use of a virtual file store. The local machine translates its file requests into the equivalent operation on the virtual file store.

The remote machine then interprets the virtual file store request in terms of its local file store. Thus, each system on the network need only translate from local file operations to virtual file store; no knowledge of the internal specifics of other machines' real file stores is required.

The virtual file store structure is shown in Exhibit IV-4-14. The virtual file store provides an independent implementation methodology for describing the data structure of almost any file. It is described by a general hierarchical model, and any node in the general tree may have a name and a data unit associated with it. This association is optional; nodes may exist without a name or data attached.

This structure is extremely flexible. Almost any kind of file structure can be represented. Examples of a few common file types are shown in Exhibit IV-4-15. The simplest is the unstructured file: the entire file is a large data unit associated with a single, nameless node at the root of the tree. Flat files and random access files are similar; the only difference is the use of node names to allow specification of particular data units in the random access file model. The file mappings are also not limited to simple file types. Modeling of complex structures (e.g., indexed sequential) is also possible.

The virtual file store provides the basis for all FTAM operations. In addition to the ability to read, extend, replace, insert, erase, or locate data units

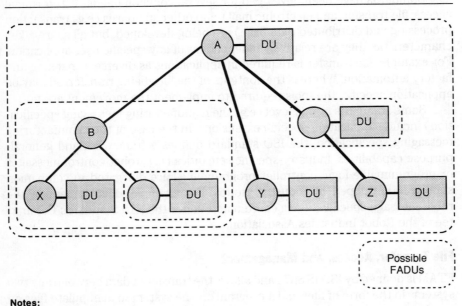

Notes:
DU   Data unit
FADU   File access data unit

Exhibit IV-4-14. The ISO FTAM Virtual File Store

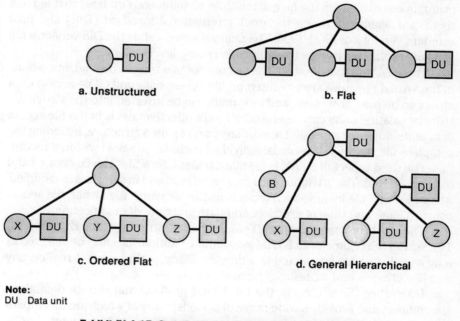

a. Unstructured

b. Flat

c. Ordered Flat

d. General Hierarchical

Note:
DU   Data unit

Exhibit IV-4-15. Sample Virtual File Store Structure Mappings

or combinations of data units in the virtual file store, the FTAM protocol provides for equivalent operations on entire files and the attributes associated with files. These operations can then be combined to transfer, access, or manage files.

File transfer is reliable or user correctable. In reliable file transfer, the FTAM protocols handle all checkpointing and error recovery. If a file transfer is interrupted or otherwise fails while in progress, this mode of operation will automatically recover. The user-correctable mode leaves all checkpointing and recovery up to the FTAM user. In the OSI environment, the user may not be a person at a data entry terminal but the application software in the local system environment that is using the FTAM services.

File and record access allow an FTAM user to manipulate remote files with many of the same methods that are available on local files. Unlike file transfer, which focuses on efficient movement of bulk data, file access is more concerned with flexible and rapid access to small amounts of data—typically on the order of records in a file. File access allows multiple users to share a single copy of a particular file, thereby eliminating the use of multiple copies spread around the network. This ability to share is particularly important when multiple users are making changes to the file, because keeping multiple copies consistent throughout the network can be difficult at best. Indeed, it was this need to maintain consistency in the face of multiple, simultaneous updates that led to a significant change between the draft international standard (DIS) and final standard versions of ISO FTAM. The final version extends the DIS version's file locking capabilities to effectively include record-level locking.

The FTAM virtual file store has no concept of a record. Instead, operations in the virtual file store are executed on file access data units. File access data units can be read or written, and new units can be inserted into the virtual file store or existing units can be erased. FTAM's effectiveness is in the file access data units' ability to represent almost any part of a file's structure, including the complete file, a group of records, individual records, or a field within a record.

The third aspect of FTAM is file management. New files can be created and old files deleted. The attributes of a file can be read and in some cases modified. Attributes of a file include such aspects as the file name, file owner, file access controls, date and time of creation, and date and time of modification.

The protocol implementing FTAM is a regime structure (see Exhibit IV-4-16). Within the regime of an FTAM association, multiple files may be selected as long as only one file is selected at a time. Similarly, within a select regime, any number of reads and writes may be made on the file.

Like other OSI protocols, the full FTAM protocol and service definitions are complex and provide a wide range of options, many of which are incompatible with each other. It is unrealistic to expect vendors to independently imple-

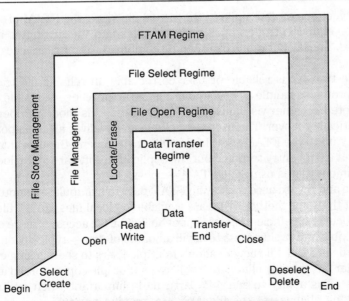

Exhibit IV-4-16. Operating Regimes in ISO FTAM

ment OSI capabilities that actually interoperate, yet the intent of OSI is to get away from vendor-dependent networking. This situation presents a quandary. Resolution is found in the various OSI profiles (e.g., the Manufacturing Automation Protocol [MAP], the Technical and Office Protocol [TOP], and the government OSI profile [GOSIP]). In turn, these profiles have relied on the Workshop for Implementers of OSI. This ongoing series of meetings for vendors and concerned users is moderated by the US National Institute for Standards and Technology (NIST); ambiguities can be resolved and options negotiated at these meetings. The output of the meetings is then documented in *The Implementation Agreements for Open Systems Interconnection Protocols.* These workshops have had such a critical impact on the implementation and practicality of OSI that the European Workshop for Open Systems and the Asian-Oceanic Workshop were developed to provide more international harmonization.

The implementation agreements concerning FTAM are divided into three generations or phases. Phase 1 is the basis for MAP 2.1 and provides a very limited capability based on the draft proposal version of FTAM that was available in 1985. Basically, it provides the ability to move a simple text or raw binary file from one machine to another.

Phase 2 FTAM forms the basis for MAP 3.0, TOP 3.0, and US GOSIP. Phase 2 is based on the international standard version of FTAM and provides far more capability than phase 1. In particular, it includes file access in addition to file transfer and the ability to work with different data types and file structures. The full range of capabilities defined are listed in Exhibit IV-4-17.

Phase 3 is still being defined. Expected to be included are additional file structures, support for reliable transfer, and application access to concurrency controls.

Message Handling Systems

Ranking in importance with file services is message handling, or electronic mail. The OSI standard for message handling is defined by the International Telephone and Telegraph Consultative Committee (CCITT). Commonly referred to as X.400, the OSI standard is actually a series of standards, only one of which is

---

Data Types	**File Structures**
Integer	Flat, Unstructured Binary
Floating Point	Simple Text
Date and Time	Random Access
Boolean	Indexed Sequential
String of Characters	Directory
String of Octets	

Exhibit IV-4-17. Phase 2 FTAM Capabilities

X.400. The various standards that constitute X.400 message handling are listed in Exhibit IV-4-18.

X.400 provides global interconnection of multimedia mail systems. Theoretically, any information that can be digitally encoded (including text, graphics, facsimile, and voice media) can be enclosed in an envelope and mailed to another user. Interoperability with the existing telex message system is also provided. In practice, initial implementations of X.400 support only simple text consisting of the IA5 character set—seven-bit US ASCII with a few US-only characters (e.g., the dollar sign) modified. Other information can be sent, but the ability of the recipient to correctly read it cannot be assumed except by prior arrangement. In time, however, a wide range of capabilities should be available.

The initial service offered by X.400 is interpersonal messaging, which provides the ability to deliver a message to a remote user without both users being connected in real time by the network. Otherwise, interpersonal messaging is similar to file transfer. Both services support moving digital data from one machine to another. However, whereas FTAM requires both systems to be simultaneously on the network to establish a connection, interpersonal messaging works with a third-party message transfer service to defer delivery until it is convenient for the receiving party. This split in functional capability is shown in Exhibit IV-4-19.

The originator of the message interacts with the user agent service on the local machine to prepare the message for transmission. The originator can be a person using a terminal or a user application process on a host machine. When ready to send the message, the user agent connects to the local message-transfer agent and releases the message for delivery. Once this local transaction is completed, the originator and user agent are no longer required to maintain contact with the serving message-transfer agent. The message-transfer agent can wait until less expensive transport facilities are available and then communicate peer-to-peer with other message-transfer agents to move accumulated messages toward their destinations. Once at the recipient's message-transfer agent, the message is stored until the recipient's user agent connects to the message-transfer agent to pick up mail with another local transaction.

X.400	Message Handling System
X.401	User Service Elements
X.408	Conversion Rules
X.409	Abstract Syntax Notation
X.410	Reliable Transfer Service
X.411	Message Transfer Protocols
X.420	Interpersonal Message Protocol
X.430	Teletex Access

Exhibit IV-4-18. CCITT X.400 Series of Standards

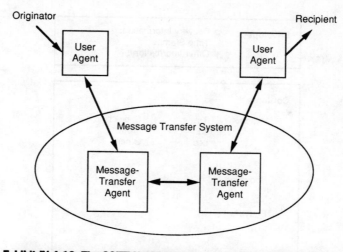

Exhibit IV-4-19. The CCITT X.400 Interpersonal Messaging Architecture

X.400 defines a wide range of service elements for electronic mail support. In addition to indicating subjects, cross-references, expiration dates, and message sensitivity, X.400 provides submission and delivery time stamps, allows multiple destinations, and provides carbon copies, distribution lists, access controls (e.g., recipient authentication), and delivery confirmation. Presentation layer services convert encoded information between otherwise incompatible machines. Conversion today is generally limited to envelope information and simple text body parts but will eventually expand to include other body-part types (e.g., extended character sets, formatted documents, spreadsheets, and graphics).

The message structure of an X.400 interpersonal message is shown in Exhibit IV-4-20. Some of the available fields are listed in Exhibit IV-4-21.

Job Transfer and Management

Job transfer and management is derived from the concept of remote job entry but is much more comprehensive. Defined by ISO 8831 job transfer and management (i.e., concepts and services) and 8832 job transfer and management (i.e., basic class protocol), job transfer and management is designed to support arbitrarily distributed processing elements. The basic class protocol provides for the submission of a job, collection of data from diverse sources, execution of the job, and distribution of the output. The various agencies involved in a job transfer and management application are shown in Exhibit IV-4-22.

Commitment, concurrency, and recovery is used to control individual actions and allow them to be controlled and rolled back as required. Job

```
┌──────────────────────────────────────────────────┐
│ Envelope      Delivery Information:                │
│               Time Stamps:                         │
│               Other Information:                   │
└──────────────────────────────────────────────────┘

┌──────────────────────────────────────────────────┐
│ Contents                                           │
│                                                    │
│     Header     To:            Subject:             │
│                cc:            From:                 │
│                bcc:           Other:               │
│                                                    │
│                                                    │
│     Body Part                                      │
│                                                    │
│                                                    │
│     Body Part                                      │
│                                                    │
└──────────────────────────────────────────────────┘
```

Exhibit IV-4-20. X.400 Message Structure

transfer and management maintains tight control of all aspects of job progress, allowing monitoring, control, and modification of the job in progress. Whereas the basic class supports only suspending, killing, or displaying the status of a job in progress, the full class also permits modifying, holding and releasing subjobs, and reporting of user messages.

More sophisticated control is possible through use of a transfer control record, which governs attempts to transfer documents in terms of timing and retries. These transfer control records may be modified during the progress of individual subjobs. Job transfer and management also makes use of document registration for time stamping, authorization, and audit trails. It allows separate, heterogeneous systems to participate in distributed batch processing. Unfor-

IPM Message Identification	Subject
Authorizing User	Importance
Originator	Sensitivity
Primary Recipients	Reply by (time)
Copy Recipients	Reply to Users
Blind-Copy Recipients	Expiration Date
In Reply to	Autoforwarded
Cross-References	Obsoletes

Note:
IPM   Interpersonal messaging

Exhibit IV-4-21. X.400 Interpersonal Message Fields

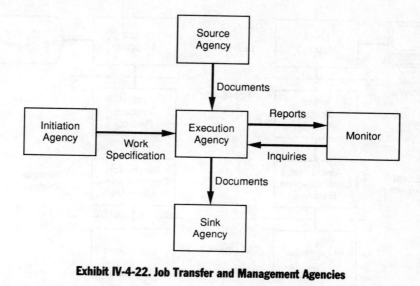

Exhibit IV-4-22. Job Transfer and Management Agencies

tunately, its emphasis on batch processing puts it in conflict with today's trend toward distributed interactive systems, and job transfer and management is not included in popular North American OSI profiles.

Virtual Terminal Protocol

The ISO standard for virtual terminal is defined in ISO 9040 (i.e., virtual terminal service) and ISO 9041 (i.e., virtual terminal protocol). Virtual terminal service resolves the differences between various terminals and hosts by defining a virtual terminal capability in the same way FTAM defines a virtual file store. Each end of the virtual terminal session then translates between the local expectations of terminal capability to those defined by the network virtual representation.

The ISO standard specifies the operations available on the virtual terminal and any associated characteristics. Characteristics include such details as the number of characters per line, the number of lines on the screen, the colors available for display, and available emphasis modes (e.g., underline, bold, or inverse video). Operations may be character, line, or page oriented and include such items as protected fields, light pens, and mouse input. The particular characteristics and operations to be used during any session are negotiated at the start of the virtual terminal session.

The virtual terminal service is based on the model illustrated in Exhibit IV-4-23. The local mapping function is an addition to the host operating system that breaks the usual data path between the user's terminal and the user's

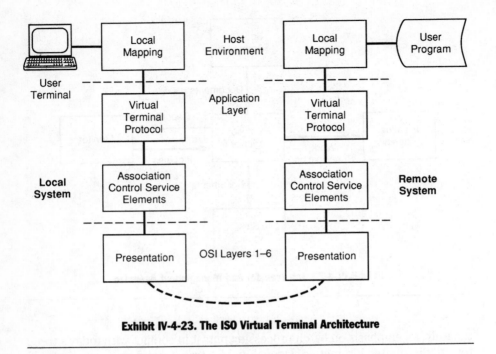

Exhibit IV-4-23. The ISO Virtual Terminal Architecture

program and allows the data path to be redirected. On the local system, the local mapping connects the user's terminal to the virtual terminal protocol. Similarly, on the remote system, the local mapping allows the virtual terminal protocol to control the user's program as if it were a local terminal.

The basic class virtual terminal protocol defines three service levels. The simplest subset establishes and terminates associations, transfers data, controls delivery of information, and recovers from errors. Delivery control provides the ability to buffer transferred data at the destination and deliver it to the receiver when commanded by the sender. Virtual terminal B extends the virtual terminal A definition with the ability to negotiate profile switches. This allows negotiating use of more powerful terminal features (e.g., cursor addressing) if supported by both end systems. Virtual terminal C adds the ability to negotiate multiple interactions over the same connection, permitting the user to control multiple independent programs from a single terminal.

Two modes of operation are defined for the virtual terminal. All the protocol subsets can operate in asynchronous or synchronous mode. In asynchronous mode, the two directions of data flow, terminal to program and program to terminal, are independent. Synchronous mode coordinates the two data flows. The definition is being reworked to include a forms-oriented virtual terminal, a graphics virtual terminal, and a mixed-mode (e.g., text, graphics, and voice) virtual terminal. The actual form of future enhancements to ISO virtual terminal are not clear. The general concept of terminal-oriented computing is being eclipsed by the microcomputer and workstation trend toward distributed computing. X-Windows is a typical equivalent protocol concept, extending the concept of virtual terminal to that of virtual user interface.

Manufacturing Messaging Specification

Factory floor communications with programmable devices (e.g., numerical controllers, programmable logic controllers, and robot controllers) are enhanced by a standard messaging language. The manufacturing messaging specification, ISO standard 9506, allows many communications functions to be implemented independent of the specific programmable device being controlled. For example, a robot can be issued emergency stop or cycle stop commands from a cell controller, thereby eliminating the need for a unique encoding of bits for each brand of robot controller.

Like the files and terminal services, the manufacturing messaging specification achieves machine independence by defining a conceptual virtual machine. A computer wishing to interact with any device writes only one translation into the model of the virtual machine. Each specific machine then translates from virtual machine operations to the appropriate operation on the particular machine. The virtual machine (see Exhibit IV-4-24) is general and allows a variety of manufacturing processes and devices to be mapped.

The executive function is common to all virtual protocol machines. This function provides overall control and a pathway to individual device functions.

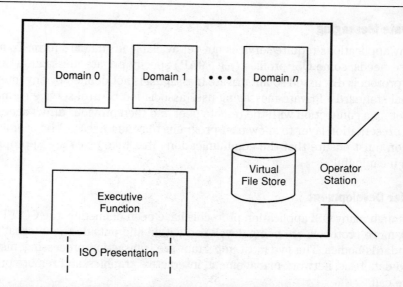

Exhibit IV-4-24. Manufacturing Messaging Specification Virtual Protocol Machine

A file system is defined to allow for simple file operations (e.g., create, copy, and delete), which allows recipes, control programs, and other files to be transferred without the full FTAM protocol. A simple operator interface is also defined to allow for operator interaction with a cell controller. Like the virtual machine's file system, this is an optional feature that provides minimal capabilities with minimal protocol overhead. The expectation of the protocol designers was that if extensive operator interface or file system manipulations were required, the user would implement an appropriate full-powered OSI protocol in addition to the manufacturing messaging specification.

The other primary capability for the virtual protocol machine is the operating domains. A virtual machine must define at least one operating domain; additional domains are optional and may be implemented, if appropriate, for the specific device. The operating domain is where the specific operations for a manufacturing device are defined. Outside of general capabilities (e.g., journaling and variable definition), the specifics of the operating domain are not defined by the ISO manufacturing messaging specification. Instead, they are defined in what are called companion standards, developed by specific industry groups for specific device classes. For example, the Robot Institute of America is developing a companion standard for robot controller operations.

Taken as a whole, the virtual machine concept provides several basic services. It allows a controller to read and write variables on the device, to define variables to be read or written, to upload and download files, to interact with an operator at a keyboard or through indicators and switches, to maintain and read journals, to define and use semaphores to control multiple machine interaction, and to generate and report events.

Private Messaging

Many applications require services not yet available in standard form. To meet those needs, some OSI profiles (e.g., MAP) specify private messaging. Unlike the protocols discussed so far, private messaging is not defined by any international standards. Private messaging uses association control service elements to set up a connection with the remote peer and then provides direct access to the presentation layer to allow user programs to communicate. The user application must ensure that the communications that take place are appropriate and meaningful.

Under Development

Although many OSI application protocols have been defined by the CCITT and ISO, more protocols are being developed within and outside the international standards bodies. The five most important are transaction processing, distributed data base, network management, interactive graphics, and remote procedure call.

Transaction processing is being developed by the ISO. Current expectations are that the services will be similar to those defined by the IBM LU 6.2 protocol. The protocols to implement those services will be independently defined, however, and may bear no resemblance to the IBM version.

The development of distributed data base functional capabilities is closely related to transaction processing. Whereas the structured query language (SQL) has been standardized for encoding access requests to a centralized data base, little progress has been made in defining a truly distributed data base in which the information required to satisfy a request is distributed among multiple machines. A true distributed data base is beyond the current state of the art; it is not even clear if a perfect solution to the problems involved is logically possible, let alone technically feasible.

The standardization process—determining which imperfections are acceptable—is difficult in the politically charged arena of international standards, and the ultimate solution cannot be predicted at this time. In the meantime, transaction processing and standardized query languages substitute for full-distributed data bases.

The most critical missing OSI protocol is probably network management. The need for useful network management is recognized in the standards community, and work is progressing; a general framework for network management is already standardized. Although work on the communications protocols required to support the framework is progressing well, the critical missing piece is the definition of what to manage. The OSI network management framework identifies five key areas requiring network management: fault management, performance management, configuration management, security management, and accounting management.

OSI network management does not specify how a network is managed. Rather, it should provide the tools that are necessary for a vendor's network manager application to manage any other vendor's network objects by using a standard manager-agent protocol. The functional capability of the management application, or how the tools provided are used to manage the network, is not specified. The expectation is that network management applications will be proprietary, single-vendor developments. Unlike today's proprietary network management tools, however, they will be able to manage network resources unhampered by the vendor of any particular resource. This can be seen in the current vendor offerings, such as IBM's NetView, Digital Equipment Corp's Enterprise Network Management Architecture, Hewlett-Packard's OpenView, and AT&T's Unified Network Management Architecture. Originally, these companies supported only vendor-specific devices, but all have announced their intent to support other vendors' OSI-compliant products as OSI standards solidify.

Standards for distributed computing are being developed outside of the ISO and CCITT. Two of the most important projects, X-Windows and the network computing system (NCS), are described in the following paragraphs. As these projects near completion and stabilize, they will be given ISO standard status. This method of operation in standards development is becoming common because it minimizes duplication of effort and maximizes the scope and speed of standards development.

X-Windows from Project Athena at Massachusetts Institute of Technology and the network computing system developed by Apollo Computers, a division of Hewlett-Packard, are results of the trend in UNIX workstations toward distributed, integrated environments.

Unlike traditional mainframe networks (in which the emphasis is on bulk transfers) and personal computer networks (in which the emphasis is on file system, communication, and other servers for processes running on local personal computers), the best environment for workstation networking is a true distributed processing environment. The goal of both X-Windows and the network computing system is to distinguish between the presentation of services to a user and the provision of those services, removing the artificial ties that plague current environments and frustrate users.

X-Windows accomplishes this goal for interactive applications by separating the display functions from the program function. An application written to X-Windows can then communicate with the user without concern for the specifics of that user's display. This allows software developers to create applications that can be run from various vendors' machines rather than require the redesign of the user interface for each platform. The benefits to the user are tremendous: a user on any machine can access an application on any other machine—or locally on the user's own machine—without concern for where the application runs or whether it is compatible.

In some ways, X-Windows is the state of the art in graphics virtual terminal capability; however, it does more than perform traditional virtual terminal operations. In many ways, it defines yet another standard terminal type, although a flexible and highly extensible one. By separating the application from the specifics of the display implementation, it allows applications developers to concentrate on the mechanics of computing and display developers to enhance their products without rendering them incompatible with existing applications.

X-Windows also illustrates the client-server model of distributed computing, which is becoming prevalent in emerging protocols. As shown in Exhibit IV-4-25, X-Windows is an asymmetric protocol, unlike traditional ISO OSI protocols. The X-Windows client on the application server uses the X-Windows server on the client workstation to provide the human interface. The X-Windows client and server roles are apparently the reverse of most client-server protocols, in which the client is on the end-user workstation and the server executes on the larger computer. This reverse relationship is not perceived by the X-Windows protocol. From its perspective, the client workstation provides the display service to the application server. From a more global viewpoint, however, the X-Windows server runs on the application client machine and the X-Windows client runs on the application server.

The X-Windows protocol itself provides a wide range of interactive display

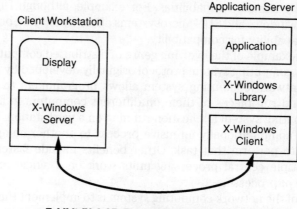

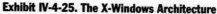

Exhibit IV-4-25. The X-Windows Architecture

services for the user and application. It allows the user to have multiple windows open—each associated with a client application, independent of the physical location of the client. Engineering users, for example, can have a word processing window open to their local machine, an electronic mail window open to the departmental mail server, a design application running on a high-powered workstation, and a simulation program running on the corporate supercomputer.

It is this flexibility, however, that is the Achilles' heel of X-Windows. If each application uses a different paradigm for user interaction (e.g., if one uses the escape key to execute commands and another uses the same key to cancel them), users can become hopelessly confused, and the benefit of having a wealth of applications available is greatly diminished by the productivity that is lost in trying to figure out how each one works. This problem is being attacked on several fronts, all with the goal of providing a user interface standard that allows distributed computer users to gain some of the advantages long enjoyed by Apple Macintosh users (i.e., consistent user interfaces). Digital Equipment, for example, is standardizing on DECview, a common corporate specification for the use of windows in the DEC VMS, UNIX, and IBM PC worlds. DECview adds standard toolkits to X-Windows for applications developers to provide consistent interfaces between applications.

The first product of the Open Software Foundation (OSF) was OSF/MOTIF—a standard windowing user interface that, although built on X-Windows and the DEC windows toolkit, is similar in appearance and methods of use to the Microsoft/IBM Presentation Manager in the personal computer environment. Although caught up in the proprietary battles being fought in the UNIX arena between OSF and Unix International, OSF/MOTIF has become the dominant interface standard. Proprietary offerings continue but are generally accompanied by standard capabilities. For example, although Digital Equipment has DECwindows and SUN Microsystems offers OpenView, both also offer OSF/MOTIF capability for compatibility.

A second example of the evolving genre of distributed computer protocols is the network computing system protocol originally developed by Apollo Computers. The network computing system allows programmers to break apart applications and run pieces of them on different computers in a network. A network computing system application running on a workstation, for example, can off-load a computationally intensive process to another computer that is better suited to perform that task. Other benefits include faster processing (because multiple central processing units work on a single problem) and optimized use of processors.

The goal of the network computing system is to implement the dream of all computer users to employ all central processing unit cycles on every machine in the network. The network computing system provides three primary components to developers of networked programs: remote procedure calls, a network interface definition language, and a location broker. The general architecture is shown in Exhibit IV-4-26. When a user executes a program, the workstation application queries the location broker, requesting the network addresses of the computers needed for specific remote procedure calls. Subroutine calls are then routed to the specified processors, where they execute and return their results to the client application.

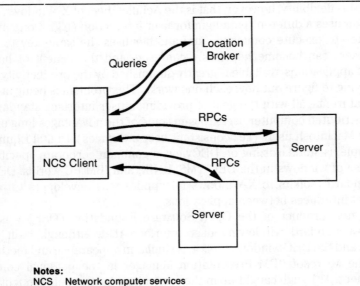

Notes:
NCS   Network computer services
RPC   Remote procedure call

Exhibit IV-4-26. Network Computer Services Architecture

The network interface definition language is used to define interfaces, called stubs, between the local application (i.e., the client) and the remote procedures that run on servers. The network interface definition language compiler converts the stubs and subroutines into C-language source code for loading onto the local and remote processors. The stubs on the local application then communicate with the stubs on the remote systems specified by the location broker. The stubs hide the physical distribution from the application and remote procedure.

The network computing system frees users from having to find remote resources, log on to them, and use their applications. A user can sit down at a workstation and have the network computing systems application indicate that it needs an array processor to run a program. The network computing system makes those connections for the user. It allows users to access a diversity of machines and highly specialized servers for data bases and vector processing.

Although the durability of the network computing system as an OSI standard was not proved at the time of this writing, more than 100 vendors have licensed the technology, including IBM, Digital Equipment, and Hewlett-Packard. Even if the network computing system does not succeed commercially—it does have competition, such as Sun Microsystem's open network computing product—it provides insight into the directions being pursued in distributed processing and demonstrates that distributed processing in the truest sense is both possible and practical.

ABOVE THE OSI MODEL

Although the OSI reference model provides basic networking services, it does not include the ability to transfer the meaning of the data (i.e., the true informational content)—that is the province of information exchange protocols. These protocols serve as the network equivalent of data base dictionaries, allowing the information transferred to be correctly interpreted by the recipient. Standards for document interchange, business transactions, and product data (i.e., computer-aided design/computer-aided manufacturing, or CAD/CAM) interchange are being refined.

The development of information exchange protocols increases as users discover that even though computers can now talk to each other, they cannot necessarily communicate. The lower-layer services are comparable to the telephone system. A user in New York can call a user in France, but unless the New Yorker speaks French or the French person speaks English, not much communication is going to occur, because a path for data, though necessary, is insufficient to ensure the exchange of meaningful information. OSI is sometimes called digital Esperanto because of its role as a universal language for computers. Some cynics contend that OSI will suffer the same fate as Esperanto, ignoring the fact that to computers, the stability of a standard is far more important than the richness of a proprietary format.

Standards use is becoming less an option and more a necessity. The competitive nature of the marketplace no longer allows for inefficiencies, such as plotting out drawings from a three-dimensional modeling package used in the design laboratory and having the manufacturing engineers rebuild the solid model from the drawings to develop their machining programs. Besides increasing the probability of introducing errors, the company with inadequate communications is still at the keyboard while its competitors are shipping products.

Document Interchange Standards

Anyone who has tried to use a word processor to work on a document that was originally developed on a different word processor can understand the reason for document exchange standards. The goal of these standards is to allow a work group to cooperate on the development and production of documents ranging from memos to books without constraining the entire group to use a particular word processing package. Ideally, each group member could use the package best suited for his or her specific needs and skills without constraining the exchange of documents in any way.

This goal is not completely attainable because different packages have different capabilities, and a word processor that lacks the means to merge text and graphics cannot effectively edit the output of a publishing package containing multiple text fonts, line drawings, and scanned images. But more capability can be provided than when converting everything to unformatted ASCII text, which entails losing all of a document's logical structure from page headings to paragraph boundaries.

From an implementation viewpoint, there are two approaches to the document exchange problem. One technique is to define a document definition architecture, in which the different features of exchangeable documents are encoded in a standard data structure. This is the approach taken by the office document architecture and office document interchange format standard. The alternative, defined by the standard generalized mark-up language standard, takes the text of the document and adds all layout and structure with escape sequences. This approach was initiated by the publishing industry because it allowed the use of simple alphanumeric display terminals to perform sophisticated layouts. Both international standards are published by the ISO.

ISO 8613, office document architecture and office document interchange format, allows the exchange of documents of any kind across a network. It is designed to enable the user to reproduce, revise, and otherwise work on documents ranging from traditional word processing to typeset format (e.g., spreadsheets, images, or line drawings).

The ISO office document architecture is built around the conceptual model of the document generation process shown in Exhibit IV-4-27. Generation of a document is divided into three distinct phases: the editing process, the layout process, and the imaging process.

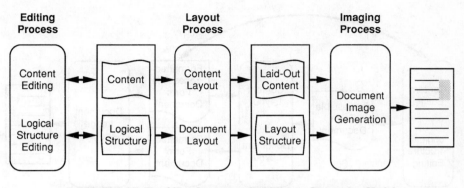

Exhibit IV-4-27. The Office Document Architecture Processing Model

The document editing process is divided between the content editing and the logical structure editing. In a text document, the content consists of the words that make up the document and the logical structure is the organization of those words into paragraphs, headings, footnotes,.and chapters. In a compound document, the logical structure defines which contents are text and which are illustrations. The output of the editing phase is a document that can either proceed to the layout phase or return to the editing phase for modification.

The output of the editing phase is not suitable for generating a formatted document—that is the task of the layout process. Like the editing process, the layout process consists of two interacting processes: content layout and the document layout. The document layout process allocates the presentation medium being used to the various components making up the logical structure of the document. For example, a display screen may have areas reserved for menus, command entry, help notations, and data display. Similarly, the pages of a book have specific margins surrounding the main text, and illustrations fit inside the area used for text. The contents are formatted by the content layout process to fit within the areas defined by the document layout. This may require sizing and scaling of graphic elements or breaking paragraphs of text across page boundaries.

Once the contents and appearance are fully defined, it is possible to proceed to the final step. The imaging process takes the document layout structure and the individually laid out contents in that structure and generates a usable physical document. This may be a display screen, printed paper, film, or whatever is appropriate for the document being produced.

The office document architecture defines three formats of standard document interchange: processible form, formatted form, and formatted processible form. The relationship of these forms to the document processing model is shown in Exhibit IV-4-28.

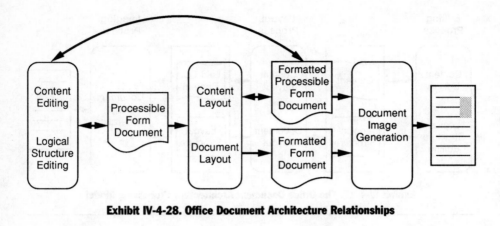

Exhibit IV-4-28. Office Document Architecture Relationships

Processible form is the output of the editing process and may be further edited or laid out. Formatted form and formatted processible form are the interchange output from the layout process. Formatted form is suitable only for input to the imaging process; no further editing or layout changes are possible because the information used to create the current layout is not included in the document. Formatted processible form can be used as input to any of the three generation processes. This form contains not only the layout structure and laid-out content required to image the document but the content and logical structure the final layout is based on.

The power of the office document architecture is demonstrated by TOP, which specifies all three forms of document interchange (i.e., formatted, processible, and processible formatted). Content architectures are specified to allow interchange of character data (i.e., text), raster graphics (i.e., scanned images), and geometric graphics (i.e., line drawings encoded in either the computer graphics metafile or the initial graphics exchange standard. Character content includes specification of such details as justification, fonts, character orientation, line spacing, and character spacing. Raster and geometric graphics provide similar flexibility within their domains.

Electronic Data Interchange

Electronic data interchange (EDI) allows a wide range of standard business documents to be exchanged. It provides a common syntax and common transaction format for direct computer-to-computer execution of typical business transactions. The range of transactions covered is shown in Exhibit IV-4-29. It includes electronic funds transfers as well as purchase orders, shipping acknowledgments, and invoices.

The format of an EDI message is defined by the three layers of envelopes shown in Exhibit IV-4-30. The innermost level is the envelope around each

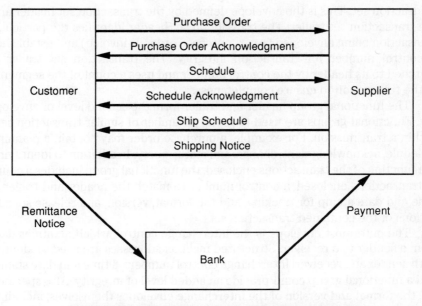

Exhibit IV-4-29. Typical Uses for Electronic Data Interchange

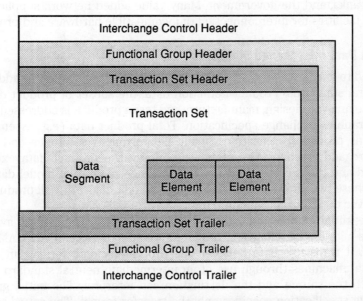

Exhibit IV-4-30. Format of an Electronic Data Interchange Message

transaction set. This is the envelope defined by the transaction set header and the transaction set trailer. The transaction set header identifies the particular transaction being enveloped (e.g., a purchase order or invoice) and establishes a control number for transaction integrity. The transaction set trailer is matched to its header by the control number and uses a count of the segments in the transaction to ensure completeness.

The functional group header and trailer form the second level of enveloping. Functional groups are used to group a number of similar transaction sets within a transmission. For example, a purchase order may contain a planning schedule, acknowledgment, change, and status query. In addition to identifying the function of the transactions enclosed, the functional group includes a count of transactions enclosed, a control number to match the header and trailer, a time and date stamp for tracking, and the format, version, and release specifications of the contained transaction sets.

The outermost envelope is the interchange control, which identifies data from a sender to a receiver. Structured mailbox addresses are used to identify both sender and receiver. Interchange control numbers, a time and date stamp, and a functional group count provide an added level of integrity. Also specified are the format and version of the interchange envelopes themselves, including the specific characters being used in the interchange for data element separators and segment terminators.

When used with electronic mail service, EDI can act as a bridge between incompatible operation schedules and numerous participants. A typical purchaser might require links to brokers, suppliers, customers, rail carriers, wholesalers, banks, and the government. Many value-added network suppliers also provide facilities for interconnection of incompatible hardware and protocols.

Product Data Interchange Standards

The need to exchange product data among users and applications is addressed by several standards. Product definition data, the subset of product data required to analyze, design, manufacture, and test a product, is addressed by the initial graphics exchange specification. Total product data (e.g., assembly instructions, process specifications, financial data, quality assurance, and testing data) are addressed by two standards efforts: the product data exchange standard and the ISO standard for the exchange of product model data. The goal of these two efforts is to define a single standard covering all product data needs over the entire product life cycle.

The initial graphics exchange specification, which is currently available, provides high-level exchange of design information between CAD/CAM workstations. It translates data between the proprietary data formats in use on individual machines through use of an intermediate neutral standard format that both the source and the destination can interpret. The initial graphics exchange specification specifies only the transfer format. The actual transfer may be provided by any convenient file transfer mechanism, from ISO FTAM to IBM bisynchronous remote job entry.

The key to the initial graphics exchange specification is that the meaning and structure of the data making up the drawing are transferred, not just the final image. For example, dimension lines retain their meaning as denoting dimensions of features rather than just arbitrary lines, arrowheads, and meaningless text. If a design is altered, the dimensions can change along with it.

This philosophy can be seen from the composition of an initial graphics exchange specification file, illustrated in Exhibit IV-4-31. The product definition data is divided into five sections. The start section is a text message for easy identification of the file contents. This is followed by the global section, which contains product-oriented information (e.g., the name of the product, the responsible engineer, and the company). The directory section describes the product data to follow, and the parameters section contains the actual design information. The terminate section provides error checks on the contents.

The initial graphics exchange specification has gone through several revisions since its first publication, with each version providing more capability. Version 3.0 provides for the exchange of data for drafting, curve modeling, surface modeling, finite-element modeling, parametric design modeling, and electrical and electronic design. Version 4.0, which is currently being implemented, adds solids modeling, plant design, manufacturing technology, architecture, engineering, and construction data exchange. Data encodings are de-

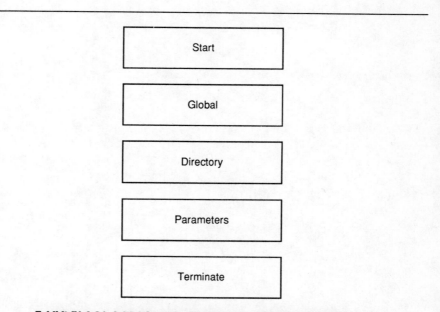

Exhibit IV-4-31. Initial Graphics Exchange Specification File Structure

fined in ASCII, compressed ASCII, and binary formats, with normal ASCII being the most popular despite the fact that it has the lowest storage efficiency of the three options.

SUMMARY

The OSI reference model—in particular the session, presentation, and application layers—has been developed to provide the basis for functional network interoperability. For this level of communication to be fully realized, however, continued development of higher-level standards, to allow information exchange between applications, is necessary. Further work on graphic user interfaces and document and graphics exchange standards will eventually simplify the use and management of computer networks and their applications.

IV-5

An Introduction to the DARPA Internet Project and the TCP/IP Protocol Family

JEFFREY EARL TYRE

TCP/IP is the combined acronym for a pair of networking protocols, the Transmission Control Protocol (TCP) and Internet Protocol (IP). These protocols are part of a family of protocols that have evolved from the Internet project, a national research effort initiated by the Department of Defense (DoD) that today networks thousands of government, commercial, and educational computers located around the world. TCP/IP has become synonymous with the Internet project, because these two protocols provide the major network communication procedures within this family of protocols. The two most familiar application protocols of the TCP/IP protocol family are the file transfer protocol (FTP) and Telnet, a terminal access protocol.

Exhibit IV-5-1 illustrates some typical components of the Internet environment. These devices, physically attached to various networks, internetwork through the support of the TCP/IP protocol family. Specifically, this exhibit shows devices connected to two LANs that are bridged together and that have wide-area access, by means of a gateway, to the Defense Data Network (DDN) packet-switching network. Each computer that has access to the Internet can be networked to any other computer on the Internet through the use of a unique address assigned to each computer. The networks and packet routing techniques employed make it possible to readily address computers within a building or across the nation.

The TCP/IP protocols have been readily embraced by the industry as a standardized thread connecting many heterogeneous computing environments. Because of the maturity and nonproprietary nature of these protocols, the TCP/IP protocol family is widely used outside the scope of the Internet project and its administrative jurisdiction, as a networking platform between any given group of computers for which protocol software and complementary network interface hardware are available. To help distinguish between a particular Internet project (the national networking project) and a generic TCP/IP internet project (which could be used either within or outside the context of

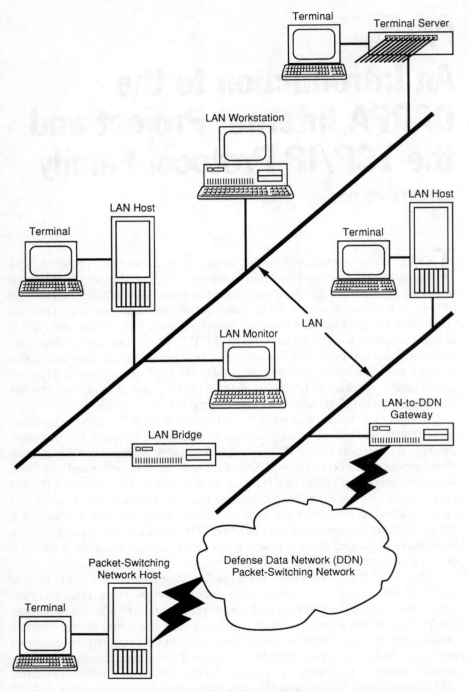

Exhibit IV-5-1. An Internet Environment

the Internet), this chapter refers to the former with an initial capital letter and the latter with a lowercase initial letter.

A major focus of this chapter is to review the history and administration of the Internet project. In addition, it discusses individual protocols that are part of the TCP/IP family and illustrates how the protocols provide a layered set of rules by which computer processes communicate.

HISTORY

The Internet project began in research supported by the DoD. The Advanced Research Project Agency Network (ARPANET) is a DoD-funded project that was established in 1969 as an experimental packet-switching network, the forerunner of today's X.25 wide area networks. The ARPANET led to the development of protocols that work on several administratively separate yet interconnected networks.

These networks provide communication services for hundreds of computers, primarily in the defense industry and scientific research communities. For example, the Military Network (MILNET) was splintered off from ARPANET to provide a separate military network facility. Along with several other classified networks, ARPANET and MILNET come under the authority of the DDN.

One of the fastest-growing segments of the Internet community is the NSFNET, a project primarily funded through the National Science Foundation to provide networking services to academic and industrial research groups. The internet backbone of the NFSNET is actually being used to replace sections of the ARPANET (which is limited to phone lines and modems) with T1 and T3 transmission capabilities. Data traffic rates are increasing in some regional areas of the NSFNET at the rate of 20% to 30% per month. Such a growth rate indicates that the NSFNET will become an important national data network.

The TCP/IP protocol family also has become a de facto standard for business and industry, where it is often used in non-Internet situations. A principal reason for this is that the International Standards Organization (ISO) set of networking protocols, the Open Systems Interconnection (OSI) reference model, has not been comprehensively formalized to the point of full implementation by vendors or their customers. In comparison, the TCP/IP protocols are one of the most mature and widely supported sets of networking protocols.

For example, TCP/IP has been programmed as an integral part of the University of California at Berkeley's BSD version of the UNIX operating system. Support of these networking protocols within the UNIX operating system has facilitated its use by such companies as Amdahl Corp, Data General Corp, Hewlett-Packard Co, Sun Microsystems Inc, and Unisys Corp. Other computing environments also enhanced with the TCP/IP protocol family include the Apple Macintosh, IBM Corp PC-DOS and VM, Digital Equipment Corp VMS and Micro-

VMS, SCO Inc XENIX, and Wang Laboratories Inc VS. Much of this can be attributed to the open forum within which the TCP/IP protocol family has evolved.

PROTOCOL STANDARDIZATION

Internet activities are coordinated by the DDN Network Information Center (NIC), which is part of SRI International (Menlo Park CA). This organization oversees the evolution of Internet standards through the distribution and review of technical reports called requests for comments (RFCs). RFCs can be formalized into official protocols (e.g., TCP and IP), which are standards issued for compliance by those groups using the Internet. Furthermore, these protocols may be adopted by the DoD as a military standard (Mil-Std) specification. For example, TCP and IP are respectively listed as RFC 793 and RFC 791 as well as being Mil-Std-1778 and Mil-Std-1777 specifications. Important RFCs continue to emerge (e.g., IBM's NetBIOS, which is being implemented on top of the TCP/IP networking functions). In general, it is hoped that by openly publishing RFCs, a uniform set of standards will be available to all who use them.

NETWORK ADMINISTRATION

The administration of any TCP/IP network depends on whether a connection to the Internet is to be provided, as opposed to use of the TCP/IP protocol family without a requirement for access to the Internet. If an Internet connection is desired, a network number must be obtained from the DDN NIC. Essentially, internetworking between TCP/IP networks is supported by the assignment of network numbers unique to each network. All devices attached to the same network have the same network number, with individual devices on a network having a different host address. The local administrator has the authority to assign a host address to the NIC network number, and the two in combination form a complete IP address for each network device.

This process identifies any device that has access to the Internet. If no access to the Internet is required, administrators are free to assign both network numbers and host addresses, as long as the basic rules regarding network and host addressing are followed in the manner previously described.

In reality, an IP address consists of four parts, commonly represented by the variable $a.b.c.d$, with each part consisting of 8 bits (decimal values actually range from 0 to 255) and yielding IP addresses that look something like 121.10.4.1. The four-part format yields three classes of networks, with each class effectively defining the number of hosts that can be identified through the use of this addressing convention. Using n to represent the network component and h to represent the host component, the four-part format yields three possible addressing schemes, which are discussed in the following sections.

Class A: *n.h.h.h.* In this class, the first byte represents the network number and the remaining three bytes represent the host address. This class is used for networks with a large number of hosts.

Class B: *n.n.h.h.* In this class, the first and second bytes represent the network number. The third and fourth bytes are used for the host address. This class is used for networks with an intermediate number of hosts.

Class C: *n.n.n.h.* This class has many networks, indicated by use of the first, second, and third bytes in combination to represent the network number. Only the fourth number is used to assign a host address. This class is used for networks with a small number of hosts.

ARCHITECTURAL DESIGN

As with many network protocol architectures, the TCP/IP protocols are functionally grouped into layers. The principal benefit of a layered architectural design is to provide protocols that specialize in network services and that work with processes in adjacent layers to form a comprehensive set of network communication mechanisms. Exhibit IV-5-2 presents both an architectural model for the TCP/IP protocols and the seven-layered OSI standard reference model. As can be seen from the exhibit, the OSI and TCP/IP architectural models share major structural elements. However, an important aspect of the

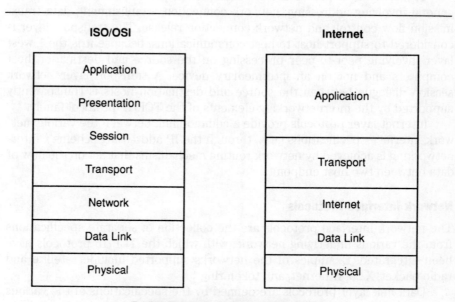

Exhibit IV-5-2. Architectural Comparison

evolution of the TCP/IP protocols has been their integration with communications specifications from a variety of underlying network interfaces. Specifications for these network interfaces are often derived from standards set by committees outside the Internet forum, such as X.25 from the International Telephone and Telegraph Consultative Committee (CCITT) and the 802 committee standards from the Institute of Electrical and Electronic Engineers (IEEE).

This chapter distinguishes between those protocols that are administered by the DDN NIC and those standards set by other organizations. It does not detail the standards set by the other organizations but does introduce the essential elements of these network interfaces.

Internet Protocols

The core of the TCP/IP family of protocols provides the essential application, host-to-host (i.e., endpoint) transport, and internetworking (i.e., intermediary point) protocols that have been implemented on a variety of network interfaces.

Application layer protocols of the TCP/IP model are designed to provide services similar to the protocols that are segregated between the upper three layers of the OSI model, including application user and programming interfaces, data and file type declaration, and network session initiation requests to the transport layer protocols.

Transport layer protocols from both models provide similar functions, in general involving addressing, network connection establishment, data transmission flow control, and network connection release. The transport layer is considered to support host-to-host communications, because it is the lowest layer involving peer-to-peer processing on the source and destination host computers and not on an intermediary device. A transport-layer network session dialogue between the source and destination hosts is transparently supported by the internetworking elements of the TCP/IP protocol family.

Internet layer protocols provide a common link between the various network interface specifications (e.g., through the IP addressing scheme). Internetworking is achieved by network routing mechanisms that act on the flow of data between two host endpoints.

Network Interface Protocols

The network interface protocols are the collection of separate specifications from the various underlying networks with which the TCP/IP protocols have been integrated. Examples of the networks supported include satellite and radio packet, X.25, Ethernet, and token ring.

Data link layer protocols are defined by the specifications of the various network interface standards. These protocols initiate, control, and terminate the flow of the communications link across the physical network. This includes error checking for reliable data transmission across the physical media. Some networks implement their own addressing scheme for network device identification with address specifications at this layer.

Physical layer protocols from networking standards supported in both architectural models define reliable, bit-level data transmission on network media. Primary concerns include mechanical, electrical, and procedural functions of the interface between the network device and the physical network.

NETWORKING DEVICES AND UNDERLYING MECHANISMS

Three general types of entities are involved in network communications: software processes, network devices, and physical networks. A process is a software program that is executing on a computer. All executing computer programs consist of one or more processes. The networking protocols discussed are implemented as executable computer programs and, therefore, consist of computer processes.

Network devices are computer units physically attached to the network (e.g., host computers, terminal servers, network monitors, gateways, routers, and bridges). Network devices have software processes executing on them that support network communications.

The term *network*, in a strict sense, applies to the media involved in network communications. This chapter applies the term *physical network* to distinguish the network media entity from the more generalized concept of a network, which commonly refers to all three types of entities involved in network communications.

Exhibit IV-5-3 illustrates the concept of process-to-process communication, within the context of the TCP/IP layered architecture presented in Exhibit IV-5-2. Two major components constitute process-to-process communication over a TCP/IP network. Dialogue between protocols of corresponding layers on physically separated devices is termed peer-to-peer communication and is represented by the horizontal arrows. The vertical arrows depict the flow of data within a device, between adjacent protocol layers, which is commonly referred to as layer-to-layer communication processing.

Several major network components are represented in Exhibit IV-5-3, along with the conceptual features mentioned previously.

Applications are represented by the letters X, Y, and Z to illustrate paired application layer processes on networked host computers. These can be either the standard TCP/IP protocol family applications (e.g., Telnet and FTP) or other programs that make programming calls as part of an application programming interface (API). An example of the latter is the BSD UNIX socket library of programming function calls, which interface to the lower-layer (i.e., transport layer and below) protocols.

Host computers are designated A and B in the exhibit. These are the computational platforms for the source (A) and destination (B) networking

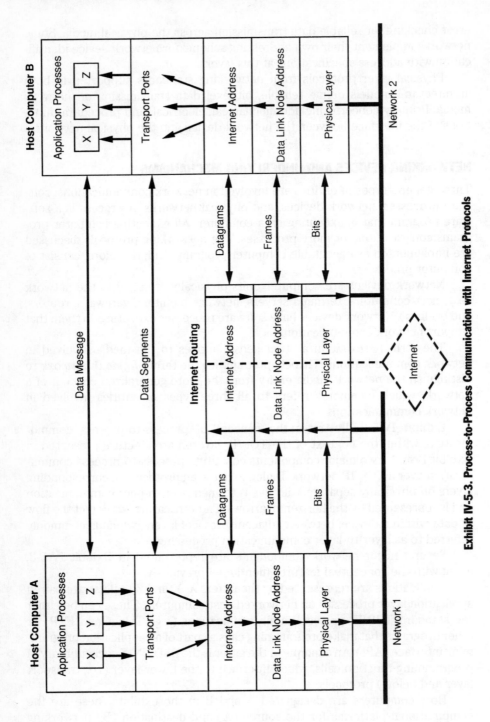

Exhibit IV-5-3. Process-to-Process Communication with Internet Protocols

processes. These devices can range from personal computers to supermainframes. As long as the device designates a TCP/IP networking endpoint, including such specialized devices as terminal servers, it is considered to be a host.

Physical networks are designated network 1 and network 2 in the exhibit to represent the local or packet-switching network to which a host computer is attached. The TCP/IP protocol family is supported by a range of network interfaces (e.g., Ethernet and X.25) and media types (e.g., coaxial and twisted-pair cable and optical fiber) that these interfaces use.

Internet gateways, referred to in the exhibit as internet routing, are network devices that reside between network hosts to provide internetwork routing mechanisms. Gateways either can be statically preset or can dynamically determine the optimal datagram path across networks, with the topology of the internetwork retained in memory on each gateway. Information is exchanged between gateways to determine current network traffic loads across specific networks and to adjust accordingly to lighten traffic loads.

Underlying Mechanisms

Exhibit IV-5-4 extends the concepts introduced in Exhibit IV-5-3 by illustrating the transformation of application data into network packets, packet transmission and routing, and the reassembling of data packets. Beginning from the application layer of the source host, the data unit that is handled by application processes can be thought of as a data message. The term *data* is used in Exhibit IV-5-4 to designate the original application layer data message. Depending on the size of the data message, it may be necessary to transmit data over the network in the form of smaller data units than are being handled at the application layer. Therefore, an initial modification of the data message may be to divide it into smaller pieces, termed data segments. This mechanism is called segmentation and is performed at the transport layer, along with the countermechanism of reassembly of the data message at the destination host computer.

Once segmentation has occurred, further processing is performed to supplement each data segment with control information, a mechanism referred to as encapsulation. Control information includes features such as addressing (i.e., identification), destination receipt acknowledgment, and error correction.

Encapsulation can occur at each subsequent architectural layer, beginning at the transport layer, as information is added to each data segment during processing by each protocol that handles it. This is designated in Exhibit IV-5-4 by TP for transport layer protocols, IP for internet layer protocols, and NI for the network interface protocols. The control information added to the data segments is often referred to as a header, to distinguish it from the original application layer data. Data units that have undergone encapsulation at the Internet layer are referred to as Internet datagrams. In addition, the terms *packet, frame,* and *bit* refer to data units that are applicable to the protocol

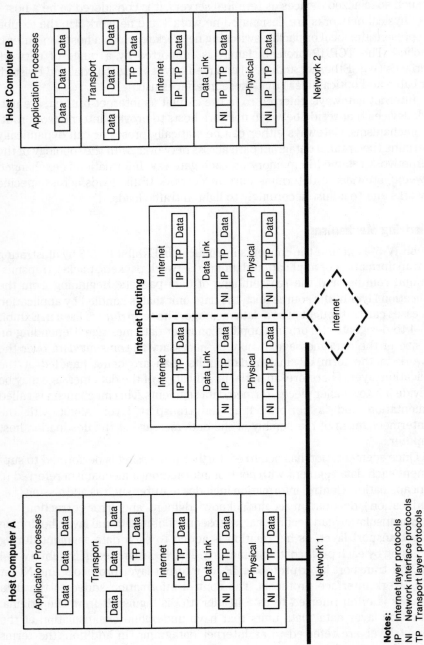

Exhibit IV-5-4. Data Segmentation, Encapsulation, and Reassembly

Notes:

IP   Internet layer protocols
NI   Network interface protocols
TP   Transport layer protocols

format for the various network interfaces supporting the TCP/IP protocol family.

A major component of the control information is addressing—that is, identification of network entities. Earlier in this chapter, the identification of network devices (i.e., the host address) and physical networks (i.e., the network number) was included in the discussion of network administration. Identification of each process endpoint active over the Internet must also be available to provide true process-to-process communications. Endpoints are data structures that are under the control of the computer processes that constitute the transport layer protocols and are commonly referred to as ports. Coresident endpoints on a host are distinguished from each other by a port number. In summary, to specify an endpoint (e.g., TCP port) with which to communicate on a specific destination host, a three-part address is used that consists of:

- The port number.
- The host, identified in the Internet protocol address.
- The physical network, identified in the Internet protocol address.

Intermediary Processing. This discussion concentrates on networking mechanisms that are involved at the communications endpoints, in the source and destination hosts. Intermediary processing during internetworking can involve a series of IP datagram routing events on gateways and networks that are located between the source and destination hosts. Exhibits IV-5-3 and IV-5-4 symbolically represent all possible routing events under the label internet routing. Each internetworking transmission uses the Internet layer protocols to perform routing decisions based on the Internet address (i.e., the packet's ultimate destination) and routing control information (i.e., the best way to get it there at the time). As with network hosts, each Internet gateway has a unique Internet address that is used not only for communication between gateways but for communication between the source host and the local gateway when it has been determined that the destination host does not reside locally. Internetwork routing relies on the Internet layer and does not use the facilities of the transport layer, as illustrated in Exhibits IV-5-3 and IV-5-4.

The reverse of the mechanisms described occurs at the destination or intermediary network device, as data is processed from lower- to upper-layer protocols and the header information pertinent to each layer is examined. In the case of intermediary devices, the processes involved in going from upper to lower layers will be invoked again as data is being forwarded to the destination host. As the network packets successively reach the transport layer of the destination host, they are fully reassembled into the original data message that is usable at the application layer.

OVERVIEW OF THE TCP/IP PROTOCOLS

Many discussions of networking protocol architectures begin with the lowest layer, the one defining physical attachment to the network, and work their way up to the application layer. This chapter emphasizes the user's perspective—essentially, how user data that resides on a local host computer is transformed into data packets, transmitted across the network, and reassembled into user data on a remote host computer—a top-down discussion. The architectural layers of the TCP/IP protocols have been designed to provide the networking services discussed in the following sections. Although not specific to the TCP/IP protocols, overviews of the network interface layers (i.e., data link and physical) are included as part of a complete architectural discussion.

Internet Protocols

The Application Layer. This layer consists of programs that interface users or host processes with the lower-layer networking protocols. These programs essentially are starting points for the support of basic host computer applications (e.g., terminal access, file copy, and electronic mail) beyond the local host computer. Application layer programs initiate network communication requests to the protocols of the transport layer, which are then active in establishing, controlling, and closing communications process endpoints. TCP/IP includes the following application layer protocols:

- Telnet (RFC 854 and RFC 855/Mil-Std-1782)—This virtual terminal service provides network access to destination hosts from terminals attached to source hosts, which include terminal servers. In many applications, destination host computers use a device driver, called the network virtual terminal, to negotiate sessions with a wide variety of terminal types.
- File transfer protocol (RFC 959/Mil-Std-1780)—This file transfer protocol (FTP) is used between hosts. One FTP session requires at least two TCP port connections: one that facilitates a command mode and one or more others that provide the connection used for the actual data transfer. In command mode, such activities as file directory administration and file parameter settings (e.g., ASCII versus binary) are performed.
- Simple mail transfer protocol (RFC 821 and RFC 822/Mil-Std-1781)—This electronic mail protocol is intended for use between existing host mail systems. In other words, the user interfaces with a local host mail program, which uses the local simple mail transfer protocol (SMTP) sender module to communicate with an SMTP receiver module on the remote host system. The receiving agent of the SMTP protocol interfaces with the reciprocal electronic mail service on the remote host system.
- Domain name service (RFC 822 and RFC 823)—This protocol provides a distributed name service that is accessible by system administrators and programs from host sites. Users can query a domain name service (DNS) for the Internet address by providing the host name. Because the DNS is a data base, information other than the Internet address can be maintained, including records of the types of services provided by different hosts.
- NetBIOS (RFC 1001 and RFC 1002)—Implementation on the TCP/IP

protocols is a recent RFC development that has been introduced to make use of this widely supported IBM PC standard. NetBIOS provides an application program interface that provides front-end-to-networking services similar to those found in the transport layer. An inherent NetBIOS limitation is that it does not define internetworking capabilities. Combining NetBIOS with the TCP/IP protocols is mutually beneficial to both sets of protocols because it provides TCP/IP with NetBIOS's broad personal computer hardware and software support and supplements NetBIOS with TCP/IP's inherent support of internetworking services.

The Transport Layer. The transport layer contains the protocols that are responsible for the establishment, control, and termination of network connection between the data structure endpoints that reside on the source and destination hosts. Transport protocols service communication initiation requests from application layer processes while also servicing requests from the internet layer below by identifying the destination port of incoming data. The TCP/IP transport layer includes the following protocols:

- Transmission Control Protocol (RFC 793/Mil-Std-1780)—This protocol provides reliable, bidirectional network communications between peer processes. TCP is reliable because it maintains and controls the state of the connection and ensures that all data has been received by the destination host. TCP breaks an application layer data message into segments and adds a TCP header to the beginning of each segment that contains control information. Part of this control information is segment order, which is maintained through use of a sequence number field. Data flow control is provided through the exchange of current and expected sequence numbers between the source and destination ports. Each data segment is addressed with source and destination port numbers. In addition, a checksum field is used for bit-level error checking of both the TCP header and the data.

- User datagram protocol (RFC 768)—Like TCP, the user datagram protocol (UDP) provides source and destination port numbering within a header. However, UDP provides unreliable network communications between peer processes. UDP is unreliable because it does not provide destination receipt acknowledgment and thus cannot guarantee delivery of data to the destination host. In addition, UDP does not implement mechanisms for data flow control, because segmentation is not supported (all data must fit into one segment). The principal gain achieved by lack of data flow control and error checking is that UDP provides faster data throughput as compared to TCP.

The Internet Layer. The internet layer protocols implement device and network addressing that supports communication between network devices and provides routing services for transmitting data across an internet. By

403

providing internetworkwide addressing and routing, these protocols handle the underlying data transmission and switching mechanisms in support of the transport layer protocols. The internetwork route that the data takes is transparent to the transport layer protocols. The internet includes the following protocols:

- Internet Protocol (RFC 791/Mil-Std-1777)—This protocol provides the Internet address to identify network devices and physical networks. A second set of important mechanisms is IP fragmentation and reassembly. During routing, datagrams may need to travel across a variety of network types (e.g., X.25, Ethernet, packet radio, and phone lines). Because each type of network defines a different maximum packet size, IP must provide a way to resolve size conflicts. If a maximum packet size is less than the datagram size, fragmentation must be applied to divide the datagram into smaller units. IP is designed to maintain the integrity of the datagrams through a reassembly process at their destination. An IP header is attached to the outgoing transport layer segments, forming an IP datagram. Major elements within the IP header are the Internet source address, Internet destination address, and IP header checksum fields.
- Internetwork control message protocol (RFC 792)—This protocol provides a mechanism for IP devices to communicate control information about the network. The information usually consists of error messages sent back to the datagram source when an IP device determines that a problem has occurred in the transmission of a datagram that it has received.
- Address resolution protocol (RFC 826)—This protocol provides a method for translating between a 32-bit IP address and a 48-bit Ethernet address. The Ethernet address is actually implemented at the data link layer. Both of these addresses can be used to reference a network device, but only the Internet address is usable across all subnetworks. This is a critical step in that translation is between an Internet address and the node address of the underlying network interface.

The Network Interface

The various network interfaces to which the Internet protocols have been ported contain specifications that are defined by other standard organizations. Primary examples of these underlying networks are X.25 and Ethernet. The most common features of these interfaces can be discussed in general within the context of a data link layer and a physical layer.

The Data Link Layer. Data link control protocols to which the TCP/IP protocols have been implemented include the ISO high-level data link control (HDLC), the CCITT link access procedure (LAP) and link access procedure balanced (LAPB), and the IEEE 802.2 logical link control (LLC). Networking specifications are concerned at this layer with two general considerations: reliable data transmission across the physical media—including initiation of data transmission, error checking of the active link, and termination of data transmission—and addressing network devices with format and procedures governed by the underlying physical network's specifications.

Framing is a data link layer mechanism performed by many networking specifications to surround the data unit with both a header and trailer, creating a data unit referred to as a frame. This is the final encapsulation prior to transmitting the data on the network. A frame error control mechanism used by many data link protocols is based on a cyclic redundancy check (CRC) method and incorporated as an inherent part of framing, usually termed the frame check sequence (FCS). Framing involves a specific format for each type of network standard involved. For example, RFC 894 is a TCP/IP specification that defines how Internet datagrams are to be framed for transmission on an Ethernet.

A link-level node address, identifying the physically attached devices, has the Internet address mapped to it, as was discussed with the address resolution protocol. The addressing mechanism involved at this layer is dependent on the specifications of the underlying network. For example, HDLC provides a frame address field. It is used to identify secondary devices dependent on a primary device that is providing the principal data communication link. This type of multiple link is classified as a tiered-multipoint network. In comparison, the Ethernet standard demonstrates how a node is addressed on a peer-multipoint network, in which each node has an equivalent addressing status.

The Physical Layer. The physical layer of each networking standard defines reliable bit-level data transmission on a network medium. Major functions include mechanical properties (i.e., the size and physical configuration of the device interface) and electrical properties (i.e., changes in voltage represent bits) as well as procedural concerns of transmitting data. A wide variety of physical interface standards have been implemented for the TCP/IP protocols, including the EIA RS-232 and RS-449, IEEE 802.3, Ethernet, DDN 1822, and CCITT V.35.

SUMMARY

Support of the TCP/IP protocol family has grown significantly. The TCP/IP protocol family offers a well-documented and mature set of rules for networking. TCP/IP's technical merits, as well as its documentation and maturity factors, contribute to decisions to select these networking protocols for connectivity to numerous types of hosts. Many of these decisions are based on the fact that there is a void between the need for networking and the broad implementation of the OSI standards. TCP/IP has served the needs of a diverse set of groups, ranging from those that require a nonproprietary R&D networking environment to commercial interests who could not wait for OSI.

There is little doubt that OSI will eventually be the most widely supported networking standard. Two of the most interesting questions that need to be asked are how soon will this occur and what will be the real driving force behind the transition. If OSI technically and functionally offered little advantage over TCP/IP networking, then, on the basis of the large number of hosts currently implementing TCP/IP networking, OSI replacement of TCP/IP and other networking protocols would be a lengthy process.

However, there are distinct improvements in OSI's protocols in the area of applications. It is here that a robust functional capability—such as that offered with file transfer, access, and management (FTAM), message handling system (X.400), directory (X.500), and the common management information protocol (CMIP)—currently provides advantages that are distinctly appealing to users. This user appeal, especially in the commercial sector, may provide widespread support of OSI. Many estimates indicate that support of OSI will increase during most of the 1990s in much the same way that use of TCP/IP grew during the 1980s. The federal government has clearly stated that OSI—through GOSIP, the government open systems interconnection profile—will be the networking protocol of choice and will be mandatory in network product and service acquisitions. This is the most definitive indication, at least in the US, of the transition from TCP/IP to OSI.

IV-6
TCP/IP and OSI

DANIEL C. LYNCH

Many central computer facilities are disappearing as organizations set up a more distributed computing environment. Technology has made the desktop computer commonplace, and most companies are using LANs. Networking relies on the ability of different computer systems to speak the same communications language. A protocol is a set of precisely defined interactions that allows this communication to take place.

THE TCP/IP PROTOCOL SUITE

The Transmission Control Protocol (TCP) and the Internet Protocol (IP) were developed for the Department of Defense (DoD) by the researchers who built ARPAnet. ARPAnet, one of the first wide area packet-switched networks, was sponsored by the Defense Advanced Research Projects Agency (DARPA). The term *TCP/IP* is often used to refer to the whole suite of DoD protocols, including TCP, IP, and the three most common application protocols, which are simple mail transfer, file transfer, and Telnet, the virtual terminal protocol.

TCP is a transport protocol that guarantees reliable delivery of datagrams from one computer to another through the use of checksums, duplicate detection, and retransmission of lost segments. Many machines using the TCP/IP protocol structure provide a software interface to the TCP functions, allowing application programs to detect incoming requests for sessions, respond actively by requesting a connect to other programs (or processes) on a network, send and receive data, and close sessions.

IP is the envelope that allows TCP segments to travel between different networks; a collection of IP networks is called an internet.

The three major application protocols in the TCP/IP protocol suite are described in the following sections.

Telnet. Telnet is an application-level protocol that allows a terminal on one computer to pass through to another computer on a local or remote network, appearing there as a local terminal. (The name Telnet comes from *tele*type *net*work, referring to the predominant terminal used in the early days of computing.) There are two sides to the Telnet protocol: one for the user or client and one for the server or remote host. Telnet allows either the client or the server to request or respond to option settings that are related to the pass-through session—for example, a choice of character set (e.g., ASCII or EBCDIC). Most Telnet sessions operate in ASCII full-duplex mode. This makes it possible for any dumb ASCII terminal to pass through to remote equipment, though Telnet options also support other types of data streams, including the transmission of 3270 data in EBCDIC mode for communicating with IBM equipment.

The File Transfer Protocol. The file transfer protocol supports the transfer of data files between any pair of hosts. Like Telnet, this protocol is usually provided as a pair of client and server applications, in which the client application connects with the actual user (usually a human, occasionally another program) and the server application is an unattended process on the remote machine that receives requests to store or retrieve files. The file transfer protocol supports a small variety of file types: ASCII, EBCDIC, binary, and paged. (A paged file type is a special mechanism for passing structured files between systems of the same type.)

The Simple Mail Transfer Protocol. The simple mail transfer protocol is a mechanism for exchanging messages between users. One machine may connect to another simple mail transfer protocol server process and transfer a message to a list of mailboxes on the destination machine. It can also request to receive messages immediately that are waiting to be sent in the reverse direction. The format of the messages is governed by a standard on what the headers must look like, so that user-level agent processes can easily parse the messages and present them to the user in an easily understood form. This standard, called RFC 822, establishes all typical fields (including to, from, subject, date, reply-to, and copy-to) and has an escape mechanism that allows new fields to be added by mutual agreement among users.

Multivendor Compatibility

One particularly important design feature of TCP/IP is its ability to operate over a variety of underlying network technologies. Currently, there are large TCP/IP networks that run over T1 links, X.25 public data networks, local area networks (e.g., Ethernet or token ring), satellite networks, and packet radio networks, making TCP/IP the de facto standard for multivendor computer networking. More than 200 vendors now offer products based on TCP/IP.

Requests for Comments

All TCP/IP protocols are documented in a set of written specifications, called requests for comments, that were started by the small group of computer scientists who formed the early ARPAnet research community. They decided to write down their ideas along with their proposed solutions and distribute the documents to interested colleagues for comments, thereby both improving the ideas and documenting the actual protocols. The name is still used even though most modern requests for comments are actual standards and say so in the first paragraph. More than 1,050 requests for comments are available from the Network Information Center at SRI International in Menlo Park CA (800-235-3155).

CHARACTERISTICS OF THE TCP/IP COMMUNITY

The TCP/IP community consists of hundreds of thousands of people, ranging from novices to sophisticated computer users, who rely on computers and networks in their daily professional lives. In addition to the three basic services—electronic mail, file transfer, and remote log-in—several other capabilities are sometimes available, including:

- Network file system—This protocol provides shared file access.
- NetBIOS—This interface provides microcomputer network applications.
- Internetworking—This protocol provides connections between different networks.
- Experimental protocols—These protocols provide voice digitization, graphics, and parallel processing support.

Network File System

The network file system is a protocol originally developed by Sun Microsystems that allows clients to transfer parts of files rather than only entire files with the file transfer protocol. This feature is frequently used when users want to keep files in a central location while using them at a remote location, leaving the home location of the file unchanged. The network file system supports the concept of diskless workstations; users can also choose either to have exclusive use of the files or to allow shared use if that makes sense for a distributed application.

NetBIOS

NetBIOS (Network Basic Input Output System) was developed for IBM to allow microcomputers on a local area network to exchange data from one computer application to another; many such applications have been developed. Because TCP/IP networks are usually much larger than microcomputer networks, a method was developed to allow the NetBIOS applications to run on top of the TCP/IP protocols in a manner that leaves the actual application unchanged. Making a microcomputer network application part of a large TCP/IP network greatly enhances the scope of operation of the microcomputer application.

Internetworking

A major factor for the TCP/IP user community is the concept of internetworking. A single network is usually described by its physical link characteristics (i.e., Ethernet, token ring, token bus, RS-232, satellite, radio, and optical fiber). Exhibit IV-6-1 shows five networks with various hosts (called end systems in OSI) on them. An internet is a collection of networks that all run the same communications protocols from OSI layer 3 upward; the component networks are connected to each other by routers. (Routers are sometimes referred to as gateways in the TCP/IP community; OSI calls them intermediate systems.) Exhibit IV-6-1 illustrates an example of an internet of five networks connected by the routers. Although TCP/IP can easily transfer data between hosts on the same network (e.g., from H1 to H2 in network 2), its real strength is shown in its ability to transfer that same data to H3 on network 4.

As information needs expand dramatically, the number of communications networks is increasing into the millions and the need for internetworking is becoming more critical. In light of this situation, many TCP/IP users are simultaneously anarchic and cooperative in their views on how to use networks. They understand that although it is highly desirable to be able to access data that resides on another network, it is also necessary to insulate their own network from random access by unknown outsiders.

Building bridges to other electronic mail systems has been a hallmark of the TCP/IP community. Many mail systems do not quite conform to the specifications of the protocols in the TCP/IP suite. Because mail is so important, several mail translation packages have been developed that allow users of

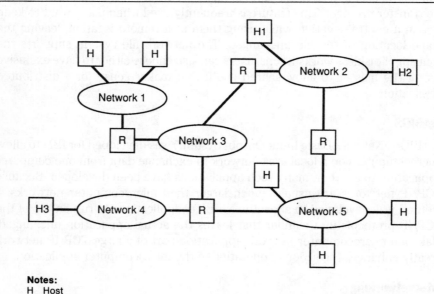

Notes:
H   Host
R   Router

Exhibit IV-6-1 An Internet of Five Networks

foreign mail systems (e.g., Usenet, the UNIX users' network; PROFS, IBM's electronic mail system; DECmail; MCImail; and BITNET, a public domain network) to exchange electronic mail with TCP/IP-based mail users.

THE BENEFITS OF THE ISO/OSI PROTOCOL SUITE

The International Standards Organization (ISO) defines standards in several areas, including computer communications. ISO has developed the well-known seven-layer protocol model called open systems interconnection (OSI). These protocols will play a major role in worldwide communications because almost all countries in the world have made a major political commitment to the adoption of OSI.

The Transition from the TCP/IP Suite to the OSI Suite

What can be done to convince TCP/IP users to make the transition to OSI? Mandates are not very effective and take a long time. Therefore, the services that OSI-based protocols offer must provide the lure that will convince TCP/IP users to undergo the difficulties of change. The TCP/IP suite is deficient in three main areas. If OSI can provide services to these three areas, there should be little resistance to making a transition from a functional standpoint. (There will always be a cost issue that can delay transition; this must be addressed by each organization.) The services are discussed in the following sections.

X.400 Electronic Mail. X.400 mail appears to be a significant improvement over the mail services provided in the TCP/IP arena. X.400 offers true multimedia services and many more sophisticated options for sending, handling, cataloging, and filing mail. Protocol translators between X.400 and TCP/IP mail do exist that perform adequately in simple cases when translation in both directions is possible. Therefore, it is possible to have meaningful communication between the two communities. When the TCP/IP users realize that they are missing some valuable services that their colleagues using X.400 enjoy, they will be eager to change to OSI.

Seamless Cut and Paste. A major weakness of the existing TCP/IP suite is that few applications have been built that allow one application to freely call another to obtain data for insertion into a local computation. This deficiency takes two forms:

- No general mechanism is available in the TCP/IP environment for hooking up computers from multiple vendors—This is important because different computer architectures lend themselves to different tasks. OSI protocols have such a general mechanism built in, allowing a supercomputer to have a graphics workstation as a front end.
- It is difficult for a user in a TCP/IP environment who is composing a document (e.g., spreadsheet text, graphics, voice, or data base) to extract

information from existing sources to integrate into the new document—Microcomputer users today can extract information from multiple documents easily, using application packages provided by many vendors. Performing this same task in a networking environment across applications from multiple vendors would be a significant gain to TCP/IP users. OSI provides many generic tools for building such a capability.

Hiding the Operating Systems from the User. Working in the networking world often requires that the user know numerous system commands and file manipulation primitives for each operating system used. This is a significant burden for most users, particularly application users who do not care to learn the intricacies of the computer system they are using. TCP/IP is the stick shift of networking; OSI is like automatic transmission.

Methods for Transition

Many factors must be considered in the plan for a transition from TCP/IP to OSI, including cost, ease of training, length of time to accomplish, access to services from either side, and user confidence in the new system. Such a transition is not completely transparent.

Because the seven-layer model of open systems is so appealing, it is possible to consider the solution to the transition problem as a clever substitution of layers until there are only OSI layers doing the work. Unfortunately, the substitution must take place in all the end systems and all the intermediate systems simultaneously. This could be accomplished by essentially doubling up in certain places, putting parts of both protocol stacks in key places, and running both sets of protocol suites in parallel until users gain confidence in the pure OSI stack. It is important to identify these key places.

Within an end system, the protocol stack can be considered as two parts: the application itself and the movement of the data. New OSI applications (e.g., the X.400 mail system and file transfer, access, and management [FTAM]) can run on top of existing TCP/IP networks as if they were just new TCP/IP applications. Code must be designed, however, to provide a seam between the two protocols, translating the requests of the upper OSI layer into the expectations of the lower TCP/IP layer. The ISO Development Environment developed by researchers at Northrop Research and Technology Center is a public domain code that provides this seam. The advantage of using this code is that a new OSI application can run on an existing large TCP/IP network with its existing large installed base of users. It still does not offer true interoperability because it allows OSI applications to communicate only with other OSI applications over TCP/IP networks, not with TCP/IP applications. For example, the file transfer protocol cannot work directly with FTAM. If FTAM transferred a file from one system to another, however, that file would be effectively transferred as if it were done by the file transfer protocol, which could then be used to move the file into a pure TCP/IP environment. (The reverse situation also works.)

Beyond using OSI applications within a TCP/IP network, managers with a pure OSI network will want to construct an application gateway that can take in both OSI and TCP/IP data streams, translate one to the other, and send the resulting packet on the proper route. For example, such a gateway would allow data coming from a TCP/IP network that is running FTAM to communicate with a pure OSI stack running FTAM. Although this application gateway does not yet exist, it will become increasingly critical as more organizations establish pure OSI networks and still need to communicate with users on TCP/IP networks.

Undoubtedly, the most important case will be to develop an electronic-mail application gateway that can move simple mail transfer protocol messages to and from X.400 messages. Similar gateways have been built to move simple mail transfer protocol messages to the UNIX system's file transfer protocol and others, but it would be much preferable to develop a user interface application to manage the contents of a user's mailbox that is able to process both styles of mail. Unfortunately, this solution requires numerous changes to existing software that may prohibit its easy implementation, resulting in a mail-only gateway as a short-term reality.

Other possible solutions—for example, running TCP/IP applications in OSI networks—are available, but the mechanisms described in this article should be sufficient to allow organizations to make the transition from TCP/IP to OSI with minimum pain and cost. In particular, network managers should be careful when designing and building gateways because they can be tremendous performance bottlenecks.

SUMMARY

True interoperability among different computer systems is an important global goal. TCP/IP users have been pioneers in beginning to achieve this goal. They are natural first customers for the improved services offered to the international community by OSI protocols. The transition from an existing TCP/IP installed base to the OSI world will become increasingly essential, and careful implementation of interim mechanisms can prevent it from being exceedingly difficult or painful.

IV-7
Personal Computer Networking in a TCP/IP Environment

LEO J. McLAUGHLIN III

IBM's original personal computer, equipped with a cassette port, 16K bytes of random access memory, and a built-in BASIC interpreter, was a somewhat uninspiring though perfectly serviceable product. Its most remarkable feature was its open architecture, which made it capable of supporting a variety of new types of hardware and software.

One of these new products was a networking package described in the *IBM PC Network Technical Reference*. This document contained a description of a programming interface known as NetBIOS. At the same time, several proprietary networking products were introduced by other manufacturers. The Net-BIOS specification became so widely used that more than 99% of all the personal computer LANs currently installed support NetBIOS. Because of the popularity of Novell products, however, less than half of the personal computer LANs that have NetBIOS actually use it for their own applications. Even those networking products that do use NetBIOS are not interoperable because differing protocols and hardware media are used in their implementation.

About nine years ago, the ARPAnet, a store-and-forward packet network built by the Defense Advanced Research Projects Agency (DARPA) to conduct computer science and military research into networking technologies, was converting to a new suite of protocols, the Transmission Control Protocol and Internet Protocol (TCP/IP). These protocols were designed to allow interoperability between dissimilar computer systems and were endorsed by the Department of Defense.

The TCP/IP protocol suite includes a variety of applications and protocols to provide connectivity. These include Telnet and TN3270, a variation of Telnet, which provide virtual terminal access to minicomputers and mainframes; the file transfer protocol (FTP) and trivial file transfer protocol (TFTP), which allow remote file transfer; and the simple mail transfer protocol (SMTP), which transfers mail. In addition, protocols exist for network management, file shar-

415

ing, remote operations, data representation, name resolution, and many other networking tasks.

The TCP/IP protocol suite achieved widespread use when, as part of the University of California at Berkeley's UNIX 4.1, 4.2, and 4.3 distributions, it was installed in most of the educational and scientific environments in the country. Again, use of the TCP/IP suite of protocols became increasingly widespread as business and manufacturing environments adopted UNIX and its networking applications.

Today, TCP/IP is the protocol suite of choice for heterogeneous LANs and WANs. Therefore, the question of how to integrate the plethora of personal computer LANs into a coherent corporate network is often the question of how to integrate those networks into the larger TCP/IP environment.

PERSONAL COMPUTER CONNECTIVITY CRITERIA

Generally, the evaluation of any proposed connectivity solution determines whether it will work, how well it will perform, and how much it will cost. These three issues may be resolved into a set of evaluation criteria.

Will It Work? The purpose of an internetworking solution is to make available to one networking environment those applications and services usually found only in the other environment. Therefore, the most important evaluation criterion of any particular solution is the range of services it supports. However, just because a particular service is claimed to be supported does not mean that that solution's support is sufficient for all environments. For example, some services may be supported in only one direction or for only a fixed number of users.

How Well Will It Perform? Performance is determined by the details of a particular internetworking implementation rather than by the general type of internetworking solution. General statements, however, can be made about the advantages and disadvantages of those connectivity solutions that directly connect LANs rather than use a gateway of some kind. The principal advantage of direct solutions is higher throughput from a LAN workstation to a TCP/IP host. Application gateways are slow; almost all gateway solutions reduce performance. Another advantage of direct solutions is that no host is needed to serve as the gateway. If the gateway is dedicated, a machine is wasted; if the gateway is nondedicated, the performance of the file server or workstation serving double duty may be severely reduced. In addition, because there is no data flow bottleneck, there is no chance of running out of some critical resource in the gateway.

The principal disadvantage of direct solutions is that personal computer LAN products can produce extraordinary amounts of network traffic, particularly broadcast traffic. Therefore, in many environments, it may not be wise to connect a LAN directly to a company's backbone network. Furthermore, if the gateway is part of a more general-purpose bridge or router, it can provide flexibility and security solutions that may be desired in some environments.

How Much Will It Cost? The cost of the solution entails more than the vendor's price. A connectivity solution that requires a great deal of change in the existing networking environment will probably be costly to purchase and install, particularly if new hardware as well as new software is required. The installation of a large amount of new equipment will likely also be expensive in terms of disruption to the existing network environments.

A secondary but often more expensive cost to consider is the level of effort required to maintain and manage the networks once they are connected. The more the connectivity solution allows networking software functions to be controlled by network management protocols, the less expensive the solution will be to operate.

Two distinct types of connectivity solutions allow the integration of personal computer LANs into larger networks. The first solution is the use of NetBIOS over TCP/IP to support the traditional personal computer resource-sharing networking applications. Although this approach has many advantages in terms of simplicity, memory use, performance, and the range of applications supported, it may require replacement of some or perhaps all of the personal computer networking software currently installed.

The second solution relies on the extant personal computer networking software to provide the resource-sharing applications, and some sort of inter-operability solution to provide the TCP/IP applications (i.e., remote log-in, file transfer, and mail). The principal advantage of this approach is that it is less disruptive to an existing network; however, most interoperability solutions have limited usefulness, degrade performance, and may place a prohibitively high demand on scarce CPU and memory resources.

TCP/IP LAN CONNECTIVITY SOLUTIONS

Personal Computer LANs Using NetBIOS over TCP/IP

The use of NetBIOS over TCP/IP to provide LAN connectivity is simple to diagram (see Exhibit IV-7-1). The proprietary personal computer network host and the TCP/IP host differ only in name.

The primary advantage of implementing NetBIOS over TCP/IP is that it is a complete solution. All applications traditionally found in both the personal computer and minicomputer-mainframe environments are transparent to the user. Because no special gateways, routers, or bridges are required, performance, reliability, and ease of installation are improved. Users must learn only one set of applications, which reduces network complexity to both users and administrators, and only one network management protocol is required for operation and maintenance. In addition, only one protocol stack is required, decreasing memory use.

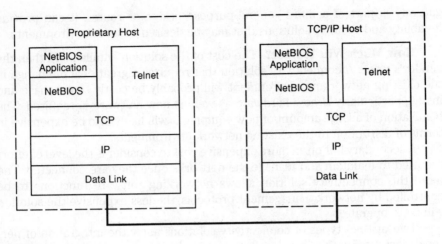

Notes:
IP   Internet protocol
TCP   Transmission control protocol

Exhibit IV-7-1. NetBIOS over TCP/IP LAN Solution

Until recently, a NetBIOS LAN based on TCP/IP could not be recommended for most environments. Either a prohibitively large amount of memory had to be devoted to the protocol stack or an expensive smart network interface was needed to run the TCP/IP protocols. However, advances in TCP/IP technology have made host-resident TCP/IP-based NetBIOS systems feasible.

The single disadvantage of a LAN that runs NetBIOS over TCP/IP is that if the existing personal computer networking software is not NetBIOS based, it must be replaced. Therefore, it is not an appropriate solution for an organization with a substantial investment in non-NetBIOS networking products. LANs that run NetBIOS over TCP/IP provide either the final connectivity solution or no solution at all.

NetBIOS Bridges

A NetBIOS bridge allows two or more dissimilar NetBIOS protocol stacks to be joined into one logical LAN. For example, with the aid of a NetBIOS bridge, a client on a NetBIOS LAN that runs over NetBEUI could share the files stored on a server that runs NetBIOS over TCP/IP (see Exhibit IV-7-2).

This solution has several advantages. As with the LAN that runs NetBIOS over TCP/IP, all NetBIOS applications are supported on all hosts on both the personal computer LAN and the TCP/IP-based networks. Furthermore, NetBIOS bridges can connect dissimilar NetBIOS-based proprietary networks.

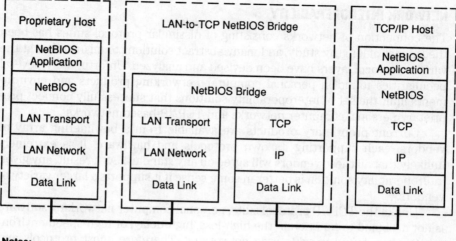

Notes:
IP   Internet protocol
TCP Transmission control protocol

Exhibit IV-7-2. NetBIOS Bridge Solution

Unlike the LAN that runs NetBIOS over TCP/IP, however, each host on the proprietary network need not obtain a new protocol stack.

There are, however, many caveats. First, NetBIOS bridging requires that the existing proprietary personal computer networking software be NetBIOS based.

Second, although NetBIOS applications are supported on all hosts, Advanced Research Projects Agency (ARPA) applications (e.g., Telnet) are not. To serve as a complete solution, the NetBIOS bridge must be combined with an interoperability solution (e.g., a network tunnel) that provides ARPA application connectivity. Third, because TCP/IP is not on the nodes on the proprietary network, the proprietary network cannot be managed by an SNMP or CMOT network management station.

Fourth, because NetBIOS name resolution happens below the interface, the bridge is limited. Several methods circumvent this name space limitation. One method is to add to each client needing to communicate with hosts on another NetBIOS network a small program that forwards name requests to the NetBIOS bridge. Another method is to list on the bridge the NetBIOS name of every distant node that the hosts on the local NetBIOS network might wish to access. A third method is to delve into the particular NetBIOS implementations on either side of the NetBIOS bridge and pass on all packets bearing NetBIOS name information.

NETWORK INTEROPERABILITY

The connection of networks consisting of dissimilar protocol suites has been the subject of lengthy study, and many abstract solutions to mismatches at the various protocol layers have been devised and analyzed. Unfortunately, several peculiarities found in personal computer networking products and environments limit the set of interoperability solutions that successfully connect proprietary personal computer networks and TCP/IP-based networks.

Current proprietary products are available from a bewildering array of vendors, each supporting its own protocols and hardware. It is extremely unlikely that all these vendors will agree on any standard. As a result, any given interoperability solution is better in some sense if it supports a larger variety of vendors.

Unlike the TCP/IP protocol suite, personal computer networking software is not designed to function in the high-loss, high-delay, or high-speed environments often found in wide area networking. Therefore, most protocols and many applications written for a LAN environment will not work well over larger networks. Furthermore, few proprietary protocol suites were designed to scale well into networks consisting of thousands and millions of interconnected hosts.

The relatively low cost of personal computer systems and the internetworking inexperience of their operators constrains internetworking solutions. A solution that is expensive compared to the cost of a proprietary personal computer network is unacceptable, as is any solution that requires, at every site that needs personal computer LAN-to-TCP/IP connectivity, the services of a sophisticated system administrator.

These difficulties are by no means insurmountable, and there are several solutions to the problem of integrating proprietary personal computer networks and TCP/IP networks. These solutions are discussed in the following section.

TCP/IP–TO–PROPRIETARY LAN INTEROPERABILITY SOLUTIONS

Dual Stacks

The dual-stack solution simply proposes that each workstation in the proprietary LAN contains two separate protocol stacks, each supporting its own applications. A user on the dual-stack host shown in Exhibit IV-7-3, for example, could retrieve a file from the TCP/IP host and copy it to the proprietary host by using the FTP and NetBIOS redirector applications respectively.

The primary advantage of the dual-stack approach is the wide range of services supported. Each workstation in the LAN becomes a full-featured TCP/IP host capable of supporting any application written for the TCP/IP environment. If the Network File System is not supported by the TCP/IP networking software, the TCP/IP hosts cannot function as local file servers.

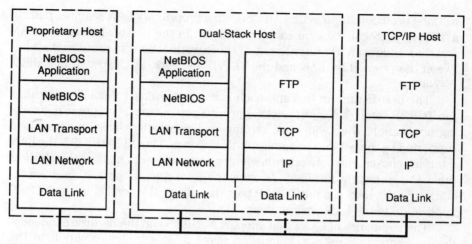

Notes:
FTP   File transfer protocol
IP   Internet protocol
TCP   Transmission control protocol

Exhibit IV-7-3. Dual-Stack Solution

Although this solution requires that new software be added to each LAN workstation, nothing else must be changed. The presence of two protocol stacks, however, may cause interference in the networking software. Unless the software has been designed for this type of application, simultaneous use of the protocol stacks is impossible without two hardware cards in each workstation. Furthermore, because of the proliferation of ARCnet and token-ring LANs, and because the neighboring TCP/IP and proprietary LAN systems run over different hardware media, two network interface cards are often necessary even when the two software packages are compatible.

Traditionally, dual-stack installations have been viewed as difficult to manage successfully. However, because of the simplicity of most personal computer LAN products and the advantages of introducing TCP/IP-based management protocols to the personal computer LAN environment, management of a dual-stack installation should not be much more difficult than managing a host running only TCP/IP.

Network Tunneling

Network tunneling is the connection of two like networks through a dissimilar network that is used as a communications link, or tunnel. To connect a system to a foreign host that uses a protocol not found in that system's environment, connectivity is provided through an intermediate system running both networking protocols. Connecting a TCP/IP to a proprietary LAN requires putting a TCP/IP protocol stack on each workstation in the personal computer LAN and then adding an IP router to one of those workstations to route packets between the proprietary LAN and the TCP/IP network, as illustrated in Exhibit IV-7-4.

The best feature of this approach is its extraordinary flexibility. Because the TCP/IP services are just another proprietary personal computer networking application, they will work on any implementation over any hardware supported by the personal computer LAN software. Thus, if NetBIOS is the LAN interface chosen, the network tunneling solution will work in more than 99% of the LANs currently installed. As with the dual-stack approach, each workstation on the LAN is a full TCP/IP host that allows the porting of any TCP/IP application to the LAN environment.

The popularity of LANs that support NetBIOS and the hardware independence inherent in network tunneling make it an excellent solution to the problem of personal computer LAN interoperability. The network tunneling solution requires more changes to the network than the dual-stack approach, because one station must serve as a router and new software is required on every proprietary LAN workstation. Because the TCP/IP software is just an-

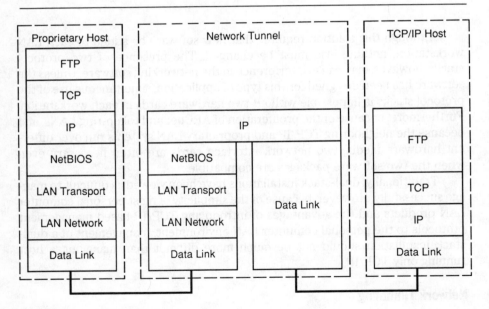

Notes:
FTP   File transfer protocol
IP   Internet protocol
TCP   Transmission control protocol

Exhibit IV-7-4. Network Tunnel Solution

other application, however, the requirement for new software can be eliminated if the TCP/IP software is installed on the personal computer LAN file server.

Management of a network-tunneled installation should be slightly easier than a dual-stack installation because the proprietary network traffic is limited to its own network.

Application Gateways

An application gateway is a program specifically designed to allow communication between similar applications that are based on dissimilar protocols. Few types of applications are supported by both personal computer LAN networks and TCP/IP networks. There is, however, one type of application—mail—that exists in both environments and lends itself to use in an application gateway. A NetBIOS-to-SMTP mail application gateway is shown in Exhibit IV-7-5.

Because an application gateway is designed to support only one application, the range of services provided is rather small. That application, however, is provided efficiently. In the case of the NetBIOS-to-SMTP mail application gateway, users may freely send and receive mail on their proprietary LAN to and from the larger TCP/IP environment. Once connectivity has been established to these larger TCP/IP networks, SMTP-to-X.400 gateways provide mail

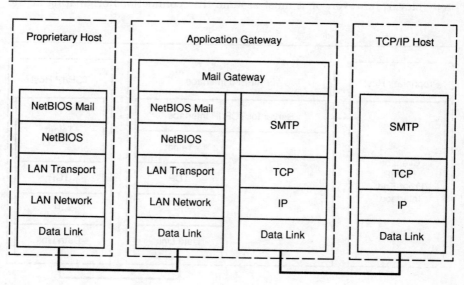

Notes:
IP   Internet protocol
SMTP   Simple mail transfer protocol
TCP   Transmission control protocol

Exhibit IV-7-5. Application Gateway Solution

connectivity to OSI networks. When mail gateways are built for different proprietary LAN products, personal computer LAN–to–personal computer LAN interconnectivity solutions are created. Addressing problems and type of service may be mismatched, but this should not present insurmountable difficulties.

The greatest benefit of mail application gateways is that very little change in the personal computer LAN is required. Only the mail gateway is new. Furthermore, the traffic generated by mail on the personal computer network introduces no new network management problems.

Front-End Interfaces

Front-end interfaces encompass solutions that attempt to connect personal computer LANs to TCP/IP networks by adding one proprietary host to the TCP/IP network and having it provide some kind of interface for the rest of the LAN's hosts. If a proprietary LAN, for example, supports a remote procedure call mechanism, a sophisticated Telnet application could be created that accepts connection requests from any host on the LAN and initiates a Telnet session with the desired host (see Exhibit IV-7-6).

In many environments, this solution may yield an insufficient range of services. A front-end interface can handle requests for connection to a TCP/IP host that originates at a LAN host. Either the implementation must be exceedingly clever, however, or it must assume that connections originating at the

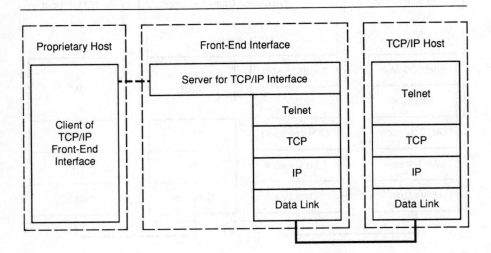

Notes:
IP   Internet protocol
TCP Transmission control protocol

Exhibit IV-7-6. Front-End Interface Solution

TCP/IP network destined for an arbitrary host on the LAN will not occur. Furthermore, because each host on the personal computer LAN is not actually a TCP/IP host, intranetwork TCP/IP-based applications are not possible.

Additional limitations may result from insufficient resources in the host serving as the front-end system. Because all the proprietary LAN–to–TCP/IP network connections reside on one host, the number of sessions may be severely limited.

A front-end interface does have one significant benefit: its nonintrusiveness. The required TCP/IP connectivity product must be installed only on one node in the LAN. However, a front-end interface does not allow the entry of TCP/IP network management protocols into the proprietary LAN environment. Because each LAN workstation is an unknown TCP/IP host, successful management of such a network can be rather difficult.

SUMMARY

Not surprisingly, no one solution will answer the personal computer connectivity needs of every environment. Nevertheless, a few observations can be made regarding networking strategies.

First, those installations that already have personal computer networking equipment, particularly non-NetBIOS–based equipment, have a narrower range of options available to them. Connectivity without the use of some sort of gateway mechanism may be difficult and may in fact be impossible if a hardware medium other than Ethernet was chosen.

Second, the prospective consumer of connectivity equipment must decide if access to both TCP/IP applications and LAN applications for all hosts is required. If so, one of the TCP/IP LAN connectivity solutions is required. However, if TCP/IP application connectivity for all hosts is sufficient, the interoperability solutions are sufficient.

Finally, the wide variety of connectivity solutions available ensures that the successful integration of personal computer networks into larger IP-based networks is a reasonable goal for almost any environment.

IV-8
Evaluating Gateways for Network Interconnection

LADAN POROOSHANI • JOHN MORENCY • DAVID K. PORTER • RICHARD PITKIN

The connection of IBM networks with networks based on the products of other vendors is frequently accomplished through the use of gateways. Several criteria simplify the evaluation of gateway products. These criteria can be applied to the gateway independent of the actual application of the networks and to certain mainstream network functions that gateways are required to support.

GATEWAYS

The term *gateway* is frequently used in the vendor and user community. In this chapter, a gateway is the means by which applications interoperability occurs between a non-IBM networking environment (which may be either an OSI, TCP/IP, or vendor-proprietary environment) and an IBM environment, which is usually based on SNA protocols.

Applications Interoperability

The term *applications interoperability* means the ability of a turnkey function (e.g., terminal-host access, user mail exchange, or file transfer) to be logically extended. Interoperability with IBM networks typically means support of the 3270 data stream (for access from a terminal to an IBM host or from a 3270 terminal to a non-IBM host) and support of IBM proprietary mail and file transfer protocols (i.e., SNA distribution services or DDM) relative to either OSI (i.e., virtual terminal protocol, X.400, and file transfer, access, and management), TCP/IP (i.e., Telnet, simple mail transfer protocol, and file transfer protocol), or vendor-specific protocols that perform similar functions.

For an end user, the net result is the ability, either from an individual personal computer or workstation or from a multiple user host, to sign on as an interactive user to such a subsystem as CMS, IMS, CICS, or TSO. Applications interoperability may also enable a user in the IBM network to sign on interactively to the workstation or multiple-user host in the non-IBM environment. In addition, mail can be addressed to IBM-based users from a non-IBM environment and vice versa with a suitable extension to the addressing conventions of the non-IBM mail system. The arrangement for file transfers is similar.

Gateway Platforms for Interoperability

Gateway functions provide applications-level interoperability between an IBM network and a non-IBM one. The means by which this interoperability is achieved, however, varies from vendor to vendor. Fortunately, the systems-level aspects of all gateway solutions are similar.

Most gateways operate by way of a packaged system physically connected to both the IBM network and the vendor network. The IBM connection is made through synchronous circuit connections to a front-end processor (e.g., the 3705, 3725, or 3745), direct channel connection to the mainframe, or an IBM-supported LAN. The connection to the vendor network may be implemented by an industry-standard LAN (e.g., Ethernet, token bus, or token ring).

The physical connection to the IBM network generally must make allowances for three variables: the interconnect bandwidth and data rate, the proximity of the IBM and non-IBM networks, and the additional cost required to make the connection within the IBM domain (e.g., the cost of an additional channel connection versus the cost of extra communications front-end resources). A general illustration of the target environment is shown in Exhibit IV-8-1.

The system shown in the exhibit is typically termed a gateway. However, to satisfy the definition of gateway used in this chapter, this packaged system may need to be complemented by appropriate client software, within either the vendor or the IBM network. Whether additional client software is required depends on the internal architecture of the gateway product and the nature of the application.

Gateway internal architectures use two principal approaches to realize protocol interoperability: encapsulation and full conversion. The approach used largely depends on how closely the IBM protocols align with the protocols used by a particular vendor to support the function in question.

In the encapsulation approach, some portion of the foreign network protocol is placed between the packet headers of the native network protocol—for example, the encapsulation of the IBM 3270 data stream within the transport packets of a particular vendor network. The overall objective is to provide vendor-specific terminals the ability to appear to the IBM-based application as real 3270 devices. Similarly, protocols specific to that vendor's terminal-to-host access functions could be encapsulated in client software based on an IBM host to cause native 3270 devices to appear as interactive terminals in the non-IBM vendor's network. In either case, encapsulation takes place in the client systems, so additional client software is usually required.

The base transport functions (i.e., the IBM and vendor-specific end-to-end protocols) within the respective networks carry the encapsulated protocol

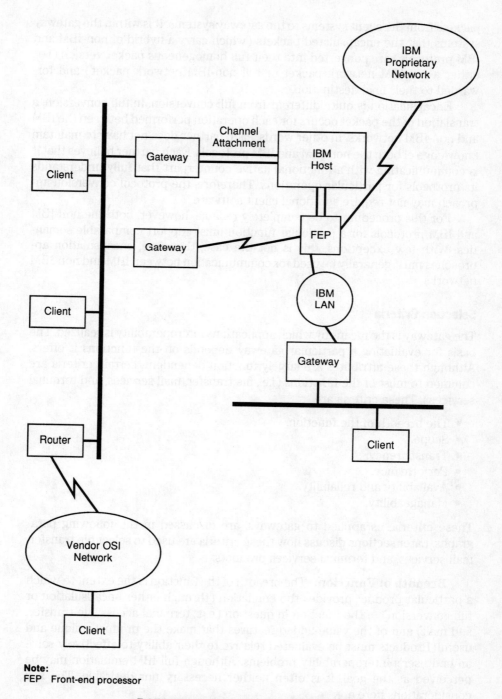

Note:
FEP   Front-end processor

Exhibit IV-8-1. Generic Gateway Configuration

429

packets from the client systems to the gateway systems. It is within the gateway systems that the encapsulated packets (which carry a hybrid of non-IBM and IBM protocols) are converted into their full homogeneous packet version (i.e., either a full IBM network packet or full non-IBM network packet) and forwarded to their final destination.

Encapsulation is quite different from full conversion. In full conversion, a translation of the packet occurs for each operation performed between the IBM and non-IBM networks. In other words, each partner does not have to maintain knowledge of both the non-IBM and IBM protocols. Each partner believes that it is communicating with a functional native counterpart that fully understands its protocols for particular operations. Therefore, the protocol conversion approach may not require additional client software.

For this procedure to be completely reliable, however, both the non-IBM and IBM protocols for a particular function must support comparable semantics. With few exceptions, this is not the case; therefore, encapsulation approaches must generally be used for communication between IBM and non-IBM networks.

Selection Criteria

The gateway is the means by which applications interoperability is realized. The basis for evaluating a particular gateway depends on the functions it offers. Although these attributes are largely function dependent, certain criteria are common to most of the functions (i.e., file transfer, mail services, and terminal services). These criteria are:

- The breadth of the function.
- Scope.
- Transparency.
- Performance.
- Availability and reliability.
- Manageability.

These criteria, as applied to gateways, are discussed in the following paragraphs. Later sections discuss how these criteria are used to select file transfer, mail services, and terminal services products.

Breadth of Function. The breadth of the function is the extent to which a particular product provides the emulation (through either encapsulation or full conversion) of the function in question (e.g., terminal access, file transfer, and mail) and of the value-added features that make the product unique and useful. Products must be evaluated relative to their ability to effectively solve an end user's interoperability problems. Although full IBM emulation may be perceived as the goal, it is often neither necessary nor desirable. The key considerations here are:

- What is the nature of the intended application? What business problem will it help solve?
- What existing applications, either IBM or non-IBM, will it be required to interoperate with?
- How effectively will the gateway supply the desired interoperability? What required features are present or not present?
- What effect will the gateway have on end-user work flow and habits? Is it replacing existing IBM equipment or is it simply making IBM services available to those on the non-IBM system?
- What vendor services exist to make the application more effective from a productivity standpoint?
- How consistent is the emulation offering with other layered products from the same vendor? How easily can the end user make data from the emulation available to other layered products to effect higher orders of application composition?

Scope. Scope refers to the range over which the gateway's functions are available to users. Can an end user access the gateway effectively, regardless of the user's location on the network (assuming that such issues as performance are not critical)? Are all subfunctions location independent?

Because the focus of this chapter is on gateways as a network-to-network connection, a key concern is the availability of gateway functions across the network. Furthermore, because a gateway connects two networks to form a larger, composite network, the bidirectional nature of the function and its associated scope are key concerns. Additional considerations with respect to scope include the following:

- To what extent are the gateway's services provided independently of the type of the end-user computing platform?
- To what extent must services on the gateway be complemented by modules that reside on the end-user computing platform (e.g., use of an encapsulation approach) as opposed to provision of the entire service within the gateway itself (e.g., a full conversion approach)?
- To what extent are the services bidirectional, allowing users in the non-IBM and IBM networks equal use of the gateway?
- How effective is the product, in function and cost/performance ratio, with networks that range in size from small to large?
- What impact will the product have on an existing IBM network, from either a functional or a performance standpoint? Similarly, what effect does the IBM network have on the non-IBM network?

Transparency. Transparency primarily involves the extent to which the end user needs to understand the naming, addressing, and command syntax conventions of either network. In other words, to what extent are naming and

431

addressing tokens present in commands used to effect particular functions? It is much simpler to log on to the accounting system or send mail to John Doe than to explicitly specify all the networking attributes necessary to accomplish these functions.

Achieving transparency is largely a function of the extent to which naming services and command substitution (i.e., the ability to replace a large, complex command with a shorter, more intuitive one) are present as well as the product's ability to use the naming conventions most effectively within the IBM environment. The most effective solutions are generally those that completely hide the presence of the IBM network within the vendor's command suite and make use of natural command and naming extensions within existing IBM products.

Performance. Descriptions of desired performance are sometimes contradictory. With respect to bulk transfer functions (e.g., file transfer or mail exchange), more performance is better; with respect to interactive response time, however, less is better. Clearly, both cannot be achieved simultaneously in terms of a single function.

Therefore, it is important to understand not only the product's basic performance (i.e., the maximum speed at which it interconnects into the IBM environment) but how effectively the product can be managed and controlled. Performance evaluation questions follow:

- Function separation—During concurrent bulk transfer and interactive functions, to what extent can the functions and priorities be separated so that one is not optimized at the expense of the other?
- Performance certification—To what extent can the vendor predict the performance of its product with respect to the anticipated end-user work load?
- Management—What tools are available for monitoring and tuning performance?
- System scaling—What level of load sharing exists across multiple implementations of the same product?
- Side effects—Could the product adversely affect the performance of the IBM network, and can this situation be diagnosed if it does arise?

Performance considerations are complex. An evaluation has to include the performance potential of the individual gateway within the context of the overall system. This requires an understanding of the configuration of the system, and the means used by the product to achieve its maximum performance must be understood.

Availability and Reliability. Availability is the product's ability to provide the expected services without disruption. Reliability is the product's ability to provide correct operation over a sustained period of time, often despite unusual or even abnormal operating conditions. A product must be both highly robust in its operation and sufficiently flexible to circumvent faults when they do occur.

Reliability and availability are more likely to be present in mature products. The vendor's philosophy regarding fault tolerance and management can also be important.

Manageability. As the corporate information network evolves, the ability to manage the network's service delivery becomes crucial. The key areas are configuration, fault, performance, security, and accounting management. Because the entire network is regarded as a single corporate entity, the network is rarely divided by product boundaries. Services required by the enterprise exist on all systems. Therefore, to realize service synergy, some level of synergy must be attained in all the management areas previously identified.

The fit of the gateway into the overall enterprise network management structure, if such a structure exists, is important. Few standards currently exist in the network management area, so a user must be flexible and creative in merging the IBM and non-IBM systems. The vendor may be helpful in adapting existing network management structures to the new network. In the long run, the best course of action is to aim for implementation of true network management standards, such as those provided by OSI.

APPLICATIONS

File Transfer

File transfer products range from simple programs that transfer sequential text files between a personal computer and a host system to rich and complex subsystems that support a variety of file and data types and access methods. A selection of criteria by which to evaluate a file transfer product follows. In using these, both immediate and future applications should be considered.

Breadth of Function. Breadth of function refers to the file transfer product's features, support of the intended operating environment (i.e., operating systems and hardware configurations), and interoperability with existing network components. Breadth of function should always be evaluated with respect to the effective solution of business problems.

What Operating Systems and Hardware Configurations Are Supported? This is the most basic question; it includes not only a consideration of the end-user systems involved in the transfer but the configuration of any necessary intermediary (e.g., a file transfer server to support networked personal computers).

What Communications Environment Is Required by the Product? Many products presuppose the existence of particular network protocols—for example, SNA on an IBM system. This requirement can also be reversed; if a network is already in place, it is preferable to have a file transfer product that uses the existing communications software.

What File Systems or Access Methods Are Supported? This question is particularly relevant for such operating systems as IBM's MVS family, which supports various file access methods (e.g., the virtual sequential access method).

Are There Any Implications for Simultaneous Data Access? For example, can the file transfer product read a file that is currently opened by a data base manager? For such access to be useful, there must be some way of ensuring that the transferred copy is internally consistent; it should not be possible to catch the file in the middle of an update.

What File Organizations Are Supported? File organizations may include sequential, random-access, and indexed organizations of various types. Furthermore, because the source and destination systems will usually differ in the details of their support for particular file organizations, it is necessary to check that the essential details of file organization are preserved during the transfer.

Are There Any Restrictions to File Organizations? There may, for example, be some limit on the number or length of key fields for an indexed file. If so, the limitations may have more to do with the target file system than with the file transfer product; careful comparison is required.

What Record Formats Are Supported? Record formats may include fixed length, variable length, byte stream, and print format. It must be determined whether there are any restrictions for particular formats or format conversions. One potential problem area is that some personal computer operating systems do not support record-structured files, and conversions must therefore be performed to and from a stream format. Another concern, when print formats are involved, is maintaining absolute print fidelity, including such features as overprinting and underlining.

What Kinds of Data Conversion Are Supported? Data conversion is usually necessary in order that information transferred from one system to another can be meaningfully interpreted at the destination system. The data to be converted may be text, in which case the character code may need to be translated—for example, from EBCDIC to ASCII. The data may be numeric (i.e., in several possible formats), in which case it can require conversion between the different formats used by different systems hardware.

Supported conversions may range from simple text translation to much more sophisticated schemes that allow different fields within a record to be subject to different translations. For example, the first 20 bytes of a record may be converted as five 4-byte integers, with the remainder being converted as EBCDIC text. In such cases, the user must be able to specify the conversion to be invoked.

It should be known whether these conversions are fully reversible. If a file is copied from the host system and then copied back to the same system, the new host copy should be identical to the old.

For text conversions, the user should know whether alternative translation tables are specifiable and whether these tables are supplied by the vendor or by the customer. This is particularly important information outside North America because a national variant of the standard character set may be in use. Another issue is whether there are characters in one character set that have no equivalent in the translation. Last, it may be necessary to transfer files in the binary mode and perform no conversions of any kind on the data as it is transferred.

Does the Product Support Record-Level Access? It is often unnecessary to transfer an entire file to accomplish a given task. Although it may be possible to run an extraction job to create a subset of the original file, which is then transferred, it is often more convenient if the file transfer product itself offers some means of reading or writing particular records in the file.

Although record-level access is most often found in conjunction with an applications programming interface, utility programs may also provide for some sort of data extraction. Because two dissimilar systems are involved in the transfer, it may be necessary to determine whether both systems support record-level access.

Is a Programming Interface Provided for Customer Applications? A programming interface may provide the ability to initiate a complete file transfer from within a customer application, or it may provide a data access interface to the remote file system itself. Although both interfaces are useful, the latter may give added flexibility to applications. A programming interface may be available on either or both sides of the transport connection.

Does the Product Provide Any Hooks into Other System Services? For example, it may be necessary to transfer a print file and then spool it to a printer on the remote system. This feature may be explicitly provided as a feature of the file transfer product, or it may be implicit in the structure of the target operating system (perhaps as a spooled printer device accessible through the file system). Some features required in this category may overlap with features of other products (e.g., remote job entry systems).

What Data Storage Media Are Supported? Disk storage is usually provided, but the capability to use other media (e.g., magnetic tape) is advantageous. If magnetic tape, for example, is supported, it must be determined how tape-specific processing (e.g., label processing) is handled.

Scope. The term *scope* refers to the degree to which the product is available to end users regardless of their location on the network and regardless of the type of computing hardware on which they base their work. The following questions will help to focus this aspect of the investigation of the product.

What Is the Scope of the Product? Does the product provide a true network-to-network data transfer facility, or is it a system-to-system interconnection? A product that transfers data between networks can usually transfer a file from any authorized node in one network to any other authorized node in the connected network, without the need for a direct physical connection between the two endpoints. A product that interconnects systems usually restricts access to the systems that support the physical connection itself.

The scope must be determined for each of the connected networks because some products, such as micro-to-mainframe gateways, provide network-to-system connectivity.

Where Is the Software Located? It may be necessary to install some component of the file transfer product on every network node that needs to use it. Alternatively, the file transfer product may be implemented as a server on a particular node; all other authorized nodes in the same network transfer data through the server node by using the file transfer mechanisms that are native to their own network. There may be asymmetry between the two networks with respect to software location; it often depends on whether a particular network supports a standard file transfer protocol in the first place.

Software location affects the network management and the overall cost of using the product. However, it may still be necessary for all accessing nodes to pay a licensing fee to the software vendor.

Who Can Initiate Data Transfer? It should be ascertained whether data transfer must be initiated by the user of either network or whether the user must be logged on to one particular network. For example, with a network-to-network file transfer product, it is reasonable to expect equal access from both sides. For a micro-to-mainframe product, it is more likely that transfers can be initiated only by the personal computer.

An important point is whether, in a given network, data transfer can be initiated from any node or the user must log on to some particular node or type of node. In other words, the product should be available on all operating systems and hardware bases that can exist in the network.

Does the Product Scale Well? It should be determined whether the product scales well in both cost/performance ratio and in performance, from small to large networks. A given product may be too expensive for consideration at the low end or may not offer adequate performance at the high end. The possibility of upgrading any dedicated systems to more powerful versions (i.e., those that handle higher throughput, more simultaneous users, or both), preferably without significant adverse effect on end users, should be determined.

Transparency. This is related to the product's ease of use. If the product's operation is suitably transparent, learning times will be reduced and training costs will be lowered. The following questions highlight the different ways the user will be aware of transparency.

How Transparent Is the User Interface? The integration of the user interface into the standard user interface for each system should be checked. If, for example, there is already a user command to perform intranetwork file transfers, the user should know if the same command is used for internetwork transfers.

Whether the file transfer product provides different styles of user interface (e.g., menu and command line) that will support different classes of users or applications should be determined. Whether the product can be accessed from command procedures, batch jobs, or similar job streams is also important.

How Transparent Is the Programming Interface? The user must determine:

- Whether the programming interface is unique to this application or is a standard system interface.
- The programming languages that can use the programming interface.
- Whether standard high-level language input/output statements will be used.
- Whether the same interface will be used to transfer files between the two networks and within one of the networks.

How Transparent Are File Names? There may be two conflicting requirements concerning how the other network's file names appear to the user. The first consideration is that a given file should have a name that looks similar in either network; for example, if an IBM system file is known as **PORTER.PROJ. STUFF** in the IBM network, the name by which it is known in the non-IBM network should resemble **PORTER.PROJ.STUFF** as closely as possible. The second consideration is that a user of one network may not care to know the syntactic conventions of the other; it may be preferable to convert the file name to something like **[PORTER] PROJ.STUFF** in the file transfer software.

Performance. Performance is often one of the most important concerns about a file transfer product; the rate of data transfer should be known. Performance is also one of the most difficult areas to evaluate. The following questions must be answered to facilitate the evaluation of file transfer performance.

What End-User Data Throughput Can the Product Sustain? When comparing performance, it is necessary to compare like with like. Ensure in particular that bits-per-second figures are compared at the same level, whether at the level of the transmission medium itself or at the level of the user data. It is also useful to distinguish between the aggregate throughput of a file transfer system and the throughput that is achievable in a single session.

On What Variables Does the Achievable Throughput Depend? Typically, throughput depends on such factors as the speed of the physical links, the size of the message units transmitted, the record sizes of the files, and the CPU and memory resources available at each end of the transfer session and in intervening communications processors. Some of these factors can be tuned to maximize transfer rates; others (e.g., record size) may be predetermined by existing software.

What Are the Effects on the Systems at Either End of the Transfer? Transmitting data at very high rates can consume large quantities of system resources at the transfer endpoints. Concurrent use of the systems can reduce the actual throughput rate; on the other hand, the file transfer software can degrade response times for other systems users.

Mail Services

There are two types of mail services: immediate delivery and store and forward. In an immediate-delivery mail system, the user establishes a connection to the destination mail system, delivers mail, and then exits. It is very similar to a standard telephone call, in which an individual dials a number, the party on the other line answers, information is exchanged, and the connection is broken when the telephone is hung up.

In a store-and-forward mail system, the user delivers a mail message to the local system, then exits. The local mail system establishes a connection to the mail message destination and delivers the message when the system or network resources are available. An example of store-and-forward mail service is the US Post Office. Mail is dropped in a mailbox, and the local post office picks up the mail, determines the destination post office and the path to it, determines the vehicles for delivery, and finally delivers the mail to the destination post office. The destination post office then delivers the mail to the mail receiver.

The main difference between the two types of mail service is that with immediate delivery, the user and the user's resources are occupied until the message is delivered; the delivery results (i.e., success or failure) are known immediately. With store and forward, the system does the work on behalf of the user, and the delivery results are not known until later.

If the mail exchange is between two proprietary mail protocols, mail gateway software is needed to provide the mapping and translation between the two proprietary protocols. If the mail exchange is among systems that have adopted the OSI reference model standard for mail (X.400), a software mail gateway is not needed.

For either type of mail service (i.e., immediate delivery or store and forward) or protocol (i.e., proprietary or X.400), a network planner should consider certain factors before choosing a mail interconnect vendor. For mail products, the areas of consideration are breadth of function, scope, transparency, performance, reliability, and manageability. These criteria are discussed in the following paragraphs.

Breadth of Function. This refers to a mail product's features and functions. The questions to consider are discussed in the following paragraphs.

What Types of Documents, Messages, and Notes Are Supported? This question refers to the different computer systems that may exist in a network and the need for each to participate in a multivendor mail network, even though each system may use a different format for files, documents, and messages. A network manager whose network consists of IBM SNADS, IBM PROFS, Digital's ALL-IN-1, and personal computers may require that all these systems, regardless of their protocols and file structures, go through the mail interconnect product and exchange mail among themselves. If certain files (e.g., personal computer stream files) are not supported, the effect on the network manager's business task should be evaluated.

What Functions and Features Are Preserved by the Mail Interconnect Product? Mapping between proprietary protocols generally entails the loss of some functions and features. It must be determined what is lost and whether that loss is acceptable to the network manager. The following are examples of questions to ask when determining whether functions and features are preserved:

- Are mail priorities and classes preserved or at least mapped as closely as possible?
- Does the business depend on acknowledgment receipts, and if so, does the mail interconnect product support it?
- Which mail commands (e.g., **SEND, RECEIVE, REPLY,** and **FORWARD**) are necessary to the business, and which are optional?
- Does the mail interconnect product support the required commands?
- How accurately is the mail content of a particular command preserved and presented at the receiving end? For example, if the command **REPLY** to a mail message does not carry some kind of unique identifier (it can be the original mail **SUBJECT** line), the receiving end cannot determine what the reply was to.

Network managers need to understand and outline the features of the mail systems that their business depends on and then check those requirements against a vendor's mail gateway features and functions.

Is a Programming Interface Available? If a programming interface to the mail system is available, network managers will be able to develop in-house products to extend the use of their preferred mail platform.

To What Degree Does the Mail Interconnect Product Take Advantage of Directory Services? Vendors have proprietary directory service as well as proprietary mail systems. Directory service is a collection of user information. Users of a mail network store in a central place such information as their full name, network address, telephone number, and their department, much like a telephone directory. Mapping among these directory services is an important, complex task because each proprietary directory service has certain information that is not necessarily found in the other vendor's directory service; the key is to be able to find the user location regardless of the proprietary directory service involved.

One important issue is whether a user can be moved to a different location on the network while network transparency is retained—that is, while the need for other system users to make adjustments to accommodate the move is eliminated. Another important issue is how efficiently the mail gateway uses these directory services. Does the mail gateway require duplication of user information in its domain? For example, if a 1,000-node Digital Equipment network is connected to an IBM SNA network of 1,500 users and all 2,500 users need to exchange mail, a mail gateway product should perform this with minimal to no duplication of directory services information in its domain. A mail gateway product should take advantage of existing directory services as much as possible.

Scope. Scope refers to the degree that mail service is independent of the network users' locations and operating systems. Some questions that will help evaluate the scope of the function follow.

What Is the Scope of the Product? It should be determined whether the mail gateway is a true network-to-network mail system. That is, existing or future nodes should be able to use this mail system and access any other nodes for mail.

Where Does the Mail Interconnect Software Exist? If the network topology consists of many nodes, it may not be desirable to install and license the mail interconnect software on each node. One or more nodes should be able to serve the whole network; therefore, a mail server product may be more desirable. Immediate-delivery mail software usually requires client software on every node; otherwise, the users have to log into a node that has the software installed. A store-and-forward mail system is more easily adaptable to a network server model and hence can serve a large number of network nodes simultaneously without requiring each user to log on to the mail server node.

Who Can Exchange Mail? It cannot be taken for granted that a mail gateway will allow everyone on the network equal use of the mail message function. The following aspects of the product's operation should be checked:

- Whether users on either network will have to log on to an intermediate system to send and receive mail messages.
- Whether the mail gateway serves all operating systems on the network.
- Whether send and receive functions are supported for all users.

The effect on the organization of some network users' not having access to mail service should be carefully evaluated.

Does the Mail Interconnect Product Scale Well? The product should be checked for the following:

- Whether additional nodes can be added and, if so, the effect on performance (i.e., will it be degraded, and at what point will the system no longer be useable?).
- Options when the maximum number of allowable nodes is reached.
- Impact on the mail users of the addition of new nodes to the network.

Transparency. As with other products, mail system transparency directly affects ease of use. The following questions should be answered.

How Well Is the Mail Product Integrated with the User Environment? Can user X on mail system A exchange mail with user Y on mail system B as if Y were an A mail user, or does user X have to know extra information? For example, a Digital Equipment user should be able to exchange mail with an IBM, Wang, or Data General user as if it were another Digital Equipment node in the network, and vice versa.

Performance. Performance goals for an immediate-delivery mail system could be translated into response time—that is, the total time it takes a user to issue a SEND mail command, establish connection to the destination, send mail across the network, and get the return of the screen prompt. The expected response time for an immediate-delivery system is usually a matter of seconds. For a store-and-forward system, response time is a measure of hours, days, or sometimes weeks, depending on the network topology, location, and resources available. The following questions should be asked.

How Fast Can It Transmit the Data? The mail system may be able to use several pipes to transmit data from a large network to another large network. The techniques for accomplishing this and the effects on network or system resources should be evaluated.

What Are the Upper Limits? Upper limits for the number of users (i.e., the number of nodes) must be considered to allow efficient exchange of mail. Sample response times for predefined networks can help determine the expected response time.

Reliability. Businesses that depend on electronic mail for communication cannot afford a mail system that loses mail, is incapable of recovery from simple errors, or cannot identify an alternate route to a destination. Some key questions that can help identify the reliability of mail interconnect products are discussed in the following paragraphs.

If a Link Goes Down, Can Mail Recover? The mail product should not stall when a link goes down. Instead, it should be able to search for alternate routes or reestablish the broken link so that the delivery process can continue.

What Error Reporting Features Are Included? Information about the following features will be useful:

- Whether the mail system reports on problems in the mail delivery process.
- The length of time it takes to generate a report about a problem.
- The content of the status report.
- Notification of the sender of a failed delivery attempt.
- A list of reasons for failure of mail delivery.

Manageability. Manageability refers to the tools provided by the mail interconnect product that assist the mail network manager in setting up the product and in determining and tracking the problem mail in the hearts of the system. Some key questions that can help determine the manageability of mail interconnect products are discussed in the following paragraphs.

What Management and Problem Determination Tools Are Included? The following should be investigated:

- The availability of error log files with the mail interconnect product and their level of detail and usefulness.
- The ability to trace mail from source to destination.
- The degree of difficulty in tracking mail that has traversed several hops in the network.
- Whether the mail manager has to log on to each system and track the mail message or information is provided automatically through management and problem determination tools.
- Whether the tools provided by this mail interconnect product are user-friendly and easy to use.

The amount of training required to manage, use, and run a mail network is an important factor that is often overlooked. Products that are well integrated and user-friendly and that take advantage of common architectures can reduce training costs in the long term. Therefore, each network application, including mail, should be examined in the context of its effect on the whole network and the requirements of the business. A vendor that delivers integrated solutions based on common architectures usually offers point products that operate together harmoniously yet save money for the businesses in the long term.

Terminal Services

Terminal services typically allow access to any application running on any system from any type of terminal. For example, in a network that consists of SNA and DECnet and OSI elements, IBM applications are accessed through IBM 3270 terminals, and Digitial Equipment applications are accessed through VTXXX terminals. If a business requires that VTXXX users have access to IBM applications and 3270 users have access to Digital applications, a 3270 and a VT emulator are required. A network planner in a situation such as this should consider the following criteria before choosing a terminal emulator.

Breadth of Function. This refers to the supported applications and the access devices. The following questions serve as guidelines.

What Applications Are Supported? Terminal users must access different types of applications. Some applications use color and graphics, some are character oriented, some use block mode (transaction processing), and some are similar to editors. The nature of the applications must first be determined, then emulator features and functions must be examined.

What Are the Characteristics of Access Devices? Two types of terminal devices—character cell terminals and bit-map devices (i.e., work stations)—are in use. Emulation performed on a bit-map device will more closely represent the actual terminal than emulation on a character cell device. Therefore, an emulator product should provide the closest match between the application features and features of the terminal device that emulation is performed on. This match should be found for the network manager's current and future network. An emulator product should also be able to take advantage of new device technologies (e.g., bit mapping) to satisfy future as well as current needs.

Scope. As with other products, scope refers to the physical separation of elements of the network. The following questions provide guidelines.

Where Are the Network Terminals Located? Terminal location should not matter. Any terminal in the network should be able to access any application in the network, regardless of whether it is local or remote. Local terminals are physically within reach; remote terminals can be miles away, perhaps even in another country. A vendor's offering should accommodate both local and remote terminals. How a vendor does this—and what that means to the business in terms of budget, excess hardware requirements, and impact on the user—needs to be examined.

How Are Terminals Connected? The following considerations should be addressed:

- Whether extra hardware is required to connect terminals.
- The need for extra hardware if more terminals are added or if a different type of terminal is added.
- Whether a vendor's terminal offering scales appropriately for the current and future needs of an organization in terms of how those terminals are connected.

How Many Terminals Are Supported? This refers to the number of terminals that can use the terminal emulator product efficiently. A terminal

443

emulator may allow x number of users, while a network planner may have requirements for many more than x. In terms of capacity and efficiency, a network manager must know the precise number of terminal users before shopping for a vendor.

Transparency. Terminal services should be transparent to the application and the user. User transparency means that a user accessing an IBM application from a VTXXX terminal device uses the keys on the VTXXX keyboard that are equivalent to those on the 3270. The emulator maps the 3270 keyboard onto the VTXXX keyboard so that the 3270 keyboard can be used as if it were a VTXXX. Keyboard mapping is a nontrivial task; keyboards are physically different from each other, so a direct, one-to-one mapping among keyboards cannot be achieved. Transparency can be achieved to a limited extent, and the more transparent (i.e., the better the keyboard mapping), the better off the user will be.

Application transparency means that applications require no information about terminal devices on the part of the user; the emulator provides the application with any information it needs.

Performance. Terminal emulation uses CPU cycles. Which CPU has cycles to support an emulator product is a decision the network manager must make. The application hosts should not be bogged down with emulation processing. A business that depends on timely applications processing and predictable response times cannot afford to lose processing power to such activities as terminal emulation.

Predictable (i.e., deterministic) response time is an important factor for a terminal emulator product. A function that requires three seconds today should not take one hour tomorrow, because this could be costly to the business and distracting to the user. Because response time is sensitive to network topology, it is illogical to expect to be able to maintain the same response time when the topology is changed. Topology tuning to achieve optimal terminal emulator response time is a nontrivial task and requires extensive understanding of the network, topology, and work loads. This is an area in which a vendor's expertise can play a major role not only in providing a suitable terminal emulator product but in tuning for the best response time results.

Manageability. A local or remote terminal user should be able to access any application. Security requirements necessitate tracking users throughout the network to ensure that unauthorized users and terminals do not have access to privileged systems or applications. Management tools provided by a vendor should facilitate this task and are therefore an important consideration in choosing a vendor.

A terminal emulator product should have fault detection and correction capabilities. If such capabilities are not provided, a management tool or product from the same vendor should be able to detect and recover the fault so that services can continue. A management tool should also help determine the response time of a terminal emulator product and help fine tune it when necessary.

SUMMARY

The network manager, by following the evaluation guidelines provided in this chapter and carefully ascertaining the capabilities of various gateway solutions, can ensure that a LAN will have fully functioning interoperability with the targeted 3270, OSI, SNA, or TCP/IP environment.

Section V
Applied Technologies and Standards

The strength of LAN technology lies in its versatility, which is best demonstrated when LANs are used in conjunction with other technologies to address real-world business and technical problems. This section presents three major topics to illustrate this versatility. The first topic is technologies developed largely because of LANs—in particular, NetBIOS, servers, and network operating systems. The next topic is the use of LANs according to open systems interconnection (OSI) standards, which results in the development of a mainstream systems utility function based on LANs. Finally, how LANs can coexist with and extend the capabilities of traditional, hierarchical, mainframe networks is discussed.

Since it was first introduced by IBM in 1984, NetBIOS has grown to become one of the more important network interfaces used by personal computer applications developers. Chapter V-1, "The NetBIOS Interface," details the structure and capability of the interface and discusses efforts taking place in the Transmission Control Protocol and Internet Protocol (TCP/IP) and International Standards Organization (ISO) communities to extend NetBIOS beyond personal computer and LAN environments.

During the 1990s, many organizations will use LANs as an enabling technology, allowing the adoption of client-server computing architectures. Chapter V-2, "Server Concepts and Technologies," explores the development of the client-server model and discusses several important existing and emerging server types.

A technology related to servers is discussed in Chapter V-3, "Network Operating Systems." The functions of network operating systems are discussed, followed by a quick overview of each of the more popular current network operating systems. NetWare, the most common, is reviewed in detail. The future of network operating systems, especially as they relate to OSI, is also discussed.

The first three chapters of this section focus on the application of LAN technologies and standards to the issue of making LAN-based resources available to end users and application programs. The remaining five chapters of this section focus on how LAN technologies and standards can be applied as integral, key components of an organization's overall information systems strategy. Such applications can take two basic forms: the use of LANs as the primary communications vehicle in a distributed architecture, and the use of LANs to provide connectivity in the traditional, host-centered network.

Section IV of the *Handbook of Local Area Networks* provides a discussion of interoperability architectures, including the OSI reference model. As discussed in Section IV, OSI merely provides a framework. To make that framework truly useful, it is first necessary to flesh it out in the form of a specification. Chapter V-4, "The Manufacturing Automation Protocol and the Technical and Office Protocol," discusses the manufacturing automation protocol (MAP) and the technical and office protocol (TOP), two of the most important specifications developed to date. A brief history of MAP and TOP is presented, the specific standards contained within the specifications are introduced, and the future relationship between MAP, TOP, and other emerging specifications, such as government OSI profile (GOSIP), is discussed.

The ability to apply such specifications as MAP and TOP to the solution of real-world problems is a subject of considerable interest. As shown in Chapter V-5, "GMT-400: A MAP Implementation Case Study," General Motors (GM) not only was instrumental in the development of MAP but was also a leader in implementing real systems based on MAP. This chapter discusses the background leading up to the implementation of MAP 2.1 in two GM assembly plants. The discussion includes the business requirement, the alternatives considered, and the network selection itself. Experiences during and after installation are also reviewed.

The preceding specifications are primarily designed to solve the problems associated with networking in a heterogeneous, peer-to-peer environment. However, many organizations' environments are characterized as neither heterogeneous nor peer-to-peer. Rather, they are single-vendor shops using traditional mainframes, the vast majority of which are IBM or IBM compatible. For this type of environment, proprietary systems have a valid place because they can often provide performance enhancements without the economic penalties associated with proprietary systems in a multivendor environment. The most important proprietary LAN technology is IBM's Token-Ring. In fact, at the time of this writing, IBM has already shipped well in excess of one million Token-Ring Adapters. Although the token ring has been standardized as IEEE 802.5, applications have been almost exclusively dominated by IBM's version. Despite the token ring's proprietary nature, it is considered important enough to warrant considerable discussion in the *Handbook*.

Chapter V-6, "Connectivity Options for the IBM Token-Ring Network," introduces the basic concepts of token-ring connectivity. Included in the discussions are basic terminology and connectivity approaches, the user's perspective, and a general overview of the options available.

IBM's Token-Ring, by itself, is essentially a peer-to-peer implementation. The typical IBM environment, however, is not. Full migration to a peer-to-peer scenario is expected to be very slow and methodical. Therefore, it is important to consider the Token-Ring's coexistence with Systems Network Architecture

(SNA). The most important element in providing LAN connectivity to an SNA environment is the LAN-to-SNA gateway. Chapter V-7, "SNA and LANs: The Gateway Function," provides a detailed look at the primary types of LAN-to-SNA gateways, including the functions provided by each. Selection guidelines are provided. This chapter assumes that the reader has a working knowledge of SNA terminology.

V-1
The NetBIOS Interface

STEPHEN A. THOMAS

A key standard for local networks in the IBM microcomputer environment is the Network Basic Input/Output System (NetBIOS). All network operating systems and software applications for PC-DOS, MS-DOS, and OS/2 use or support some form of NetBIOS, and NetBIOS's existence has been a major factor in the explosive growth of LANs for personal computers. This chapter defines NetBIOS, outlines the services that it provides, and describes several of the most important versions of NetBIOS.

NetBIOS is not a true standard, despite the fact that many people refer to it as such, because no national or international standards organization defines NetBIOS. Rather, NetBIOS is a de facto standard; IBM introduced NetBIOS when it released its first serious LAN for personal computers—the PC Network. As part of that network, IBM sold the PC Network Adapter and a technical description of that adapter, the *PC Network Technical Reference*, that includes a detailed description of NetBIOS, the interface to the PC Network Adapter.

The fact that NetBIOS is not a true standard is important because what actually constitutes NetBIOS is therefore open to interpretation. One vendor may decide a certain group of features makes up NetBIOS, whereas another vendor may choose a different set. Because no standards organization oversees NetBIOS, no one can dictate which vendor is correct. This also means that no official conformance tests for NetBIOS are available; each NetBIOS vendor must decide how to conduct its own test of conformance to the NetBIOS standard.

Another important fact about the NetBIOS standard is that it defines only an interface. Specifically, NetBIOS defines the software interface between application programs and a network adapter. NetBIOS does not specify anything about how an adapter should carry out its operations. For example, it does not specify the communications protocols that the adapter must use. (The *PC Network Technical Reference* does describe the PC Network Adapter's communications protocols, but that information is not part of NetBIOS.) As illustrated in Exhibit V-1-1, NetBIOS defines how applications software communicates with network adapters, not how network adapters communicate with each other over the network. Because different vendors may use different communications protocols, NetBIOS-compatible adapters from different ven-

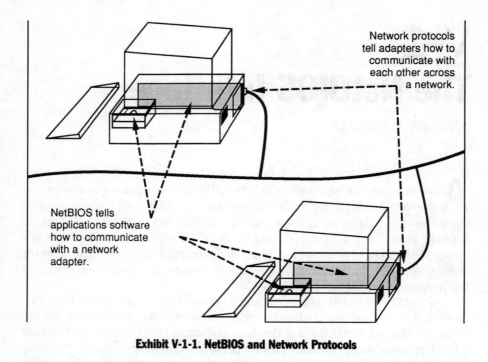

Network protocols tell adapters how to communicate with each other across a network.

NetBIOS tells applications software how to communicate with a network adapter.

Exhibit V-1-1. NetBIOS and Network Protocols

dors cannot always communicate with each other. IBM, for example, sold both the original PC Network Adapter and the Token-Ring Adapter. Both of these adapters conform to the NetBIOS interface; however, not only can they not communicate with each other, they cannot even connect to the same network cabling.

Because NetBIOS specifies an interface only, it cannot guarantee that different network adapters will be able to communicate with each other. NetBIOS does, however, provide a consistent, defined interface for applications software. It can guarantee that different network adapters will support the same applications. For example, applications software that works with the PC Network Adapter will continue to work if a Token-Ring Adapter replaces that PC Network Adapter. For an entire network to continue functioning, however, all PC Network Adapters on the network must be replaced by Token-Ring Adapters, although in some cases, bridges, gateways, or protocol converters can be used instead.

Like most software interfaces in the MS-DOS environment, NetBIOS is accessed through a software interrupt. When an application needs a NetBIOS service, it executes a specific software interrupt. This interrupt directs the microprocessor to transfer control to the network adapter's software, which can then process the request.

The specific interrupt used by NetBIOS is interrupt 5C (in hexadecimal). Applications execute the INT 5C instruction to pass control to the adapter software. Other software interrupts, including interrupts 21, 2A, and 2F, provide some network services. Those interrupts, however, are not part of NetBIOS but are part of a network operating system such as IBM's PC LAN program. The software that responds to these interrupts can, in turn, issue NetBIOS interrupts to request NetBIOS services.

The most important structure defined by the NetBIOS interface is the network-control block (NCB), which is the structure through which applications software and the adapter software communicate. Each time a program issues a NetBIOS interrupt, it must set aside enough memory for a network-control block, fill it in, and set up specific registers to point to it. The adapter software can then use those registers to locate the network-control block and, after examining it, decide what actions to perform. The adapter software also indicates the results of those actions by updating information in the network-control block.

As shown in Exhibit V-1-2, a network-control block consists of 14 fields that specify the command to perform as well as the data, parameters, and options for that command. Application programs fill in these fields before issuing the NetBIOS interrupt. Other fields in the network-control block tell the application the result of its request. The adapter software fills in these fields both while it processes the command and after it finishes the processing.

NETBIOS SERVICES

When an application program issues a NetBIOS interrupt, it requests a network service. Because the NetBIOS interface defines exactly how applications can

NCB__COMMAND	1 byte	Command requested
NCB__RETCODE	1 byte	Result of command
NCB__LSN	1 byte	Local session number
NCB__NUM	1 byte	Name number
NCB__BUFFER@	4 bytes	Address of message buffer
NCB__LENGTH	2 bytes	Length of message
NCB__CALLNAME	16 bytes	Remote name
NCB__NAME	16 bytes	Local name
NCB__RTO	1 byte	Receive time-out
NCB__STO	1 byte	Send time-out
NCB__POST@	4 bytes	Address of completion routine
NCB__LANA__NUM	1 byte	LAN adapter number
NCB__CMD__CPLT	1 byte	Command completion status
NCB__RESERVE	14 bytes	Reserved for use by adapter

Note:
NCB   Network-control block

Exhibit V-1-2. Network-Control Block Fields

use the NetBIOS interrupt, it effectively defines the network services available from NetBIOS. NetBIOS identifies those services with the NCB_COMMAND field of the network-control block, which specifies a particular NetBIOS command. Exhibit V-1-3 lists the available NetBIOS commands that are usually divided into four groups for four different classes of network service. The four classes—general services, naming services, session services, and datagram services—are discussed in the following sections.

General Services

The NetBIOS general services manage and configure the network adapter. Five NetBIOS commands provide general services: RESET, CANCEL, ADAPTER STATUS, UNLINK, and TRACE. The RESET command, as its name implies, resets the adapter; it can also specify some configuration parameters. The CANCEL command cancels a previously issued command. There are a few NetBIOS commands that cannot be canceled; CANCEL has no effect on these commands.

The ADAPTER STATUS command returns status information about a network adapter. The command can get this information for either the local adapter or a remote adapter. This remote operation allows software that is executing on one computer to find out the status of an adapter installed in a different computer. The information returned by an ADAPTER STATUS command can include self-test results, software version numbers, traffic and error

General Services	RESET	Reset local adapter
	CANCEL	Cancel prior command
	ADAPTER STATUS	Get status of adapter
	UNLINK	End a remote program load
	TRACE	Enable diagnostic tracing
Naming Services	ADD NAME	Register a unique name
	ADD GROUP NAME	Register a group name
	FIND NAME	Discover a name
	DELETE NAME	Delete a name
Session Services	LISTEN	Wait for a session
	CALL	Establish a session
	RECEIVE	Receive a message on a session
	RECEIVE ANY	Receive from a set of sessions
	SEND	Send a message on a session
	CHAIN SEND	Send multiple messages
	SEND NO ACK	Send without guaranteed delivery
	CHAIN SEND NO ACK	Chain send without guarantee
	HANG UP	End a session
	SESSION STATUS	Get status of a session or sessions
Datagram Services	RECEIVE DATAGRAM	Receive a datagram
	SEND DATAGRAM	Send a datagram
	RECEIVE BROADCAST DATAGRAM	Receive a broadcast datagram
	SEND BROADCAST DATAGRAM	Send a broadcast datagram

Exhibit V-1-3. NetBIOS Commands

statistics, resource statistics, and name-status information. Some implementations of NetBIOS provide only subsets of this information.

The final two general commands are specialized commands available with only a few NetBIOS implementations. The UNLINK command ends a special communication known as remote-program load that provides primitive support for diskless workstations. Because the support is so primitive, however, many vendors choose not to provide it at all and consequently do not support UNLINK in their NetBIOS implementations. TRACE suffers a similar fate. IBM defined TRACE for its NetBIOS implementation for Token-Ring Adapters, where it enables special diagnostic software. Because this feature is specific to the token-ring implementation, few other vendors support the TRACE command.

Naming Services

When IBM first introduced NetBIOS, one of its most innovative features was its naming services, which manage network names. When applications software refers to network adapters, NetBIOS allows it to use a network name of its own (or of the remote software's) choosing, which can be simple, logical, and mnemonic. Most applications extend this convenience to their users so that they can use simple, logical, and mnemonic names as well. When a user accesses a computer that stores marketing information, for example, application programs allow the user to refer to that computer as MARKETING__PC. Neither users nor application programs need to keep track of cryptic hexadecimal numbers or other forms of network addresses.

The use of network names is not new to NetBIOS, but NetBIOS popularized the idea that names could be dynamic. When names are dynamic, they can move from one system to another, and the network automatically keeps track of them. A user named ABRAHAM LINCOLN, for example, could continually move from one computer to another, and as long as all the computers were on the same network, the network would keep up-to-date information about this user's location automatically. Any mail sent to ABRAHAM LINCOLN would automatically arrive at the computer where this user was active at the time.

Name services occur in three phases: name registration, name discovery, and name deletion. These phases are discussed in the following sections.

Name Registration. Before anyone can use a network name, someone has to register that name. When an application program registers a name, it identifies itself and its name to the network adapter. Before granting the registration, the adapter makes sure that the name is a valid name and that using this name will not cause a conflict with other names on the network.

Two NetBIOS commands provide name registration services: ADD NAME and ADD GROUP NAME. Each tells the adapter to register a network name, but they differ in the type of name they identify. ADD NAME registers a unique name—only one application at a time can use a unique name. As part of the registration process, the adapter must be sure that no other application is already trying to use the name. **ADD GROUP NAME,** on the other hand, registers a group name—many applications on a network can use the same group name at the same time. In many cases, data sent to a group name will arrive at all the application programs using that name. For group name registration, an adapter need only make sure that no application is using the name as a unique name.

Name Discovery. The second phase of naming services is name discovery, which identifies the specific network adapter at which a name exists. For example, an application program that sends mail must transfer data to an application program that receives mail. Both of these programs can simply use network names to identify each other, but the adapter software on the sending computer must actually locate the network adapter of the receiving program. In other words, the sending adapter must discover the network address of the receiving adapter.

Most of the time, name discovery takes place without the knowledge of application programs. When an application establishes a session or transfers a datagram, the application uses only names. The adapter software, on the other hand, must translate these names to network addresses. It is the adapter software itself, therefore, that most often uses name discovery.

Some implementations of NetBIOS provide a **FIND NAME** command so that application software can access the name discovery service directly. Once an application discovers a name, however, there is not much it can do with the information. Because **FIND NAME** provides little useful information and because it is not part of the original NetBIOS standard, most implementations do not support it.

Name Deletion. Once an application program has no further use for a name, it may delete it. Name deletion is the opposite of name registration; it cancels any association between the name and the application, and it allows other applications to use the name. An application must delete a name before the name can move to another computer, even if the second computer is using a copy of the same application. Although users may think of these two applications as being the same program, NetBIOS views them as two separate applications.

NetBIOS provides the **DELETE NAME** command for deleting a name. Applications use this command to delete both unique names and group names. In addition, an adapter deletes all names when it receives a **RESET** command or when its computer is rebooted or powered down.

Session Services

The third type of service NetBIOS provides is session services, which allow programs to exchange information. As valuable as naming services are, they only allow applications to identify each other. The main business of a network is the transfer of information, and naming services cannot provide for data transfer.

Session services provide connection-oriented communications, much like an ordinary telephone call. One application program calls to establish a session, and the other application answers the call. Once the application establishes a session, each may send data to the other on that session. Finally, when either application no longer needs the session, it ends the session by hanging up. This operation naturally divides session services into three phases—establishment, data transfer, and termination—which are discussed in the following sections.

Session Establishment. Session establishment occurs when two application programs start to communicate. One application issues a LISTEN command, which tells the adapter software that the application is willing to accept a session. The second application executes a CALL command, which directs the adapter software to actively attempt to establish a session. The adapter must discover the remote name specified in the command and try to set up a connection to that name. If the remote adapter has accepted a matching LISTEN command, the local CALL command succeeds. If the remote adapter has no appropriate LISTEN outstanding, however, the CALL command fails.

Data Transfer. Once applications establish a session, they can then transfer data. The simplest way to transfer data is with the RECEIVE and SEND commands—a RECEIVE command tells the adapter that its application is willing to receive data, and a SEND command gives the adapter the data that its application wants to send. The CHAIN SEND command, which is very similar to the SEND command, lets an application send more data with a single NetBIOS command.

Applications can also use RECEIVE ANY commands to receive data; a RECEIVE ANY command differs from a RECEIVE command in that it applies to a set of sessions instead of a single session. Applications that use more than one session at the same time frequently use RECEIVE ANY commands to avoid having to issue separate RECEIVE commands for each active session.

When applications use SEND and CHAIN SEND commands, they gain the important benefit of reliability because NetBIOS guarantees delivery of any data sent with a SEND or CHAIN SEND command. If an unusual network event prevents delivery, NetBIOS will notify the sender of this condition before completing the SEND or CHAIN SEND. If the sender application does not get such a notification, it can be assured that the remote application successfully used a RECEIVE or RECEIVE ANY command to obtain the transferred data.

NetBIOS also provides a less reliable method of data transfer for sessions. Two other commands—the SEND NO ACK and CHAIN SEND NO ACK commands—transfer data without guaranteeing reliable delivery. Because these commands do not require that NetBIOS perform the work involved in guaranteeing delivery, they can offer a significant performance improvement over SEND and CHAIN SEND commands. Because many networks provide some degree of reliability automatically, the extra reliability provided by NetBIOS may be redundant.

Despite these advantages, **SEND NO ACK** and **CHAIN SEND NO ACK** have not yet become popular with NetBIOS implementors or applications developers. The original NetBIOS standard did not include the **NO ACK** commands, so the first applications did not have the option of using them. Because few applications make use of them, NetBIOS implementors have been reluctant to support these commands.

Session Termination. When an application no longer needs a session, it can end the session with a **HANG UP** command. Either application involved in a session may issue a **HANG UP**. When only one application hangs up, NetBIOS notifies the other application by returning an error code in one of its commands.

Other circumstances can also cause session termination. Network errors that prevent reliable data transfer can force NetBIOS to end a session. A session may also be terminated if an application deletes the name it is using for the session. Finally, an adapter automatically terminates its sessions when it receives a **RESET** command or when its computer is rebooted or powered down.

Datagram Services

As an alternative to sessions, application programs may exchange information with datagrams, a connectionless service. Datagrams resemble mailed letters in the manner that sessions resemble phone calls. When an application sends data in a datagram, it simply gives the data to the adapter software and tells the adapter to whom it should be sent. The application need not bother with preliminary commands to establish a session.

Datagrams have two significant disadvantages compared with session-data transfer. First, datagrams support only a limited amount of data. Whereas an application can send as much as 131,072 bytes of data with a single **CHAIN SEND** command, datagrams limit the application to 512 bytes at a time. Second, datagrams are not reliable. NetBIOS gives a sender no assurance that data sent by a datagram will ever be delivered to the recipient.

An application can use datagrams in three ways: it can send data to a single remote application, it can send data to a group of applications, or it can send data to all NetBIOS applications. These methods are discussed in the following sections.

Point-to-Point Data Transfer. The simplest way an application can use datagrams is to send data to one other application. Because this type of transfer involves one sender and one recipient, it is called a point-to-point transfer. (Session-data transfer is also a form of point-to-point transfer.) To prepare for receiving a point-to-point datagram, an application issues a **RECEIVE DATAGRAM** command, and the sending application executes a **SEND DATAGRAM** command. If an application sends a datagram to a remote name that has not issued an appropriate **RECEIVE DATAGRAM** command, the data is simply lost and the sender is not notified.

Group-Data Transfer. Applications use the same NetBIOS commands for group-data transfer that they use for point-to-point transfer: RECEIVE DATAGRAM and SEND DATAGRAM. For group transfer, however, the recipient's name is a group name instead of a unique name. Many applications on many different adapters can all issue RECEIVE DATAGRAM commands for the same group name. Then when someone sends a datagram to that name, all of these applications can receive a copy of the data.

Broadcast-Data Transfer. The final way in which applications use datagrams is for broadcast-data transfer. NetBIOS provides two commands just for broadcast transfer: RECEIVE BROADCAST DATAGRAM and SEND BROAD-CAST DATAGRAM. These commands behave like the regular datagram commands except that they do not require a specified destination name for the datagram. For broadcast traffic, the implied destination is every adapter on the network. However, not everybody will receive a broadcast datagram; only those applications that have issued RECEIVE BROADCAST DATAGRAM commands can do so.

IMPORTANT NETBIOS IMPLEMENTATIONS

A network adapter that can provide the network services outlined in the previous section can also provide a NetBIOS interface, and many network adapters have done just that. Because there are many ways to provide the network services, different implementations of NetBIOS have emerged.

The NetBIOS implementations covered in this chapter do not represent an exhaustive list—NetBIOS has been used in everything from LANs to wide area networks (WANs) to asynchronous communications. In fact, the following list does not even include the most widely distributed NetBIOS version—Novell includes a NetBIOS software program with every copy of NetWare. (Instead of NetBIOS, Novell promotes its own network interface, which has been fairly successful.) The versions of NetBIOS discussed here, however, do represent the most important versions of the interface.

NetBIOS for the PC Network Adapter

NetBIOS for the PC Network Adapter is an important NetBIOS implementation because it was the first. IBM's release of the PC Network in August 1984 introduced NetBIOS to the world. In its initial form, NetBIOS was simply the interface to the PC Network Adapter. It served as a network extension to the standard BIOS interface for keyboards, display adapters, disk drives, and other devices. Because it was the first network interface, NetBIOS for the PC Network Adapter became the reference NetBIOS.

The original PC Network Adapter, though marketed and sold by IBM, was developed by Sytek Inc of Mountain View CA. Sytek developed both the hardware and software for the adapter, including the data communications protocols the adapter uses to access the network. Exhibit V-1-4 shows the protocols Sytek developed. It is important to note that Sytek's protocols are not based on any standard network protocols but are, in fact, proprietary to Sytek. No other vendor may use the protocols without licensing them from Sytek.

Because of the proprietary nature of its network protocols, few vendors have been eager to develop network products that interoperate with the PC Network Adapter. Other factors, such as the relatively small LAN market in 1984, also influenced vendors' decisions. Users of the IBM PC Network, therefore, can purchase products only from IBM or, in some cases, Sytek. Currently, Sytek no longer makes PC Network Adapters for IBM, and although IBM supports the PC Network, it strongly encourages its customers to use the Token-Ring Network instead.

NetBIOS for the Token-Ring Adapter

As IBM has deemphasized the PC Network, the Token-Ring Network has taken its place. Because Token-Ring is IBM's preferred LAN and because IBM is

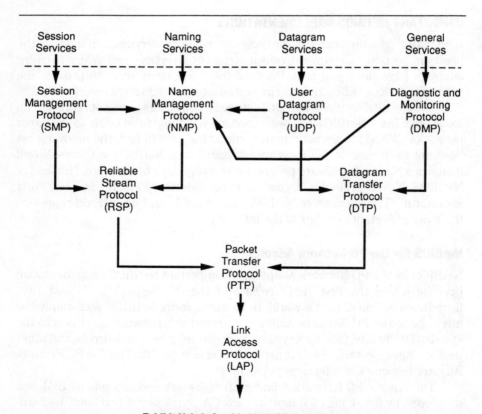

Exhibit V-1-4. Sytek's NetBIOS Protocols

closest to being an owner of NetBIOS, NetBIOS for the Token-Ring Adapter has become the reference NetBIOS implementation, replacing NetBIOS for the PC Network Adapter.

An important difference between the Token-Ring Adapter NetBIOS and the original PC Network NetBIOS is that the NetBIOS interface is not the primary interface to the Token-Ring Adapter. The Token-Ring Adapter, in fact, does not naturally provide the same network services as the PC Network Adapter. Because it cannot provide the services NetBIOS needs, the Token-Ring Adapter has its own interface.

Despite the need for its own distinct interface, the Token-Ring Adapter still supports NetBIOS through a software emulation of the NetBIOS interface. The original Token-Ring Adapter software included two programs, **TOKREUI-.COM** and **NETBEUI.COM**, that together provided a NetBIOS interface. Currently, the **DXMTOMOD.SYS** module of the PC LAN support program provides the same function. In both cases, the programs use the primary adapter interface and the network protocols built into the adapter and supplement these network protocols with protocols of their own. The additional protocols provide the network services that a NetBIOS interface needs. As with the Sytek protocols for the PC Network, the additional Token-Ring protocols are proprietary. Exhibit V-1-5 shows the difference between the PC Network Adapter's NetBIOS interface and the Token-Ring Adapter's NetBIOS interface.

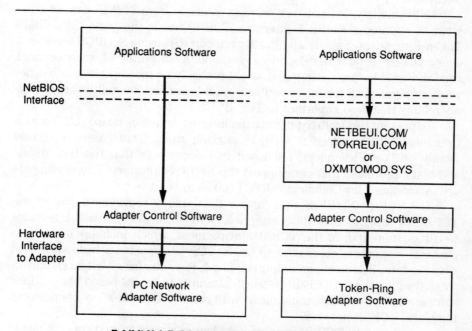

Exhibit V-1-5. PC Network and Token-Ring Adapters

It is irrelevant to applications software whether a NetBIOS interface is a primary interface to a network adapter or a software emulation. As long as the software emulation functions properly, application programs need not know the difference. With the Token-Ring NetBIOS, IBM showed that an adapter other than the PC Network Adapter could still provide a NetBIOS interface. This principle has served as the basis for all NetBIOS implementations since the original PC Network.

NetBIOS for Department of Defense Protocols

One concern surrounding both IBM NetBIOS implementations is their reliance on proprietary network protocols. For the PC Network, those protocols are built into the adapter; the Token-Ring Network includes proprietary protocols in its NetBIOS emulation software. Proprietary protocols limit users to products sold by or licensed from a single vendor. In today's multivendor networking environment, this limitation is quickly becoming unacceptable.

A well-known set of standard protocols are those of the US Department of Defense (DoD). Those protocols are often referred to by the name of their two most prominent components: the Transmission Control Protocol (TCP) and the Internet Protocol (IP). During the mid-1980s, TCP/IP became increasingly popular as a basis for commercial, multivendor LANs. As TCP/IP vendors became interested in the MS-DOS market, they also became interested in NetBIOS.

Unfortunately, the network services available from TCP/IP are not sufficient to support a NetBIOS interface. TCP/IP needs the same thing IBM's Token-Ring Adapter needs: additional protocols to provide NetBIOS services. If every TCP/IP vendor developed its own additional protocols, each vendor's version would be proprietary and would probably be incompatible with other vendors' versions. Such incompatibility would sacrifice the multivendor interoperability that is so important to TCP/IP.

To prevent this from happening, the Internet Activities Board (IAB), which oversees TCP/IP, formed a NetBIOS working group. That group, composed mostly of TCP/IP vendors, published two documents that together define additional protocols that can support the NetBIOS interface. The documents are IAB Request for Comments (RFC) 1001 and 1002.

The TCP/IP NetBIOS goes further than simply providing a way to use TCP/IP to support a NetBIOS interface, however. It also partially integrates NetBIOS support into the TCP/IP environment, which includes more than personal computers connected to LANs. TCP/IP supports a wide variety of systems from PCs to supercomputers, and it provides for global interconnectivity through WANs. TCP/IP NetBIOS attempts to let PC-based applications software using NetBIOS communicate with both PC and non-PC systems across the global TCP/IP network.

Unfortunately, TCP/IP vendors have had only very limited success meeting these goals. Several of the NetBIOS services, including dynamic naming and group and broadcast datagrams, simply cannot function efficiently outside of a local network. Even if inefficient operations across a global network are tolerated, TCP/ICP NetBIOS still requires complex protocols that no vendor has yet implemented. Interoperation with non-PC systems also requires that these non-PC systems include the additional NetBIOS support protocols, and few large systems have added these extra protocols.

TCP/IP NetBIOS also suffered because of its lack of a conformance test. Several vendors took liberties with the IAB RFC 1001/1002 standard in their initial products, and ambiguities in the standard led to different interpretations. As a result, TCP/IP NetBIOS products from different vendors have had difficulty interoperating. These problems are not unexpected in a brand-new standard. As the standard matures, however, support should become both more reliable and more uniform.

NetBIOS for International Standards Organization Protocols

Another set of standard network protocols that has become increasingly popular is the set published by the International Standards Organization (ISO). This set of standards, based on ISO's open systems interconnection (OSI) reference model, has strong international support and will someday replace TCP/IP. In the US, most of the initial support for ISO protocols came from the Manufacturing Automation Protocols (MAP) and Technical and Office Protocols (TOP) user groups. The ISO protocols suffer from the same basic problem as TCP/IP, however, in terms of supporting the NetBIOS interface. ISO protocols alone do not provide all the network services NetBIOS needs, so additional protocols are still necessary.

To ensure multivendor interoperability, the MAP/TOP user group formed a NetBIOS migration special interest group, which has defined a specification for supporting NetBIOS using ISO protocols. Although the MAP/TOP user group's activity resembles the IAB's formation of a NetBIOS working group, there are two important political differences between the two efforts. First, MAP/TOP does not directly control the ISO standardization process, as MAP/TOP is only one of many organizations interested in ISO protocols. Because nothing developed by MAP/TOP is binding in any way on ISO or other parties concerned with ISO, other organizations are free to develop different means of supporting NetBIOS through ISO protocols. As yet, however, no other ISO-based organization has expressed an interest in NetBIOS. In the future, other ISO-based organizations will most likely simply adopt MAP/TOP's specification.

Second, MAP/TOP views NetBIOS purely as a migration aid. True ISO protocols exist that provide most of the functions available from the applications software that uses NetBIOS. By their very nature, NetBIOS-based applications cannot use true ISO protocols. Although the MAP/TOP user group would clearly prefer that all software applications adhere strictly to ISO protocols, the user group recognizes that users have already made a significant investment in NetBIOS-based applications. By providing a NetBIOS interface, MAP/TOP allows these users to continue to use their current applications until they can phase them out and replace them with ISO-based applications.

Like the TCP/IP effort, MAP/TOP NetBIOS attempts to integrate NetBIOS support into the global ISO networking environment. The resulting MAP/TOP specification closely resembles the TCP/IP NetBIOS standard, and it suffers from some of the same shortcomings. For PCs on LANs, MAP/TOP NetBIOS should function identically to IBM's Token-Ring or PC Network NetBIOS. For non-PC systems and for systems connected by WANs, however, full NetBIOS capability may not be available, and both dynamic naming and group and broadcast datagrams are simply not efficient on WANs. Non-PC systems must also include additional software to communicate with NetBIOS-based PC systems.

SUMMARY

Both the TCP/IP and the MAP/TOP NetBIOS demonstrate the importance of NetBIOS to LANs. The TCP/IP and ISO protocols have defined standards for network applications, yet despite this fact, vendors and users have acknowledged the need to extend those standards to include support for NetBIOS. NetBIOS, in its current and future versions, will continue to be important as long as the wealth of PC-based network applications expect a NetBIOS interface.

V-2
Server Concepts and Technologies

CHRIS GLADWIN

The client-server model of computing, discussed in this chapter, is relatively new. It traces its development from the original centralized computer architecture and the later development of tiered architecture.

CENTRALIZED ARCHITECTURE

During the 1960s and 1970s, hardware was the dominant cost in computer systems. As a result, designers employed a centralized architecture, using mainframe computers, that minimized hardware utilization.

Exhibit V-2-1 is an example of such a centralized architecture. Within an organization, all of the processing and storage resources are usually at one location and are shared by all users. When a user at a terminal requests some kind of computation, the response is delayed until prior requests from other users have been serviced in turn. In this way, the overall required processing power is minimized, albeit at the expense of possible delays for the users.

TIERED ARCHITECTURE

Advances in computer technology that lowered hardware prices allowed departures from the centralized architecture model. Minicomputers, although they still share CPU time, are usually limited to fewer users than mainframes, and organizations typically have more than one minicomputer. Installations are frequently configured on a departmental basis.

Personal computers allowed a move away from the shared approach to computing. They did not, however, replace centralized and departmental computers. Mainframes still are used when very large quantities of data are involved, when the computing requirements are organizationwide, or when extremely complicated calculations must be performed. Minicomputers still find departmental applications.

Connectivity among these different computer types was minimal, leading to the development of tiered architecture. As shown in Exhibit V-2-2, all three

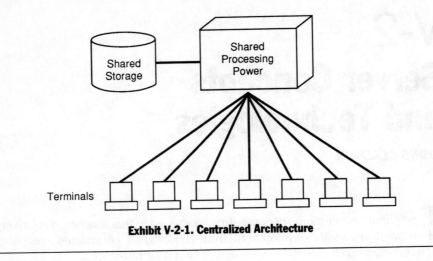

Exhibit V-2-1. Centralized Architecture

types of computers can coexist within an organization, but they are isolated and operate independently.

CLIENT-SERVER ARCHITECTURE

During the 1990s, the variable with the most influence on computing architectures will not be related to computer hardware or software but to the experience of the end users. As the portion of the work force that uses computers increases, organizations will focus primarily on the benefits derived by their computer users and the cost of the time that their employees spend learning and using computing tools. The dominant computing architecture, therefore, will be one that is oriented toward maximizing the productivity and effectiveness of end users.

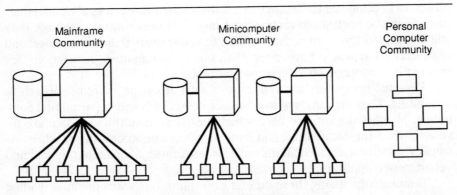

Exhibit V-2-2. Tiered Architecture

This evolving architecture is the client-server architecture. As shown in Exhibit V-2-3, all of an organization's computing resources are networked together so that all resources are available to all users. The client-server architecture allows every computer user to best benefit from all of the computing resources of the entire organization.

The key to the client-server architecture is communication among computers as intelligent peers. The computing devices within a client-server architecture are networked together, with communication among the computers typically in the form of requests and responses. For example, one computer requests a piece of information from another, and the other computer responds with that piece of information. The end user is typically not aware of these requests and responses and can focus on the functional rather than the technical aspects of the task at hand.

The end user's device is an intelligent workstation, which is capable of performing such computing tasks as document preparation and numerical calculations. It also performs the computing tasks required to interface and present information to the user. In addition, the workstation formulates requests to and receives responses from other computers functioning as servers. Servers can be microcomputers, minicomputers, or mainframes. Computers functioning as servers typically handle requests from many clients; the type of computer chosen as a server depends on the nature of the service. For example, some activities are very storage-access intensive, whereas others are very processor intensive. This architecture provides the end user with an easy-to-use interface to a flexible set of resources that includes both the computing resources at the workstation and all the resources to which the workstation is connected.

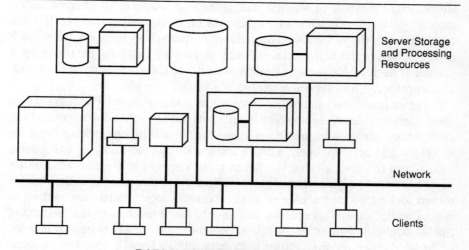

Exhibit V-2-3. Client-Server Architecture

The client-server architecture may seem to be the computing architecture that should have always been used. All of the technologies for this architecture, however, were not available until the late 1980s. Advances in microelectronics are the basis of today's small, inexpensive, yet powerful personal computing workstations. Sophisticated communications technologies (e.g., local and wide area networks) are the result of years of development work. The third technology required for a client-server architecture—interprocess communications—has been the last to mature. Intelligent devices with the capability to communicate with each other still need a common language to exchange information effectively; this common language is interprocess communications. Two examples of interprocess communications are structured query language (SQL) and X.400. SQL is a standard method of requesting information from a data base. X.400 is an industry standard for sending messages between computers.

TYPES OF SERVERS
Disk and File Servers

Although not commonly used, disk servers provide an excellent starting point for a discussion of the evolution of server technologies. Some of the first personal computer LANs employed disk servers so that expensive hard disks could be shared. Disk servers provided each user with a dedicated amount of hard disk storage. If, for example, three personal computer users wanted to share a 60M-byte hard disk, they could divide the hard disk so that one of the users had 40M bytes and the other two had 10M bytes each. The users of a disk server, however, could not share the same files, nor could one user who needed extra space access that allotted to another user.

Although similar to disk servers, file servers provide a more sophisticated and efficient method of sharing disk storage in addition to offering added capability. The users of a file server share the entire storage capacity of the hard disk. Although the file server management software may limit what files each user can see or limit the total amount of storage that can be taken by a particular user, all file server users have access to the entire shared hard disk. This approach offers several advantages over disk sharing.

For example, overall unused storage space is minimized. File servers also allow users to share the same files in different ways—either one user at a time or simultaneously—and provide routines for file and record locking. With file locking, a user or, more likely, a user's application can mark a file as being used. This allows the user locking the file to make changes to the file, while other users have read-only access to that file. File servers also provide a platform for record locking so that a user or application can lock a particular section or record within a file. This enables that user to make changes to that section of the file, while allowing other users to access the entire file in a read-only manner or to lock other records within that same file and make changes to those records.

File servers have become very popular among personal computer users. Novell's NetWare, although it offers additional services, is an example of a popular file server for personal computers. Network file systems (NFS) is a standard for file services supported by many vendors in many computing environments.

Data Base Servers

For those applications in which server requests are primarily requests for data within a file instead of for entire files, a data base server is more efficient and capable than a file or disk server. When a client's application needs a piece of data from a data base server, the application can specifically request the data desired. To get that same data using a file server, the application would essentially have to access the entire file and sort through it to find the desired data.

Therefore, a data base server is a more efficient and higher-performance approach than a file server for shared data applications. By transmitting only the desired data to the client, traffic on the network is minimized. In addition, the data base server hardware and software can be optimized for data base operations.

The interprocess communications language understood by the server and used by the client is an important element of a data base server. SQL is the dominant standard for data base query languages. SQL is supported by almost all data base server vendors and is being included in an increasing number of client applications. Even though SQL is an English-like language, the generation of SQL calls is transparent to users of most applications. Client-based applications (e.g., spreadsheets and charting packages) collect data through SQL calls without requiring the user to understand SQL or even know SQL is being used. The use of data base servers, especially SQL servers, is expected to increase drastically during the 1990s and will complement, not replace, the functions offered by file servers.

Print Servers

A print server allows several computer users to share one or more printers. It usually includes a queue in which print jobs are held until the printer is available. Printer servers are usually not sold as separate products but are included with other types of products, such as network operating systems. Print servers are currently very common and will continue to be so.

Communications Servers

To communicate with different computers in different locations, a sophisticated personal computer user needs various types of communications hardware, including a terminal emulation board, a modem, a LAN board, and a fax board. An alternative approach to having separate add-in cards for each of these is a communications server. As shown in Exhibit V-2-4, a communications server allows communications resources to be shared by several users. With this architecture, both the number and the aggregate expense of required communications hardware is reduced because communications hardware is more efficiently used.

A communications server is typically used on a LAN and provides the LAN users and their applications with one or more types of communications services, including the following: asynchronous dial-in and dial-out, fax sending and receiving, and various types of terminal emulation. A communications server can also be used by server-based applications. For example, a data base server may use a communications server to access data that resides at other locations. A single product that will do all these things is not on the market, but it is possible to assemble a communications server that provides these functions.

Message Servers

A store-and-forward message server functions like a post office. A user addresses a message and gives it to the message server. The message server stores the message until the recipient is available and then forwards the message to the recipient. A message server is also capable of other functions. For example, if the recipient never becomes available to receive the message, the server informs the sender that the message could not be sent. In addition, a message server can route messages through other message servers similar to the way mail is often routed through several post offices.

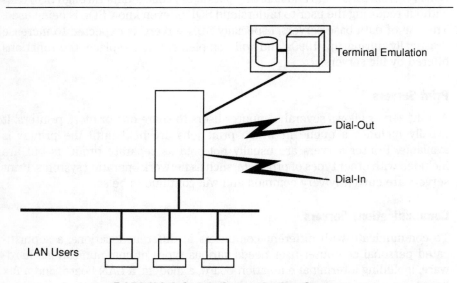

Exhibit V-2-4. Sample Communications Server

Just as standards for data base query languages are important for data base servers, a standard messaging language is important for message servers. The International Telephone and Telegraph Consultative Committee (CCITT) X.400 standard includes standards for addressing messages, programming interfaces to mail servers, and routing messages.

Emerging Server Types

The potential for server-based applications will continue to expand with the increase in use of computer networks. In addition to file, data base, print, communications, and message servers, other server types will become commonly used. One of these will be processing servers. A processing server can receive a request for processing and return the result. One use for processing servers is to perform complex mathematical calculations. If an economist, for example, wants to solve an economic model that would take several minutes or even hours at a workstation, the modeling application could request that the model be solved on a powerful processing server (e.g., a supercomputer). This is an example of cooperative processing.

In contrast to the generic processing server, other types will emerge that will be very application specific. An example of such an application server would be a server for a large computer-aided drafting (CAD) application. This CAD server could store the detailed drawing of an entire airplane and allow clients using various CAD packages to simultaneously access various sections of the drawing (e.g., the wing or the tail) for design changes or aerodynamic simulations.

Other server types are being developed as the client-server environment matures. The creation of networks with multiple clients sharing multiple server resources will require naming and authentication servers. To date, naming and security services have typically been a part of a file server's network operating system. The file server maintains information describing which files a particular user can view or delete and which printers can be used. With multiple server systems, maintaining separate naming and authentication information on each server is inefficient. A naming and authentication server maintains information for other servers so that user accounts have rights that extend across multiple server types.

SUMMARY

The key to successfully managing the conversion of computer networks to the client-server model is to understand the reasons for the model's development. It is designed to make all of an organization's computing resources available to the computer user. These users will grow in number and in sophistication, and as LANs provide more services on which the organization's success depends, LANs will be held to higher standards of reliability and usability.

V-3
Network Operating Systems

CHRIS GLADWIN • FRITZ E. NELSON

Although there are as many definitions of a network operating system as there are network operating system products, most operating systems have certain features in common. These features, listed in Exhibit V-3-1, may provide the most useful definition of a network operating system. This chapter discusses these features.

MESSAGING

A network operating system frequently provides a mail-like utility that allows for basic communication among all the machines on a network. Novell's NetWare, for example, has a **SEND** command that delivers a short message, which appears on the bottom of the screen, to a specified network user. Most network operating systems allow users, as part of this type of message utility, to send files.

SECURITY AND NAMING SERVICES

Network security is usually under the control of the network administrator, using services provided by the network operating system. These usually take the form of a naming service that can provide network user's names and passwords and a list of attributes or services, including user access rights. The service can also set up accounts that allow the administrator to determine a balance or allotment of access rights for a particular user.

A nondistributed naming service sets up separate accounts for each file server. A distributed naming service creates accounts that span the entire network and all its file servers, making administration of the network easier.

FILE SERVICES

A network operating system allows users to share data, typically in the form of stored files. The network structure can be centralized, allowing everyone to see common data, or decentralized, allowing the storage devices of all machines on a network to be shared. The network also provides centralized backup, data integrity, and data security resources.

Feature	Function
Messaging	Provides the mechanism for computers to exchange electronic messages
Security and naming services	Control access to network resources
File services	Allow users to share data storage devices; manage access to shared files
Print services	Enable users to share printers
Administration utilities	Provide tools for network management and administration
Application programming interfaces	Define methods for programs to use network resources

Exhibit V-3-1. Basic Components of a Network Operating System

---

File sharing allows users access to files created by other users, enabling users to add, modify, or delete information or data. It is the basis of the popularity of networks in today's work groups.

File sharing primarily allows users to access shared files one at a time, but file- and record-locking features allow users to share files at the same time. With file and record locking, everyone on the network can see a file (or a record within the file) but only one user can modify it at a time.

PRINT SERVICES

Network operating systems allow workstations to share printers, so it is not necessary to purchase a printer for each workstation. The operating system also administers printer sharing by building a queue that serves as a storage zone or buffer on the file server. The queue stores print jobs, sending them to the printer in the order they were received in case several users decide to print at once.

ADMINISTRATION UTILITIES

A typical network operating system includes various utilities that manage the other network services (e.g., file and printer sharing and messaging). The network administrator uses these utilities to optimize network performance.

An administrator can enhance a file server's performance, for example, by adding memory, a faster hard drive, or a better network adapter. A management utility gives the administrator a picture of the inner workings of a network so that it is possible to determine which enhancement would work best.

Users may be concerned about printing on a shared printer or sharing a file, but when something goes wrong, the administrator needs utilities of this type to troubleshoot the network. Apple's AppleShare, for example, can display at the file server a list of who is logged on to the network and display a reading of overall relative network use. The administrator can then study the amount of network traffic and general use patterns and, with that information, allocate resources (e.g., memory) to reflect these patterns.

APPLICATION PROGRAMMING INTERFACES

A network operating system is not limited to the turnkey functions that come with the product. Vendors include application programming interfaces (APIs), which are commands that programmers can use to incorporate the services of the network operating system into their programs. These commands are the specific instructions that define, for example, how a programmer may send data from a program on one workstation to a program on another.

Named Pipes, which is quickly evolving into an API standard, is a set of calls that allows a programmer to open a pipe, or channel, from one program to another. The pipe can carry a message or data between the programs. Named Pipes has become successful because it is very useful as well as simple to work with.

ADD-ON PRODUCTS

Network users can obtain added value from their network operating system by using products that network vendors or third parties offer to complement the network operating system.

Although third-party products are separate utilities, they function as a part of the network operating system. LAN Systems Inc's LAN Spool, which runs as part of Novell's NetWare 286, allows all printers on a network—the centrally located ones and those attached to a workstation—to be shared. Novell provides a similar utility as a standard feature in its NetWare 3.0. In either case, the utility is part of the network operating system from the user's perspective.

Add-on products also provide automated data backup and communication between separate similar or dissimilar network operating systems and allow different types of computers to be included on the network—for example, 3+Mac allows Macintosh computers to work on 3Com's 3+ network operating system.

These features can be used to create a practical definition of a network operating system. The features, however, do not limit whether a product can be defined as a network operating system; some systems include all of these features and more and some include only a few.

A network operating system can be thought of as an extension of the operating system already on a workstation. That is, although users still have their operating system and all of its functions, they get the added capabilities of the network operating system. A redirector at the workstation looks at commands and requests from the workstation, for example, and determines whether the request is for the workstation's operating system or the network operating system (see Exhibit V-3-2). If the request is for the workstation operating system, the redirector passes it on. If it is for the network operating system, it directs the request to the server or printer, or wherever it needs to go.

USER BENEFITS

In making a decision between network operating systems, potential system users need to consider which system features are the most important. Current network operating systems (future ones will be discussed later in the chapter) are most often used for two basic functions: printing and data sharing. In both cases, the network operating system does not change the user's environment; it simply adds new capabilities.

A printer attached to a file server is available to any user on that network. The network operating system makes it appear as if it is a local printer, which means that the user does not notice any difference between directing a file to a local printer and directing one to the remote printer through the network.

The same principle of operation holds with data sharing: the network operating system allows data on the file server to be accessed by any user on the network, just as if it were the user's own file on the user's own system. The data is live—that is, everyone sees the same thing at once. Again, the user does not notice a difference.

APPLICATION RELATIONSHIPS

Software applications are increasingly being written to take advantage of network operating systems. Software vendors realize that network capabilities can

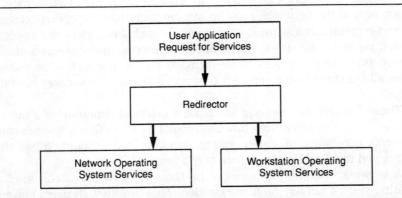

Exhibit V-3-2. Cooperation Between the Workstation and the Network Operating System

be an added sales feature for their products. The relationships between an application and a network operating system fall into five general categories: coexistence with LANs, incompatibility with LANs, LAN versions of standalone products, LAN-aware applications, or LAN-specific applications. These categories are discussed in the following sections.

Coexistence with LANs. Applications can coexist with a network operating system without using it or benefiting from it. A microcomputer-based word processing application written before network operating systems existed, for example, may still work on networked microcomputers, printing as it always has, maybe even to a printer on the network. In other words, it does not behave any differently on the network than it does on a standalone machine.

Incompatibility with LANs. Incompatible applications cannot function on networked microcomputers. Some of the older copy protection software, for example, performs disk operations by going straight to the drive, bypassing the operating system. Because these applications assume that the hard drive is local, they also bypass the network operating system.

Although many older applications were not designed to recognize that additional storage devices may exist, very few of today's applications are incompatible with network operating systems. Software developers may not want to take advantage of a network operating system's features but still want the application to be able to function on a networked system.

LAN Versions of Standalone Products. Some applications are available in LAN versions that are very similar to the standalone product. In fact, they may be the standalone product licensed for multiple use. For example, instead of requiring that 10 users of the software each have an individual copy, the assumption is made that only two or three users need the program at any one time. So two or three copies of the software are licensed and installed on the file server. To users, it appears that each has a personal copy of the software. The advantages of this approach are that the LAN version may be less expensive than multiple single copies and that it is usually easier and more cost-effective to upgrade and manage.

LAN-Aware Applications. LAN-aware applications function the same way as the standalone version of the same programs but are designed to recognize that they are in a LAN environment. LAN-aware applications take advantage, for example, of such network functions as user preferences. That is, many software packages have preference files like color, style sheets, and default directories. The LAN versions of the software can accommodate preferences by storing individual user preferences.

These applications, then, can be called LAN aware. That is, they are aware a network is out there. And although they do not provide any new functions, they do provide the appearance that multiple users each have a single copy of the application when in reality only one exists on a central file server. This allows users to save storage space on their own hard drives and save money as well.

LAN-Specific Applications. These applications have features built in so users can take advantage of the network operating system's services. They are designed for multiple users and essentially have functions that require a network operating system.

LAN-specific applications may have features built in so that users can simultaneously and transparently share data using file and record locking or may have built-in messaging capabilities.

Group productivity software, like a group calendar package in which everyone records schedules and appointments, is a real growth area in LAN-specific applications. If someone wants to schedule a meeting with four other network users on Tuesday, the application can look up everyone's Tuesday schedule and give the user a status report. If the meeting time is available to everyone, the application marks the meeting on the calendar and sends a note to all the users. This kind of function cannot exist without a network.

POPULAR NETWORK OPERATING SYSTEMS

The use of network operating systems has proliferated rapidly over the last few years. The most popular ones contain some form of all of the features previously discussed; however, all are slightly different in their solutions to providing LAN functions (see Exhibit V-3-3). Some of the popular network operating systems are discussed in the following sections.

NetWare

Novell's NetWare is considered the market leader in personal computer networking. Most estimates give Novell a 60% to 80% market share. It has become the industry's de facto standard in network operating systems.

NetWare's popularity is a result of its being a fast, high-performance network operating system that provides a work group with a file server and allows a laser printer to be shared. NetWare is hardware independent, running on Ethernet, token-ring, ArcNet, GNet, and other networks.

NetWare was optimized as a file server. That is, its file system was built to be a file-server file system. In 1989, Novell released NetWare 386, a program that provides true 32-bit processing and up to 16 terabytes of storage capacity. The rich development environment of NetWare 386 allows developers to take full advantage of the 80386 processor.

It is instructive to look at NetWare to get an accurate idea of the overall services a network operating system provides and how someone would use them. NetWare supports the file and print services that most users expect from a network operating system. DOS, Macintosh, and OS/2 applications are avail-

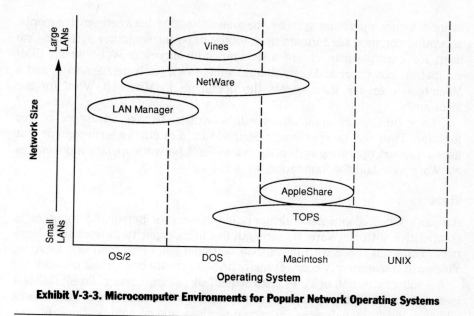

Exhibit V-3-3. Microcomputer Environments for Popular Network Operating Systems

able over NetWare, so network services are provided in the user's native environment.

Typical users may have printers attached to their personal computers; if they do not, they may share one on the network. Most applications print as they usually do, so the user still gets the benefit of being able to print. The only difference from printing locally is that the user may have to use NetWare's redirector command to redirect the printer.

In addition, users may have their own storage, but they can also store data and applications on the file server. The appearance to users is the same as storing data on the hard drive; users may not even realize when they are storing data or applications in the usual manner or on a file server. The file server may be located anywhere, even across the country.

Users do know that they have accounts with certain restrictions and limits. They must log on, using an identification number and password.

Some applications are custom-developed to take advantage of NetWare's functional capabilities. For example, data base applications allow everyone on a network to share data, look at a file, and make changes to a file or record. When one user is accessing a record within the data base, however, that record is locked so that data integrity is maintained. Again, a user's perception is one of equal access as everyone else.

Other applications are written to allow communication between different computer environments so that users on, for example, a Macintosh can create a document that can then be converted for use on a DOS machine. NetWare, like other network operating systems, becomes the glue between environments, accepting common file formats from totally different computer systems. One user, for example, can create a document in Microsoft Word on an IBM-compatible computer and copy that document to a NetWare file server, and a Macintosh user can then access the document in Microsoft Word for the Macintosh.

Over time, more applications will be written to take advantage of this function. They will be specifically designed for a multiuser environment that uses a network operating system's services. Such network operating systems as NetWare have laid the foundation for doing so.

Vines

Banyan's Vines, also a network operating system for personal computers, is competitive with NetWare. Its strength lies in its capacity to work with large networks, even those with more than 500 nodes in more than one location. Vines can transparently connect many LANs to create one virtual network.

Another strength of Vines is its StreetTalk naming service. StreetTalk is a global, distributed data base that maintains lists of the names and attributes of all users, file storage devices, individual services, and communications devices on the network. Vines file servers run a variant of UNIX.

MS-Net

Microsoft has always loomed large in the microcomputer networking world because of its dominance in personal computer operating systems. Microsoft's MS-Net network operating system, which is based on the DOS filing system, was not sold directly to the end user but was licensed to third parties, who added specific enhancements and sold their own versions.

During the mid-1980s, many of the major hardware vendors (e.g., 3Com, IBM, and Ungermann-Bass) offered products based on MS-Net. The products experienced limited success because they did not offer the high performance and capabilities offered by other network operating systems.

LAN Manager

Microsoft has introduced an OS/2 network operating system as the successor to MS-Net, using the same strategy as with MS-Net. Other vendors license LAN Manager and sell their own enhanced product. What Microsoft is in effect providing is the engine for the network operating system. The car that goes around the engine (i.e., the print services and file services) is built by other companies.

LAN Manager is evolving. Microsoft has upgraded to a higher-performance OS/2-based file system and is expected to release a 32-bit or 386-specific version. IBM's LAN Server and 3Com's 3+Open are the most popular LAN Manager–based network operating systems.

TOPS

Most of the popular network operating systems are based on a centralized file server architecture. TOPS, developed by Centram Systems West, offers a peer-to-peer architecture in which workstations can share the resources of other workstations.

TOPS's popularity results from being one of the first network operating systems to support Macintoshes, IBM PCs, and UNIX workstations, but it offers some other significant advantages as well.

For example, TOPS does not require a dedicated centralized machine, which saves money. Just as important, users can install the TOPS software and everyone can immediately have access to existing files on other machines. Everyone's hard drive becomes a file-storage medium, eliminating the dependence on a fixed amount of storage on a centralized machine.

With TOPS, the hard drive (i.e., station) being accessed essentially becomes a file server, with the owner of the workstation publishing specific volumes for others to share. Other users (i.e., clients) can then mount the server and the published volumes, which transparently become theirs. Although TOPS is well suited for smaller networks because of its peer-to-peer nature, it is also beneficial in mixed hardware environments.

AppleShare

AppleShare, produced by Apple and designed for the Macintosh environment, is easy to use, manage, and install and uses the Apple Filing Protocol. It is a low-end product with very few security features but is extremely popular because it is a network operating system that is native to the Macintosh.

AppleShare supports only 25 to 50 users (depending on the type of Macintosh running the AppleShare software); other popular network operating systems support hundreds of users. AppleShare is most often used in small to mid-sized homogeneous Macintosh networks.

OSI AND NETWORK OPERATING SYSTEMS

Network environments have become more heterogeneous, supporting equipment from more vendors and of greater variety. That trend will accelerate even more during the next few years. It is hoped that the open systems interconnection (OSI), particularly upper-layer OSI services, will have a profound effect on how network operating systems will offer more services and capabilities and keep up with the changing network environments.

Many organizations currently have distinct network operating system communities. For example, there may be separate 3COM, Novell, and Banyan LANs. At best, it may be possible to install a gateway to allow some communication between the different LANs, but this adds to the administrative burden and introduces such problems as reduced levels of function between the network operating systems. At worst, there may be nothing to allow communication between the network operating system communities. The intent of OSI is to make this situation easier.

OSI is not a product but an architecture. Its seven layers establish standard protocols for communication, categorizing and organizing different communications components. In particular, OSI defines the services provided by each communications layer and how peer protocols within a given layer will talk to each other. If all vendors write their network operating systems to adhere to OSI, there will be an important consistency among products.

Right now, network operating systems are largely tied to certain types of hardware. All of a network operating system's services are tied together. A user cannot use the file service of Novell's NetWare and the print service of 3Com's 3+Open because they are not written the same way.

However, the OSI concept, if followed, will further this kind of interchange. If all network operating systems are based on OSI, it will not matter what type of hardware a network uses or even if the hardware environment is a mixed one. OSI provides the hope that network operating systems will become more generic and independent because its protocols are not tied to specific hardware.

Networking has already become complex enough that a network operating system vendor cannot simply write a network operating system for one environment. All vendors must be concerned with accommodating multiple environments. With OSI, vendors can be less concerned with the other products their network operating system communicates with and can concentrate instead on improving the function of their network operating systems. For the computer user, this means a greater stress on increasing function within the product.

OSI will also allow the introduction of unbundled server-based applications. For example, network operating system vendors will sell a print server, file server, or data base server. Users will benefit by being able to choose exactly which services they want; if Novell's file server and 3Com's print server are the most useful, they can both be installed on the same network.

SUMMARY

No longer are computers the only resource and networks simply the tool to connect those resources; networks are also a resource. Network operating systems have played a large role in bringing this evolution about. And as network operating systems continue to grow, they will help bring this evolution to all users. Although many consider the network operating system the central nervous system of a network, it may well be the heart that pumps new life into an already dynamic system and drives a strong desire to make the network an even better resource.

V-4
The Manufacturing Automation Protocol and the Technical and Office Protocol

VINCENT C. JONES

The manufacturing automation protocol (MAP) and technical and office protocol (TOP) represent an attempt to create a complete set of specifications for factory and office networks that conforms to the open systems interconnection (OSI) model proposed by the International Standards Organization (ISO). This chapter discusses the history of the MAP/TOP movement, describes and compares early versions of MAP and TOP with MAP 3.0 and TOP 3.0, and discusses the relationship between MAP/TOP and the government open systems interconnection profile (GOSIP).

The goal of the MAP/TOP movement was captured in the specification for MAP version 2.1, published in March 1985:

> The driving force behind the General Motors MAP effort is the need for compatibility of communications to integrate the many factory floor devices. These devices are now provided by many different vendors, and it is our continued intention to use many vendors in the future. It is GM's goal to provide an environment for multiple vendors to participate on a standard communications network.

The problem faced by General Motors (GM) and other large corporations was described by Roger B. Smith, chairman of GM, in 1984:

> We are limited in the manufacturing efficiency we can achieve by the Tower of Babel that exists among robots and other computer-aided programmable devices. Only about 15% of the 40,000 programmable devices in GM plants now can communicate outside their own processes. That is because each uses vendor-unique communications methods. It's as if each of these machines were speaking its own language—French, Italian, Russian, Chinese, Hungarian, or whatever. They need an interpreter. And that interpreter

comes in the very costly form of custom hardware and custom software needed to interface between different processes.

GM had realized before 1984 that the problem of incompatible devices threatened its plans for automation. As Exhibit V-4-1 shows, however, by 1984 the number of programmable devices in use in GM plants had grown dramatically and the problem was getting out of control.

The company could not meet its plans for computer-integrated manufacturing with a proprietary network because no single vendor could meet all its needs. Relying on multiple vendors was impossible because of communications incompatibilities, and developing customized solutions would be so expensive that it would allow for only a few functions to be addressed.

GM was not alone in this quandary; virtually every large manufacturer has had to confront it. Nor was the problem limited to manufacturers; organizations trying to implement office automation also faced it—and some still do. Vendors' offerings for such basic services as electronic mail, for example, are often incompatible with each other. Isolated on islands of automation, users often cannot retrieve the information they need to perform a task because it is located on a system that is incompatible with theirs. The MAP/TOP movement can be considered a revolt of the users because it is aimed at removing control of distributed computing from computer vendors and giving it to user organizations.

The state of computer automation today is like the state of the tire and automobile industry 50 years ago. Then, the owner of a Stutz Bearcat that needed new tires could get them only from Stutz and could choose only from the options Stutz offered. The same was true of other manufacturers. This situation raised costs in two ways. First, the engineers designing a car had to design wheels and tires also; they could not rely on existing standards because none existed. Second, owners with special needs (e.g., extra-wide balloon tires for soft ground) had to have them custom made because the demand was insufficient to justify production of special tires for each brand and model of car.

Device	1983	1984	1986
Programmable Controllers	3	256	350
Robots	0	136	180
Vision Systems	0	0	10
Weld Controllers	0	200	200
Cell Controllers	0	0	25
AGV Systems	0	1	6
Process Computers	3	8	12
Host Computers	1	2	2

Note:
AGV   Automated guided vehicle

Exhibit V-4-1. Technology Growth in Typical General Motors Truck Plants

In contrast, current standards, although they have reduced the number of tire sizes available, have dramatically increased the variety of types available. Almost any type of tire is readily available from many tire manufacturers for just about any vehicle. Car owners can select cars suitable for their transportation needs and tires for specific driving conditions.

The goal of the MAP/TOP effort is to create similar conditions for computer automation users, freeing them from dependence on a single vendor and allowing them to select computers and other automation hardware that fit their needs.

EARLY MAP/TOP

The first commercially available versions of MAP/TOP were MAP versions 2.1 and 2.2 and TOP version 1.0. All three are based on the protocol suite shown in Exhibit V-4-2. MAP 2.1 established the baseline capability for MAP/TOP. It provides three application-level services: file transfer, manufacturing, and interprocess communications. These services are provided at the top of a protocol stack built on international standards under development by the International Standards Organization (ISO). The layer 1 specification for physical media uses the Institute of Electrical and Electronics Engineers (IEEE) 802.4 standard, which has become the international standard for broadband, token-passing LANs. The layer 3 specification for communications among geographically dispersed sites uses the International Telephone and Telegraph Consultative Committee (CCITT) X.25 standard for packet-switched networks.

As shown in Exhibit V-4-3, MAP 2.2 provided the same application-level services as version 2.1 but added carrier-band media as an option at the physical layer and introduced the enhanced performance architecture and miniMAP options. The enhanced performance architecture permits the optional bypassing of several layers of the OSI reference model to promote faster response time for certain real-time applications. MiniMAP similarly provides for limited-function devices that require access only to layers 1, 2, and 7.

TOP 1.0 is an adaptation of MAP 2.1 for the office environment. It provides for file transfer on an IEEE 802.3 (Ethernet) LAN. It is primarily used to provide access to MAP 2.X networks from an Ethernet-based office. With the exception of miniMAP, the only differences among MAP 2.1, MAP 2.2, and TOP 1.0 are in the application services each provides and in the LAN media and media-access methods each supports. Even at the application and physical layers, the three share many specifications. All three have the same file transfer, access, and management (FTAM) standard and the same implementation of IEEE 802.4. The specifications of each for layers 2 through 6 of the OSI reference model are identical.

Because the prototype MAP 2.1 was issued before stable international standards were available for several layers, MAP 2.X and TOP 1.0 have major limitations. Specifically, the protocols for file transfer and interprocess commu-

Layers	MAP 2.1 Protocols	TOP 1.0 Protocols
Layer 7: Application	ISO FTAM (DP 8571) File Transfer Protocol, Manufacturing Messaging Format Standard, and Common Application Service Elements	ISO FTAM (DP 8571) File Transfer Protocol
Layer 6: Presentation	ASCII and Binary Encoding Only	
Layer 5: Session	ISO Session (IS 8327), Kernel and Full-Duplex Functional Units Only	
Layer 4: Transport	ISO Transport (IS 8073), Class 4 Only	
Layer 3: Network	ISO Connectionless Internet (DIS 8473), with Optional Use of CCITT X.25 as a Subnetwork Under ISO 8473	
Layer 2: Data Link	ISO Logical Link Control (DIS 8802/2) (IEEE 802.2, Type 1, Class 1); Optional Use of CCITT X.25 Requires Appropriate Link and Physical Layers for X.25	
Layer 1: Physical	IEEE 802.4 Token-Passing Bus, for 10M-bps Broadband Media	ISO CSMA/CD (DIS 8802/3) CSMA/CD Media Access Control, for 10M-bps Baseband Media

Exhibit V-4-2. MAP 2.1 and TOP 1.0 Protocol Suite

---

nications are based on draft proposals that have since been revised. In 1985, work had not even begun on an international manufacturing protocol, so MAP 2.X includes a unique manufacturing protocol developed by GM.

MAP's designers were aware of these limitations but felt it was better to proceed than to wait for the international committees. As a result, the goal of vendor-independent networking was achieved years sooner than would otherwise have been possible. The implementation of the early versions of MAP also helped the standards committees identify and correct deficiencies in their draft proposals that might otherwise have been overlooked.

The problem with implementing draft standards, however, is that the

Layers	Standard MAP 2.1 Stack	MAP 2.2: Enhanced Performance Architecture, and MiniMAP
Layer 7: Application	ISO FTAM (DP 8571) File Transfer Protocol, Manufacturing Messaging Format Standard, and Common Application Service Elements	Equivalent to MAP 2.1
Layer 6: Presentation	ASCII and Binary Encoding Only	Bypassed
Layer 5: Session	ISO Session (IS 8327), Kernel and Full-Duplex Functional Units	Bypassed
Layer 4: Transport	ISO Transport (IS 8073), Class 4 Only	Bypassed
Layer 3: Network	ISO Connectionless Internet (DIS 8473), with Optional Use of X.25 Under ISO 8473	Bypassed
Layer 2: Data Link	ISO Logical Link Control (DIS 8802/2) (IEEE 802.2, Type 1, Class 1), with Appropriate Link and Physical Layers for X.25	IEEE Single-Frame Confirmed Service (IEEE 802.2, Type 3, Class 3)
Layer 1: Physical	IEEE 802.4 Token-Passing Bus, for 10M-bps Broadband Media or 5M-bps Carrier-Band Media	

Exhibit V-4-3. MAP 2.2 Protocol Suite

standards have since changed. As a result, MAP/TOP 3.0, based on the stable versions of the international standards, is incompatible with the earlier versions of MAP/TOP. In anticipation of this problem, MAP 2.1 was deliberately restricted to minimize the risk to vendors of investing in the development of products that would become obsolete. In particular, the file transfer service, based on the ISO FTAM protocol, supports only transparent binary bit stream and simple text transfer, and the interprocess communications facility, based on the ISO common applications service elements, provides no data translation services—the user application must determine how data being transferred is to be represented in binary octets.

For similar reasons, MAP 2.1's network management and directory services are just sufficient to allow a reasonably sized network to operate under stable conditions. Proprietary extensions to the specification are required for managment tools to provide such capabilities as directory updates, failure reports, and diagnostics.

The manufacturing messaging format standard (MMFS), the manufacturing messaging service of MAP 2.1, suffers from the opposite problem in that it is too powerful. Developed by GM before OSI protocols for most layers were available, MMFS assumes a network with only minimal transport service and includes many of the functions that OSI networks handle in presentation-, session-, and transport-layer protocols. In MAP/TOP 3.0, MMFS has been replaced by the ISO manufacturing messaging specification (MMS), which assumes a network with a full OSI stack and does not provide the lower-layer functions available in MMFS.

MAP 3.0

Both MAP 3.0 and TOP 3.0 were originally scheduled for publication in mid-1986, but delays in the development of stable international standards caused the release of preliminary versions to be postponed until July 1987. The final versions were not ready for publication until July 1988, almost two years later than planned.

All the services in MAP 2.1 are available in MAP 3.0 but have been considerably enhanced. Among the enhancements are the following:

- The addition of remote file access, improved file management, and the ability to handle structured files and multiple data bases to network file transfer services.
- The extension of the interface to network interprocess communications to permit access to more underlying capabilities.
- The replacement of the GM-developed MMFS with the ISO standard MMS.

All core protocols in MAP 3.0 are based on international standards. All additional protocols, with the exception of network management, are based on either international standards or draft international standards. The standards for the three user application services—manufacturing messaging, file transfer, and association control—are:

- The EIA RS-511 MMS—This provides for communications tuned to the needs of factory floor devices (e.g., for programmable controllers, numerical controllers, and robots).
- ISO FTAM—This provides the ability to transfer files from one machine to another, to retrieve files on remote devices as if they were local, and to manage such file attributes as names and protection schemes.
- ISO association control service elements (ACSEs)—These allow inter-

process communications to support distributed applications that are not explicitly supported by other protocols.

The physical layer standard for MAP 3.0 remains the same as that for MAP 2.1: the IEEE 802.4 broadband cable, token-passing bus. This continuity protects the investment in cable of MAP 2.X system users.

The network management and directory services in MAP 3.0, although they have been substantially upgraded from the 2.X services, are still incomplete because accepted international standards for these services are not yet in place. Full capability in these areas may not be available until the early 1990s.

Exhibit V-4-4 illustrates the protocols that make up MAP 3.0 and their interrelationships.

Because of substantial incompatibilities between MAP 2.X and MAP 3.0, the upgrade was traumatic for users and vendors. To avoid additional trauma, the MAP users group has issued a stability statement that promises a six-year moratorium on incompatible extensions.

TOP 3.0

Unlike TOP 1.0, which was a subset of MAP 2.1, TOP 3.0 is a superset of MAP 3.0. All the capabilities of MAP 3.0 except manufacturing messaging, miniMAP, and

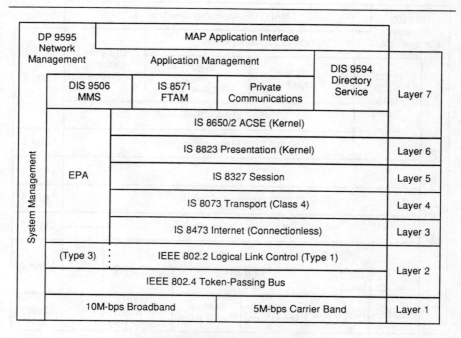

Exhibit V-4-4. MAP 3.0 Protocol Suite

the enhanced performance architecture are also available in TOP 3.0. A comparison of Exhibit V-4-5, which shows the TOP 3.0 protocol stack, with Exhibit V-4-4, which shows the MAP 3.0 protocol stack, reveals that TOP 3.0 uses the same protocol specifications as MAP 3.0 at every layer for all functions they share.

An underlying assumption of the specifications for both MAP 3.0 and TOP 3.0 is that MAP and TOP networks should be interoperable. The differences between them in layers 2 through 6 involve compatible extensions that permit the support of additional capabilities in the application layer and additional cable plants in the physical layer. All political and technical reasons for the continued independence of MAP and TOP disappeared years ago. The only reason they have not completely merged is that they have incompatible document-generation systems; the costs involved in overcoming this incompatibility have so far outweighed the benefits.

The features of TOP rival those of any proprietary network available today

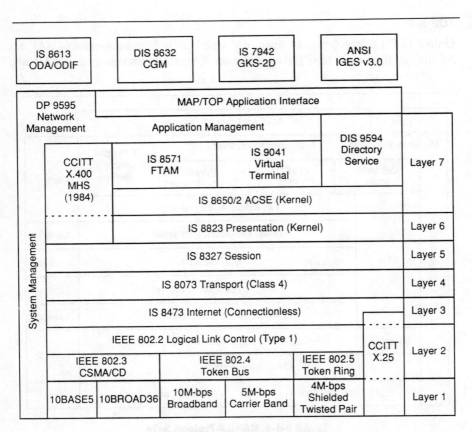

Exhibit V-4-5. TOP 3.0 Protocol Suite

for office and engineering use. In addition to all the capabilities of MAP 3.0, TOP 3.0 includes a wide range of protocols that support engineering and office applications. The application services TOP 3.0 provides are:

- The ISO basic class virtual terminal protocol—This permits a terminal on any machine to log on to any other machine as a simple character-mode terminal.
- ISO FTAM (as defined in the discussion of MAP 3.0).
- The CCITT X.400 message-handling service (MHS)—This permits electronic mail transfers of all kinds of documents within facilities, between facilities, and internationally.

The information exchange protocols TOP 3.0 provides are:

- ISO office document architecture and office document interchange format (ODA/ODIF)—These protocols permit formatted documents like those produced by word processing and desktop publishing programs to be transmitted independently of the package used to create them. They include support for text, raster graphics, and line graphics data.
- The American National Standards Institute (ANSI) initial graphics exchange standard (IGES)—This protocol permits the exchange of product design information among CAD/CAM workstations independently of the CAD/CAM package used to create the information.
- The ISO computer graphics metafile (CGM)—This protocol permits the exchange of geometric graphics independently of the devices used to create them.

TOP 3.0 provides many more physical media options than TOP 1.0. These include the IEEE 802.3 (Ethernet) protocol on 10BROAD36 as well as 10BASE5 media, the IEEE 802.4 token-bus protocol on 10M-bps broadband and 5M-bps carrier-band media, and for compatibility with IBM networks, the IEEE 802.5 token-ring protocol on 4M-bps twisted-pair media. The preferred protocol is IEEE 802.5 on 10BASE5 media. The other protocols and media are recommended only when 802.3 10BASE5 is not practical. The specification requires that any alternative implementations be able to interoperate through bridges with an 802.3 10BASE5 network.

TOP committees are currently studying many extensions to version 3.0. The fiber distributed data interface (FDDI) standard will be incorporated at the physical layer when it is complete. Likewise, fiber optic–based additions to the IEEE 802 series are being considered as they are defined. At the network layer, a work group is studying better use of connection-oriented services. At the application layer, the critical services of transaction processing and remote data base access, for which international standards are being defined, could be available in the early 1990s. Committees are also evaluating electronic data interchange (EDI) and the standard generalized markup language for inclusion in TOP and are considering upgrading from version 3 to version 4 of IGES.

MAP, TOP, AND GOSIP

Recognizing the importance of the open systems movement for government computer users, the US government has developed the government open systems interconnection profile (GOSIP). As Exhibit V-4-6 indicates, the GOSIP protocol stack is closely related to that of TOP 3.0. This similarity is no coincidence; it reflects close cooperation between the MAP/TOP community and the National Institute of Standards and Technology (NIST).

GOSIP is a proper subset of TOP 3.0, with the exception of extensions for addressing assignments and security specified by NIST. GOSIP includes those aspects of TOP 3.0 that were stable in 1987; other services, including the virtual terminal service and directory service, will be added as they mature.

Other governments have made similar commitments to the open systems movement. The UK has developed its own OSI profile, which is also called GOSIP, and other countries have equivalent specifications.

SUMMARY

The goal of the MAP/TOP movement has been to create specifications for manufacturing, office, and technical products based entirely on accepted international standards. The shift from MAP 2.X and TOP 1.0, which are based largely on draft proposal standards, to MAP 3.0 and TOP 3.0, which use interna-

CCITT X.400 (Red Book, 1984)		IS 8571 FTAM		Layer 7
Public Data Network : Private Network		IS 8650/2 ACSE (Kernel)		
		IS 8823 Presentation (Kernel)		Layer 6
IS 8327 Session				Layer 5
(Class 0): (Class 4)		IS 8073 Transport		Layer 4
CCITT X.25	IS 8473 Internet (Connectionless)			Layer 3
			X.25 PLP	
IEEE 802.2 Logical Link Control (Type 1)			HDLC LAP-B	Layer 2
IEEE 802.3 CSMA/CD	IEEE 802.4 Token Bus	IEEE 802.5 Token Ring	MIL-STD 188-114-A	EIA RS-232D	Layer 1

Exhibit V-4-6. GOSIP Protocol Suite

tional standard protocols at all layers, represents a significant step in the achievement of that goal. Users and vendors can expect a series of 3.X releases as the standards for additional capabilities (e.g., security and concurrency control) are developed, refined, and added to the specifications.

V-5
GMT-400:
A MAP Implementation
Case Study

VINCENT C. JONES

The General Motors Truck and Bus Group is responsible for the manufacture of commercial vehicles for General Motors (GM). When the changing market for pickup trucks required the improvement of manufacturing facilities to remain competitive, GM's decision was that higher levels of automation and device integration at their assembly plants were needed and maintenance and support costs had to be reduced. Their new manufacturing system was to have a 10- to 15-year life span and the ability to expand and adapt to support new business needs and new products with a minimum of downtime.

GMT-400 was the project code name for the development of the facilities required to build, in high volume and with world-class quality, a new pickup truck. The project spanned three assembly plants (the Fort Wayne plant in Fort Wayne IN, the East Pontiac plant in Pontiac MI, and the Oshawa truck plant in Oshawa, Ontario, Canada) and two supporting fabrication plants (the Flint Metal Fab in Flint MI and the Indianapolis Metal Fab in Indianapolis). This case study considers the Fort Wayne and East Pontiac plants only. The Oshawa plant, though architecturally similar, did not develop its automated system at the same pace as the Fort Wayne and East Pontiac plants.

PROCESS BEING AUTOMATED

The level of automation and device integration represented by GMT-400 is orders of magnitude higher than at prior GM truck plants. The dramatic increase is shown in Exhibit V-5-1, which lists some of the numbers involved in GMT-400 and those for other GM plants designed just two and three years earlier. These numbers represent extensive automation in the body shop, the paint shop, cab and engine trim, and frame and final assembly. GMT-400's use of new technology includes automated guided vehicles, automatic vehicle identification, computer vision, online inspection, and flexible scheduling.

Technology	Number of Devices		
	Pre M-Van (1983)	M-Van (1984)	GMT-400 (1986)
Programmable Controllers	3	256	350
Robots	2	136	180
Vision Systems	0	0	10
Weld Controllers	0	200	200
Cell Controllers	0	0	25
Automated Guided Vehicle Systems	0	1	6
Process Computers	3	8	12
Host Computers	1	2	2

Exhibit V-5-1. Technology Growth in Typical Truck Plants

THE NEED FOR NETWORKING

The computer networking requirements were driven by the computer architecture chosen to support the increased level of automation. Traditionally, GM plants met their automation needs with centralized plant computer systems. The central computer system would support all plant computing and information processing from a single location. Data requests from the plant floor flow up to the central facility; after processing, the responses are sent back down to the plant floor. This architecture was never powerful enough to support all applications, and even before the decision to expand the use of automation, many devices had to run on a standalone basis. A centralized computing architecture clearly could not meet the needs of GMT-400.

The computer architecture selected was the distributed processing system based on communicating cell controllers (see Exhibit V-5-2). The challenge was to network the cell controllers and the centralized support computers. Cell controllers, distributed throughout the facility, were to be selected on the basis of how well they met functional needs rather than on whether or not they could connect to the network.

The computer architecture and the network to support it were developed over a three-month period by a team of 10 GM employees. The team included representatives from all areas affected, including staff function control engineering people. (Control engineering within the GM Truck and Bus Group is responsible for coordinating the specifications for the systems to build the vehicles.) The team was chartered to develop a plant floor architecture, using state-of-the-art technology whenever appropriate, that would meet the objectives of the GMT-400 project.

The team visited high-technology manufacturing facilities in the US and Canada to observe existing approaches to automation. Resultant ideas were discussed with potential vendors, the number of which gives some indication of the communications challenges GM's team faced. Computer requirements were discussed with such suppliers as IBM, Digital Equipment Corp, and Hewlett-

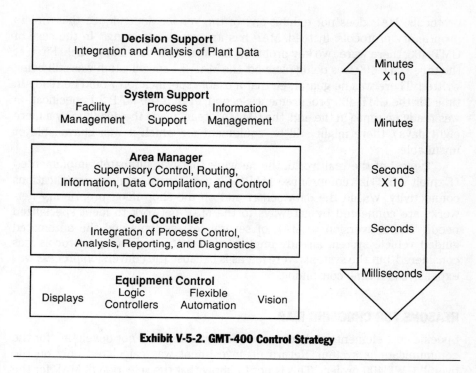

Exhibit V-5-2. GMT-400 Control Strategy

Packard (HP); factory floor devices, with such plant floor controller suppliers as Allen-Bradley, Gould-Modicon, and General Electric. Such specialty suppliers and integrators as Industrial Networking Inc (INI) and Concord Data Systems also participated. The team used the information derived from these meetings and discussions to solidify the desired distributed architecture and develop availability time frames.

NETWORKING ALTERNATIVES CONSIDERED

Two decentralized network architectures were considered, one supported by proprietary protocols and one supported by the manufacturing automation protocol (MAP). The key disadvantage associated with basing the plant communications on a proprietary network was the loss of control over equipment selection. Cell controller and central support computers would all have to be selected on the basis of their ability to attach to the proprietary network. Their suitability for the job, their cost, and their range of functions could only be secondary considerations. Past GM experience had also shown that the network and attached devices would constantly require modification to support new equipment.

The same decentralized architecture could also be built according to MAP

497

protocols. MAP does not exhibit any of the vendor dependence that afflicts proprietary protocols. Instead, MAP has its own shortcomings. In the case of GMT-400, there were two key problems facing a MAP-based approach. First, at the time GMT-400 was being planned, the MAP 2.1 specification was still being written. There was no guarantee that a usable specification would be ready in time for the GMT-400 procurement. Second, even if the MAP 2.1 specification was ready on time (in the end, the GM MAP team made the deadline by a mere eight days), there might still be equipment for which it was unavailable or unsuitable.

Typical of the real world, the network that was ultimately implemented (Exhibit V-5-3) is a compromise. MAP 2.1 is used for backbone communications connectivity. Within the data center and on the shop floor, proprietary networks are connected by gateways to the MAP network to meet specialized needs. The conversion to MAP of several test systems and the automated guided vehicle system already implemented with proprietary protocols was considered, but the systems were left as is because the conversion process was expensive and time consuming.

REASONS FOR CHOOSING MAP

Specific cost elements and economic justifications were not developed for the communications system. Return on investment was calculated only on the overall GMT-400 project. This is not to imply that the selection of MAP for the backbone network architecture was arbitrary. The arguments, however, were more qualitative than quantitative.

The analysis in Exhibit V-5-4 comparing the proprietary and MAP interface development costs is informative, but it is important to keep in mind the ground rules under which it was developed. The use of a broadband cable plant was assumed, eliminating a cost advantage held by many proprietary systems. The proprietary estimate is also based on the acquisition of incompatible equipment from different vendors; it ignores the potential use of commercially available intervendor products.

The selection of MAP was really because of the company's long-term outlook on the GMT-400 program. The expense involved in writing communications drivers in the proprietary scenario was balanced by the dangerous dependence on timely completion of the MAP 2.1 specification and availability of usable products, but the potential flexibility provided by MAP over the planned 10- to 15-year lifetime of the GMT-400 project was the deciding factor. The competitive environment of the automotive industry ensures a continuing need to handle product and process changes. The need for support of additional computers and controllers is inevitable, and each new vendor or model supported increases the complexity of effective custom communications solutions. If the multivendor connectivity promised by MAP could cut the model changeover process by just one day, the plants could produce more than $10

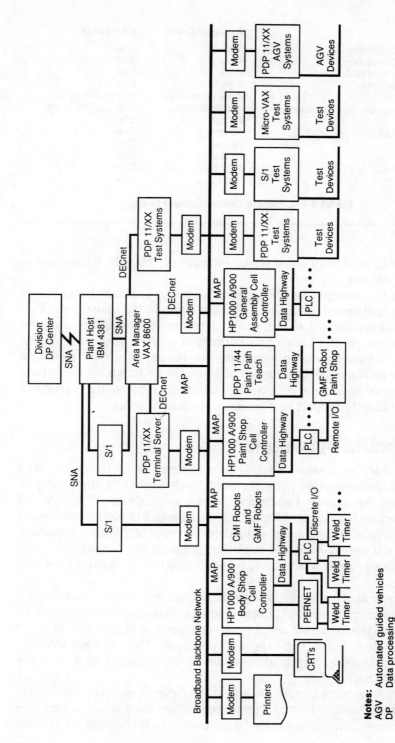

Notes:
AGV   Automated guided vehicles
DP   Data processing
CMI   Cincinnati Milacron Inc
GMF   General Motors Fanuc
PLC   Programmable logic controller

Exhibit V-5-3. GMT-400 Connectivity

Element	Non-MAP Costs	MAP Costs
System Complexity	High	Low
Protocol Converters	Many	None
Gateway Implementations	Many	Few
Installation Times	High	Low
Validations	Many (in-house)	One (outside)
Data Throughput (bps per device)	Low (2,400 bps)	High (230,000 bps)
Training	Various	One
Documentation	Various	One
Hardware	Various	One
Software	Various	One
Diagnostics	Various	One
Maintainers	Many	Few

Exhibit V-5-4. Relative Communications Costs

million more in products (based on an estimate of 960 vehicles per day at $12,000 per vehicle).

MAP 2.1 was selected for the network backbone primarily for its future expandability and growth, despite its untested status at the time the decision was made. The advantages of an open architecture, providing the ability to select equipment on the basis of its performance rather than its ability to integrate into a custom or proprietary network, remain to be fully quantified. However, the feeling of GMT-400 was that a proprietary backbone would have led to ineffective operations because of a lack of integration and a potential inability to change to support new business needs and profits.

NETWORK OPERATIONAL EXPERIENCE

The GMT-400 MAP 2.1 network has been operational since 1986. Compared with the custom proprietary networks used previously at GM, the MAP 2.1–based network has provided savings in several areas already. The cost per device connection has averaged $8,500, compared with $12,000 for proprietary solutions. There also have been reductions in costs of personnel training, installation, and development and validation of interdevice compatibility; network downtime (currently averaging better than 99.9% availability) has also been reduced.

The current MAP networks, described in Exhibit V-5-5, are used strictly for plant floor communications. Additional uses (e.g., bulk data transfers) may be implemented in the future but are not currently planned. Migration to MAP 3.0 will be considered but is not expected to happen. The installed MAP 2.1 network is not a temporary holding action or experimental pilot; it is the production system.

The actual network installation was free of surprises. The network was installed as scheduled, and initial operating costs have been as anticipated. The per-device connection cost has ranged from a low of $2,900 to a high of $10,000.

	Pontiac East	Fort Wayne
Plant Size	2,400,000 ft²	2,200,000 ft²
Broadband Cable	105,558 ft	55,000 ft
Cable Taps	1,300	700
Available Ports	10,192	5,040
MAP Nodes	97	102
Intelligent Devices	800	1,143
Cable Systems (totally redundant)	2	2

Note:
MAP   Manufacturing automation protocol

Exhibit V-5-5. GMT-400 Network Specifics

(The wide range is primarily due to the one-time purchase of networking software for the GMF robots. The cost per connection at the time of purchase was skewed higher by the development fee, but subsequent connections have been skewed lower because the software was already paid for.) More typical connections have cost between $5,000 and $7,000, and costs are expected to drop to about $4,000 per connection as products mature.

The management and maintenance of the broadband communications system has been a larger challenge than the MAP network itself. The broadband system is the communications utility at both plants, carrying all plantwide data communications, not just the MAP network. Production in both plants depends on the broadband system; redundant systems are installed to allow maximum availability, and the equivalent of approximately one worker per shift is devoted to managing and maintaining the broadband system.

Not all applications in the plants use MAP. The communications system installed is a pragmatic balance between the OSI ideal and proprietary reality. IBM's SNA is used to connect IBM host equipment in the computer room. The Digital Equipment Corp equipment is interconnected using DECnet. On the plant floor, rewriting some existing plant process control and test systems for MAP 2.1 was not economically feasible, so they remain point-to-point network implementations (typically over the broadband communications utility).

The MAP network serves as the glue binding the plant floor systems together. All pertinent construction requirements, equipment diagnostics, facility monitoring, programmable device support, and quality information go over MAP. The cell controllers act as gateways to and from the MAP network as required.

SUMMARY

GMT-400 as an application of MAP to factory floor automation is a major success. The network has been in continuous operation since its installation in April 1986 and is accepted as a basic utility, just like telephones and electrical power. The greatest benefit has been the ability to select products on the basis

501

of their cost and performance rather than their fit into or adaptation to a proprietary or custom network. The flexibility to change or improve portions of a process with minimal effect on other operations is also considered an enormous benefit. An unexpected fringe benefit has been the simplification of training requirements and reduction in troubleshooting times. Nobody on the GMT-400 team has disputed the wisdom of making MAP 2.1 the chosen networking system for the project.

V-6
Connectivity Options for the IBM Token-Ring Network

GILBERT HELD

The IBM Token-Ring Network has evolved into a family of products providing communications connectivity between microcomputers, terminals, control units, and mainframes. As a result of the emphasis that IBM has placed on the introduction of token-ring products, this LAN can be expected to become the dominant one, replacing Ethernet-based networks in the near future.

The expected emergence of the token-ring configuration as the leading network has led network managers at IBM and non-IBM installations to become conversant in the networking strategies such products provide. By understanding how hardware devices are connected through a Token-Ring Network, network managers can consider the connectivity options available to meet their current and future networking requirements. This chapter describes various methods used to connect different devices to a Token-Ring Network.

PRODUCT ANNOUNCEMENTS

The first IBM Token-Ring Network announcement was limited to hardware and software products for the IBM PC series. Devices announced included a token-ring adapter card to be installed in each PC that required access to the network, a multistation access unit that provided an interface among as many as eight terminal devices, and a cable connection to the Token-Ring Network. After the first IBM announcement, only a single ring with the ability to support a maximum of 260 devices was available for use. In addition, the total ring distance was restricted to 1,000 ft, which limited the appeal of the network to small organizations whose computational facilities were localized.

The second IBM Token-Ring Network announcement introduced several products that significantly expanded the use and connectivity of the network. Included in the announcement were copper and fiber-optic repeaters, which extended the cabling distance of the network; a bridging program, which permitted multiple rings to be interconnected; and attachments, which permitted System/36 minicomputers and System/370 mainframes to be connected to the network. The System/36 attachment to the LAN was through an IBM PC AT serving as a gateway; access to System/370 mainframes was through a special hardware option that had to be installed in a 3725 communications controller, which serves as a front-end processor to the mainframe.

In 1986, IBM introduced a new 3174 cluster controller that, when configured with a token-ring option, could be connected to the LAN. IBM also announced token-ring support for the 3270-PC and 3270-PC AT. In 1987, in conjunction with the introduction of the PS/2 family of computers, IBM announced a new Token-Ring Adapter designed for use in the Micro Channel of the PS/2 models 50 and higher.

Since 1987, IBM has introduced several communications products and a new series of minicomputers that can be attached to Token-Ring Networks. Communications products include IBM 3720 and 3745 communications controllers and the channel-attached 3174 control unit. The new series of minicomputers, marketed as AS/400, can also be connected to Token-Ring Networks.

NETWORK OPERATION

Token-Ring Network stations are first connected to a multistation access unit (MAU), which in turn is connected to a node on the ring. Up to eight network stations can be connected to one MAU, and multiple MAUs can be connected to one another to form a ring. Exhibit V-6-1 illustrates the physical structure of a Token-Ring Network. As indicated, the actual configuration is a star ring. A PC station gains access to the ring through the MAU and transfers information onto the ring, which enables it to circulate to the next station. This is accomplished after a station detects a free token, which is a distinct sequence of bits indicating that the station can transmit data onto the network. When a station receives information addressed to it, it copies the data as it passes through the interface and modifies a portion of the frame format to signify that data has been correctly received at its destination. The data continues to circulate around the ring, eventually returning to the station that originally transmitted it. By examining the frame of data, the source can determine whether it was received correctly at its destination and then remove the information from the ring.

The PC LAN program operates as follows. After starting the Disk Operating System (DOS), the operator initiates the PC LAN program and assigns a network name to the computer. The operator then identifies the devices being shared or used. For example, if the operator's computer is assigned the network name **RESEARCH** and a letter-quality printer is attached to the computer being shared with other users, the printer could be named **LTRPRINT**. After the printer is identified as a shared device to the program, other users on the network could direct print jobs to that printer by assigning the path \\ **RESEARCH** \ **LTRPRINT** to their print job. (The double backslash [\\] denotes the beginning of the network name of the computer, and the single backslash [\] denotes the beginning of the device name assigned to that computer.)

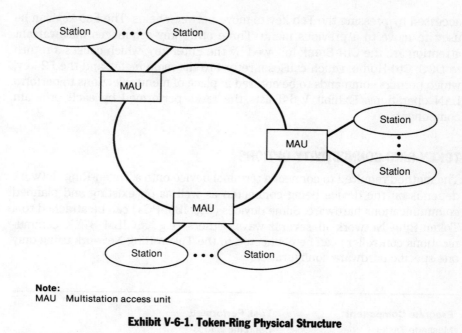

Note:
MAU   Multistation access unit

Exhibit V-6-1. Token-Ring Physical Structure

Once the PC LAN program is loaded, the computer operator can switch between using local application programs and using the PC LAN program. This change is accomplished by using network request keys. The **Ctrl-Alt-Break** key sequence is used to switch from an application program to the PC LAN program; the **Ctrl-Break** key sequence followed by the **Enter** key can be used to switch from the PC LAN program back to an application program.

Exhibit V-6-2 illustrates the major components of the PC LAN program. Each component is menu driven and includes a help screen activated by pressing the **F1** key. The menus consist of one or more fields that can be rapidly

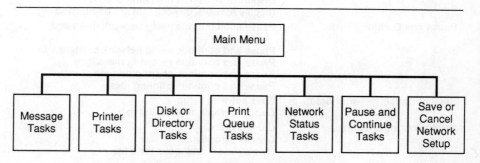

Exhibit V-6-2. PC LAN Program Components

accessed by pressing the **Tab** key to move between fields. The **Esc** key can be used to move to a previous menu. Three other key sequences that warrant attention are the **Ctrl-Break** followed by the **Enter** key, which causes a return to DOS; **Ctrl-Home**, which causes a return to the main menu; and the **F2** key, which permits commands to be entered in place of menu selections to perform LAN operations. Exhibit V-6-3 lists the tasks performed by each program component.

TOKEN-RING CONNECTIVITY OPTIONS

The method required to connect a terminal device onto a Token-Ring Network depends on the device being connected as well as on existing and planned communications hardware. Some devices (e.g., IBM PCs) can be attached to a Token-Ring Network in several ways. Others (e.g., an IBM 37XX communications controller) can be connected to the Token-Ring Network using only one specific hardware configuration.

Program Component	Task Performed
Message Tasks	Send messages
	View received messages
	Start or stop saving messages
	Start or stop receiving messages for another name
	Start or stop forwarding messages
Printer or Print Queue Tasks	Start or stop sharing the printer
	Start or stop using a network printer
	Print a file
	Change the print size on a network printer
	Start or stop printing a separator page
Disk or Directory Tasks	Start or stop sharing the disk directory
	Start or stop using a network disk or directory
Network Status Tasks	Check or change print queue on computer
	Check print queue on another computer
	Display names that can receive messages at the computer
	Display devices that are being shared
	Display network devices that are being used
Pause and Continue Tasks	Pause and continue using network disks and directories
	Pause and continue using network printers
	Pause and continue receiving messages
	Pause and continue sharing devices
	Pause and continue printing files
Save or Cancel Network Setup	Save network setup
	Cancel current network setup
Network Control Tasks	Close a file
	Display error list
	Display users and locks for a file

Exhibit V-6-3. PC LAN Program Component Tasks

PCs

The IBM PC series can be connected to a Token-Ring Network through the installation of a token-ring adapter card into the system unit of the computer; this enables the PC to be connected to the network through a MAU. For most small to medium-sized organizations, this is the preferred method of attachment.

For large organizations that have mainframe systems and an IBM 3270 Information Display System network, connectivity can be accomplished through an IBM 3174 cluster controller that contains a Token-Ring Network option. With this option, microcomputers can be attached to the controller through an emulation board. The cluster controller serves as an intermediate device in providing access to the Token-Ring Network. The advantage of this method is that the PC can access either the host computer (through the cluster controller as an emulated 3278/9 terminal) or the Token-Ring Network; in either situation, access is obtained through the use of one adapter card. In comparison, a microcomputer connected to a Token-Ring Network requires a token-ring adapter card. If the token-ring does not have a gateway to the mainframe or if older 3274 cluster controllers are used, a 3278/9 terminal emulation adapter is required to obtain access to the mainframe through the cluster controller.

System/36 Connection

The attachment of an IBM System/36 minicomputer to a Token-Ring Network requires using a dedicated PC AT that functions as a network communications controller. Once a System/36 is attached to the network, it can communicate with other devices attached to the network, including System/36s, PCs, 3278/9 terminal devices, and a System/370.

In addition to the use of a PC AT, special hardware and software is required to connect the System/36 to the Token-Ring Network. The IBM System/36 LAN attachment feature contains three adapter cards—two for installation in the PC AT and the third for installation in the System/36—as well as connecting cables. The first adapter card installed in the PC AT is used to connect it to the System/36; the second adapter card is a token-ring PC adapter that connects the computer to the Token-Ring Network. In addition to the System/36 LAN attachment feature, an IBM System/36 LAN communications licensed software program is required, enabling the PC AT to serve as a gateway between the System/36 and the LAN.

AS/400 Connection

Unlike the older System/36 connection, which requires the use of a PC AT, the AS/400 can be directly connected to a Token-Ring Network. It requires the installation of an integrated Token-Ring Network Adapter in the AS/400. This adapter is then cabled to a MAU, permitting the AS/400 to communicate with other systems, controllers, and PCs connected to the network.

Mainframe Connection

Three methods can be employed to connect a Token-Ring Network to a mainframe. First, an IBM 3270 PC or 3270 PC AT can serve as a gateway. These devices are connected to the 37XX communications controller in the same manner that a computer is usually connected to obtain host access. Next, a token-ring adapter is installed in the system unit, allowing connection to the Token-Ring Network as well as serving as a gateway between the mainframe and the LAN.

A second method used to obtain connectivity between a Token-Ring Network and a mainframe is by using a 3174 cluster controller containing a token-ring option. This option permits devices connected to the token ring to access the mainframe by means of the cluster controller connection to a communications controller or directly connected to a channel on a host.

Compared with the two previous methods, which permit only one network to be connected to a mainframe, the third connectivity option permits connection to eight networks. This is accomplished by installing a token-ring line attachment base in an IBM 37XX communications controller. The line attachment base can support eight separate token rings, with as many as 260 devices per ring, bringing the total of network devices that can be connected to the mainframe to 2,080.

Network Bridge

Although the line attachment base of an IBM 37XX communications controller permits multiple Token-Ring Networks to be interconnected, in many cases a network bridge may be a more practical solution to connecting LANs. A network bridge is an IBM PC AT or another 80286- or 80386-microprocessor–based microcomputer that contains two token-ring adapter cards in its system and operates a token-ring bridge software program. By cabling each adapter to a different token ring, the bridge computer serves as a connection between networks, permitting devices on one network to access devices located on the other network and vice versa.

CONNECTIVITY SUMMARY

Exhibit V-6-4 illustrates the methods by which different terminals and computers can be connected to an IBM Token-Ring Network. In the exhibit, two Token-Ring Networks are illustrated, with the lower network connected to the upper network through the use of a dedicated microcomputer. In the upper portion of the exhibit, the major methods by which terminal devices, minicom-

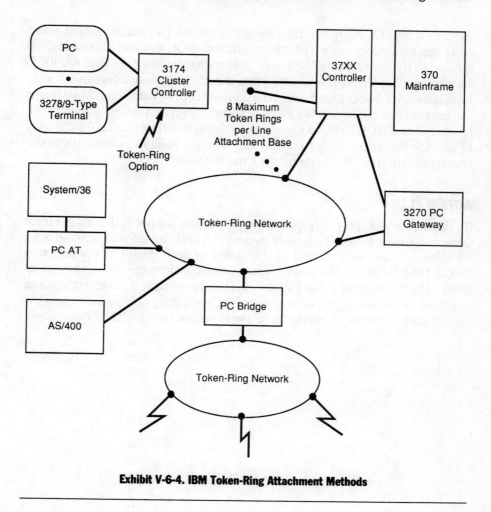

Exhibit V-6-4. IBM Token-Ring Attachment Methods

puters, microcomputers, and mainframes can be attached to a Token-Ring Network are illustrated.

In the middle left portion of Exhibit V-6-4, an IBM System/36 is shown connected to the Token-Ring Network through an IBM PC AT. Above that illustration, PC and 3278/9 terminal devices are shown connected to an IBM 3174 cluster controller. Assuming that the cluster controller has a token-ring option installed, devices connected to the 3174 can be routed to the LAN or the mainframe by way of the 37XX communications controller or by way of a direct attachment to a channel on a host computer.

Above the top Token-Ring Network, a connection between that LAN and the 37XX communications controller is illustrated through a line attachment base on the 37XX. By using this connectivity option, as many as eight token rings can gain access to a 370-type mainframe (e.g., the IBM 4300 and 3090 series). In the lower left of the upper Token-Ring Network, an IBM AS/400 is shown connected. Here it is assumed that the AS/400 has an integrated Token-Ring Network adapter that permits that computer to be cabled to a MAU that is the backbone of the network. Finally, in the middle right portion of the exhibit, the use of an IBM 3270 PC as a gateway is illustrated. Here the 3270 PC is used to provide the Token-Ring Network user with the ability to access the mainframe through the 37XX communications controller.

ACTION PLAN

To determine an appropriate method of connection, the network manager must consider several items. The type of devices currently installed or ordered must be taken into account as well as the ability of each device to connect to a Token-Ring Network. The manager must also consider the different connectivity options and their costs. By following this procedure, the communications manager can examine Token-Ring Network connectivity options and assess the cost of each option in satisfying the network requirements of the organization.

V-7
SNA and LANs: The Gateway Function

KEVIN TOLLY

The early applications of local area networks were primarily to connect personal computers so that relatively expensive resources (e.g., file servers and laser printers) could be shared by several machines. This chapter discusses one aspect of the integration of LANs into an organization's larger computing environment—specifically, connecting IBM Token-Ring LANs to a host environment that is based on IBM's Systems Network Architecture (SNA).

DEFINITION OF TERMS

The communications connection between a System/370 architecture host and a LAN is called a variety of names. Some, such as gateway, are not well defined. Others, such as token-ring network, are well defined but are still frequently misunderstood. The following sections define several important terms used in this chapter.

Token-Ring LAN

LANs were first used in most organizations as transport mechanisms for file servers and print servers. They allowed personal computers to read data from disk files on other personal computers and send the output to printers attached to another personal computer some distance away (i.e., yards or meters). Therefore, many people think of a token ring, which is a kind of LAN, as inextricably linked to the first application to run on it—a file server.

The design of the token-ring LANs running today is based on an architecture document drafted by the IEEE 802.5 committee and approved by the Institute of Electrical and Electronics Engineers (IEEE), the American National Standards Institute (ANSI), and the International Standards Organization (ISO) in 1985. The token ring is one of several competing LAN standards defined and approved by those organizations. The IEEE standard presents the token ring as it relates to the ISO open systems interconnection (OSI) model. Of the seven layers of the OSI model, the part that we call the token-ring network

511

maps to layer 1 (the physical layer) and part of layer 2 (the data link layer). Technically, this is referred to as the media access control (MAC) sublayer.

Few, if any, programs are actually written to the MAC interface. The IEEE has defined a more flexible, higher-level interface common to all of the IEEE MAC LAN network standards. This sublayer is called logical link control (LLC). Because LLC was specified by the IEEE 802.2 subcommittee, the interface is usually referred to as simply 802.2. Along with MAC, it completes the definition of the data link layer. It is at the 802.2 interface that token ring and SNA actually interface.

SNA

SNA (Systems Network Architecture) is IBM's grand design for communications compatibility among computers built on any or all of the three major hardware platforms: microcomputers, minicomputers, and mainframes. Although it may seem obvious, it is important to keep in mind that SNA is not a product to buy but a set of specifications.

Gateway

The word *gateway* is necessarily so generic that without adjectives it is almost meaningless. A gateway could be defined as a device connected to both the LAN and SNA environments that provides the devices attached to the LAN access to the SNA network. The inclusion of specific SNA capabilities would invalidate the definition.

Gateway User

Several names have been applied to the general category of gateway users. Some names imply specific functions, and others are meant to be generic.

Downstream physical unit (DSPU) is a term associated with the users of both physical unit (PU) pass-through and PU concentrator gateways. As the name implies, this variety of gateway user provides its own SNA physical unit function. The DSPU support has been implemented in a wide range of platforms, including personal computers, 3174, and AS/400.

The term *network station* has been used by IBM in different contexts with different meanings. In the case of IBM's PC 3270 Emulation version 3, network station refers to the users of that PU controller gateway. In that context, it implies the use of NetBIOS protocols between the LAN-attached personal computer and the gateway. In IBM's current PC 3270 product, network station is used more generically.

The term *LAN station*, though not often used, is probably the most accurate term to use to refer to a LAN-attached computer without inadvertently endowing that computer with particular attributes. In this discussion, LAN station refers to the users of a gateway.

TOWARD A GATEWAY ARCHITECTURE
Current State

Although IBM's SNA wide area network (WAN) standard and the IEEE LAN standards are clearly defined, no hard and fast rules exist governing the convergence of these overlapping and unequal networking protocols. Although SNA covers the network model from top to bottom (with the exception of the physical layer), the LAN protocols deal only with the lower two layers (physical and data link). Therefore, a LAN-to-SNA gateway must provide two interface points into the SNA environment: vertically into SNA path control and horizontally into SNA link-level protocols.

Furthermore, SNA demands only that certain functions take place; where they take place is not specified. Although, for example, all SNA peripheral nodes must implement a controller function, SNA has no interest in where this is done. In the case of gateways, it is performed either in the gateway or in the LAN station. This is just one of the choices not specified in the architecture that characterize differing approaches to the gateway task.

Although token ring–to–host connections provide all the functions of native SNA connections (e.g., synchronous data link control [SDLC] and S/370 channel), the token ring is not an extension or enhancement to the lower levels of SNA. Because IBM chose to hide the existence of the token ring from the control function of the SNA environment, host virtual telecommunications access method (VTAM), the job of the gateway is essentially that of a protocol converter. The token-ring MAC and logical link control formats, both foreign to the SNA host, must be mapped into a recognizable frame format and reach the host over a path recognized by the host, whether SDLC or S/370 channel.

The capabilities of a given SNA logical unit (LU) type do not vary on the basis of the link-level connectivity. Therefore, various gateway implementations can use different approaches yet offer the end user identical SNA functions.

The Scope of Gateway Connectivity

An SNA gateway is a computer (a combination of software, hardware, and microcode) attached to both a LAN and a host that allows another computer (usually a personal computer) attached to the same logical LAN to appear to the host as a cluster controller (SNA PU type 2). Implicit in this definition is the presence of a controlling host and thereby a traditional, hierarchical SNA peripheral connection. The peripheral-to-host connection supports all of the LU types implemented in host-based systems, most notably LU types 2 and 3 for 3270 data stream and LU 6.2 for advanced program-to-program communications (APPC).

However, other connections are also supported by current SNA products. Most discussions of gateways ignore several areas of increasing importance:

host-to-host SNA (cross domain), peer-to-peer SNA (PU type 2.1), and LAN-to-LAN communication over SNA (mesh networks). Although these areas of interest may not have an impact on immediate decisions, both are important elements in any corporate connectivity strategy.

Host-to-host (also called cross-domain) communications over SDLC or S/370 channel have long been in use in many organizations. In 1988, IBM delivered a new version of the front-end processor (FEP) control program, Network Control Program (NCP) version 5.2.1. This update allows FEPs (PU type 4) and 9370 gateways (PU type 5) to function as intermediate network nodes (INN), performing subarea communications across a token-ring LAN. These sessions are also supported across local and remote token-ring bridges. Because cross-domain (i.e., subarea) connections are supported only on FEP and 9370 gateways, a requirement for this type of connection restricts the gateway options.

Peer-to-peer is the subset of SNA that provides a means for connectivity without requiring the presence of a controlling S/370 host to implement the SNA system services control point (SSCP) function. Peer-to-peer is defined in the architecture as a new category: PU type 2.1. Further enhancements have been built on top of this PU type. These enhancements provide more sophisticated, dynamic routing schemes across a network of many PU type 2.1 nodes. LEN (low-entry networking) and APPN (advanced peer-to-peer networking) are the names IBM has given to these higher-function capabilities.

Standard cluster controllers are known in SNA as peripheral or boundary function nodes. PU type 2.1 nodes, which have more functions, are called enhanced boundary function nodes. The proliferation of computers that are capable of PU type 2.1 communication—personal computers and AS/400s—has made PU type 2.1 capability an important aspect of gateway functions. In 1988, IBM delivered NCP version 5.2, which allows FEPs to act as LEN nodes that can participate in PU type 2.1 session setup without involving the host. This allows a network of PU type 2.1 nodes physically connected to the host-controlled SNA network to function independent of the host. Gateway support for PU type 2.1 pass-through is also limited. Only the FEP gateway allows LAN-based PU type 2.1 devices to communicate with partner nodes elsewhere on the SNA network.

PU type 2.1 connectivity also supports sessions between LAN-based devices separated by a WAN. In the case of gateways, this type of connection is possible only when both LAN gateways support PU type 2.1 sessions. To date, only the FEP supports LAN-to-WAN-to-LAN PU type 2.1 sessions.

All gateways have some support for traditional PU type 2 cluster controller functions, which is by far the most prevalent organizational connection. Organizations requiring more sophisticated host-to-host connections over LANs or PU type 2.1 and across a gateway will find that these requirements lead to a single option: the FEP gateway.

Gateway Approaches

SNA requires a PU function in each and every device defined to it as a peripheral (i.e., boundary) node. SNA requires and recognizes only a single instance of the PU function per boundary node. The gateway environment implies the presence of at least two LAN-attached computers: the gateway and the gateway user (there could be many gateway users). Depending on the type of gateway, the LAN stations could appear to the host collectively, as one PU or individually as separate PUs. For each PU defined to the host, the PU function must be performed by one and only one of the LAN-attached computers. This controlling session that exists between the host and a peripheral node is called an SSCP-to-PU session. SSCP is the network controlling function defined by the SNA architecture and implemented on the S/370 host in the VTAM program product.

Different types of gateways support the SSCP-to-PU sessions differently. In some cases, the gateway is effectively invisible. The host SSCP communicates with the PU function in a gateway user with the gateway invisibly passing the SNA data stream between the SNA and token-ring environments. IBM calls this type of gateway a PU pass-through gateway. All FEP and 3174 gateways, local and remote, are PU pass-through gateways.

Alternatively, a gateway itself can participate actively in the SNA session by providing the PU function in the SSCP-to-PU session. The gateway appears to the SNA host as a single PU cluster controller. In this case, SNA effectively stops at the gateway; the host SNA data stream does not flow out to the stations on the LAN. The gateway provides all PU services to the LAN stations. Those LAN stations do not require full SNA support and typically communicate with the gateway by means of a non-SNA protocol (e.g., NetBIOS). Gateways of this type, unnamed by IBM, are referred to in this chapter as PU controller gateways because the gateway presents a single cluster controller appearance to the SNA host. Most personal computer gateways not made by IBM are PU controller gateways. In addition, LAN-attached AS/400s, when configured as gateways, fall into this category.

In 1989, IBM introduced a gateway product (IBM PC 3270) that combines aspects of PU pass-through and PU controller gateways. When viewed from the perspective of the host, the gateway appears as a PU controller gateway. From the perspective of the LAN station, however, the gateway appears as a PU pass-through gateway. This type of gateway, unnamed by IBM, is referred to in this chapter as a PU concentrator gateway because by simulating a PU type 4 FEP gateway, it takes many LAN stations acting as independent PUs and maps all of them to a single PU, which it presents to the SNA host SSCP.

The PU pass-through, PU controller, and PU concentrator gateways are each discussed in detail in later sections of this chapter.

SNA Device Simulation

Because there is no native VTAM support for LAN-attached devices (9370 VTAM is an exception), the sessions reaching the host through the gateway need to be mapped into standard, VTAM-supported definitions. To the end user (i.e., the LU), the session mapping is irrelevant. The capabilities of an LU type 2 (3270 terminal) connection, for example, do not vary at all between those defined as channel-attached cluster controllers and those that are defined as link-attached cluster controllers, or between cluster controllers defined on dial-up connections and those on leased-line connections. As each gateway implementation is discussed in this chapter, the SNA device simulation used by each is explained.

GATEWAY CONCEPTS

Although all three of the approaches to gateways currently marketed by IBM and other vendors—PU pass-through, PU controller, and PU concentrator—provide the end user with SNA connectivity, each type does so differently and provides different levels of SNA connectivity. In general, PU pass-through gateways provide the most flexibility to and support the broadest range of gateway users. For example, an IBM 3174 gateway can simultaneously support personal computers running DOS or OS/2, AS/400, S/36, and 3174-13R devices. In contrast, PU controller gateways tend to support only very specific LAN configurations. For example, IBM's PC 3270 version 3 PU controller gateway can support only personal computers running the same program as users of its gateway.

In very broad terms, gateways are either passive or active when it comes to the relationship between the gateway and the SNA data stream of its users. Any gateway must provide, at a minimum, a physical path that links the gateway user to the host and a means of protocol conversion. This chapter categorizes as passive a gateway that provides only these two functions. A gateway might also provide higher-level functions (e.g., PU or LU support) to the gateway user; gateways that fall into this category are referred to in this chapter as active. The terms *passive* and *active* describe the gateway's participation in the higher-level SNA functions of the gateway users. Before discussing the specifics of the three different types of gateways, the attributes of active and passive gateways are discussed.

Passive Gateways

The primary characteristic of a passive gateway is its invisibility to the host SNA system. Passive gateways, which include all models of the 3174 and FEP gateways, act merely as a conduit for fully specified SNA traffic generated by LAN-attached computers. All PU pass-through gateways are passive. Regardless of implementation, all PU pass-through gateways are concerned only with address mapping and protocol conversion. Each LAN user (called a downstream PU by IBM) maps to a specific SNA host definition. The gateway converts the LAN data frames into a format acceptable to the SNA host. The gateway component itself has no traditional SNA visibility.

There are two exceptions to this rule. In the case of FEP gateways, the physical token-ring adapter looks like a leased SDLC link to the SNA host. Although the gateway adapter does not appear to the host as such, it does have a network address and can be activated and deactivated by a network operator. In the case of the 9370 computer, the function of the FEP is integrated into its on-board communications adapter. Because the token-ring gateway is part of VTAM in the 9370, the token-ring adapter is identified as a token-ring–type node to VTAM.

The gateway does not provide any other services to the downstream PUs. That is, the gateway does not perform any higher-level processing on behalf of any gateway user. No information about the attributes of the LUs residing on a DSPU is maintained by the gateway. Only minimal address-mapping information is maintained at the gateway to describe each DSPU. This information is used to correlate MAC-layer token-ring source and destination addresses with the appropriate SNA addresses (i.e., either SDLC or S/370 channel). Essentially, the gateway is unaware of the characteristics of its users and does nothing except convert and pass the SNA data stream between the SNA and token-ring environments.

Active Gateways

An active gateway also must provide a physical link between the LAN and SNA environments. In addition, active gateways offer all or part of the higher-layer SNA functions to the gateway users. At a minimum, an active gateway implements the SNA cluster controller function (which is the PU), making the gateway visible to the SNA host and thus distinguishing it from the passive gateway.

The services that different active gateway implementations offer to their users vary significantly. In most cases, the gateway simulates an SNA cluster controller and provides its own product-specific interface (usually NetBIOS) between itself and its users. IBM's PC 3270 Emulation version 3 and IBM's AS/400 host SNA services are examples of controller gateway implementations.

A more sophisticated, extended version of the controller gateway is a concentrator gateway. Implemented in the DOS (PC 3270 version 1.0) and OS/2 (EE version 1.2) environments, this type of active gateway still appears to the host as a cluster controller (PU type 2). What is radically different is how the concentrator gateway appears to the gateway user. The concentrator gateway emulates a PU type 4 pass-through gateway, which is passive.

PU Pass-Through Gateways

PU pass-through gateways provide a transparent, flexible path between SNA-capable, LAN-attached computers and an SNA host. The gateway does not participate at all in the SNA sessions of its users. The PU function is carried out entirely by the LAN-attached computer (i.e., the gateway user). The task of the gateway is to map traffic that originates on the LAN into simulated SNA connections. This type of gateway acts as an invisible protocol converter.

Many separately defined PUs can simultaneously use a pass-through gateway. This approach is valuable because of the flexibility it allows to the LAN stations. Because the PU pass-through gateway is involved only with address translation, this approach puts no constraints on the gateway user. (It should be noted that all current implementations support PU type 2 DSPUs, whereas only FEP gateways support PU type 4 and PU type 5 DSPUs.) The LAN station communicates with the gateway using 802.2 logical link control–defined sessions.

PU pass-through gateways do not carry definitions of the PUs and LUs they support. The gateway is aware of only some very basic characteristics of the PU. The LUs are completely invisible to the gateway. The gateway knows neither the number of LUs nor the characteristics of any of the LUs.

Pass-through gateways are currently implemented in the cluster controller (3174) and FEP (3720, 3725, 3745) product lines.

Address Mapping. For a PU pass-through gateway to do its job, it needs to be able to map data from a LAN onto an SNA network address it is simulating on behalf of the LAN station. In the 3174 implementation (local and remote), this requires creating a customer-generated table into the gateway microcode. This table maps each available SNA network address being simulated by the gateway to a MAC-layer token-ring address of a LAN station. It is through this table that the gateway can make the proper address translations for data moving between the two networks.

In the FEP gateway, the simulated SNA connections are dial-up connections with each LAN station mapped over an available virtual switched circuit. In this implementation, the LAN stations are not identified to the gateway during the generation process. Rather, the mapping to the PUs and LUs takes place in VTAM using a standard SNA SDLC exchange ID (XID) sequence exactly as if the LAN station were accessing the SNA host through a real dial-up connection. Specifics of the SNA device simulation, capacity, and LAN station support are addressed in the implementation section.

PU Controller Gateways

In contrast to PU pass-through gateways, the PU controller approach presents a single PU to the SNA host. Instead of passively shipping the PU functions to LAN stations, the PU controller gateway performs all of the PU functions for all of the LAN stations it represents. The gateway user stations do not execute any SNA PU functions. In effect, SNA stops at the gateway. The data flows that are used between the gateway and the LAN stations usually are not based on SNA. This approach is often used when it is important to minimize the complexity of the LAN stations or reduce the SNA definition requirements in the host.

The PU controller is perhaps the easiest gateway to implement. The host sees what looks and acts like a single, generic PU type 2 cluster controller and is completely unaware that a LAN lurks behind the gateway controller.

Controller gateways connect to the host using SDLC or 802.2 protocols. Most commonly, the gateway connects to the host through an SDLC data link to an FEP, which in turn is channel connected to the host. Alternatively, the controller gateway can employ 802.2 protocols to reach the host indirectly over a PU pass-through gateway. This second approach is known as a double gateway and is discussed in a later section of this chapter.

The PU controller gateway is defined to host VTAM (the SNA host) as a PU type 2 cluster controller. Some recent implementations present multiple PU type 2 appearances to the same or different hosts. From the viewpoint of the host, each gateway is a separate SNA entity because the gateway maintains each connection separately. Internally, the gateway manages the control blocks representing each LU. The gateway implementation determines such specifics as how many total LUs are supported (to the architectural limit of 255 per PU type 2), what types of LUs are supported, how many simultaneous LUs a single LAN station may have active, and whether LAN station–to–LU mappings are static (i.e., predefined) or dynamic (i.e., pooled).

Although the PU type 2 support offered by PU controller gateways provides a basis for support of many LU types (1, 2, 3, and 6.2), there are architectural limits imposed on the capabilities of PU type 2. These fall into two categories:

- Subarea communications—PU type 2 nodes cannot communicate as peers with PU type 4 (FEP) or PU type 5 (9370) nodes. They can function as cluster controllers only when communicating with a subarea node. Therefore, the PU type 2 gateway architecture does not support PU type 4–to–PU type 4 communications passing through it.
- Enhanced boundary function (PU type 2.1)—This enhancement to the PU type 2 architecture allows nodes to establish sessions with peers. Whereas a PU type 2.0 node cannot have a session with another PU type 2.0 node (only with a host), a PU type 2.1 node can establish a session with another PU type 2.1 node. This connection can take place across an existing SNA backbone network without host involvement. A detailed discussion of PU type 2.1 and its various implementations (e.g., LEN and APPN) is beyond the scope of this chapter; however, it is important to note any PU type 2.1 capabilities, or the lack thereof, in future PU controller gateways. There is

nothing standing in the way of vendors wishing to add PU type 2.1 capabilities to existing PU controller architecture products.

Currently, all PU controller gateways support, at a minimum, 3270 display (LU type 2) and printer (LU type 3) sessions. The 3270 environment offers a variety of interfaces that enable the user to use the interactive 3270 session in program-to-program mode. This provides the user with some of the benefits of APPC-based applications without using LU type 6.2. Although these interfaces and features are beyond the scope of gateway discussions, they are explained in the following sections because they can play an important role in gateway selection. The most important of the optional features are file transfer, low-level application programming interface (LLAPI), high-level language application programming interface (HLLAPI), and server-requester programming interface (SRPI). None of these optional features is supported under the 3270 device emulation of the AS/400 or S/36.

File Transfer. The IBM (3270) file transfer program—also referred to by its host program name, IND$FILE—is a de facto industry standard. It provides a SEND/RECEIVE facility to move sequential files from the host to a personal computer. The file transfer program is supported on the host by CICS, MVS TSO, and VM/CMS. Typically, every personal computer gateway implementation supports the file transfer program. Some differ on the size of transmit and receive buffers supported. PU controller gateways have been implemented by IBM on both the PC and AS/400 platforms and by non-IBM vendors on personal computer and minicomputer platforms.

LLAPI. This interface provides a PC macro Assembler interface that allows user-written programs to simulate a terminal operator. The host program, which can be any program supporting LU type 2, remains unchanged and operates as though it were interacting with a 3270 terminal operator. The LLAPI is not standardized among vendors, though most vendors offer some form of LLAPI. Care must be taken if such products as IBM's Personal Services/PC are to be used. For example, Personal Services/PC requires IBM's LLAPI modules (PSCAPI), which are provided only by IBM's 3270 emulator products.

HLLAPI. Vendors often provide language interface modules that allow C, COBOL, BASIC, Pascal, or FORTRAN programs to access 3270 emulation sessions. Recently, IBM standardized a HLLAPI that will be source code compatible in both DOS and OS/2 EE 3270 emulation products. As with the LLAPI, the HLLAPI is not standard among emulation vendors. It is likely, however, that all vendors will offer an IBM-compatible HLLAPI language interface module.

It should be noted that although the AS/400 3270 device emulation does not directly support the standard 3270 APIs, the AS/400 PC 5250 emulation does. This means, essentially, that user programs that operate terminal sessions are source code compatible between the 3270 and 5250 (AS/400) terminal emulation environments and that 3270-emulated screens, provided by the

AS/400 3270 device emulation subsystem, can be manipulated indirectly by the 5250 implementation of the standard HLLAPI. An in-depth discussion of this topic is beyond the scope of this chapter.

SRPI. SRPI is an APPC-like, single-verb interface that runs on top of LU type 2 terminal sessions. It allows a program running on the personal computer to exchange buffers with a program running under MVS TSO or VM/CMS. The format of the exchange is entirely user defined. Typically, the SRPI is offered only by IBM 3270 device emulation products. SRPI is the basis and prerequisite for IBM's enhanced connectivity facilities (ECF) product. ECF offers host simulation of personal computer printers and disks as well as transparent access of certain host file types from a personal computer running ECF.

PU Concentrator Gateways

The PU concentrator is a hybrid gateway combining aspects of both pass-through and controller gateways. Each LAN station provides its own SNA PU function and communicates with what it believes is a PU pass-through gateway. However, only a single PU is presented to the host, as with the PU controller gateway. The concentrator gateway effectively collects all of the LU appearances defined in the various LAN stations (usually fewer than five per LAN station) and maps those LUs, which are hidden from the host by the gateway, into LU control blocks defined in both the gateway and the host. The host sees a single-host PU appearance controlling up to 255 LUs.

The concentrator gateway presents completely different identities to the host and to the LAN stations. The gateway conforms to the SNA PU type 2 boundary node protocol in its interaction with the SNA host. When the gateway interacts with its LAN stations, it simulates the actions usually executed by an FEP (PU type 4) gateway and host VTAM. When a LAN station wishes to connect to the host through the gateway, the request and response exchanges are the same ones it would use to communicate with an actual FEP gateway.

Because the actual PU and LU information is not carried by the FEP, an additional step is required to match the LAN stations with the appropriate PU and LU definitions. Using a real FEP gateway, the simulated connections are those of switched SNA PUs. This requires the use of SDLC XID command between LAN station and host VTAM to allow VTAM to locate the proper set of PU and LU definitions to be used when communicating with the LAN station. (The SDLC XID command uses a combination of two fields, **IDBLK** and **IDNUM**, which are supplied by the LAN station, to locate the single PU statement in the host definition file that corresponds exactly. The XID allows an incoming call from an unknown PU to be resolved to a specific, unique PU and LU definition.)

The PU concentrator simulates this VTAM XID function and uses the serial number included in the XID command from the LAN station to simulate the VTAM identification function. The PU concentrator gateway has its own manually updated configuration file, which describes the LU attributes of its LAN stations.

Using the XID sent by the LAN station, the gateway determines the LU requirements of the particular LAN station. The gateway uses this information to determine whether the LAN station LUs can be mapped into pooled LUs or must map into specific host LU names (i.e., correspond to a specific **LOCADDR**). If an LU can be mapped into a pool, the gateway further determines from the gateway configuration file which pool (e.g., LU type 2 or LU type 6.2) is appropriate for a given LU.

The actual LUs and PUs as defined in the LAN stations remain invisible to the host. The LUs are remapped into LU control blocks on the gateway, and the PUs of the LAN stations are discarded. The LAN station PUs still function as though each were in communication with a PU type 4 FEP gateway, but that gateway, in contrast to an actual PU pass-through gateway, does not pass the PU functions to the host. The LAN-based PUs remain invisible to the host.

The PU concentrator approach combines the lower host overhead of the controller gateway with the SNA flexibility of the pass-through gateway. As long as the aggregate number of simultaneous LAN-based LUs can be mapped into the allowable 255 LU slots per defined PU, the concentrator gateway is a very effective solution.

Double Gateways

Although the term *double gateway* may sound complex, it is actually a very simple concept. A double gateway exists when either a PU controller or PU concentrator gateway uses a PU pass-through gateway to access the host. For example, the IBM PC 3270 Emulation version 3 gateway (a PU controller) can be configured to use either SDLC or 802.2 protocols to reach the SNA host. When it is configured to run over 802.2, the gateway requires the services of a PU pass-through gateway. The PU gateway thus becomes a DSPU to the PU pass-through gateway.

Double gateways are typically employed as a means to reduce the number of LAN-based PUs that need to be defined at the host. Instead of each LAN station presenting a PU appearance to the host, many stations can take advantage of a PU appearance configured in the PU gateway.

It is important to note that PU concentrator gateways can accomplish the same ends, reducing the number of PUs visible to the host, but without the restrictions typically placed on LAN stations by PU controller gateways. That is, only personal computers are typically supported.

All host traffic handled in a double gateway environment requires two trips around the ring. First, the buffer must be transmitted from the LAN station to the PU controller gateway. To reach the host, the PU controller gateway then repackages and resends the buffer, this time with the PU pass-through gateway as the target. Because the token-ring environment is so quick (even at 4M bps, a LAN station will receive 10,000 to 12,000 tokens per second) and utilization is so low (most corporate LANs average 4% to 5%), this second trip is negligible and affects neither performance nor utilization.

SUMMARY

The features and functions that are relevant to gateway applications between SNA and Token-Ring networks are reviewed in the following sections.

SNA Capabilities

Hierarchical (PU Type 2). All three gateway architectures—PU pass-through, PU controller, and PU concentrator—offer support for PU type 2. Although implementations vary, support for LU types 2 and 3 is guaranteed, and support for LU type 6.2 is likely in most products.

Host-to-Host (PU Types 4 and 5). Because only the FEP gateway supports subarea traffic, a customer requiring this type of support across token-ring LANs has no decisions to make. The FEP gateway can be either channel attached or link attached to its controlling host; the type of connection affects only throughput, not function. Because of the complexity in implementing full PU type 4 support, it is unlikely that 3174s or personal computers will ever offer PU type 4 or 5 pass-through support.

Peer-to-Peer (PU Type 2.1). PU type 2.1 is used to link AS/400s, personal computers, and other computers without requiring control or intervention by an S/370 host VTAM (SSCP). IBM's OS/2 OfficeVision and OS/2 EE remote data base support require PU type 2.1 connections between personal computers. More and more corporations will require PU type 2.1 connections across the SNA backbone network or between a LAN-based machine and one elsewhere on the SNA network.

To date, only the FEP gateway will support PU type 2.1 connections. It is likely that some PU controller gateways as well as the remote implementation of the 3174 gateway will someday support PU type 2.1 traffic. Because PU type 2.1 switching is handled in the NCP and not in host VTAM, it is unlikely that the local 3174 gateway will ever be able to implement support for PU type 2.1.

Finally, enabling the PU concentrator gateway to offer PU type 2.1 support could be quite tricky. Adding PU type 2.1 support on top of the already substantial protocol imitation it is performing might be a difficult and challenging task. There is, of course, nothing prohibiting that extension to the PU concentrator architecture.

PU Pass-Through Versus PU Controller Considerations

As a rule, pass-through and controller implementations serve very different purposes and are appropriate for very different environments. Pass-through gateways tend to be installed at the mainframe site to take advantage of the

S/370 channel speed and because the mainframe site typically has higher-capacity demands (i.e., there are more users to be serviced). Controller gateways using SDLC links to the host are appropriate at remote sites when channel speed connections are not available and the user community is relatively small.

The PU controller implementations are roughly equivalent to both the local and remote 3174 PU pass-through implementations when it comes to SNA support. All offer PU type 2 support. A PU controller implementation, however, cannot begin to offer the range of SNA functions the FEP gateway can offer to users (PU type 2.1, PU type 4, and PU type 5).

IBM discontinued its PU controller product, IBM PC 3270 Emulation version 3. The choice is now between PU pass-through and PU concentrator gateways.

PU Pass-Through Versus PU Concentrator

The PU concentrator is a very attractive alternative to PU pass-through gateways, especially in remote (link-connected) environments in which the LAN station population is restricted to personal computers. Although today's PU concentrator gateway implementations support only relatively low-speed lines, they are effective replacements for remote 3174 gateways. Because the current implementations support only such personal computer software products as DSPUs, the PU concentrator gateway is not appropriate if 3174-13R or AS/400 devices exist as LAN stations.

In a personal computer–only environment, the PU concentrator truly does provide the best aspects of PU pass-through and PU controller gateways. It allows software independence for the LAN stations and eliminates polling overhead by presenting a single PU to the host.

Pass-Through: 3174 Versus FEP Considerations

As a rule, the 3174 implementations are appropriate in the local (i.e., channel-attached) environment in which a relatively small number of users require only PU type 2 functions. When more sophisticated SNA functions are required, a large user base must be supported, or quality performance is required from a remote LAN to a host, the FEP gateway is usually appropriate.

Section VI
LAN Applications

U ltimately, a LAN's intended purpose is to support an automated applications process. The nature of this process can range from scientific to
manufacturing or to business. This section of the handbook takes a look at the
diversity of applications that LANs can support as well as some of the issues
that surface in a LAN-based applications environment.

The potential uses of LANs in office applications are as limitless as the
number of applications themselves. Chapter VI-1, "Applications for LANs in
the Office," discusses three such applications: electronic mail, desktop publishing,
and color imaging. By example, the chapter illustrates how LANs can be used
both to solve incompatibility issues and to optimize the productivity of people
and office machinery.

Data communications is fast becoming an integral part of today's
computer-aided design and manufacturing systems, for a host of reasons. Yet its
growing prominence has raised several questions related to management control. Chapter VI-2, "The Role of Communications Standards in CAD/CAM,"
reviews the many communications-related standards that are involved in managing a distributed CAD/CAM environment. In particular, it examines the role
of LANs in linking distributed design workstations, data exchange among CAD
systems, centralized data management, and the emergence of international
standards for the factory and office environments.

A third applications area in which LANs can be effectively used is manufacturing. Nowhere is this more evident than in the manufacturing automation
protocol (MAP) arena. One MAP installation is at an Alcoa plant in Tennessee,
supporting the operation of the plant's materials-handling system. That system
takes 30-ton aluminum coils from the hot rolling mill, through the annealing
process, and on to the cold rolling process. Chapter VI-3, "Alcoa Tennessee
MAP/TOP Case Study," takes a close-up look at this particular case. Included in
the study are discussions of a number of implementation and operational
experiences.

Among the implementation experiences highlighted for Alcoa was the
divergence of perspectives between applications developers and hardware
developers. The importance of involving the right people in the design of LAN
systems and the applications that run on them is the focus of Chapter VI-4, "The
Role of LANs in Departmental Computing." In this chapter, the author presents
a process for systems design that departs significantly from traditional systems

design processes and therefore better meets the needs of users in a departmental computing environment.

To round out the discussion of LAN applications, Chapter VI-5 illustrates how LANs can be used in support of mainstream applications in the epitome of the business community—a large bank. "Southeast Bank: A Case Study of LANs in a Business Environment" discusses how a small staff of information center personnel transformed the widespread, ad hoc use of microcomputers into a cohesive network and applications strategy across the corporation.

VI-1
Applications for LANs in the Office

STEPHEN E. YOUNG

Despite references by office equipment vendors to office automation, end users are really looking for office applications. Offices are not automated; rather, users need computer applications at the desktop and should not be concerned with the operating system protocol or transport necessary to deliver the applications. In this chapter, applications that depend on LAN office solutions (specifically electronic mail, desktop publishing, and color imaging) are reviewed as examples of office LAN applications.

ELECTRONIC MAIL

Although sophisticated applications and connectivity for the desktop were available by the early 1970s, the products posed problems in terms of their cost and their inability to connect mail packages of different vendors. Sending a message worldwide and attaching other electronic information to that message was possible, but only if users limited themselves to one vendor. Interoperability between vendors was virtually nonexistent.

Vendors with a large installed equipment base did well with electronic mail systems, although both the applications and the networks remained proprietary. Among these companies were IBM Corp, Digital Equipment Corp, and Wang. As user demand for interoperability grew, LAN vendors began to offer products that allowed the development of interoperability solutions, and high-speed connections between electronic mail applications were eventually made available. The introduction of the personal computer and the greater variety of networks available to the end user made interoperability a growth path for companies, resulting in the development of better and more versatile interoperability solutions.

An example of a situation requiring interoperability is a corporation that depends on two computer systems (see Exhibit VI-1-1). Some parts of the corporation use a DEC VAX system for manufacturing control, order processing, and running an ALL-IN-1 office automation package. The company LAN connects personal computers procured one at a time by individual department

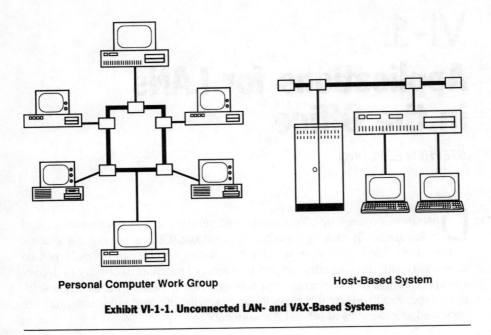

Personal Computer Work Group   **Host-Based System**

Exhibit VI-1-1. Unconnected LAN- and VAX-Based Systems

---

managers. MIS has provided Novell file servers to limit the number of printers required and to allow data to be shared over the network.

The Novell users have access to CC:MAIL. This electronic message system is well liked, particularly for its ability to deliver a message while the user is on another application. The Novell network uses the proprietary IPX/SPX protocol and an ARCnet subnet for inexpensive connection to the file server.

The VAX uses a VMS operating system native to that environment; DECnet is the network used to link local and remote systems together. Local area transport (LAT) terminal servers also function on the network and are used to access the system from asynchronous terminals. An Ethernet backbone connects multiple file servers on the DECnet and carries the proprietary IPX/SPX protocol to transfer CC:MAIL messages.

To provide a connection between these two applications, hardware and software have to be added to the systems. The transport is already available: the existing Ethernet cabling system used for the DECnet and NetWare IPX protocols. An illustration of the network layers is shown in Exhibit VI-1-2.

Changes to the DEC VAX

Because there is no gateway available to bridge CC:MAIL to the DECnet protocol or the ALL-IN-1 application, a protocol providing interoperability must be added to the VAX system. There are two choices: intelligent cards that are added to the system, or host-based software. The major difference is that the

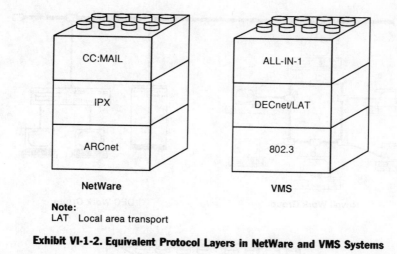

NetWare   **VMS**

Note:
LAT   Local area transport

Exhibit VI-1-2. Equivalent Protocol Layers in NetWare and VMS Systems

---

board-based solution requires less CPU cycle time than the host-based option. For an electronic mail application, either option would be adequate. The choice is the MIS department's. Both intelligent cards and host-based software solutions provide the same application options necessary for interoperability, including Telnet, file transfer protocol (FTP), and simple mail transfer protocol (SMTP). In this situation, SMTP is a good choice to provide a gateway from ALL-IN-1 to CC:MAIL.

Changes to the NetWare Server

The Novell NetWare server has a proprietary network operating system referred to as IPX/SPX. This protocol provides high-speed file access, but personal computer users on the network need a gateway to communicate with networks that use other operating systems. Installing a Transmission Control Protocol/Internet Protocol (TCP/IP) gateway, such as Racal InterLan's TCP/IP gateway for NetWare, will allow the standard applications such as Telnet, FTP, and SMTP to provide interoperability to the VAX systems.

As shown in Exhibit VI-1-3, both work groups have been given a physical connection and a compatible network application, making the electronic mail packages accessible to all the end users.

The system operates as follows. By using the sockets library in the TCP/IP gateway, a call can be made to the CC:MAIL application when a message needs to be routed to a user on the VAX ALL-IN-1 application. The TCP/IP protocol then becomes the transport for the mail destined for the VAX. Once the information arrives at the VAX, the process reverses, providing the message to the ALL-IN-1 application.

Both users maintain a familiar electronic mail application but can now

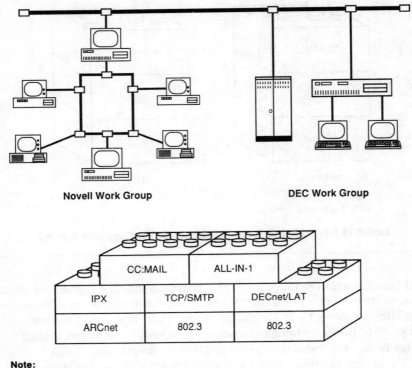

Novell Work Group

DEC Work Group

CC:MAIL	ALL-IN-1	
IPX	TCP/SMTP	DECnet/LAT
ARCnet	802.3	802.3

Note:
LAT   Local area transport

Exhibit VI-1-3. The DEC and Novell Work Groups Combined Through a TCP/IP Gateway

perform mail and messaging between systems with different applications, operating systems, protocols, and computer bus structures.

DESKTOP PUBLISHING

One application that has become popular with personal computer users is desktop publishing, available through such programs as Ventura Publisher (Ventura Software Inc, San Diego) and PageMaker (Aldus Corp, Seattle). These programs have become so successful that typesetting vendors are networking their $100,000-and-up typesetting systems with the desktop systems of their customers.

The problem is lack of compatibility among all of the equipment types required to accomplish this level of service. Dissimilar operating systems and file formats can lead users to resort to a so-called sneakernet to integrate their systems. The resolution of these problems is found in the technology of local area networking.

The technical and office protocol (TOP) offers one solution. When used on a high-speed Ethernet network, TOP enables the typesetter to manipulate text and graphics and perform all prepress functions with ease (see Exhibit VI-1-4).

Such a system could be used as follows. A customer could deliver a disk or transfer files to the vendor using an electronic bulletin board. The customer decides whether to simply have the file typeset on the vendor's high-quality typesetter for submission to the press room or to have the file enhanced. In the former case, the file is placed in the proper directory, converted to Postscript if necessary, and spooled to a typesetter. A document that requires enhancement is submitted first to one of the vendor's prepress professionals. The importance of TOP is the interoperability between different personal computer environments (e.g., Macintosh and MS-DOS) that it provides.

Publishing Work Groups

End users have also been taking advantage of LAN technology to form integrated desktop publishing environments. One organization uses the personal computer file server Banyan VINES. Either Ventura or PageMaker desktop publishing packages can be accommodated.

By means of an Ethernet, all users have equal access to all network servers. Directories have been created on the servers to deposit or to act on files that are created in the application related to the particular discipline of each professional. The choice of applications package belongs to the end user. Writers can use their favorite word processing package. Graphics illustrators can use one of the popular graphics packages. Desktop publishing programs (e.g., Ventura) support networks. The operator calls up the proper drive and proceeds through the directory tree to find and load the proper files (see Exhibit VI-1-5). The advantage of networking a desktop publishing application is

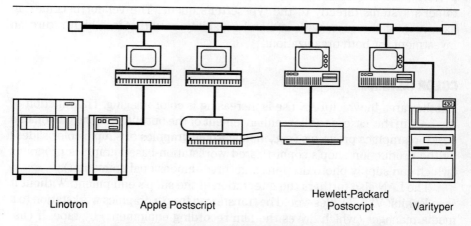

| Linotron | Apple Postscript | Hewlett-Packard Postscript | Varityper |

Exhibit VI-1-4. Compositor's Network for Manipulation of Text and Graphics

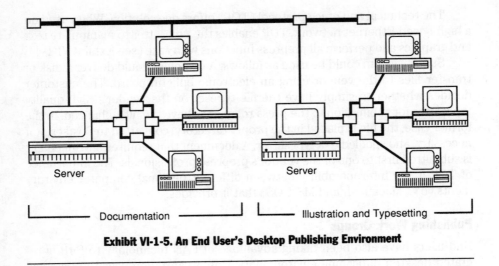

Server   Server

└───── Documentation ──────┘ └────── Illustration and Typesetting ──────┘

Exhibit VI-1-5. An End User's Desktop Publishing Environment

that changes made by either the typesetter or the file's originator will update the source file.

Interoperation Between the User and the Printer

With printers and customers each using their own LANs, it becomes possible to provide a gateway between the two LANs using, for example, a learning bridge that operates over T1, fiber-optic, X.25, or high-speed dial-up connections (see Exhibit VI-1-6).

With a learning bridge, which adapts automatically to changes in network configuration, traffic on the two networks can be isolated to provide higher performance and security. Postscript files can be transferred from the customer's systems directly to the typesetter's queue. The vendor becomes an extension of the customer's site and capability, resulting in a high return on investment for both organizations.

COLOR IMAGING

Another area in which LAN use is increasing is color imaging. The function of the LAN in this case is to allow enhancement of the output from the customer's desktop graphics programs (e.g., monochrome graphics or simple color slides) by the production shop's sophisticated workstation-based graphics programs (which can supply photo drop-ins and three-dimensional animation).

The LAN also furthers the integration of the shop's equipment. Without it (see Exhibit VI-1-7), files would be transferred from a graphics workstation to a media manager (which drives the film recording equipment) by tape. If customers supply graphics files, the files may have to go through a file type or

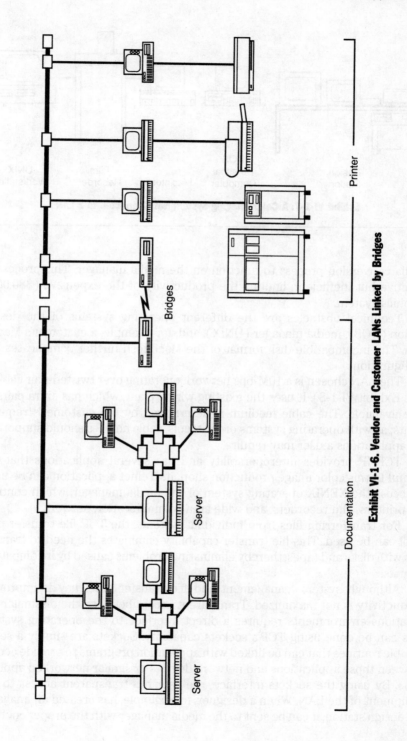

Exhibit VI-1-6. Vendor and Customer LANs Linked by Bridges

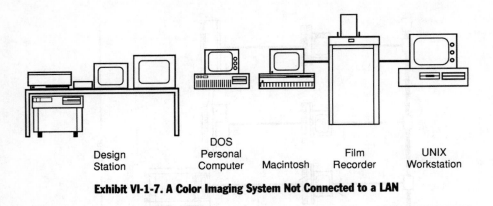

| Design
Station | DOS
Personal
Computer | Macintosh | Film
Recorder | UNIX
Workstation |

Exhibit VI-1-7. A Color Imaging System Not Connected to a LAN

media conversion process to function on the media manager. This process is effective but inefficient, limiting the productivity of the expensive ($80,000) graphics system.

Technical obstacles are the different operating systems of the design station (DOS), media manager (UNIX), and, for example, a customer's Macintosh. The incompatible disk format of the Macintosh further complicates the configuration.

The LAN chosen is a 10M-bps network operating over twisted-pair cabling (see Exhibit VI-1-8). It uses the existing wiring plant, which has extra pairs of wire available. The cable medium is determined by the customer's requirements; as with operating systems or protocols, cable choices should support all the applications a user may require.

TCP/IP provides interoperability and has several applications that are helpful to this color image production shop. Its Telnet application can be used to access the XENIX operating system of the media manager, which controls the printers, film recorders, and wide area communication network.

For transferring files from individual systems, the TCP file transfer protocol can be used. This file transfer capability eliminates the need to transfer files with disks and tapes, thereby eliminating problems caused by incompatible formats.

Although system management and file transfer efficiency is improved, productivity is not maximized. Transparent access between the dissimilar applications environments requires a direct interface to the operating system. This can be done using TCP's sockets capability. Sockets are simply a set of callable routines that can be linked with application programs to provide access between those applications and network devices or similar networked applications. By using the sockets interface, the user has transparent access to the equipment of the LAN. When a designer, for example, has created an image on the design station, it can be sent to the media manager with the proper controls

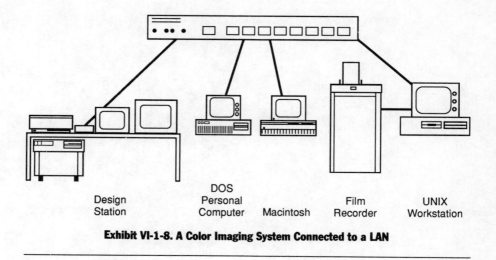

Design Station   DOS Personal Computer   Macintosh   Film Recorder   UNIX Workstation

Exhibit VI-1-8. A Color Imaging System Connected to a LAN

to produce the required output. With one request, the designer can print slides, overhead transparencies, color prints, or speakers' notes. This requires no special mechanical or technical knowledge. A customer that supplies a file by means of a Macintosh need only select **print** to achieve the same results as the designer.

SUMMARY

It is very important that both users and vendors recognize their respective roles in the marketplace. In the three applications described in this chapter, the users decided which functions they wished to perform themselves. They did not allow the vendors to use the limitations of networking technology as an excuse to dictate to them what they could or could not do. If both vendors and their customers are to prosper, vendors of networking technologies and user applications must work to improve the solutions to users' problems.

VI-2
The Role of Communications Standards in CAD/CAM

JAMES F. MOLLENAUER

During the last few years, data communications has emerged as a critical component of CAD/CAM. Its growing importance represents both a response to changes in computer technology and an attempt to increase the application of CAD/CAM to the production process.

The first generation of CAD systems typically involved multiple users sharing a mainframe or minicomputer. Finished designs were printed out on plotters, and the resulting plots were handled in a manner similar to manually generated engineering drawings. They could be copied on blueprint machines and marked up in red pencil, but the design data remained on the CAD computer (except for its storage on a reel of magnetic tape).

For automated production, the CAD computer could be equipped with a paper-tape punch. The design could be converted to tool-path instructions on the tape, which would then be hand-carried to a numerically controlled milling machine. This level of automation in manufacturing is not at all new. The weaving of cloth under the control of punched cards was introduced on the Jacquard loom during the 1830s. The most significant changes in product design have concerned not the application of computers but their rapid proliferation.

The availability of inexpensive microprocessor computing power has changed the development environment significantly over the past several years. Intelligent workstations have replaced terminals that provided only a keyboard, screen, and printer for design work. In many cases, the computing power of these new workstations substantially exceeds that of the shared computers of the previous generation. Nevertheless, large projects require the cooperative efforts of many designers, and for this the workstations must be interconnected.

In tandem with the need to share data on large projects is the desirability of centralized program storage. A CAD system comprehensive enough to support the design of an airliner, together with the applications built on it, might involve tens or even hundreds of megabytes of software. Efficient networking can obviate the need to supply each workstation with the disk space to store this amount of data.

In fact, networking allows for a further partitioning of the CAD process, separating the task into the CAD operations performed on the data representing the part and support of the user interface, including graphics and a variety of I/O devices. Although microprocessor speed can double each year, speed does not come at a constant price. Assigning the computing-intensive and data-intensive aspects of the design process to a centralized server makes sense when the performance of the server is 5 to 20 times that of a DEC VAX 11/780, the flagship superminicomputer of 10 years ago.

The result of this partitioning is a clustering of workstations around servers. Small local area networks (LANs) provide communications links between servers and their client workstations; the servers, in turn, are interconnected by a backbone network. An example of such a configuration is the Prime/Computervision CADDSnetwork system, shown in Exhibit VI-2-1, which features CADDServers and CADDStation clients. (CADDS is an acronym for

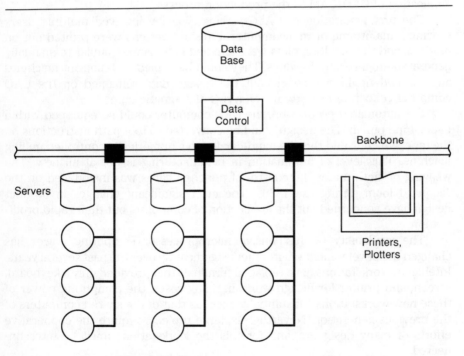

Note:
Servers provide file storage and perform computationally intensive CAD operations. Clusters are internally connected through Ethernet; an Ethernet backbone interconnects the clusters and attaches to the data management system and shared peripherals.

Exhibit VI-2-1. Workstation-Based CAD Network

Computer-Aided Design and Drafting System.) The CADDS 4X program is partitioned; one copy of the main task is in the server, and copies of the graphics and I/O support software are distributed to each workstation. Both the server and its workstations use a UNIX-based operating system. Local storage is provided on the client stations for frequently used files, although diskless stations are also supported.

Other steps in the overall CAD/CAM process also depend on networking. Specifically, networking provides the necessary links to analysis machines, engineering and manufacturing data bases, and the factory floor. Design analysis for thermal and mechanical stress, aerodynamics, and other computing-intensive properties typically takes place on a specialized analysis computer. Depending on the application, this machine may range from a supermini-computer (e.g., a VAX) to a very large supercomputer (e.g., a Cray). Although the recent introduction of workstations capable of running at a rate of more than 10 MIPS may alter the distribution of work, the need for specialized crunch nodes is unlikely to disappear. Networking is necessary to convey the data to these machines.

Although the design process is being decentralized to workstations, centralized control of data remains essential. Both work-in-process and finished designs must be archived, and access and modification controls must be implemented to prevent simultaneous design modification by two or more engineers.

The solution to this control issue is a centralized data base. These data management systems differ from typical data bases that are optimized for retrieval of small records. The CAD/CAM data base is optimized for retrieval of very large items, and it is concerned with authorization level, concurrent access, and the associativity of components in assemblies. Representative data base systems include Prime/Computervision's PDM and Digital Equipment's EDSC.

From the engineering data base the product design is sent to the factory. Numerically controlled tools and robotic assembly equipment can run directly from CAD data with little human intervention. In most cases, however, the data does not come directly from the engineering data base. For reasons of geography or efficiency, the factory may well run its own computer system. Finished designs are sent to this system along a communications path that need not be as fast as the links between the workstations and the engineering data base; only completed designs are transmitted across the link. Within the factory, the need for speed resurfaces as data is fed repetitively to the manufacturing machines. This arrangement is illustrated in Exhibit VI-2-2.

The passage of data from a concept to a finished product generally involves a succession of computers; rarely does one vendor supply the best solution for all stages of the process. Thus, computers from many vendors are found in the typical manufacturing corporation. As a result, standards are needed to move the data from one computer to another and to specify the meaning of the data once it arrives at its destination.

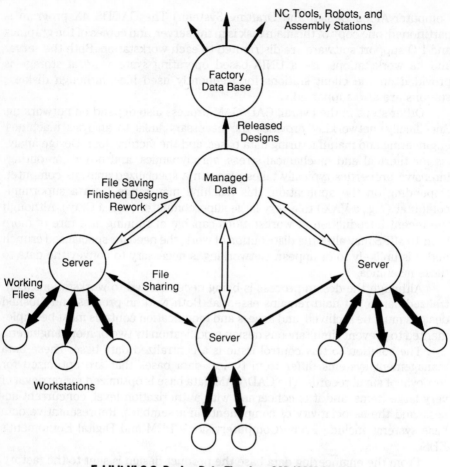

Exhibit VI-2-2. Design Data Flow in a CAD/CAM System

STANDARDS FOR DISTRIBUTED APPLICATIONS

The dispersal of design activities to individual workstations has created a demand for data communications both among workstations and between workstations and servers. Whether the servers store files, provide access to shared peripherals, or carry out computation, high-speed communications geared for bursts of data is imperative. CAD files often comprise many megabytes of data and generally must be transmitted within a minute or so. High-resolution graphics usually involve transfers of a megabyte or less, but the time requirements are even more demanding, generally on the order of just a few seconds. LANs are able to meet both these demands.

The Ethernet LAN

The preferred LAN in computer-aided design is Ethernet. Ethernet features a peak speed of 10M bps and a cable-sharing mechanism that is highly efficient at low to moderate loads. Response can degrade under high load factors, but these are rare in practice. Most Ethernet networks in production environments run at load factors of 3% or less, and peaks rarely exceed 10%. The ability of current workstations and minicomputers to obtain data from a file system, process the higher-level protocols, and then put the data on an Ethernet network limits the contribution from any one data source. If the load grows substantially, partitioning the network into clusters of workstations interconnected by a backbone cable can keep the load on any one Ethernet at a moderate and workable level.

The importance of proprietary LAN designs in the workstation area is declining. These networks, however, are still popular in the microcomputer market, with its lower speed requirements and greater cost sensitivity. A peak speed of 64K bps, for example, though much too slow for a CAD workstation, would suffice for many microcomputer file-transfer applications. If a group of microcomputers is being used for CAD purposes, however, it would probably pay to install Ethernet to take advantage of such facilities as central file storage, archiving, and access control, which are now offered by the major CAD vendors.

The recent introduction of Ethernet on existing telephone wiring makes it cost-effective with any kind of desktop computer, including IBM PCs and compatibles, Macintoshes, or UNIX-based workstations. The cost of cabling in the original Ethernet cable is significant: the Teflon jacket version required in return-air plenums is close to $3.00 per foot, not including labor. A version of the IEEE 802.3 standard for telephone twisted-pair wiring is progressing rapidly, but meanwhile the hardware is available from such vendors as Synoptics.

The TCP/IP Protocol Set

The higher network protocol layers are now entering a period of change. The current preferred protocol set is Transmission Control Protocol/Internet Protocol (TCP/IP), which was developed by DARPA, an agency of the Department of Defense. This protocol set likely will give way during the next five or so years to international standards, but for now it is supported by most CAD/CAM networks.

The IP layer provides internet routing, moving data from one Ethernet LAN to another. It is generally used to route data from a cluster over the backbone to another workstation or server, either on the backbone or on another subnetwork. Data can also be routed over wide-area networks (WANs), in which remote systems or networks are connected to form a coherent whole.

An increasingly popular alternative to IP-based routing is the use of a bridge. A bridge interconnects two LANs, in some cases by means of an intermediate wide-area link, through the use of the link-level address rather than an explicit internet address. Because no assumptions are made about the network protocols above Ethernet, this approach provides a high degree of flexibility.

Bridges can usually be classified into two types. Preloaded bridges contain a list of stations on the home network; other destinations are assumed to be located on the other side of the bridge. Learning bridges determine the location of stations from the source addresses in the data packets. A learning bridge may forward some packets unnecessarily, but it adapts automatically to changes in the network configuration, sparing the administrative burden of maintaining duplicate tables in several systems.

TCP, for its part, integrates a multiple-hop journey into a reliable transmission. The protocol checks sequencing, sets timers to detect lost or discarded packets, and runs an end-to-end checksum. Because these functions consume overhead, most TCP/IP implementations also provide, for less-demanding applications, a simpler, nonconnected protocol known as the user datagram protocol. Applications that use this can perform their own checks on data sequencing and integrity. These applications include file access, remote log-in, and graphics transfer.

In addition to these transport protocols, there are two application protocols. The file transfer protocol is used to move files from one system to another. Because it transfers files in their entirety, the file transfer protocol is not the protocol of choice for accessing large CAD files. Telnet, on the other hand, provides a mechanism that enables a terminal to access a remote computer. It works well for text but has no graphics capability; remote CAD terminals must therefore use another access method.

Remote File Access

In the case of remote file access, proprietary or de facto standards provide the capability missing in the TCP/IP package. The two systems that have achieved the widest implementation are Sun Microsystems' Network File System (NES) for workstations and Novell's NetWare for microcomputers. Both allow files located on remote servers to be treated at the application level as if they were located on the local machine. Files are accessed piecemeal: only the requested records are sent over the network.

An important distinction between these systems lies in their degree of openness. Sun has actively encouraged adoption of the NFS standard by other manufacturers; more than 100 firms have licensed it, although not all have products on the market yet. Because it includes a protocol—called XDR—for treating the diverse data formats of different machines, NFS works well in a heterogeneous environment. NetWare, on the other hand, involves a proprietary operating system on a microcomputer-based server and addresses only microcomputers as clients.

Other LAN Standards

Other LAN standards find application in the CAD/CAM environment, although to a lesser degree. Even in the case of Ethernet, the version used most commonly is not the official IEEE 802.3 version, but the earlier proprietary version promulgated by Digital Equipment Corp, Intel, and Xerox. In fact, Digital Equipment alone accounts for about 42% of the installed Ethernet base. The IEEE standard differs relatively little from the proprietary version in most respects, but it does add a logical-link sublayer that provides most of the link services of the wide-area X.25 protocol set as an option. Because TCP/IP predates these services, it does not use them, and it is usually teamed with Ethernet Version 1 or 2 rather than with IEEE 802.3.

This situation, however, is certain to change in the future. The federal government is starting to require compliance with its government OSI protocol (GOSIP) stack, and this will require the use of not only 802.3 for Ethernet installations but also the ISO standards for higher layers.

Token-based standards have not yet made a presence in the CAD/CAM environment. IBM's token-passing ring is just coming into use, primarily to interconnect PCs. However, the new 16M-bps version of the token ring may attract users for such performance-sensitive applications as CAD. Most IBM CAD installations use IBM's 5080 workstation, which is directly connected to a mainframe I/O channel without an intervening LAN. Digital Equipment workstations and mainframes, on the other hand, are usually interconnected through Ethernet, using the proprietary DECnet protocols for the higher layers.

Among the standards organizations there is consensus that the token-passing bus (IEEE 802.4) is the appropriate standard for the factory environment. It offers bounded delay time and a rigid cabling system, based on cable television technology, that is resistant to electrical noise. Network buyers, however, have not shared this unanimity. Thousands of Ethernets have been installed in manufacturing companies without a significant incidence of problems. Although Ethernet delays can become considerable under heavy load conditions, such conditions are far from the norm. Extremely critical applications (e.g., emergency plant shutdown) can justify dedicated wiring in any case. Because the Ethernet cabling has four ground wraps, its noise immunity is very effective: at least two orders of magnitude better than the levels of radio frequency noise found around heavy electrical machinery.

The success of Ethernet in the CAM environment can be attributed to its earlier availability. Token-bus standards and associated equipment have come on the market only within the last two years. Whether Ethernet will maintain its momentum remains to be seen; as long as it is backed by vendors like Digital Equipment, its presence is unlikely to diminish soon.

Future LAN Technology

As processing power increases, so too does the need for increased speed in network connections. The current generation of LANs, with speeds as high as 10M bps, handles existing CAD requirements quite well. Shortly, however, CAD applications will demand higher-speed networks. This need will be met by fiber-optic systems.

The first fiber-optic standard to emerge is the Fiber Distributed Data Interface (FDDI). This standard is being developed by American Standard Committee X3T9.5. FDDI is a ring-based system that runs at 100 M bps, using a token-passing protocol that is a modified version of the one used in IEEE 802.5. Originally conceived as a computer-room interconnection, FDDI is considerably less distance-sensitive than many other LAN protocols, and as a result, it achieves a total loop length of almost 200 km (about 125 miles).

FDDI maintains compatibility with the IEEE 802 family of standards by running under the logical link control specified by IEEE 802.2. Samples of FDDI chips began circulating in the industry in early 1988; FDDI networks should become widely available in 1990.

A second thrust of development is metropolitan area networks (MANs), which are being standardized by IEEE working group 802.6. The 802.6 technology is a dual-fiber bus installed in the form of a ring with a capacity of 310M bps. Because the majority of the bits transferred between corporate locations are digital voice, the MAN effort has been optimized to support voice as well as data communications.

The 802.6 standard has been developed with the participation of the communications industry, and it can be expected to be compatible both with the other IEEE 802 standards through the logical link control layer as well as with the broadband integrated services digital network (ISDN) standards in the international communications community. Trial installations of 802.6 began in early 1990.

The 802.6 standard is the basis for the switched multimegabit data service being planned by the telephone companies. This system will provide the data service of 802.6 but not the isochronous capability designed for voice. It will provide a bandwidth guarantee to the user (in amounts less than the total capacity of 45M bits) as well as such services as address screening and group addressing.

THE ROLE OF CENTRALIZED CONTROL

The proliferation of computing power, although it has broadened the engineer's design capabilities, has created some significant management challenges. When data is distributed over many workstations, it becomes more difficult to organize projects. File backup becomes more cumbersome, and the likelihood of concurrent modification increases. Clearly, some degree of centralized control must be imposed.

Managing CAD Data

The high-speed LAN provides the solution to the control problem: a managed central file store. This is not simply a file system with transparent access, as is the case with Sun Microsystems' NFS, but an organized data base that relates to the structure of both the corporate organization and the data itself.

A local area network moves data in and out of a data base quickly. Older data communications technologies would prove too slow in transmitting CAD files, which can easily run several megabytes in size. With a LAN, a designer who needs to work on a specific part requests copies of the relevant files, which are then sent over the network to the workstation. The original data remains in the data base, available to others on a read-only basis until the user returns it, modified or not.

Permission to access and modify the data is set up to correspond to the design organization. Hierarchical levels of authority grant users the ability to read, modify, and approve designs. These levels can become complex, reflecting the real working practices of engineering departments. For example, certain individuals may be allowed to mark up a design but not to alter any elements. The design originator retains control over modifications and uses the notations to guide rework.

A given part can be represented by a multiplicity of files. One may contain the basic geometry, or model, of the part; others may contain drawings from diverse perspectives derived from the first file. Still another file may contain finite-element meshes superimposed on the part as an aid to simulation studies. Different permission schemes may apply to each of these related files. For example, in the Prime/Computervision PDM data base product, 99 levels of authority can be specified to accommodate this multiplicity.

Managing such complexity requires state-of-the art data base technology. Relational data bases can provide the needed access control, but they are slow in coping with the large volumes of data generated in CAD. Hence, as a compromise, access control is handled by a relational data base, but the data itself resides outside the data base, in the file system of the host computer. The relational data base contains indices that point to the location of the data.

Standard Interfaces to the Data Base

Standards are equally important in dealing with the data base. IBM's Structured Query Language (SQL), as a de facto standard, makes it possible to provide equivalent facilities on a variety of platforms—both hardware and data base—from different vendors. Although SQL is not an official standard, it enjoys wide acceptance, and it is available from a variety of manufacturers of mainframes to microcomputers.

Data management systems designed for CAD lend themselves to other purposes as well. The content of the managed files need not necessarily be understood by the management system. Some applications may make use of the data content when, for example, reconstituting drawings for display or plotting; however, in general, files of any type can be managed. This means that CAD files from diverse vendors can be accommodated; such utilities as the file transfer protocol are used to move the files into the managed environment.

Software components can be handled in a similar manner. Source code entails the same management concerns as mechanical design: access and concurrency control and associativity among the modules that make up a complete software system. For example, Boeing applies a CAD data management system to software components.

DATA EXCHANGE

The exchange of data among different CAD systems has long been a primary goal. Although not yet fully realized, the capability does exist for many kinds of parts and graphic entities. A limitation on the exchange of data between two systems is—and always will be—that both must support the same entities. If not, data must somehow be approximated or simulated on the system to which it is sent; as a result, a round trip may entail a loss of information.

In a multiple-system environment, the number of translations is of the order n^2 when individual source-to-target translations are used. Through the use of an intermediate format, however, translations into and out of that format require only $2n$ translations. Although two translation steps are needed, the low cost of computing power makes this a judicious move. Of course, the intermediate format must represent a superset of all the individual system's capabilities; otherwise, a loss of information will occur. Although currently a limiting factor in data exchange, the incompatibilities here are being reduced.

The first and still most prevalent data exchange standard is the Initial Graphics Exchange Specification (IGES). Drafted in 1979, it was officially adopted by the American National Standards Institute (ANSI) in 1981. The current version of IGES, Version 3.0, incorporates such features as electrical and printed circuit board support as well as data compression.

Although not yet widely implemented, data compression is valuable in relation to IGES because of its cumbersome format. IGES relies on punched-card images, in which information is arranged in specific columns or character positions. As a result, IGES files are almost always much larger than the native formats of vendor systems. Of course, general-purpose compression techniques (e.g., Huffman coding) can be applied to the file, but then the file must be decompressed before each use.

A spin-off of IGES has recently become popular in Europe. SET, an exchange standard originated by Aerospatiale in France, is conceptually rooted in IGES but it addresses two of IGES's drawbacks: the bulkiness of its implementation and its less-than-complete coverage of all vendors' features. SET attempts to represent fully any vendor's features; whether those features can be translated out of SET and into another vendor's system is still not guaranteed.

Compactness of representation has been achieved with files one-fifth to one-third the size of uncompressed IGES files.

Beyond IGES, the adoption of the newer Product Data Exchange Standard (PDES) is likely. The PDES is a reworking of IGES that better meets international requirements. The standard relies on a constructive representation of solids instead of wideframe boundaries. Although PDES data formats are not upwardly compatible with IGES, it will be possible to translate IGES files to PDES when PDES gains wider acceptance.

THE ERA OF INTERNATIONAL STANDARDS: MAP, TOP, AND STEP

In networking as well as in data exchange, international standards being developed under the auspices of the International Standards Organization (ISO) are certain to play a dominant role in the future.

The ISO protocol layering scheme is the open systems interconnection (OSI). Although this set of standards is just now reaching completion, the conceptual division of the communications process on which it is based has already become the norm. For example, TCP/IP, although not an ISO standard, largely conforms to the OSI reference model. ISO counterparts of the TCP/IP protocols and its higher-level utilities have been developed, as shown in Exhibit VI-2-3. The ISO approach adds an explicit presentation layer to control page and screen formatting and character sets (although not content) as well as a separate session layer. Functions are either similar to or a superset of the corresponding TCP/IP function.

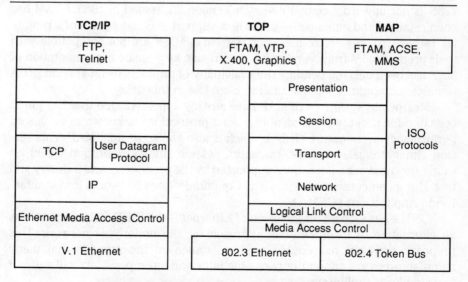

Exhibit VI-2-3. A Comparison of TCP/IP, MAP, and TOP

One of the drawbacks of the renewed focus on standards today is that there simply are too many of them. Interoperability of diverse equipment is, in fact, hindered by the presence of multiple options at each of the seven levels of the protocol. As a result, it has become necessary to create a profile, or second-order standard, to indicate which standard to use. Two such profiles are of major interest in CAD/CAM: MAP and TOP.

MAP for the Factory

The Manufacturing Automation Protocol (MAP), sponsored by General Motors, is a means of specifying data transport and semantics for factory-floor automation. MAP endorses the IEEE 802.4 token-passing bus as the preferred LAN; added to this are the standard ISO network, transport, session, and presentation layers. At the application layer, the protocol specifies the file transfer access method (FTAM) for file transfer, the manufacturing message system (MMS) for the content of messages bound for robotic equipment, and the association control for service elements (ACSE) for program-to-program communication.

This set of protocols should make communication possible between heterogeneous devices, not only in moving data from point to point but in communicating the meaning of that data. MMS, based on the Electronic Industries Association's EIA-511 standard, provides the coding for controlling the equipment that machines parts and assembles them into a finished product.

Problems of compatibility have arisen, however—not among vendors using MAP but between versions of the standard itself. Version 3.0, issued in 1988, is not upwardly compatible with Version 2.1, issued in 1985. FTAM has been retained and enhanced—it can now support accessing parts of a remote file rather than the entire file—but MMS and ACSE are not compatible with their predecessors from Version 2.1. As a result, large-scale implementation of MAP has been delayed pending the availability of products using Version 3.0. A significant amount of momentum has been lost in this delay.

Meanwhile, variations of MAP have already appeared. One that has found considerable acceptance is an abbreviated protocol stack known as enhanced performance architecture (EPA), which is also known as mini-MAP. This version eliminates the network, transport, session, and presentation layers on single-hop networks. It has been supported by the process control industry and by a European consortium known as Communications Networks for Manufacturing Applications (CNMA).

CNMA has lobbied for inclusion of Ethernet—the IEEE 802.3 version—as an alternative to the token-bus approach for the underlying network. This proposal, however, has encountered resistance on the grounds that many manufacturers will support only one medium, and interoperability will suffer if two standards proliferate.

TOP for the Office

A companion protocol set to MAP is Technical and Office Protocols (TOP). MAP is optimized for the factory floor, TOP for the office environment. As shown in Exhibit VI-2-3, its middle protocol layers are identical to those of MAP, but it diverges at the top and bottom layers.

The lower layers are based on the 802.3 version of Ethernet. Although token-bus cabling is readily installed in open-bay factories, Ethernet cabling is better suited to individual offices. In addition, the perceived token-bus advantages of noise immunity and bounded worst-case delay are not critical in office work.

At the top of the protocol stack, TOP retains FTAM and ACSE and adds electronic mail (X.400) and virtual terminal facilities. MMS is not needed.

Because CAD is essentially an office activity and CAM extends to the factory floor, support of both protocols is desirable in CAD/CAM installations. The natural dividing point between the two activities is at the data base level, in the separation of the engineering and factory data bases. CAD workstations will embrace TOP (at least, when potential performance problems with ISO protocols are resolved), and numerical control (NC) tools and controllers will gravitate toward MAP.

Originally proposed by Boeing, TOP today is benefiting from a boost by the federal government. Government contracts are stipulating the use of the POSIX protocol set, which is essentially identical to TOP; TCP/IP is being allowed only as a temporary alternative.

STEP: International Data Exchange

Paralleling the work on international standards for data transport is a corresponding effort in data exchange representations. Work on the PDES has been expanded in scope and has now joined forces with the ISO effort in a program known as STEP. The situation indicates the eventual acceptance of the IEEE 802 LAN standards as ISO standards.

When it is released during the 1990s, STEP—the French acronym for Standard for the Exchange of Product Data—will complete the evolution of CAD/CAM standards from proprietary conventions through national standards to international standards. As production of goods takes place on an increasingly international scale, the standards necessary to expedite the process should be in place.

VI-3
Alcoa Tennessee MAP/TOP Case Study

VINCENT C. JONES

In 1985, Alcoa (the Aluminum Company of America), with the aid of outside consultants, completed a two-year, multiplant study on strategic planning for computer-integrated manufacturing. One basic conclusion reached by the study was the desirability of using nonproprietary communications, such as the Manufacturing Automation Protocol (MAP), for all levels of the computer hierarchy except the lowest (Exhibit VI-3-1). Only at the process control layer were proprietary communications considered to be appropriate. On the basis of the results of this study, an internal corporate statement of direction was issued stating that within the corporation, level-1 communications (the process control level) could be proprietary, but levels 2 through 5 (stations, cell, system, and factory) should be based on broadband cable plant technology and use MAP communications.

The plant examined in this case study is the Alcoa aluminum can plant in Tennessee. Within the corporate structure of Alcoa, each plant is an independent business unit, so the corporate statement of direction promulgating MAP use is only a guideline; actual networking implementation is up to the individual plants. The raw material of the Tennessee can plant is aluminum ore, and its finished product is container stock. The plant processes include smelting alumina ore, casting it into ingots, hot rolling it, annealing it, and then cold rolling and finishing the aluminum to customer specifications.

PROCESS BEING AUTOMATED

The particular process chosen for automation within the overall process at the plant was the materials-handling system. This system takes coils of aluminum from the hot-rolling mill, moves them through the annealing process, and delivers the coils to the cold-rolling process to be cold rolled and finished. Overhead cranes and automatic guided vehicles are used to transport the coils. The networking challenge is providing the real-time control and coordination between the workers on the factory floors, the equipment moving the material, and the production centers processing the material.

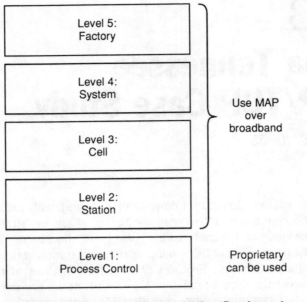

Exhibit VI-3-1. Hierarchical Communications Requirements

NEED FOR NETWORKING

The networking requirements were straightforward. The cable plant must provide connectivity between all the computers and controllers in the automated materials-handling system. The many individual computers in the system (see Exhibit VI-3-2) are distributed throughout a facility of more than 1 million sq ft. The complete block diagram is much more complicated; the numbers in the circles indicate how many of each computer are attached. The computers control 12 automated guided vehicles, seven overhead cranes, and two automated transfer charge cars to move coils to and from the annealing furnace. Fifteen operator-to-machine interfaces based on IBM PC ATs allow workers to monitor and control all aspects of operation from any control station and are the sole user interface into the system. The use of intelligent network nodes for system control provides a single, consistent interface to all the different processes controlled by the system.

The flow of control information through the network for the automated manufacturing system is only one facet of the communications requirements. Perhaps even more important is the movement, as part of the moving process, of information about the material being handled. In other words, as the crane is moving a coil from one process step to the next, the customer requirements and the processing required to meet those requirements are moving through the network along with the material.

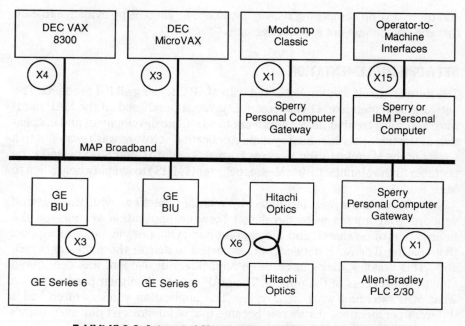

Exhibit VI-3-2. Automated Materials-Handling System Architecture

NETWORKING ALTERNATIVES CONSIDERED

The networking services selection was difficult. The strategic goal was to use MAP 3.0; however, MAP 3.0 was not available during the implementation. Two alternatives were considered. Both assumed a broadband cable plant suitable for MAP 3.0. One choice was to implement with MAP 2.1 immediately; the alternative was to use point-to-point twisted-pair communications while waiting for MAP 3.0. For two reasons, MAP 2.1 was selected as the short-term network. First, it eliminated the replacement of the twisted-pair cabling, saving hardware and redundant cabling costs. Second, it minimized the custom software development required to implement network communications services. Initial estimates placed the MAP 2.1 alternative at half the cost of point-to-point (note that both estimates included migration to MAP 3.0 when available). Networking costs have run about 50% more than estimated, primarily because of software development costs, but still well under the point-to-point estimate.

The broadband cable plant was justified simply as a utility. Redundant backups for all active components are used for higher reliability. A redundant cable system was not considered necessary.

Return on investment (ROI) analysis was not used to select or justify the network, but an ROI analysis was done on the materials-handling system as a whole. MAP 2.1 was selected because it was in line with corporate directions and there was no compelling reason not to use it. There is no evidence to date that the choice was not an effective one.

NETWORK IMPLEMENTATION

The network itself was implemented with MAP 2.1, using all INI products. The network is treated like a black-box utility. Alcoa purchased all the MAP hardware and software that its vendors were to use in the development and installation of the materials-handling system. Application software was restricted to a subset of the Manufacturing Message Format Standard (MMFS) expected to be portable to the Manufacturing Message System (MMS) to simplify upgrading to MAP 3.0.

Implementation was facilitated by monthly meetings with the selected vendors. Agreements were developed between application vendors on the information to be shared and the content and syntax of messages to support that sharing. The MAP network was expected to deliver those messages reliably. This ongoing dialogue between application developers was considered vital to the success of the project. The MAP vendors had their perspective on what MAP was and what it provided. The application vendors often had a different perspective. Alcoa's role became that of integrator, tying everybody's perspective into a unified solution.

NETWORK OPERATIONAL EXPERIENCE

The network has been operational since February 1987. The materials-handling system started testing during the summer of that year. The MAP standard aspects of the network have not been an issue; however, the use of beta version software has caused problems and delays in system development. The restriction on capabilities to ensure migration was also a limitation imposed by MAP 2.1. The only other significant limitation observed so far has been on performance, caused by the high protocol overhead. However, network capacity has not been a problem, nor is it expected to be.

Maintenance responsibility for the network is split. Plant electricians maintain the broadband cable plant. The MIS department is responsible for troubleshooting the upper layers. Training is considered a critical element in successful implementation and ongoing maintenance. For example, broadband requires new maintenance technology.

SUMMARY

The bottom line is positive for both MAP networking and broadband cable plant. At Alcoa Tennessee, a shop floor system for data collection is being evaluated as a next MAP project. Other Alcoa facilities are installing broadband cable plants, and the Alcoa Tennessee broadband cable plant has been expanded to cover the entire facility (6 million sq ft).

VI-4
The Role of LANs in Departmental Computing

HUGH W. RYAN

The goal in computerizing any process is to develop an approach that anticipates and controls problems and ensures that information reaches end users when they need it. An organization must address effectively the issues of people (both end users and MIS personnel), tools, and methods (as shown in Exhibit VI-4-1). In a certain sense, tools are the most interesting element in that they tend to be visible and concrete. Certainly, LAN technology is one of the key tools; LANs can deliver critical information to the right people in the right time frame for use in departmental computing. The key to making this tool work, however, is to ensure that it is indeed serving the right people with the right information. This leads to the other concerns in the diagram: people and method. The people are important: end user, systems developer, and information center consultant. The benefit of a methodology is that it provides a common framework and language so that people of different backgrounds may talk and work together effectively to determine what information they need. A methodology suitable for the introduction of departmental computing includes the following major phases:

- The development of a list of functional requirements.
- Data design.
- Selection of a technical architecture.
- System design.
- Implementation (i.e., coding).
- Testing.

This chapter reviews each of these phases as applied to LAN-based departmental computing. An important point to recognize is that development of the list of functional requirements precedes and creates the structure for data design; data design, in turn, precedes and largely dictates system design.

FUNCTIONAL REQUIREMENTS

In compiling a list of the users' functional requirements, the systems developer first identifies what the users want the system to do and then proposes a design

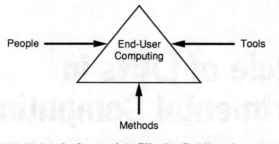

Exhibit VI-4-1. An Approach to Effective End-User Computing

---

consisting of input and output and a schematic that presents the behavior of the system from the users' perspective. Once approved, this becomes the basis for the data design.

In the typical departmental computing environment, however, users are often unclear about what they want the system to do and use iterations of the system to refine their requirements. That is, users employ the system to refine their requirements and then revise the system to accommodate the modified requirements. This approach cannot be based on asking users what kind of system they want. Users often do not know what they want until they have it; even then, subsequent iterations may be needed to refine the final system. The most systems developers can hope for from users is an identification of the data they would like to see from the system. From a methodology standpoint, this means that the process of development must, at the outset, be built on an assumption of iterative development.

In the context of LAN-based departmental computing, this often means conducting an initial installation of appropriate LANs and computing hardware and prototyping some applications for the user. This may mean putting up a few key forms that the user employs, providing some data management capability, and then patterning an information flow with the forms on the basis of the current departmental policies and procedures. This initial effort demonstrates how the LAN can benefit the department by improving communication and access to information.

At the same time, this effort will help the users see the potential of LAN-based departmental computing for support of current and future work. This in turn will lead to more precise estimates of the number of users benefiting from network access, the volume of work they could place on the network, and any particular recovery or security concerns.

DATA DESIGN

The users' requirements (as identified by the input and output) and system flow are the source of information for a data design. The key point to recognize is that user requirements cannot be put into final form. This presents a consid-erable problem in the data design stage: systems development may have an idea of what data the user wants but not how the data should interrelate to support the requirements.

Given this prototyping technique, the analyst can begin to deal with two issues. The first is the identification of forms and documents that will require LAN support for the department's operations. At an insurance agency, for example, the insurance application forms were identified as a key starting place. The second issue is the technical support that will be provided to the department as it continues to develop its own computing applications.

The design of the departmental data base that supports departmental operations is based on the forms and documents. This process is essentially one of deciding the content and structure of the data base on the basis of the content and structure of the documents.

In addition, the analyst must consider the mapping of information flow on the LAN. One of the key advantages of LANs is that they allow the analyst to create an electronic flow of information that matches and enhances the flow of information within the department. The importance of the ability of the LAN to be able to model the departmental information flow easily cannot be over-emphasized. It is a capability that many communications specialists take for granted but tends to be poorly understood by systems analysts and end users.

As a result, systems analysts and end users tend to think in terms of communications data transfer typified by information moving into and out of the mainframe, not from user to user in the department (e.g., a client that uses LAN technology to deal with insurance claims). On the basis of the nature of the claim (including the site of the claim and the type of injuries), LAN technology was used to route it to analysts trained in the appropriate situations. Prior to this all claims were stored on the mainframe, and retrieval was based on shouted conversations between claims taker and claims analyst. The LAN provided a much better mechanism for the flow of information.

This mapping of information flow leads to the second major data design issue: the design of the tables to describe who is to receive what forms. Creativity on the part of the analyst can produce a design that the user can maintain, changing flows as time passes and experience with the LAN grows.

Once the flows are identified and the tables to support the flows are established, the analyst must deal with the third issue of where data is to be stored. In this regard, there are three levels to consider: the workstation, the departmental file server, and the enterprise level system—which often trans-lates to the organization's mainframe.

Data on the workstation can be easily and quickly accessed by the user of the workstation. It is not, however, easily shared with others. So the data appropriate for storage at this level is data that will be of interest primarily to the user of the workstation; sales prospects are a common example. In addition, data that is accessed frequently for workstation processing but tends to be stable at the departmental level may find a place on the workstation.

At the departmental level, the data should be of interest to the department and not need to be shared with other departments. Common examples of such information include departmental work in process. An insurance department, for example, keeps the insurance applications that it needs at the department level while the application is being processed. Then a version of the data is moved to the mainframe. The department may also maintain performance statistics. These statistics are typically those measures that the department deems to be critical performance indicators. In a telephone sales business, this could be number of calls made, number and dollar amount of sales, or number and reason for lost sales. One of the benefits of departmental computing is that since it is in direct support of such business processing, it can facilitate performance reporting by capturing such statistics in a natural and transparent fashion.

At the enterprise level, the data has several characteristics. One is that it must be reflected in the main enterprise accounting ledgers. Second, if the data must be shared with others in the enterprise, it should reside in the mainframe. Thus, information about a completed sale, for example, must be shared with the billing department and thus needs to migrate to the enterprise level. Finally, if data is particularly sensitive or in need of security and protection, this is best done from the enterprise level.

TECHNICAL ARCHITECTURE

The next issue is to define the processing components that are to be found in the workstation, in the departmental file servers, and on the mainframe. Defining these components and their locations is the process of defining the application's technical architecture.

The workstation component is established mainly with the use of a fourth-generation language (4GL). Such a language imposes its own structure on the application. Access to local workstation data is usually provided by the 4GL. In addition, those 4GLs that have developed in conjunction with a LAN-based data base server will usually provide access to a LAN file server. In those cases in which the language is independent of the data base management system on the LAN file server, the data base management system will often provide some means of transparently accessing the data for the 4GL.

A problem often arises in record protection for the data. LAN-based file servers have begun to address this in a way that is transparent to the application. Before now, it was often necessary to design a process based on LAN semaphores to protect access to records being updated. The analyst should find out what protection is provided for records and ascertain whether the protection system meets the needs for security and protection defined in the functional requirements phase.

Access from the workstation to both the LAN data base management services and data at the enterprise level is more of a problem. An architecture is rapidly evolving today in which the access occurs through the LAN file server. This is desirable because of the saving in workstation cost. Being able to access the mainframe through the file server over the LAN can reduce the cost of the workstation and thus make the departmental processing concept more acceptable as a whole.

It should be noted that this technology is in development; there is a risk that its first users will encounter performance limits or find that there are currently unknown reliability issues.

SYSTEMS DOCUMENTATION

Systems design usually involves careful documentation of the design being implemented. Documentation requirements are different for end-user computing; short, one-person projects are often designed as they are implemented. This may appear unwise initially, but an end-user project may be the creation of a report that is designed in only 20 minutes. In this case, insisting on detailed design documentation is a sure means of losing credibility.

A second problem of systems design is that techniques that work well with traditional tools are less appropriate for 4GLs, in part because these newer tools incorporate such techniques as part of their processing. Insisting on standard documentation in this case may lead users to document the internal processing of the tool they are using.

Situations in which systems design documentation is required should be identified through the length of development time, the number of people involved in the effort, and whether the application is expected to be used by people other than the development team. In cases requiring design documentation, appropriate standards and examples must be established for the user. A documentation format that is acceptable for a mainframe report writer may be extremely confusing if the user tries to apply it to a micro-based spreadsheet program. As the organization adds tools to the end-user environment, it should plan to add standards specific to the new tools.

Implementation

In the implementation phase, the design is translated to a machine-executable format. It may be critical that the information center consultant advise the user on the best means of implementation. Standards regarding the recommended ways to implement logic should be established so that the user is not sidetracked. For example, some 4GLs have a notorious reputation for constructs not working as expected or exhibiting operational changes with new releases. Standards can be useful in avoiding these constructs.

As the organization adds new tools, it should expect to add standards and also provide expertise in the tool to resolve implementation difficulties.

Testing

Testing is one of the most difficult phases of departmental computing. When asked for the results of testing, users often answer that "the numbers looked okay" or, even more disturbing, "it quit blowing up."

Most users do not object to testing; they simply do not recognize the need for it nor do they know how to proceed on a planned basis. The user-developer must understand that testing is critical, and an approach to testing must be clearly identified.

Explaining how to test is much more difficult. There is no consensus within the data processing industry on the issue. One widely used approach is to establish specific test cases with predicted results, execute the test, and review the actual results against those predicted. Even this technique has limitations when models that predict future trends must be tested. The information center consultant can once again serve a key role by convincing users of the need for testing, helping them develop a testing approach, and ensuring that the approach is followed.

A key point in testing LAN-based departmental computing is to observe the users. They quickly learn that problems go away when they turn the file servers and LANs off and on again. In addition, most LANs do a poor job of noting and reporting problems. As a result, it is critical that the analyst spend time in the users' areas watching for and tracing the causes of problems as they occur. Otherwise, users will adopt the off-again–on-again repair technique and develop the idea that the system is not reliable.

The test period is also a good time to observe the performance of the LAN. Although models that predict performance exist, the fact is that actual loads often vary from plan. It is important to monitor LAN performance so as to be aware of its degrading as new users are added to the network. On occasion, departmental computing can become its own worst enemy because of what has been called the turnpike effect. When a LAN system is available, it is used to do more work more quickly. The result is that use of the system may exceed expected volumes, degrading performance as a result. To avoid the turnpike effect, careful monitoring of planned performance versus actual performance is essential.

Testing is a good time to note areas in which the system falls short of expectations and to decide which of these problems to address on subsequent iterations of the system. Identifying shortcomings is particularly important to enhance the iterative nature of end-user development.

SUMMARY OF DEVELOPMENT PROCESS CONSIDERATIONS

The development process is summarized in Exhibit VI-4-2. Departmental computing has a significant effect on the traditional process of systems development. Differences arise not out of misunderstandings on the part of the end user but because the iterative approach and the tools used in that environment

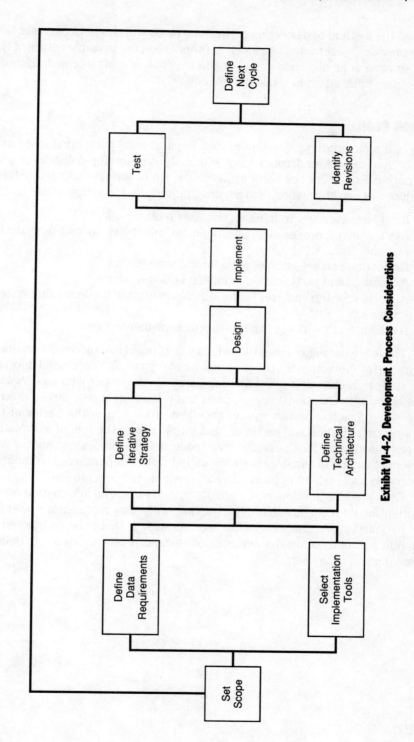

Exhibit VI-4-2. Development Process Considerations

change the method of development. In some cases, utilities perform tasks that were previously left to the developer. In other cases, the dynamic nature of the user environment demands speed at the expense of completeness. Systems developers must adapt to those differences.

ACTION PLAN

Although many systems developers view departmental computing more as a threat than an aid, end users have legitimate reasons for doing their own computing. End users need and welcome the aid of the professional systems developer as an information center consultant in the following areas:

- Introduction to and training on end-user tools.
- Evaluation of proposed applications for suitability to end-user development.
- Evaluation and selection of tools for implementation.
- Assistance and participation in implementation efforts.
- Advocacy for the end user to the MIS department in implementing system changes.
- Assistance in the design and testing of implementations.

These are not minor roles. Indeed, they are critical to a successful end-user environment. Nevertheless, the job is not for everyone. The successful information center consultant is often a mature systems developer who has grown a little bored with traditional development and is looking for new career alternatives. Often, such a person has an excellent grounding in the basics of the business organization and can bring that knowledge to the role of information center consultant. This person's knowledge of data processing and of MIS personnel can be invaluable. For such an individual, departmental computing represents an excellent opportunity for career change and growth.

Even systems developers who do not wish to pursue an information center position should recognize that departmental computing represents a powerful tool in delivering information to the user. As such, it should be considered an inherent part of the tools that information systems professionals use to deliver their commodity to users.

VI-5
Southeast Bank: A Case Study of LANs in a Business Environment

CHERYL SNAPP

Southeast Bank, based in Miami FL, is an international company with 12 primary operating locations and more than 240 branches across the US. The company's assets are currently estimated at $16 billion.

Southeast has more than 8,000 employees. Approximately 1,000 of these employees are located in the company's Miami headquarters, which occupies 23 floors of a 55-story building. Southeast's data processing group, the Information Systems and Services Division (ISSD), is located in a separate Miami facility several miles from the headquarters site.

The company's vast information system was initially centered on an IBM mainframe 3270 network, which was connected to the 12 key US operating sites by leased lines. ISSD recently replaced the IBM mainframe with two National Advanced Systems (NAS) computers, which are IBM 3090-class machines. The two mainframes support nearly 6,000 terminal connections.

Like most large organizations, Southeast also has microcomputers that were purchased by the individual sites to fill a variety of office automation roles. Before 1987, however, the company had established no corporate guidelines to control microcomputer purchase or use. Southeast's microcomputer evolution had emerged as a haphazard process—users would purchase microcomputer hardware and software products as they saw fit, in much the same fashion that they bought typewriters and office supplies.

PC REQUIREMENTS

By 1987, it was clear that the company needed a program to leverage and control microcomputer use. The new program would need to meet several requirements. First, Southeast needed to establish standards for the purchase of microcomputers. By monitoring its microcomputer purchases, the bank could ensure the quality and the compatibility of its microcomputer equipment and take advantage of quantity discounts.

Second, the company needed to develop an appropriate method for providing microcomputer support. As the bank coordinated its microcomputer acquisitions, the MIS group would be able to develop a consistent strategy for office automation and would be in a better position to provide its microcomputer users with appropriate training and support. As its third requirement, Southeast wanted to ensure that its information system was both reliable and secure.

Finally, and most important, Southeast wanted to integrate its microcomputers into an enterprisewide network. This would allow microcomputer users to participate in and enhance many of the business functions already being handled by the mainframe machines. It was this final requirement that led Southeast to research its options for a network technology that could integrate both mainframes and microcomputers.

PRELIMINARY STEPS

ISSD's first step was to form a specific six-member information center (IC) team. Once the IC group had established requirements and goals for microcomputer technology, the six analysts requested proposals from a number of systems vendors to see what kind of products and services each vendor could provide.

The IC requested three different price scenarios for each system: the cost for a 20-node, a 30-node, and a 100-node network.

NETWORK PRIORITIES

The IC's highest priority is the ability to support end-user computing—in other words, to maintain individual user and workgroup autonomy and productivity while ensuring a very high level of consistency and security throughout the company's computing environment.

The various products the IC considered were evaluated in terms of security, reliability, ease of use, function, the ability to interoperate with the mainframe environment, and price.

APPLICATION REQUIREMENTS

Particular applications required for office automation included word processing, spreadsheets, and data base packages. One of the IC's objectives was to standardize on specific software packages for use by all sites.

Standardization would help to ease the problems associated with upgrades, user training, and support. With all sites networked, standard software packages would also facilitate multiuser functions and the sharing of data across multiple sites. For this reason, the IC also examined the applications that were available for each network alternative.

One system, for example, provided access from a single, consistent menu to its own proprietary applications. The IC considered the consistent interface to be a plus; however, the committee ruled the system out when it discovered that the network's proprietary word processor was not powerful enough to meet the company's requirements.

SYSTEM ALTERNATIVES

As the IC evaluated the company's options, the group considered minicomputer as well as microcomputer network solutions. Although several of the minicomputer options offered excellent applications, the committee soon discovered that minicomputer networking was a more expensive solution. Furthermore, a minicomputer scheme would have been unable to accommodate Southeast's existing 300 microcomputers, except to connect them to the minicomputers as dumb terminals.

In fact, had the company standardized on minicomputers, the IC would have had to provide all of its applications through dumb terminals and would have disallowed the purchase of additional microcomputers.

Adopting a microcomputer-based network was the only solution that would allow the company to make full use of its existing microcomputers, facilitate continued microcomputer growth, and allow the IC to choose from the full spectrum of applications written for IBM-compatible LANs.

The IC selected a PC LAN solution based on the System Fault Tolerant (SFT) NetWare LAN operating system from Novell (Provo UT). NetWare is reliable, flexible, and easy to use and is able to interoperate with multiple computing environments, including the two host-based systems at Southeast. SFT NetWare version 2.15 currently operates on all 12 Southeast LANs. The NetWare LANs were installed in 1987 to connect Southeast's 300 existing microcomputers. Since then, the company's microcomputer population has grown to 600 nodes. The IC estimates that as many as 3,000 employees make at least some use of the microcomputer networks within the course of their work.

At the onset of the network project, the IC established a 12-node Ethernet network as a pilot; however, the network was unreliable and susceptible to frequent downtime. From that time forward, Southeast's LANs have standardized on IBM token-ring adapters.

INSTALLATION CHOICES

Although many companies on the level of Southeast Bank rely on outside consultants for network design and planning, Southeast's IC committee was able to design the company's networks itself. The NetWare configuration was the result of the internal development efforts of the IC.

IBM was the only outside consultant Southeast used, providing the cabling design through a token-ring support group in Raleigh NC.

Southeast's ability to design its own network saved the company a great deal of money. One of the minicomputer vendors that the company considered, for example, had offered to establish a single pilot network for Southeast at a cost of $250,000.

By selecting a microcomputer-based system and by providing the consulting and design expertise from within its own ranks, Southeast has established its entire corporate internet, including file servers, software, network bridges, cabling, wiring closets, and uninterruptible power supply (UPS) for each server, and tape backup facilities, for a total cost of approximately $250,000.

MICROCOMPUTER LAN IMPLEMENTATION

Because Southeast's Miami building spans many floors, the design and installation of the headquarters' three LANs posed a difficult challenge. The network system needed to accommodate great distances between the servers and workstations. In addition, the network cabling would have to fit into the building's existing architectural scheme.

Southeast selected the IBM Cabling System, which provides a great deal of flexibility by offering different grades of twisted-pair wire. The primary spine connecting the floors of each building uses the highest grade of cable—IBM type 1. Each floor contains a wiring closet, which connects the individual workstations. These connections use IBM type 5 cable.

As new workstations are acquired, the IC connects them to the network by means of an inexpensive type 9 cable that is accessible to each workstation through a wall jack. New workstations are connected to the wall plate with a small piece of patch cable. This type of connection makes additions and changes to the network extremely easy—new workstations can simply be plugged in to the network through the closest wall plate.

In terms of installing the actual cable, Southeast is fortunate to have the assistance of a network services division within the company. The actual wiring was provided by an outside electrician; however, the network services division was able to provide a great deal of assistance in determining the optimum cabling procedures and locations within the building.

For the remote locations, the IC provided its network specifications to a dealer who in turn established the networks and provided initial training on how to use and maintain the network at each of the 12 remote network sites.

EARLY CHALLENGES

Early in the LAN project, Southeast experienced problems with frequent downtime on one of the company's proprietary 286-based server machines. The reason for the downtime was unclear, but one IC analyst speculated that the server's system board had warped and that the adapter cards were not fitting properly into their slots.

Again, because continuous operation is critical to the company's business, the IC committee decided that rather than dealing with the idiosyncrasies of the various IBM-compatible machines, they would make the IBM Personal System/2 (PS/2) Model 80 the company's LAN server standard. All but one of the company's networks now use the Model 80 as a dedicated server machine.

With the new servers, UPS units, and SFT NetWare operating system Southeast now has in place, the company has experienced only one hour of unplanned downtime over a period of two years.

Southeast feels that the additional expense of the Model 80 machines is more than justified by the company's requirement for reliable LAN service. Furthermore, by focusing on a single brand of servers, the IC group has improved its ability to provide remote work sites with fast, expert support.

USER SUPPORT

In some operating sites, Southeast employees had specifically requested access to LANs, but there were also a few opponents to LANs. Virtually all users, however, have responded favorably to the LAN resource once their networks were in place. To facilitate this acceptance, the IC developed a LAN users guide, which the group provides to each new user.

Local user support is provided at each site by one of the users, who is designated as the network supervisor. These network supervisors are responsible for performing a daily file server backup, establishing user levels of access to the LAN, and acting as communications liaison with the corporate network administrator.

The corporate administrator, who is one of the six members of the IC team, is responsible for adding new users to the LAN, managing log-in scripts and network shells, performing network backups for headquarters facility, putting new applications on the network, and generally ensuring that the network is operating properly at all times.

LAN CONFIGURATION—RELIABILITY CONCERNS

As with any financial institution, system reliability is a critical concern for Southeast. In addition to selecting SFT NetWare, which is the NetWare version specifically designed to provide enhanced software reliability features, Southeast installed an uninterruptible power supply on each server. Depending on power size, UPS prices range from $725 to nearly $5,000 each—a small price for a company that depends on reliable network operation as heavily as Southeast.

To further enhance reliability, the information center is planning to implement disk mirroring or disk duplexing on all Southeast LANs in the future. The first implementation of disk mirroring is in the operations center LAN.

The disk-mirroring function in SFT NetWare allows for dual writes to duplicate hard disks. If one disk should fail, the other would continue operating. The SFT NetWare operating system notifies the system supervisor of the disk failure. Once the faulty disk is repaired or replaced, the supervisor can reestablish the disk-mirroring function without shutting down the system.

Disk duplexing is a similar function that carries the hardware redundancy a step further; disk duplexing provides for duplicate disk channels as well.

Another reliability feature provided by SFT NetWare is the transaction tracking system (TTS). TTS protects data integrity by ensuring that in the event of a network failure, updates to the LAN data base are either entirely completed or entirely backed out. In this way, TTS eliminates the chance that the data base will be corrupted by a partly completed transaction.

Some data base products, such as Novell Inc's Btrieve, Zim by Zanthe Corp (Ottawa, Canada), and dBMAN by Verasoft Corp (San Jose CA), include explicit calls to signal Novell's TTS. Other products, such as dBASE by Ashton-Tate (Torrance CA), DataFlex by Data Access Corp (Miami FL), and the DataEase package by DataEase International Inc (Trumbull CT), offer implicit compatibility with TTS.

Of the data base products the IC evaluated, the group preferred DataEase, which offers three levels of security: data base, field, and functional. The first two security levels, data base and field, are established by the system supervisor during menu and field definition and control user access to the data base. The third level of security, functional security, determines what the users are able to do within a file or a record. Southeast found the product easy to use and yet sophisticated enough to meet the company's data base needs. For these reasons and for the sake of security, Southeast has selected the DataEase product as its LAN data base standard.

An additional reliability feature Southeast uses is the Hot Fix utility, which is available in all NetWare LANs. If the network is attempting to write data to a faulty area of the disk, rather than returning an error message to the user, Hot Fix dynamically locates an operational area for data to be stored and informs the operating system, for future reference, which sectors of the disk storage are faulty.

SECURITY TOOLS

In addition to providing security within its data base, it is mandatory that Southeast ensure the highest possible security for the network system overall. Breaches in security are extremely costly for any company that handles financial accounts. The network system must include mechanisms for protecting the network from accidental damage or criminal misuse.

The IC assigns and monitors access to Southeast's LANs. As new users join the networks, they submit a brief form to the IC to request a user name and password and to request access to the particular applications they require. Within the NetWare operating system, users are assigned log-in passwords that are associated with specific rights to particular areas on the LAN. These centralized security controls ensure that each user has access only to the discrete areas of the network required.

As an extra precaution, all microcomputers purchased are now diskless workstations. This forces users to store their data on the file server, and reduces the risk that users will download secure data onto diskettes or individual hard drives. Just as in the mainframe environment, users see only the areas of data they require, and only for the duration of their work.

In Southeast's corporate headquarters, which currently has 115 connected microcomputers, the IC protects network security by centralizing the three network file servers in a specially equipped room. The centralization of Southeast's file servers and network management function carries an additional benefit beyond protecting the system's security: it eliminates the expense of providing a dedicated MIS professional at each network site. In fact, Southeast is able to manage its entire collection of LANs with just one full-time administrator.

CONNECTING LANS TO THE MAINFRAME ENVIRONMENT

Before moving to LANs, Southeast provided mainframe access to each of its 12 operating sites over leased lines to a 3270 terminal at each site. This was an acceptable means for providing the work sites with access to up-to-the-minute records from the central data base. However, only one user could access the terminal at a time.

Once the company's LANs were in place, the IC's next step was to provide users with mainframe access through the LAN. Since the microcomputers were already available for office automation, using these same microcomputers for host connection would eliminate the need for remote terminals.

Southeast Bank provided LAN-to-host connections through the NetWare SNA gateway and SNA gateway entry-level system (ELS) products over the existing leased lines. The NetWare SNA gateway, which is used at Southeast's operating center, can support as many as 128 concurrent sessions. The NetWare SNA gateway ELS, which is much less expensive, is used for remote locations that require no more than 16 concurrent sessions.

GATEWAY CONFIGURATION

A LAN gateway requires a gateway server machine that can operate in dedicated or nondedicated mode. Southeast uses IBM PS/2 Model 50s as gateway servers. However, any IBM PC, XT, AT, PS/2, or compatible will do.

Users can customize the NetWare SNA gateway for coaxial, synchronous data link control (SDLC), or token-ring connectivity. SDLC or coaxial connections require an adapter in the gateway microcomputer. Token-ring connectivity can be provided through the gateway server's existing token-ring LAN adapter. Southeast employs SDLC connections through RS-232 connections to synchronous modems at each site. The gateway server software is installed on PS/2 gateway servers.

Mainframe access is provided with Novell's NetWare 3270 LAN workstation software, a terminal emulation package. The company needs only one copy of the workstation software per file server, regardless of the number of workstations that require access to the host.

The 3270 LAN workstation requires just 106K bytes of memory. If desired, the workstation software can be temporarily removed from the microcomputer's resident memory to allow the workstation to run other applications.

ENSURING GATEWAY RELIABILITY

Initially, the IC had some reliability problems with the LAN-to-mainframe gateway connections.

One of the difficulties of LAN gateways is that the technology is still relatively new. Slight microcomputer incompatibilities that are not a problem for the LAN may be accentuated in the gateway environment. ROM BIOS problems, bus timing problems, and bus noise can cause gateway connections to fail.

Furthermore, a gateway failure may indicate a problem with either the mainframe or the LAN side of the link. The system administrator must isolate the problem before it can be corrected.

There are very few diagnostic tools available for the specific challenges LAN gateways face, particularly in the multivendor environment.

The NetWare gateway, however, includes an offline test function that simulates mainframe traffic without actually being connected to the mainframe. If the test indicates that the gateway data is getting to the workstations, the network administrator can conclude that the problem is most likely within the mainframe side of the connection.

This was the case with Southeast. The information center discovered problems with transport definitions in the mainframe connection. Consequently, the group solved the problem by reconfiguring the mainframe connection. Except for occasional problems with the phone lines, the LAN gateways now provide excellent performance.

To help ensure reliability, once the IC had achieved a strong gateway implementation at the company's headquarters, the group repeated the identical configuration with exactly the same products for each of the company's 12 remote LANs. The identical configurations ensure consistent performance, and since the same products are used everywhere, potential problems are easier for the IC to diagnose and correct.

Southeast employees use the LAN gateways to provide file transfer access to host applications through 3270 terminal emulation. Remote users may access demand deposit accounting (the company's check processing system), the customer information file, the loan system, and loan balances. In addition, file transfer over the gateways provides a convenient mechanism for downloading and distributing information to employees from the human resources group.

SPECIAL-PURPOSE APPLICATION

Most of the applications Southeast uses are available off the shelf; in fact, the ability to choose from a variety of existing packages was one of the key reasons for acquiring LANs.

In one case, however, the bank has opted to create a customized application for the proof corrections department. Southeast did, however, save some programming steps by basing the customized application on the Btrieve record-level data management system. Btrieve is a Novell product that is bundled with NetWare version 2.1 and above. The single-user version of Btrieve sells for $245. For non-Novell networks, the network version of Btrieve sells for $595.

The proof corrections department receives all checks the sorting machine rejects because of such defects as ripped corners and missing signatures. When this occurs, the employees in proof corrections send a notice to the customer to request that the check be resubmitted or to report that the check's processing may be delayed.

Before the Btrieve application was installed, employees were writing each of these notices by hand. The bank's purpose for the customized application was to automate this process. The Btrieve-based system allows users to enter the item into the microcomputer, retrieve the customer's name and address from the customer information file on the mainframe host, and then produce a customized notice.

LAN PRINTERS—CONFIGURATION CONCERNS

One of the key problems Southeast encountered in installing networks in a 55-story facility was centralizing the network servers for the sake of security and yet maintaining the network's ability to provide complete network services for the 1,000 users distributed over 23 floors.

The 286-based versions of NetWare require that network printers be located next to the file servers. In Southeast's case, the three file servers are centralized on the 11th floor. The company had three options. The first was to require network users to retrieve all print jobs from the computer room on the 11th floor. This was clearly unworkable. The second option was to configure the network's shared printers as standalone resources. In this scenario, users would take turns calling up their files and requesting printouts from the nearest workstation on their floor that had a printer attached. This option, too, was unworkable.

The third option was to purchase a third-party NetWare-compatible product that would allow users to establish network printers at any location on the LAN. There are several such products on the market, including Network Assistant Plus from Cybertek Corp (Dallas), PSPrint from Brightwork Development (Red Bank NJ), and the LANspool product from LAN Systems Inc (New York).

Southeast chose the third option and selected the LANspool product. The LANspool software allows Southeast to convert any microcomputer or compatible workstation with at least 512K bytes of RAM to a print server workstation that may control as many as seven network printers each. The print servers are able to operate in dedicated or nondedicated mode. Since LANspool requires just 2.5K bytes of RAM at the print server, the software does not interfere with workstation operation.

An additional advantage LANspool provides is that it allows Southeast's users to access the shared printers even if they are not logged on to the LAN. If the LAN should go down, for example, or if secretaries who do not have network rights need to continue working after their supervisors have logged off and gone home, Southeast's print server configuration allows users to continue using the shared printer without risking a breach in the network's security. Currently, Southeast has installed a copy of LANspool on each of the company's 12 LANs.

LAN BACKUP

Southeast backs up each network file server nightly onto Emerald 2.2G-byte tape drives. Southeast makes it a practice to back up all file server files, although the ASP tape management utility in the Emerald drive also provides the option of backing up only selected files and directories or only the files that have changed since the previous backup.

As an added precaution, the backup tapes for the company's headquarters and operations center are stored offsite. Since Southeast uses office space in two Miami locations, the offsite storage for these facilities is simply a matter of the two sites swapping backup archives several times each week. In the event of a network disaster at either site, the archived data is just two miles away.

NET RESULTS

Networking all microcomputers has given Southeast several advantages. First, the company's distributed locations still have the autonomy to purchase microcomputers and to enjoy the productivity advantages of having microcomputer processing power at their individual sites. Each site continues to have responsibility for its own microcomputer budget; however, the information center reviews the purchase requirements of each site to ensure that new purchases fit within the company's required standards. In some cases, the IC can assist the group in getting equipment at a lower cost. In other cases, if the work group has requirements that cannot be met by the products the IC has approved, the IC group may evaluate additional products for the LAN or may assist the group in finding an alternate way to meet its requirements while maintaining compatibility with the rest of the company's LANs.

Second, users today are able to gain access to mainframe applications from their microcomputers. This eliminates the company's requirement to provide both terminal connections to the mainframe and personal computers for local office automation. In addition, the IC has been able to distribute computing resources while at the same time maintaining system security and management control. The current network arrangement allows Southeast to leverage the advantages of both mainframes and microcomputers. Finally, the new system saves a great deal of money by integrating the company's microcomputers into a consistent corporatewide information processing scheme.

FUTURE GOALS

With just six employees to manage Southeast's entire microcomputer structure, the IC's next step is to expand and to distribute some of the functions that are currently handled by the IC group alone. In the future, the IC would like to work with the company's data processing group to establish a microcomputer support help desk and to integrate this function with the help desk currently in place for the mainframe environment. As the IC coordinates its efforts with the traditional data processing function, data processing operations may also assume responsibility for managing the network file servers. In addition, one of Southeast's departments has 16 Macintosh machines from Apple Computer (Cupertino CA). In the next year, Southeast intends to merge these workstations into the Novell LAN using NetWare for Macintosh.

Although each of Southeast's LANs is connected to the central host, none of the remote LANs are currently connected to one another. As a result, although the LANs are able to receive up-to-the-minute infomation from the mainframe in a read-only fashion, they are unable to pass information from one LAN to another or to perform additional analysis on the mainframe's data at their own sites. Ideally, authorized users should have access to all of the data they require from any workstation on the company's LANs.

Only one of Southeast's departments is using electronic mail today. In some of the other networks, users have established a public directory in which they can leave files for other users to read or to pick up in a makeshift LAN bulletin board. Once all of the LANs are internetworked, a corporatewide electronic mail scheme would become a more feasible goal.

The information center is also looking at mechanisms for actually downloading mainframe data to the LANs, which would enhance LAN users' ability to perform local analysis and graphical reporting with the high performance and familiar environment of the microcomputer.

SUMMARY

Southeast's LAN solution has successfully met the company's highest objectives: the creation of microcomputer networks that are easy to use, and the establishment of a network environment that is both reliable and secure.

Although mainframe computing continues to be the focal point of Southeast's information system, the company's LANs have enhanced the mainframe functions by leveraging microcomputer use. Southeast's corporate management and the end-user community alike consider the company's microcomputer networks an outstanding success.

Section VII
Management and Administrative Issues

As local area networks continue to proliferate, management and administrative issues will move into the mainstream of corporate life. This section takes a look at a number of the issues that LAN managers will face.

Regardless of the discipline or technical area of expertise, one aspect of management that is of utmost importance is the ability to develop and retain qualified professionals. LANs are no different in this respect. LANs are, however, unique in that they span a variety of disciplines and do not fit neatly into any one category. More than any other field, LANs tend to fit into communications organizations' scope; thus, Chapter VII-1, "Training Communications Professionals," discusses the issue of personnel training and retention from that perspective. The concepts and principles are equally valid across the broader range of LAN disciplines.

A very closely related management topic is the need to hire new personnel as needed as a result of turnover or staff expansion. New candidates can come from a variety of sources, both from within and outside the organization. Chapter VII-2, "Screening Systems Analyst Candidates for a LAN Environment," discusses a structured method for working through the screening process and provides insight into the qualifications to be sought for this type of candidate. Particular attention is paid to those qualifications unique to a LAN environment as opposed to a traditional MIS/DP shop.

The importance of industry standards to LANs has been emphasized throughout this volume. One aspect of standards that is of significant concern to management is the degree to which the organization should be committed to standards. This commitment can range from being a totally passive participant—relying on vendors to deliver conforming, interoperable products—to being a fully committed, proactive leader in the standards development process. Chapter VII-3, "Managing the Organization's Participation in Industry Standards Development," discusses a number of levels of commitment and the associated benefits that can be derived from each. Guidelines for getting the most return for the dollars invested in the process are also presented, with emphasis on coordinating standards activity toward the attainment of specific business objectives of the enterprise.

VII-1
Training Communications Professionals

PHILLIP R. EVANS

The communications industry has experienced a technological and organizational revolution during the past few years. Such technologies as ISDN, T1, local area networks, digital PABXs, electronic mail, and fiber optics have been growing faster than the ability of organizations to exploit them. As a result, the demand for communications professionals has skyrocketed as more business, government, and educational institutions expand their private networks of information systems. Retention of talented personnel in such a market is of utmost importance but difficult to realize. One way for an organization to stay competitive in the field is to offer ongoing training for its communications personnel who will be installing and maintaining a profusion of new equipment and services. This chapter discusses the need for training and sources of training programs, which can attract more qualified candidates to the organization and reduce turnover among valuable personnel.

REASONS FOR TRAINING

The rapid and relentless advance of technology has fueled the transition of the economy from a products-based one to one that is increasingly information intensive and service oriented. As the economy changes, so do the professional requirements of the personnel who manage and support teleprocessing functions on which business progressively relies. Their training needs are further complicated by the trend toward integrating voice and data networks and by the challenge of managing today's multivendor environments, with different companies providing the local exchange connections, the interexchange portion, and the various equipment that constitutes the network. In addition, these new products and services have new terms, conditions, and prices. For example, long-distance telephone services are available from more than 50 common carriers. Each company has different names for the services they offer, and each service has different pricing schemes and contractual commitments. Without proper training, the staff responsible for billing reconciliation has no chance of performing the job accurately. Because it is not unusual for the communications bills to run in the tens of thousands of dollars per month, the potential for large losses through billing inaccuracies is very real without continual scrutiny by knowledgeable staff.

The communications function is increasing in complexity at a time when most organizations have come to recognize that a strategic deployment of information technology can have a substantial impact on their competitive advantage. To plan, engineer, install, operate, and manage that technology, however, requires training.

Finally, the efforts under way to effect worldwide communications standards that will greatly simplify the current situation are extremely complex and technical, with great political and economic ramifications. Communications personnel must be familiar with the standards and regulations that vendors are complying with as well as the degree of their compliance. The staff cannot keep up in this area without training.

TYPES OF COMMUNICATIONS PROFESSIONALS

Exhibit VII-1-1 is an organizational chart for a typical communications department of a large organization. Management usually includes the vice-president or director and managers of the engineering, operations, and planning and administration functions of the department. Generally, the communications department is part of the MIS or information resource division.

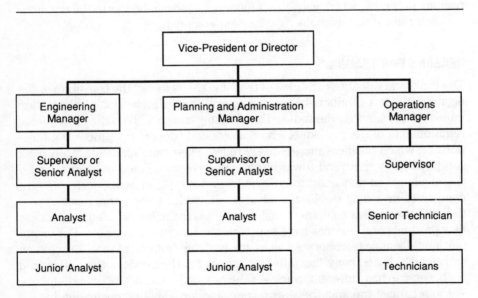

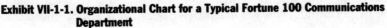

Exhibit VII-1-1. Organizational Chart for a Typical Fortune 100 Communications Department

Because organizations have given increased attention to communications applications, communications managers are included more often in business planning, and their continued training requirements are usually in business rather than technical subjects. Interpersonal skills are equally important because these managers must first sell senior management on projects and then negotiate contracts to carry out those projects. Responsibilities include managing the department budget, staff, and projects and supervising relations with in-house and outside contacts. Employees at this level usually have a college degree and more than 14 years of professional experience, including technical training from telephone companies or the military.

Supervisors or senior analysts are responsible for overseeing specific projects and selected daily operations as well as lower-level personnel and vendor and client contacts. About half hold college degrees; most of the others have some college credits. They usually have 10 years of professional experience, and most of their training has been on the job. The growth in the number of applications as well as the quantity and diversity of communications equipment and services requires that these employees receive continual vendor-specific training to handle the operations and diagnostics of networks and related components. Communication and interpersonal skills are important to the success of these employees as well.

Analysts or senior technicians have daily operational responsibilities and may also be responsible for specific projects or selected parts of specific projects. They usually have about five years of professional experience. Approximately one-third have college degrees, and most of the others have some college credits. Most of the experience of this group is gained through on-the-job training, but additional training is becoming increasingly important as more systems, equipment, and applications are installed. Vendor-specific courses are valuable to employees to facilitate their understanding of the operations, maintenance, and diagnostics procedures associated with the systems for which they are responsible.

Junior analysts or technicians are responsible for certain aspects of daily operations and specific parts of some projects. One-fourth of them have college degrees, and about one-third of the others have some college credits. Most of their training has been on the job, and they have two to three years of professional experience. Their training requirements are also usually vendor-specific. This group can focus on more specific aspects of the product or service, whereas senior levels require a broader perspective.

TYPES OF TRAINING

Training is basically focused on three areas: technical issues, business and management concerns, and interpersonal skills. Although it is desirable for all personnel to be trained in every area, time and cost constraints usually dictate that higher-level management focus on business and management concerns, operations staff (e.g., junior analysts and technicians) focus on technical issues, and supervisors and senior analysts balance their training between technical and business and management areas. As important as interpersonal skills are, training in this area is often neglected.

Technical

Engineering personnel are concerned with specifications and standards applicable to the equipment and services that constitute a system. In addition to a thorough understanding of communications engineering concepts, they must be trained regularly to keep up with new equipment, standards, and specifications. Because they are responsible for developing requests for proposals and authorization for expenditures (documents that describe various system requirements), they must also have technical writing skills. Once a project has received approval, the contracts must be awarded and the project schedule must be managed. Effective project management necessitates competence in the use of such productivity tools as spreadsheet computer-aided design (CAD), and project-management software.

Operations personnel deal daily with the technical management of communications systems. They must be competent in the operation and maintenance of the network and understand how to perform and analyze the necessary test and diagnostic routines applicable to each of its components. In addition, operations personnel must provide current and accurate documentation on inventories of maintenance spares, operational equipment, jack and cable assignments, circuit numbers, vendor maintenance and escalation procedures, client requirements, and pending work orders. Training on a routine basis is essential. It allows personnel to function effectively and to become familiar with new or modified services or equipment in a timely manner.

Training in interpersonal skills is often overlooked but is of real importance to operations personnel. These employees must interact with both vendors and clients, often in an environment of anxiety and uncertainty. The ability to communicate effectively can be of immense value in allaying concern and focusing attention on the issues at hand.

Business and Management

The communications department basically functions as a utility service company responsible for the efficient transmission of voice, data, and graphic information. The increase in the importance of these functions to the organization means that administrative, motivation, and financial skills are now required of personnel who tend to be technically oriented. Communications managers are involved in corporate planning and must have oral and written communication skills. Often, managers with technical orientation must be trained in the fundamentals of business management. Conversely, those with a business orientation must learn the technical concepts on which the networks and systems are based.

SOURCES OF TRAINING

The success of any training program depends on the selection of the most appropriate type to satisfy staff development needs. The primary sources of training are vendors, professional associations, university programs, and on-the-job training. Each is discussed in the following sections.

Vendors

Equipment and service vendors constitute one of the best sources of training opportunities. Inclusion of vendor-provided training stipulations at the time of contract negotiations can ensure that the staff members who install, operate, and maintain the new or modified equipment and services are qualified to do so. Larger vendors (e.g., AT&T, IBM Corp, and Northern Telecom Inc) have established separate divisions that are devoted solely to training. For example, AT&T publishes a quarterly catalog of the courses that it offers. The catalog describes the curriculum, instructor, duration, location, and cost of each course and whether the course is new or revised. Other companies have comparable services.

Another vendor category comprises professional education groups, including educational institutes, consulting companies, and publishing companies. A sampling of such vendors includes:

- American Institute Inc, Madison NJ.
- BCR Enterprises Inc, Hinsdale IL.
- Data-Tech Institute, Clifton NJ.
- The DMW Group, Ann Arbor MI.
- Lee's ABC of the Telephone, Geneva IL.
- Omnicom Inc, Vienna VA.
- Systems Technology Forum, Burke VA.

A third vendor category comprises companies that provide self-study courses. Audiocassettes, videotapes, and tutorial software for microcomputers have been available for some time, and interactive videodisk systems are becoming increasingly popular. With these systems, personnel can focus on courses matched to specific needs and progress at their own pace. The transportability of the training methods enhances their practicality and desirability.

Professional Associations

Several professional associations offer conferences, expositions, seminars, and short courses that address topics of current interest. The recognized need for continuing education motivated the founders of the International Communications Association (ICA) in 1948; since then, the ICA has been continually enhancing the educational services that it provides. Many of these organizations are international in scope but have local chapters. There are also regional associations that provide training. The training sources are particularly important because of the personal networking that they afford. In fact, the development of acquaintances who have similar professional responsibilities at other organizations can be of immense value. Sharing experiences at association meetings or by telephone can provide valuable insight into how vendors and their products function. Also of value are the formal educational programs. For example, the ICA sponsors an annual conference and exposition that provides an excellent opportunity to learn about numerous topics—vendors, services, and products. More than 90 technical sessions are presented, and more than 300 vendors display their products. Other international and regional groups sponsor similar conferences throughout the year.

In addition to its annual conference and exposition, the ICA offers continuing education through a series of seminars that are continually revised to respond to changes in the communications industry and member needs. Those courses, as well as the annual Winter Program and Summer Program, are available to the public. The Winter Program is a three-day course on specific management topics; the Summer Program is a one-week technical study on a specific area of network management and operation.

A sampling of professional associations includes:

- Canadian Business Telecommunications Alliance, Toronto, Canada.
- Chicago Industrial Communications Association, Chicago.
- Communications Managers Association, Bernardsville NJ.
- Energy Telecommunications & Electrical Association, Plano TX.
- Industrial Telecommunications User's Group, London, UK.
- International Communications Association, Dallas.
- Michigan-Ohio Telecommunications Association, Detroit.
- North Texas Telephone Association, Dallas.
- Southeastern Telecommunications Association, Richmond VA.
- South West Communications Association, Houston.
- TeleCommunications Association, West Covina CA.

University Programs

An increasing number of universities are responding to the growing need for communications educational programs, and many offer undergraduate or graduate degree programs in communications. Recognizing the time constraints faced by employed communications professionals, some universities now provide evening and weekend programs. The programs range from a management to a technical focus. Southern Methodist University has one of the oldest established communications degree programs; it is available through satellite transmission or videotaped classroom sessions. Some of the degree programs that cater more to employed professionals include:

- Christian Brothers University, Memphis.
- City University of New York, New York.
- Golden Gate University, San Francisco.
- New York University, New York.
- St. Mary's University, Minneapolis.
- Southern Methodist University, Dallas.
- State University of New York, Utica NY.
- University of Dallas, Dallas.
- University of Denver, Denver.
- University of San Francisco, San Francisco.

On-the-Job Training

Formal on-the-job training is often neglected. Certain personnel are experts in specific areas, including equipment, operations, diagnostics, and administration. In a formal on-the-job training program, personnel needs are measured against the expertise of current employees, and programs are established to match novices with experts. Because equipment, services, and applications are continually changing, this type of program must be reviewed regularly. A small investment of time to assess personnel needs, plan training, and motivate the staff to participate can provide big dividends in both employee technical knowledge and staff morale.

CONCLUSION

Communications is a rapidly evolving area because of radical changes caused by a combination of technological advances and the deregulation of the industry. There has never been a better time for communications professionals to enhance their careers. Because there are more opportunities than professionals to fill them, acquiring and retaining a qualified staff is critical. Training must be used to ensure technical competence and current awareness of alternatives and how to employ them profitably, as well as to satisfy personnel needs and maintain commitment. Although the organization must also provide attractive career opportunities and competitive compensation and benefits, offering a solid, ongoing training program can ensure that qualified candidates will seriously consider employment and, once hired, will display a serious commitment to the communications department and the organization as a whole.

VII-2
Screening Systems Analyst Candidates for a LAN Environment

ROBERT J. BOND

The success of a systems development project depends on the maintenance of a quality systems development staff. The loss of a key systems analyst during a project can severely damage the effectiveness of the final system. This is especially true when development is taking place using microcomputers in a LAN environment, because many applications modules draw on and depend on the development of parallel modules taking place in other departments. The loss of a specific analyst who is most aware of the interrelationship can be particularly damaging. The most common reasons for hiring a new systems analyst are staff turnover and expansion. Turnover of qualified systems analysts often occurs because:

- The systems analyst works with another department within the organization and subsequently transfers to that department.
- Another organization recruits the systems analyst by offering a higher salary and greater responsibility.
- With the increasing incidence of dual-career families, the relocation or transfer of a spouse can result in a corresponding resignation.

The systems development staff is usually expanded to accommodate increased work loads and project complexity. Whether recruiting an additional staff member or replacing a departing one, the manager needs an effective approach to the hiring process—from the authorization to hire to acceptance of the position offer. This chapter provides managers with guidelines for screening systems analyst candidates for a LAN environment. It also describes the basic qualifications for this position, outlines the areas to be addressed by the manager, and offers a detailed discussion of the type of education and experience preferred.

BASIC QUALIFICATIONS

An effective systems analyst (or a person who has the potential to be one) must be able to grasp, analyze, and resolve the numerous complex situations that arise in systems development. In a LAN environment, the analyst must also be specifically aware of the concepts of distributed data base organization, parallel and modularized system development and testing, and the techniques that enable the distributed stations to communicate with one another. This skill must be complemented by an ability to communicate, which includes gaining the trust of others and being sensitive to various user and staff member personalities. Systems analysts with these attributes can effectively elicit information from users who have difficulty recognizing and articulating system problems, clearly explain technological subjects to less knowledgeable or inexperienced users, and readily assume control of a potentially hostile situation without causing resentment.

PREPARING FOR THE SCREENING PROCESS

An accurate evaluation of the intelligence and communications ability of a systems analyst candidate can be made only during an interview. Before the interviewing begins, however, a certain amount of screening should be undertaken.

A manager can best prepare for the screening process by developing a profile of the desired systems analyst—that is, a list of required experiences and characteristics. The profile can initially be used to:

- Evaluate the qualifications of co-workers or associates.
- Write a classified advertisement for the position.
- Provide a job description to the organization's personnel department or a professional recruitment organization.

Later, applicants' qualifications can be compared with the profile to select for interviews those applicants with the most closely matched experiences and characteristics. The screening evaluation form in Exhibit VII-2-1 can be used for this comparison.

Although this profile improves screening process efficiency, it should not preclude the possibility that an individual who lacks some specific ability could be qualified to perform the assigned task. Rather, this list of prerequisites should identify only the general group of likely candidates.

The screening and selection of a systems analyst is more productive when the systems development manager scrutinizes two key areas:

- The organization's systems analysis past and future needs.
- The candidate's performance history and potential growth.

For example, if the manager knows that previous systems analysts have transferred to user departments or that the position will eventually assume

Factors	Rating	Score
Education		
Bachelor's degree	5	
Specified curriculum	3	
Related curriculum	2	
Master's degree	6	
Specified curriculum	4	
Related curriculum	3	
Subjective bonus factor for quality and reputation of institution and syllabus	—	
Professional Training		
Structured methodology	10	
Systems life cycle	10	
LAN implementation	20	
Industry Experience		
Reputable past employer	10	
Specified industry	10	
Related industry	5	
Application Experience		
Specified application	10	
Related application	5	
Use of major application package	10	
Technological Experience	*	
Data base		
Online		
Interactive		
Network		
Distributed processing		
Fourth-generation language		
Application generator		
CASE tool		
Prototyping		
Data modeling		
Microcomputer-to-mainframe integration tools		
Sponsorship		
Personally recommended by an industry professional whose judgment is respected	25	
Professionally represented by a competent placement firm	20	
	Total	

Note:

* The rating for technological experience should be based on the importance of the technology to the position requirements.

Exhibit VII-2-1. Sample Screening Evaluation Form for LAN Designers/Analysts

increased responsibilities within the MIS department, the candidate can be interviewed with future positions in mind.

CANDIDATE SOURCES

The screening process can have several iterations. The first screening usually begins with an evaluation of individuals within the MIS department and then other departments within the organization.

The manager must be sensitive to the difference between inviting individual employees to be considered for the systems analyst position versus the more formal process of posting the job, which promulgates the opening and allows any employee to apply for consideration.

Before posting the job, the manager must have a clearly defined set of qualifications and experience criteria to respond fairly to applicants from within the organization and avoid interpretations of unjustified rejection. The manager, particularly a recent arrival to the company, should thoroughly research and understand company policy and procedure regarding this topic; some organizations require job posting for a specific period before considering candidates from external sources.

User departments that participate in project evaluations and implementations are one source of internal candidates for two reasons. First, the department usually selects its project team representatives on the basis of analytical and communications skills—the two basic qualifications of a systems analyst. Second, a project team member works directly with systems analysts and is therefore familiar with their responsibilities. Many managers find that such cross-training improves the functioning of the entire MIS department. Prime sources of internal candidates include:

- Financial analysis.
- Operations analysis.
- Industrial engineering.
- Data communications.
- Strategic planning.
- Management training programs that feature rotating assignments.
- Other functions requiring strong analytical skills.

The screening process can be repeated if the organization must seek external candidates. When looking for external candidates, the manager should be guided by the position level. For example, a college or university is a source for entry-level systems analysts. Effective recruiting methods include developing a continuing relationship with a faculty member who can look for prospective systems analysts and creating an internship program. In addition, an employment agency is an external source for more experienced systems analysts. A competent placement professional who knows the kind of individual the organization is seeking can usually accurately judge a candidate's intelligence and communications ability and thus reduce the screening time for the systems development manager.

Another option increasingly available is the use of outside consultants as members of the development team. The same kind of professional screening criteria can be used for these individuals, with some additional considerations. The consultant option offers several advantages:

- A specialist with extensive experience in a particular applications area or package can be hired for a limited time, and that person's knowledge and empirical expertise can be used to an advantage.
- An individual who possesses sufficient systems analysis skills for a current project but has no long-term appeal as a career employee can be used for a limited time.
- Talented individuals who might not be attracted to a long-term position with the organization can often be persuaded with a sufficient, short-term stipend.
- If an error in judgment has been made, it is far less disruptive to dismiss an external consultant than an in-house employee.

There are two disadvantages in using consultants or contractors as systems analysts. First, permanent staff analysts sometimes form the opinion that because of their more intimate familiarity with existing systems, they are consigned to maintenance, troubleshooting, and training new users on the aging systems while outsiders obtain the more attractive new development assignments. This can be extremely damaging to employee morale and can aggravate chronic turnover problems.

Second, some permanent employees are naive to the differences between hourly consulting rates and salaried benefit packages. The manager, particularly if using consultants for the first time, should defuse the situation by explaining the differences beforehand rather than have staff members simply multiply an hourly rate by the 2,080 labor-hours in a year and go into shock.

TOPICS TO BE ADDRESSED

The screening process should address formal and professional education and experience in systems analysis, programming, and specific industries and applications. The following sections discuss the preferred requirements in these areas.

Education

The question raised most during the establishment of systems analyst candidate requirements is whether a minimum level of education should be set—and if so, what it should be. Some organizations require only a bachelor's degree, regardless of the discipline; others specify a degree in business administration, mathematics, computer science, or other related majors, often with an MBA as a preferred option. Insistence on a particular curriculum might be unnecessary; the emphasis should be on selecting individuals with strong analytical abilities, regardless of their specific course of undergraduate study.

Educational levels are generally determined by the organization's size and formality and by the function's position within the organizational structure. In evaluating the importance of education, the manager must remember that a prerequisite should not be so rigid that it eliminates qualified candidates who lack a formal degree.

Two types of education are considered appropriate for preparing an individual for systems analysis responsibilities in a LAN environment:

- Computer science or communications training.
- College business administration and systems analysis training.

Technical Training and Experience. In the older DP/MIS traditions, a systems analyst's first experience in information processing usually was as an entry-level programmer whose early training (at a vendor site or technical school) concentrated on one programming language for a specific computer. The next logical career steps were programmer/analyst and, eventually, systems analyst, often with project coordination responsibilities. For systems development in a LAN environment, however, it seems far more sensible to seek candidates from a more open-minded tradition, such as problem analysis, route selection, or solution trials. This background relies far less on the supposition of formal language training or use of brand-specific technology than it does on a conceptual understanding of microcomputers, the philosophy of problem segmentation and trial-and-error solution, and a willingness to repeat the countless iterations of system tests that allows the eventual solution to work itself out. In an oversimplification, it could be said that the older style of systems analysts took pride in trying to think of and provide for all possible system episodes before approaching the computer—the walkthrough before the run. In a LAN environment, on the other hand, the focus shifts to dealing with discrete problem modules that can be addressed as encountered, and any new problems produced by the prototype module are then addressed subsequently, until all the problems are worked out. It is the goal of the hiring manager to try to determine which of the screened candidates recognize the differences between these two philosophies, and select the kind who thrive in the distributed LAN environment.

Key elements in recognizing appropriate candidates include training and job experience. Points for the manager to look for include specific training on microcomputers and network concepts and products, use of software tools and languages appropriate to the environment, and prior experience in groups or teams similar in mission to the hiring group. These groups might include information centers, end-user computing support teams, office automation centers, and communications support areas.

Specific Industry and Applications Experience

The screening process must also address specific industry and applications experience. Ideally, the ability to perform systems analysis should be industry independent. For example, the capabilities needed to analyze and solve an inventory management problem for a wholesaler should be equally applicable to an inpatient admissions problem at a hospital. Often, the industry-specific capabilities that enhance an individual's value in that industry involve understanding the organization's business fundamentals and industry terminology. The manager should therefore only be concerned with how long the candidate will need to learn this information.

The hiring manager should also use the screening process to ascertain whether the candidate has successfully displayed analytic capabilities and whether the individual's background would make the new assignment a logical career progression.

SUMMARY

Managers should begin the screening process by evaluating and ranking the primary and secondary skills and characteristics of the systems analyst that the organization is seeking. This evaluation should determine the level of intelligence and communications ability required for the position and should provide a clear understanding of the organization's short- and long-term needs. It is important to emphasize that the systems analyst profile produced by this evaluation should be comprehensive but flexible enough to allow consideration of qualified candidates who do not exactly match the qualifications. For the screening process, the manager must measure the required characteristics against those desired.

VII-3
Managing the Organization's Participation in Industry Standards Development

JOHN L. WHEELER

Since the early 1960s, international standards bodies have been working on standards to promote compatibility among communications networks and information processing systems. One goal has been the promotion of distributed information processing by means of communications networks that connect remote locations. Since the mid-1970s, ongoing efforts have centered mainly on the development of the architecture and protocols for the concept known as Open Systems Interconnection (OSI). The architecture describes seven defined layers of services in each communicating open system, and the standard protocols provide effective communications on a peer-to-peer basis within each layer of two communicating open systems. When developed and implemented, OSI will provide the mechanism for multivendor hardware and software integration. Information processing systems from diverse vendors will be able to communicate. Vendors and users alike have known for some time that integrated communications networks and information processing systems are essential to the successful automation of business operations. The proprietary technologies of individual hardware and software vendors and communications service providers, however, have made the exchange of information in multivendor systems extremely difficult, if not impossible. The result has been many single-vendor systems, local islands of information processing, an inability to expand and extend services as businesses grow, and an inability to include suppliers and distributors within the system.

Successful development and implementation of the OSI architecture, service, and protocol standards will help overcome these constraints.

THE NEED TO PARTICIPATE

The product planning manager of Company A reads in a trade journal that a new International Standards Organization (ISO) standard for a network protocol is likely to be published later this year. The standard protocol will provide for worldwide, compatible exchange of routing information in packet-switched networks that are interconnected. The manager is concerned because it is unlikely that the large network the company is preparing to launch for an important customer will be compatible with the ISO standard.

The product planning manager checks with the software development department and discovers that the company has two people participating on the appropriate US committee working on the ISO project and that they are completely familiar with the draft standard's technical content. These two representatives have never been instructed regarding their own company's position on routing exchange protocols or its long-range business strategy for public and private packet-switched networks.

It is time for Company A to mobilize its program for participation in industry standards development activities. The firm should examine its business strategy and define its industry standards objectives to support that strategy. A manager must be assigned responsibility for overall direction and follow-up. Discipline must be established for all who participate in the outside standards meetings, and a process must be put in place that ensures operating and development units a voice in the decision on industry standards.

Participation in the development of domestic and international standards need not be a burden. If managed as an important development program, the participation can be a positive mechanism to assist in the achievement of business goals.

MAKING THE DECISION TO PARTICIPATE

The industry standards development process is similar to the legislative process. Instead of laws, the standards committee writes and approves technical standards documents. Like a legislature, the standards committee is made up of people representing constituents who assemble to discuss and develop output that meets the needs of those constituents. The standards commitee consists of subcommittees, task groups, editing groups, and formal votes. Considerable lobbying is done by those who submit written contributions and attend meetings to present their proposals. Much of the interaction of participants is informal, though the roll-call vote is what counts in approving the final output.

Categories of Participants

In the US, Committee X3 provides the means for developing domestic standards for information processing systems, and it manages domestic activity for international standards development in the same area. The grouping of voting members within X3 helps to identify the categories of participants in the development of standards. Four such categories are noted in the following sections.

Vendors of Hardware and Software. In X3, vendors are known as producers. They include manufacturers and marketers of data processing and office automation systems and of the components that are used in such systems.

Users of Hardware and Software. Users are included in Committee X3 in the group known as consumers. They include, for example, large industrial and service companies that are not in the producer category. Also included are government agencies and facilities and the user group organizations for systems supplied by the larger producers.

Trade Associations. If individual companies in the same area of business do not have the resources to participate separately, a trade association may be able to represent their interest in standards development. A number of trade associations are members of X3 or its technical committees. Some are identified as producers and some as consumers.

Professional Associations. These associations, or societies, comprise professionals with related backgrounds and objectives. In X3 and its technical committees, they are listed in the general interest group and include, for example, managers, engineers, scientists, secretaries, and production workers, with specific or general areas of interest. A number of professional associations participate in standards development. Those appointed as the representatives of these organizations will also have an opportunity, while participating in meetings, to look out for their own companies' interests.

Levels of Participation

The following levels of participation range from a simple and inexpensive involvement to a substantial commitment of resources and time. In a similar way, the levels extend from little influence to a significant influence over the standards developed.

Monitor. It is generally possible to appoint an observer to a committee or task group and to request that the observer be sent copies of meeting minutes and technical documents. In this way, it is possible to monitor progress in a particular area at minimal cost.

Education and Action. A step beyond monitoring is an active campaign within a company to distribute information about standards committee activity and to use it in developing strategy for product development and promotion. The frustration in this technique is the lack of opportunity to influence standards committee activity.

Association Membership. One way to influence the development process is to participate with other members of a trade or professional association in developing the positions and strategies of that association and in sending a delegate to the standards committee. This is generally an inexpensive process, but it assumes that association members can read a consensus on specific goals and that the goals will parallel those of the individual company.

Company Membership. Company membership in Committee X3 is the generally recommended way to participate in domestic standards activity if a corporation wants to achieve any degree of influence over the outcome of the standards development process. It sometimes requires payment of an annual secretariat fee and the commitment of a principal and one or more alternate members who will agree to attend meetings and to submit votes on behalf of the sponsor company.

Proactive Role and Specific Objectives. Obtaining company membership is only part of the necessary involvement if a company wants to achieve real influence. It is even more important that the company strategy for industry standards be developed and promoted. This is where the major resources are expended. Sending participants to standards meetings with clearly understood objectives is the best way to influence results. They should not be the individual's objectives but the company's objectives. It takes a lot of homework by many people in the company to send one instructed delegate to a meeting.

Motivation and Participation

Establishing the Business Strategy. Senior management must understand its participation in standards development, and the goals of this effort must relate to those of the overall business strategy. These goals might include, for example:

- Successful integration of its own products and services with the information processing and office automation systems acquired and used by its customers.
- Successful integration of the products and services it buys from other suppliers with the information processing and office automation systems acquired and used by its customers.
- Successful integration of its own information processing and office automation systems acquired and used to support its internal business functions.

It would be unwise to base a decision to participate on any of the following assumptions:

- Some of the engineering people are interested in this standards committee and think it would be a good source of information about what others are doing.
- Two of the people in product development have been going to these meetings for the last three years—They probably should accept assignments as committee officers because to refuse might be bad for the company's public image.

- If all those other companies are sending people to these meetings, there must be a good reason for it.
- It is a reasonable public service in the national interest for the company to pay the expenses of a member of the US delegation to an international standards meeting in another country.

In fact, none of these considerations justify involvement in standards development. There is only one reason a company should participate: to support, directly and substantially, the business strategy of the company.

Developing Goals for Participation. As noted, the levels of participation range from simple monitoring to taking a proactive role, nominating committee officers and editors, and submitting draft texts for one or more standards projects. The goals for participation determine the level of involvement. These goals may be general, for example, ensuring that none of the protocol standards under development is likely to upset the current internal information system implementation plan. On the other hand, they may be detailed and specific, such as promoting a particular operating system language as the recommended international standard. If senior management has decided that significant participation is necessary, it must agree on the goals for such participation and distribute internally the information necessary to implement plans to meet those goals.

Potential benefits that may result from participation include, for example:

- Influence over standards—A company representative may help determine the text of a new domestic or international standard or the amendment of an existing standard. This could be a significant advantage if the result is related to the firm's business strategy.
- Establishing a role and image as an industry leader—A company that aggressively supports industry standards programs is often perceived—by its customers, competitors, and the public—as a leader in the field.
- Acquiring new technology—The traditional role of standards publication is the formal documentation of specifications that have been used informally for some time. Thus, it has represented the recording of history. In contrast, today the work on new standards in information processing systems is making possible the implementation of more complex capabilities and is therefore leading development.
- Gathering market and technical intelligence—All participants assigned to standards committees should be instructed regarding the need to maintain security about proprietary information. However, even with this guarding of closely held information, it is possible to collect useful intelligence at standards meetings. The sum of intelligence is often made up of many small items added together. Participants should be instructed on gathering and reporting useful information.
- Marketing opportunities—Although it is difficult to quantify the marketing

results from participation in standards meetings, it must be remembered that such meetings result in many informal opportunities to meet with and get to know other participants. Discussions often touch on such subjects as experiences with a particular vendor's systems, potential user requirements, and methods of evaluating performance. These informal discussions may take place during coffee breaks, over meals, or while small editing task groups are meeting. Again, participants should be instructed to recognize the opportunities for making marketing contacts.

The Decision. The best way to define, discuss, and evaluate the issues and alternative responses to participation in industry standards development is to assign the task to one member of the central corporate staff. That person should be charged with reviewing the matter in detail with responsible managers in the departments concerned with the issues. These might include, depending on the business of the company, such functions as product planning, product development, information management (i.e., office automation, data processing, and communications), marketing, and customer support.

The proposed decision on participation will come out of this in-depth corporate staff review with broad participation by functional management. It must then be presented to senior management for final approval.

Management Commitment. The proposed decision on participation should include a statement concerning corporate business strategy and the related industry standards strategy for the company. If involvement is recommended, it must also contain a list of the goals of participation. If possible, it should also include a summary of the potential benefits and planned costs, in terms of human resources and anticipated delays in schedules.

It is essential that senior management become familiar with the strategic issues and participate fully in the final decision. Corporate commitment to the plan is required, because it focuses on an important aspect of business strategy and it will most likely involve more than one department, more than one geographic location, and more than one product line.

THE CORPORATE STANDARDS PROGRAM

The goals for participation in industry standards development programs may support the business of providing products and services to customers. They may promote better internal information management facilities, such as integrated office automation, data processing, and communications. In many companies, they will serve both purposes. As a result, discipline in managing this participation is most important. Representatives must be selected, instructed, and motivated with proper attention to the strategy and goals. They should not be allowed to act informally or to promote objectives different from the corporate objectives.

Establishing the Program and Organization

Establishing the corporate standards program and organization is a complex process that requires careful consideration.

Internal Standards and Industry Standards. Most companies have internal standards programs for the products and services they provide to customers. They also have standards for their internal information management facilities to ensure proper interworking of dispersed data centers and work sites.

The program established for participation in industry standards development must be closely associated with these internal standards programs. The manager of internal standards and the manager of industry standards should communicate regularly. In some cases, it may be appropriate for both functions to be assigned to the same manager. The internal standards should help determine positions to be promoted in industry standards, and the results of industry standards programs should help establish internal standards. Although this may seem obvious, it will sometimes not happen unless management makes a clear statement of policy.

Corporate Focus, Companywide Participation. The director of the industry standards participation program must be assigned by corporate management. The effort usually affects widely distributed locations, functions, and product lines. The participation of staff from many departments must be coordinated and directed so that efforts are focused on common corporate goals.

A special point must be made regarding multinational corporations participating in international industry standards development. Although a domestic corporation in the US will have the opportunity to influence positions promoted by the US delegation, a multinational corporation will generally be able to influence the goals and priorities of a number of national bodies participating in the same international development programs. Because this could represent a significant advantage, a multinational corporation should work to bring all parts of the corporation into a unified industry standards program and extend the goals of the program to include influencing the positions of a number of national bodies.

Communication Channels. Effective communication channels must be established among senior management, operating and development units, and those who serve as participants in industry standards programs. This is one of the primary responsibilities of the manager of the program. The manager must publish and regularly update documentation to cover:

- Industry committee structure, membership, scopes, schedules, and output.
- Corporate goals for participation, by committee, subcommittee, and task group.

- Status of efforts to meet those goals.
- Problem areas in which additional attention is necessary.

Senior management and operating and development unit management must respond to the publication of this documentation to make sure it continues to conform to business strategy and operating plans. Participants in committee meetings must be required to publish notices of anticipated industry standards meetings, with issues to be discussed and relevant objectives as well as reports of completed meetings, with results and projected impact on the company.

Decision Making. A formal process must be established to ensure that decisions are properly made. For a participating company, these decisions include:

- Whom the company should appoint as representative to a particular committee or task group.
- When the company should submit its written recommendation for the text of a new standard, and who will prepare and approve that text.
- The way the company representative should vote when a vote is called for at the next committee meeting.
- What the response should be when the written letter ballot is received from the parent committee by the company voting member.

It is obvious that, if there is little discipline, many of these decisions may be made on a local basis without consulting others in the company who have a decided stake in the standards being developed. The person assigned to attend the meetings, in fact, would be likely to act fairly independently if no formal process for making decisions is established. The manager of the corporate program is responsible for seeing that a formal process is followed and that participants act according to the rules and promote established corporate goals, not just the goals for their own department or functions.

The formal process for decision making requires the effective communication channels already discussed. Industry standards strategy and objectives, which sometimes must be changed to follow the developing business strategy of the company, must be reviewed and approved by senior management and by the operating and development units. This corporate strategy will determine when a draft text should be submitted and what its content should be. It also must be used to instruct participants on company voting positions. Each company participant has the responsibility to distribute information at regular intervals on proposed company actions, on issues to be discussed and voted on at meetings, and on formal letter ballot papers requiring responses before scheduled closing dates.

One method that has been used in some companies for the formal decision process is the default letter ballot. In this case, the participant, with approval of the corporate manager of the company program, establishes a list of all those who should be consulted and given an opportunity to offer opinions and recommendations. That list is used for distribution of a summary document containing the information about each decision with a proposed action that will be implemented unless a negative position is returned in writing. This means that, if there are no responses, the participant goes ahead with the proposed action. If one or more negative responses are received, then discussion is required, and a second default letter ballot may have to be distributed within the company.

Responses calling for changes in recommended action alert the corporate manager to potential issues for review and discussion at a higher level. It is the responsibility of the corporate manager, if a unanimous decision regarding action cannot be obtained and if the differences of opinion are strategically significant, to bring this fact to the attention of senior management for resolution.

Implementation of Decisions. Implementation is generally carried out by the participants who actually attend the industry standards committee meetings and by their immediate supervisors, who generally direct their priorities and work assignments. Two reports are essential in the follow-up process to ensure that approved action is taken. First, the participant must report in writing the results of each meeting soon after it occurs, giving a statement of impact and an indication of whether planned action was successfully carried out. Second, the corporate manager must publish a summary report, perhaps quarterly, showing the industry standards committees, nature of participation in each, status of action plans, unresolved problems, and noteworthy successes. This must be made available to senior management and to the operating and development units. It must also be distributed to all participants who represent the company on industry standards bodies, so that they will be able to work together. This will give participants a broader perspective and help them understand how they fit into the big picture on industry standards.

Making Resources Available. A major problem in large as well as small companies is committing financial and personnel resources to do the work of participation, including preparation, decision making, travel to meetings, reporting results, and influencing internal development programs. The reason for the problem is fairly basic: those who do the work (e.g., attending the meetings) are usually narrowly directed toward the work assignments and objectives of their own department or function. They may be concerned with one product line, one geographic location, or one function. The participants must usually come from operating and development units of the company because they will have daily experience with company products and capabilities and knowledge of current technology.

The assignment to work on an industry standards program carries a broad corporate responsibility but is taken on by a person who is usually paid to do a job with a narrow scope. The participant's immediate supervisor cannot be expected to fund this effort out of local department resources. Some corporate commitment must be made regarding reimbursement or budget approval for work of a corporate nature. There is no easy answer that fits all cases. Each company will have to work out a solution to this basic problem. If an extensive proactive plan for participation is to be carried out involving a number of technical areas and the submission of detailed proposed texts, the necessary commitment of resources will be substantial.

Finding, Training, and Developing People. The best participants in industry standards meetings are those with strong technical backgrounds who can understand complex systems, work well with other people, write clearly, follow instructions, and exercise leadership. In other words, there is a strong need for the same kind of people who are required in other functions of the company.

A company should probably look first in product development and product planning for candidates for participation in industry standards programs. A rotation plan is sometimes effective, in which a participant will join the effort part-time for a year or two and then go on to other assignments. This approach keeps the participant familiar with continuing company programs and able to return with added experience about standards. Other companies will benefit from a full-time assignment for a longer period of time.

Training and indoctrination of new people can be done by others participating in standards programs. The best in-depth development, however, can be done only through on-the-job training; all industry standards bodies are not alike.

Although many informal contacts are made at industry standards meetings, there is relatively little recruiting of people from one company to another. It would probably not be effective to plan to find and acquire company participants that way. The best company representatives are those who have been company employees for some time.

Running the Program

With the coordination and direction of the corporate manager assigned by senior management, several processes need to be carried out. These are summarized briefly in the following sections.

Establishing a Formal External Interface. One person must be designated to make commitments to the industry standards bodies on behalf of the company. This includes joining organizations, paying dues and fees, naming voting members, designating who will attend meetings with authority to represent the company, and responding to inquiries from the standards organizations.

Deciding Who Will Represent the Company. The corporate manager should maintain, in the data base on industry standards, identification of all company participants with their associated committee task groups and should oversee the decision to select new participants as required by the company objectives. A formal process of nomination, recommendation, and default letter ballot by a defined list of concerned managers would perform this function effectively.

Deciding Company Positions on Formal Votes. On the assumption that the company corporate manager has already established and published the strategy and objectives for each industry standards committee subject of interest, responsibility for carrying out the formal voting must rest with the appointed participant (voting member) of the committee. At the lower levels (e.g., in the review of first draft in the editing committee) the participant can probably use his or her judgment in developing the company response that supports the established objectives. However, in more formal written ballots, it is probably advisable to use the default letter ballot approach within the company to develop an agreement on the company vote and possible accompanying technical comments.

Data Base Management. The manager for industry standards participation should establish and maintain an automated data base of information related to the program. This should include both outside industry standards program information and internal company data, such as objectives, voting members of standards bodies, and schedules for internal meetings to discuss the development of written contributions. One of the main responsibilities of the corporate manager is the provision of accurate and updated information to all in the company who request it.

Using the Products of Office Automation. The need for prompt response and effective two-way communication about industry standards programs presents a problem for large companies with many operating and development units, particularly if there is wide geographic distribution of the people involved. Some of the functions that can help greatly in this activity are electronic mail, remote access computerized data base services, and integrated text processing systems.

Communicating Issues to Corporate Management. The company's industry standards manager should see that top management is informed about positive and negative aspects of the progress toward meeting the objectives for industry standards. These objectives, by definition, affect the business strategy of the company, and senior management should be alerted when action is needed to change the internal resources plan or to establish a different corporate policy in response to changing conditions in the industry standards community.

Establishing Company Memberships

Membership in domestic and international standards organizations enhances a company's public image and often proves a source of useful and timely information about standards development programs. When a company needs to work closely with others in promoting certain objectives for industry standards, it is often advantageous to join an association of those related companies. This is particularly true of users who often cannot justify commitment of large resources to promote industry standards objectives. The potential payback for a user is not as great as it might be for a vendor of information processing services, for example.

Establishing Individual Memberships

The decision to select a company representative is usually followed by a letter to the chairman or other officer of the committee or task group concerned. Individuals representing companies are usually members of domestic standards bodies. When delegates are sent to international meetings, they normally represent the US national body, rather than their companies. It usually is essential, however, that a person be a member of the appropriate domestic committee in order to be named a member of a US delegation.

Participating in Domestic Standards Activities

Participation in domestic standards activities requires time and dedication.

Attending Meetings. These meetings usually occur one to six times a year, depending on the work to be done. The length of each meeting might be one day or one week. They are usually more frequent and longer when active text preparation is under way. Some US committees have a rule that requires attendance to retain voting membership.

Submitting Written Votes. Voting members of standards bodies cast votes nearly every meeting in response to motions made by participants. However, when a draft standard reaches a significant milestone, such as being ready to move to the next higher organization for further processing, a written ballot is required. This may receive simple approval or approval with editorial comments. If a negative vote is submitted, a written comment explaining the reason must be submitted with the vote.

Submitting Written Working Drafts. A company voting member can submit a full text draft of a proposed standard if it has such material available. Standards are sometimes derived from this approach, but often an editing committee meets to assign sections and paragraphs to members to prepare as homework assignments. Many standards result from combinations of these two techniques.

Serving as Committee Officer. One way for a company to gain a stronger influence in a certain area of standards development is to have a voting member volunteer to be an officer. Although chairpersons, secretaries, and editing group convenors are required to be impartial in running the group activities, there is no doubt that their influence is felt, especially in the overall energy of the committee and in the speed with which results are obtained.

Influencing Results. The rules that apply to domestic standards development require that due process be provided. This means that time must be provided for the statement of all views and the promotion of positions of all voting members. Thus, all have an opportunity to influence the results of deliberation in the standards committee. The reality of participation in standards development, however, is not so evenly balanced. As in a legislative body, lobbying is permitted and practiced. There is often a great amount of behind-the-scenes negotiation among members. Informal discussions are held during coffee breaks, during meals, and in the small editing groups that are convened. In this way, positions are negotiated and agreements are made to work together on future drafting and voting.

Participating in International Standards Activities

Participation in international standards activities requires the same time and dedication as participation in domestic standards activities.

Developing US Positions. Sometimes there will be a special meeting or even a special committee to work on US participation in international standards programs, but in most cases, this work is done at the same meetings that conduct domestic standards business. It is usual for the domestic standards committee to be assigned responsibility for the US Technical Advisory Group (TAG) functions for international committees working in the same area. At these meetings, US votes are decided, draft contributions are reviewed, and delegates to international meetings are approved. A company participant can thus have influence in the international standards program without the expense of overseas travel, which could be involved with an international meeting.

Promoting US Positions. A company participant who wants to have greater influence may wish to attend an international meeting as a member of the US delegation. Approval of the appropriate US TAG must be obtained. The participant can then work directly with representatives from other countries on the development and review of texts for new international standards. Meeting frequency varies from approximately every six months to every two years.

Serving as Committee Officer. The same opportunities exist for international committees as for domestic. A company participant can volunteer, through the US TAG, to the chairperson or convenor of an international standards body, to serve as an officer of a lower-level group. Thus, a company participant might become the editor of an international standards project. In this role, there is no commitment to promoting the established US positions, because independence from national bias is expected. The opportunity for influence in overall progress and speed is significant.

Influencing Results. In international standards development, similar requirements for due process apply. The officers of these bodies take special care that all who wish to be heard have an opportunity. All written contributions must be reviewed and discussed. Again, there is a somewhat different reality, however, because lobbying also takes place in the international arena. There is much informal discussion to line up technical positions, national opinions, and voting support for motions to be put forward. International meetings often last one or two weeks, instead of the one or two days domestic meetings last. This means that participants have an opportunity for more extensive cooperation and exchange of views on issues.

ACTION PLAN

The following items are a concise action plan for managing an organization's involvement with standards:

- Make the decision—Decide what strategy and objectives should be agreed upon for the company. If the result calls for active participation, appoint a corporate program manager.
- Join ANSI—The American National Standards Institute is the overall coordinating organization for domestic standards development and for US participation in international standards activity. If the company is not already a member of ANSI, serious consideration should be given to joining. One direct benefit is the biweekly publication of announcements concerning domestic and international standards milestones, such as periods of public comment and deadlines for written letter ballots on new proposed standards.
- Join X3—Committee X3 has been accredited by ANSI as the US body for the development of standards in the information processing area. The secretariat of X3 is administered by the Computer and Business Equipment Manufacturers Association, which also sponsors US TAG activities for international standards programs in the same area.
- Select representatives carefully—Choose technically qualified people who can accept travel assignments and who will be able to take time from their other company responsibilities. If possible, be consistent, keeping their assignment unchanged for at least two years and giving them instruction about company objectives for their area of standards.
- Get someone on the international delegation—If the elected strategy is direct influence, nominate a company representative on the domestic program to be a member of the US delegation. Multinational companies may have an opportunity, in line with their strategy, to name someone on more than one national delegation.
- Submit written working drafts—One of the best ways to influence the technical content and wording of a new proposed international standard is

to develop drafts for review by the domestic committee and for submission as a US position through the TAG.

- Name someone as an ISO working group leader or project editor—The way to develop the greatest opportunity for influence is to have a company participant appointed by an international committee officer as a working group leader or project editor. Although the commitment of time and resources is significant, this method is probably the best way to promote the company objectives in international standards.

Section VIII
Network Management and Control

As the size, complexity, and number of applications of LANs continue to grow, network management and control become critical to the success of the organization. In today's business environment, this need for better control comes at a time when users' expectations of network performance and reliability are increasing, though senior management's tolerance for additional resource requests, both capital and labor, is decreasing. Therefore, management today is faced with the classic dilemma: provide more with less. This section of the *Handbook* focuses on the issues and technologies associated with solving this dilemma.

Although the primary focus of this section is on management of LANs, many of the solutions have more far-reaching implications, in particular, to network management. Chapter VIII-1, "Network Management: A Manager's Perspective," gives insight into this subject by defining a network management environment and what a network management system should do. An example is given of an ideal (although not yet implemented) network management system, and industry development areas for network management are highlighted. The chapter concludes with a management procedure for network management planning.

The discussion of network management from a manager's perspective continues in Chapter VIII-2, "LAN-WAN Management: Moving Toward the Integrated Solution." As the chapter title implies, the scope is expanded beyond LANs to address the issues of network management from a more comprehensive perspective. The fundamental issues are essentially the same as for a LAN environment, although some new issues surface as a result of the broadened scope.

In recent years, there has been considerable advancement in the area of OSI development, including open systems interconnection (OSI) systems management. Given the heavy emphasis on multivendor interconnection in LAN environments, standards-based management of LANs is likely to become critical. Chapter VIII-3, "OSI Systems Management Services and Protocols," discusses the basic structure and some of the intricacies of such a standards-based approach.

The OSI systems management standards alone, while indisputedly important, are not representative of the whole picture of standardization, or, for that matter, OSI standardization for network management. Chapter VIII-4, "Standard Management Systems to Integrate 1990s Networks," discusses such topics as standardization, implementer's agreements, and conformance, all of which are crucial steps on the road to commercialization of interoperable management systems. Particular attention is paid to the role of the Network Management Special Interest Group within the National Institute for Standards and Technology.

VIII-1
Network Management: A Manager's Perspective

CELIA A. JOSEPH • KURUDI H. MURALIDHAR

This chapter looks at network management from a technical manager's perspective and examines issues pertinent to a manager who is considering how to implement network management. These issues include: How does network management fit into an organizational environment, what products are available now, and where is network management going in the future?

In this chapter, the term *network management* is limited to the management of data communications resources that use standard interfaces—that is, to open systems. Vendor proprietary network management schemes are not considered. Although network management functions apply to all networks, some functions should be tailored to take the special needs of the applications running on the network into account. This chapter is oriented to the needs of LANs and uses the Manufacturing Automation Protocol (MAP) and Technical Office Protocol (TOP) version 3.0 network management specifications.

What is network management and why is it important? Network management can be defined as the coordination, monitoring, and control of the distributed resources in a network. Network management is important because it can provide a wide range of information about a network and a powerful set of tools for running it. The types of information that network management can provide include network configuration and status, network performance and trends, and current and historical data on network operations. Using network management tools, a network administrator can modify the network configuration, change its status, adjust parameters to tune its performance, and determine the location of faults and the best way to correct them. As organizations rely more heavily on networks and networks become increasingly complex, management information and tools become critical to the organization's operation.

BACKGROUND

As just defined, network management is the coordination, monitoring, and control of the resources that allow communications to take place over a LAN.

The term *resources* usually refers to network components, such as workstations and file servers, although it may also refer to the elements within a component, such as protocol layers or any configurable parameters that the component may have.

More specifically, network management involves ensuring the correct operation of the network, monitoring the use of network resources, maintaining network components in working order, planning for changes to the network, and producing a variety of information on network operations, such as periodic or ad hoc reports.

The Network Management Environment

Network management is frequently viewed as only a technical problem. However, the ultimate responsibility for management resides with people, not machines. Many people within an organization are often involved with network management, including users of the network, who may need access to current LAN status information, managers throughout the organization, who may be concerned about the effect the LAN's performance may have on the performance of the parts of the organization they are responsible for, and the actual network administrator in charge of the daily operation of the LAN. Thus, the integrated management environment within which network management resides is a combination of human, social, organizational, and technological resources.

Exhibit VIII-1-1 shows the main components of this integrated management environment. These include the users of the network, the network and systems resources, the organization's management, and network management. The character of each of these components is as follows:

- Users of the network are those interested in the operation and use of the network.
- Network and system resources consist of end systems (e.g., workstations, controllers, file servers), relay systems (e.g., bridges, routers, and gateways), and network components—in other words, the collection of objects that require managing.
- The organization's management directly affects network management by setting policies for the organization that have an impact on network structure and activities—Management, for example, would decide whether to implement open systems interconnection (OSI) or whether to adopt a centralized or distributed management structure.
- Network management consists of a combination of human, software, and hardware elements—The human element consists of the network administrators who make decisions on network management. The software and hardware elements are the automated network management tools that provide management capabilities for the network.

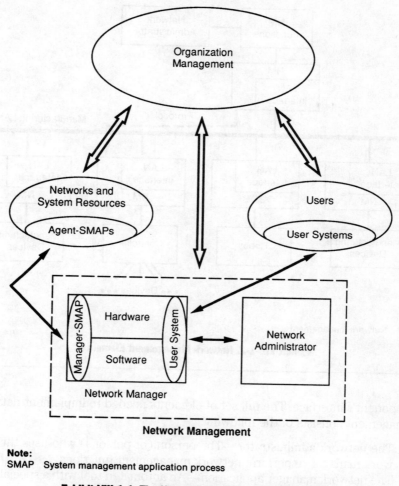

Note:
SMAP   System management application process

Exhibit VIII-1-1. The Network Management Environment

Network Management Elements

Exhibit VIII-1-2 shows an example of a manufacturing LAN with network management elements. Each device has a LAN component that permits it to attach to the LAN. In this example, all the LAN components use the standard, layered interface protocols specified by MAP and TOP. Some devices may share a LAN component. As defined by the standards groups, network management fits into and around the layered protocols in the LAN interfaces. However, more is needed to put network management in place than an element in a LAN

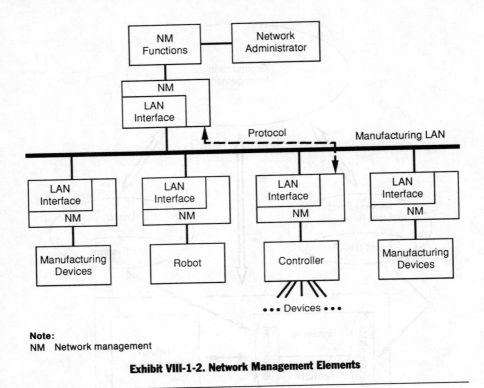

Note:
NM   Network management

Exhibit VIII-1-2. Network Management Elements

component's interface. The full set of elements needed to implement network management consists of the following:

- The network administrator—The person (or persons) who uses the network manager to perform network management functions.
- The network manager application—An automated tool with a special user system that the network administrator uses to monitor and control LAN activities. The LAN may have more than one network manager application.
- The agent-system management application process (agent-SMAP) and the manager-system management application process (manager-SMAP)— Agent-SMAP is a program that resides in each LAN component, manages the resources within the LAN component, and communicates with the manager-SMAP. The manager-SMAP is an analogous program that resides in the network manager applications LAN component.
- The network management protocol—A set of rules that defines how a manager-SMAP communicates with agent-SMAPs. This protocol is sometimes called the manager-agent protocol.
- The management information base—The data base of information that each network device maintains on its own resources. In Exhibit VIII-1-2,

the management information base is included in the network management element of each device. In addition, the network manager maintains an information base for the domain for which it is responsible, which is included in the box marked network management functions.

- The management domain—The set of all agent-SMAPs that report to the same manager-SMAP, or in other words, the set of devices that a network manager application manages. If the LAN has a single network manager application, all devices will be in that manager's domain. However, a LAN may have multiple manager applications, in which case a domain must be defined for each manager and an agent may be in more than one manager's domain.

Network Management Functions

The exact functions that network management should provide are still being defined by the standards groups. So far, they have agreed on a set of basic functions that include configuration and name management, fault management, performance management, accounting management, and security management.

Configuration and name management are mechanisms to determine and control the characteristics and state of a LAN and to associate names with managed resources. Some of the services that configurations management provides include setting LAN parameters, initializing and terminating LAN resources, collecting data on LAN status for reports, and changing LAN configuration. Some of the services that name management provides include naming the resources to be managed and managing name assignments.

Fault management includes the mechanisms to detect, isolate, and recover from or bypass faults in the LAN. The way fault management is performed depends on the LAN's application. For example, in some manufacturing applications, LAN downtime is intolerable. In these cases, fault management should be proactive, forecasting probable faults and emphasizing preventive maintenance. With LANs in which downtime is not so catastrophic, fault management could be reactive, acting only in response to faults as they occur and emphasizing accurate diagnosis and rapid repair.

Performance management includes mechanisms to monitor and tune the LAN's performance as defined by user-set criteria. Some environments may need special performance metrics. The factory environment, for example, is typically hostile to communications equipment because it is noisy, dirty, and has wide variations in temperature. Thus, instead, of classic performance metrics that assume error-free operations, these LANs should use preformability metrics that provide a means of measuring performance and reliability in a unified manner.

Accounting management includes mechanisms for controlling and monitoring charges for the use of communications resources. Security management includes mechanisms for ensuring that network management operates properly and for protecting LAN resources. Although accounting management and security management mechanisms have been defined, they have not yet been included in the MAP/TOP specifications and are not discussed further in this chapter.

AN EXAMPLE OF A NETWORK MANAGER

The standards committees have defined the basic functions that network management should provide, but they have not defined how these functions should be applied to the management of a particular type of network or network application. The standards provide a set of basic services, but they do not specify how to implement or use those services.

The example of a network manager application that follows is intended to suggest how these services could be used. The application is ideal in that some of the services described are not yet implementable.

The example system supports the three network management functions specified in MAP/TOP 3.0: configuration management, fault management, and performance management. The system provides the following configuration management services:

- Defining the LAN topology—The system provides tools to assist in setting up the network's design and in initially configuring the LAN components. For each type of component, the system suggests how the component's configurable parameters should be set.
- Displaying the LAN topology—Given the initial LAN design, the system generates a display that shows the location and the operational status of each device in the LAN.
- Reading current values—The system lets the network administrator request the current value of any communications resource within the LAN components. For example, it might tell the administrator the number of messages that have been sent or received by a specific network device.
- Setting values—The system lets the network administrator modify the value of the configurable parameters in the LAN components. The administrator could, for example, change the status of a device from active to inactive, or change the retransmission parameters of the transport layer.
- Adding or deleting devices—The system supports dynamic changes to the LAN's topology, permitting components to be addressed and removed.

The system provides the following fault management services:

- Detecting and giving notices of faults—The system gives the network administrator prompt notice that a fault has occurred somewhere in the LAN. It has an option that allows it to change from reactive to proactive fault management. In proactive mode, the system alerts the administrator of its fault predictions.

- Isolating faults—The system helps the network administrator determine where a fault has occurred in the LAN topology, which device failed, and which portion of the device failed. It does this in one of two modes: an automated mode in which the system isolates the fault without intervention from the network administrator, or an assistant mode in which the system provides suggestions to guide the network administrator in locating the fault.
- Correcting or bypassing faults—In automatic mode, the system corrects the fault or implements a bypass without intervention from the network administrator. In assistant mode, the system gives advice on how to correct or bypass the fault, but the network administrator makes the changes.

The system provides the following performance management services:

- Collecting statistics—The system maintains a set of current and historical statistics on each device in the network.
- Evaluating performance—The system uses the statistics to calculate performance metrics and evaluates these metrics against predefined user criteria for performance.
- Reporting—The system generates text reports and graphic displays of the statistics and performance evaluation results. These reports can be periodic or on demand.
- Tuning performance—The system can tune the network in either of two modes: automatic or assistant. In automatic mode, the system dynamically monitors performance levels and adjusts parameters when they move out of range. In assistant mode, the system provides advice to the network administrator on how to tune performance, but the network administrator makes any changes manually.

THE CURRENT STATUS OF LAN NETWORK MANAGEMENT

The MAP/TOP User's Group has led the OSI community in defining the mechanisms needed to provide the functions in the example network management just described. The MAP/TOP 3.0 specification includes an application layer network manager, a set of basic network management services, and a network management protocol. Other standards organizations, most notably the International Standards Organization (ISO), are progressing slowly in fully defining all of the functions of network management.

Products currently available for network management include cable monitors, modem monitors, protocol monitors and analyzers, and configuration support tools:

- Cable monitors monitor the status of low-level devices on the cable plant, such as amplifiers, and power supplies—They may also monitor the radio frequency levels on cables.
- Modem monitors keep track of the status of the modems used in the LAN.

- Protocol monitors and analyzers passively collect information on the protocol transactions of one or more network layers—They may calculate statistics, such as the average level of specific types of network traffic, and generate reports. Analyzers may also perform such additional functions as identifying patterns in network traffic or capturing a specific type of traffic for closer examination.
- Configuration support tools provide offline assistance in configuring the operating characteristics of LAN devices—Some of these products can also download software to LAN devices.

Several companies are developing network management systems for open systems that are oriented toward managing telecommunications networks. These include AT&T's unified network management architecture (UNMA), IBM's NetView, and Codex's 9800 network management system.

AT&T's unified network management architecture is a virtual network management system that provides network management information at a customer site by linking the local site to a remote network control center through a protocol based on an OSI profile. Only a few vendors supply products conforming to this architecture. IBM's NetView is an integrated network management product. NetView's main component is its command facility, which includes data collection, monitoring, and control functions. A number of vendors supply NetView-based products. The Codex 9800 network management system is based on the evolving OSI standards for network management and is currently limited to managing Codex products only.

Emerging Capabilities

Network management capabilities that should be appearing in products soon include expanded network management functions, full ISO protocol support, nonstandard interface support, and multiple network manager support.

Expanded Network Management Functions. Current LAN network management products focus on managing the lower protocol layers. To expand network management functions to cover all protocol layers, network management must be implemented in two areas: the network devices being managed and the network manager application. The network devices that implement MAP/TOP version 3.0 include network management functions. For network management applications, forthcoming systems should provide tools that interact dynamically with the LAN to manage its components. These tools provide flexible network management functions that can take the special needs of a LAN application into account. The MAP Configuration system (MAPCon) is an example of what to expect in this area. MAPCon is an expert system for configuration management that can statistically configure LANs in an offline mode. MAPCon's next versions will permit dynamic interaction with the LAN.

Protocol Suites. Network management products should support all the ISO protocols. These may be tailored to a specific platform (e.g., MAP or TOP).

Nonstandard Interfaces. Not all LAN interfaces use standard protocols. The devices using these interfaces, however, must be managed. The MAP/TOP committees have acknowledged this problem, although they have not yet solved it. As a result, creative vendor solutions may drive the standards efforts in this area.

Multiple Managers. Organizations with a distributed management structure or geographically separated LANs may wish to use more than one network manager. The standards committees will be addressing this issue in the future.

THE OUTLOOK FOR LAN NETWORK MANAGEMENT

The work of standards organizations on network management standards is progressing slowly. The International Standards Organization will probably not complete work in this area until the mid-1990s. The MAP/TOP Users' Group has taken the lead in defining some facilities sooner and may spur the standards organizations to faster progress.

Once the standards have been defined, building network management systems will still be a difficult job. The network management systems will require technologies from several areas, including artificial intelligence. Some of the applicable technologies are discrete event modeling, statistical pattern recognition, sensor fusion, control theory, distributed artificial intelligence, diagnostic reasoning, and game theory. The relation of each of these technologies to network management is as follows:

- Discrete event modeling permits detailed dynamic experiments with complex systems that can help answer what-if questions—Stochastic activity networks, for example, are particularly useful for modeling networks.
- Statistical pattern recognition permits the monitoring of the quality of processes and products and makes it possible to correct problems before the system drifts out of acceptable bounds.
- Sensor fusion synthesizes the output of several sensors to derive parameters that are not available from a single sensor.
- Control theory includes a variety of techniques for distributed control.
- Distributed artificial intelligence includes techniques for distributed problem solving.
- Diagnostic reasoning includes techniques for determining problem causes and solutions.
- Game theory includes techniques for reaching optimal solutions for games with multiple players, which may be particularly useful for multiple manager systems.

Some of the areas of network management to which these technologies are relevant are configuration management, performance management, and fault management. Applications of configuration management include helping configure a wide range of LAN devices, dynamically adding and deleting devices to and from the LAN, and dynamically setting or modifying LAN device characteristics. As mentioned, one example of an existing expert system for configuration management is the MAP Configuration system. Other applicable technologies include discrete event modeling, control theory, and distributed artificial intelligence.

Performance management applications include dynamically evaluating the LAN's performance and identifying problem areas, suggesting key parameters to watch for evaluating performance, suggesting parameter ranges when changes are needed, and dynamically tuning the LAN's performance. Applicable technologies include discrete event modeling, statistical pattern recognition, sensor fusion, control theory, and game theory.

Fault management applications include detecting and isolating a specific type of fault and suggesting corrections or detours for specific types of faults. Fault management systems should learn from experience how to respond to increasingly complex faults. Applicable technologies include diagnostic reasoning, distributed artificial intelligence, discrete event modeling, statistical pattern recognition, and sensor fusion.

SUMMARY

Network management can provide a wide range of services. Determining which are best for a particular organization and LAN application, however, requires careful consideration of many organizational and technical issues. Among the organizational issues to consider when planning network management services are the following:

- Training—Who in the organization needs training in network management? What types of training should these people receive? What types of training should network administrators receive?
- Organizational commitment to OSI—How committed is the organization to the concept of open systems? How many devices with nonstandard interfaces will have to be managed? What is the schedule, if any, for phasing out these devices?
- Budget priorities—What are the organization's investment goals? Is the emphasis on the long-range or the short-range goals? Network management and open systems are relatively high short-term expenses with long-term payoffs.
- Management information needs—Who will be permitted access to network management information? What types of information are needed? In what form? How often?

- Security—What level of security should be used to protect network management information and facilities?
- Management architecture—How should the network management structure relate to the organization's management structure? Is a centralized or distributed structure more appropriate?
- Management mode—Should the network manager work in a proactive or reactive mode?

Among the technical issues to consider when planning network management services are the following:

- Network management architecture—Will the network management architecture be centralized or distributed? If multiple managers are needed, is the organization willing to do research on how to define the functions that have not yet been addressed by the standards groups?
- Missing pieces—Two key areas have not yet been addressed by the standards groups: how to deal with multiple managers and how to manage devices with nonstandard interfaces.
- Application characteristics—What characteristics of the organization's LAN application have special network management requirements? LANs with real-time traffic, for example, need performance maintained within strict limits.
- Expert systems—Which expert system tools are applicable to the organization's network management requirements? How critical are these requirements? Should the organization consider pushing technology development in these areas by funding research or conducting its own research?

VIII-2
LAN-WAN Management: Moving Toward the Integrated Solution

NATHAN J. MULLER

Data communications professionals know that proper management of computer and communications resources can produce an efficient and economical organizational network. The network, in turn, is the key to improved customer service, increased market share, and success in new business opportunities. The network must be managed both effectively, with technical knowledge and business acumen, and continuously—something that, given the diversity of network equipment and services, is more easily said than done.

NETWORK COMPLEXITY

In addition to private branch exchanges (PBXs) and mainframes, the typical network may include hundreds of microcomputers tied together through LANs and WANs. In addition, users have an insatiable appetite for accessing more and more network resources, which is why many networks include gateways to satellite and microwave systems, as well as to packet-switched services like Tymnet and Telenet. Links to cross-connect systems provide access to the numerous services offered through the public network. And because of different electrical and transmission standards, communication to international locations requires specialized interfaces.

MANAGEMENT ALTERNATIVES

Vast networks must operate smoothly, with a minimum of downtime. While some corporations depend on computer vendors and carriers to find and correct problems on their networks, others use third-party service firms. Some of these firms tout their ability to tap into corporate networks to diagnose and isolate problems. Other firms specialize in dispatching local technicians to customer locations with portable test equipment and spare parts.

Many users prefer to retain total control over their network resources.

These organizations use internal resources to minimize their dependence on third parties. Hiring, training, and keeping a private cadre of technicians to fix problems on the network, however, is prohibitively expensive for most companies.

Vendors are therefore emphasizing their products' management capabilities, which, with regard to wide area networking, are becoming essential for leased line modems, data service units and channel service units and multiplexers, and packet assembler/disassemblers and packet switches. The management capabilities of LAN engines—the servers—can ensure optimal LAN performance. Bridges, routers, and gateways have become instrumental in partitioning large networks into more manageable subnetworks and providing the means to interconnect remote LANs. These devices, too, have sophisticated management capabilities.

With network management systems, technicians can remotely diagnose and correct problems associated with each type of device. Through bit-error rate testing, the likelihood of problems occurring can be predicted. Traffic may then be diverted from failing lines or equipment with little or no inconvenience to users.

Although there are now many diagnostic and control systems available for specific types of devices, most of them cannot be integrated at a central point of control. It is not possible, for the most part, to build networks with hardware from different vendors and manage it as if it were a coherent whole. This includes linking LANs through WANs, which has introduced a new level of complexity that many users are not yet prepared or equipped to handle. Different management systems are required even among the various product lines of the same manufacturer, and these may or may not be integrated through a higher-level management system. Network management has, consequently, become more complicated, not simpler.

NETWORK MANAGEMENT DEFINED

To the MIS manager, network management means monitoring the mainframe for proper operation and spotting problems with front-end processors and associated applications software.

To a LAN manager, network management means configuring ports on a file server or data switch to control access to various distributed data bases, bridges, gateways, and other shared resources (e.g., high-speed printers and disk storage). The data communications manager is preoccupied with monitoring the quality of leased lines to ensure data integrity and maximum network availability. This includes restoring malfunctioning equipment or bypassing failing lines—before problems get out of hand and degrade the performance of the entire network.

The telecommunications manager thinks in terms of capacity planning and monitoring use to ensure that the PBX has enough trunks to handle peak hour traffic without frustrating too many users, but not so many as to waste the organization's money on underused facilities.

None of these management approaches meets the needs of the overall organization. This is because the management system for each type of network component requires its own hardware and software, as well as specialized technicians who can interpret the alarms and reports before invoking the appropriate diagnostics and restoral actions.

This does not mean that network management systems serving the different organizational needs have nothing in common. In fact, there is agreement that network management systems will all perform the following tasks:

- Fault detection and isolation.
- Maintenance tracking.
- Performance measurement.
- Configuration management.
- Applications management.
- Security.
- Inventory and accounting.

Fault Detection

With fault detection and isolation capabilities, users can identify whether problems are caused by line or equipment failures, or by both. A top-of-the-line network management system can detect problems by continuously monitoring line performance and automatically conducting diagnostic tests on the multitude of variables that impair transmission. A summary of network management services is shown in Exhibit VIII-2-1. In the case of WANs that rely on analog leased lines, the network management system must be able to perform and report the results of the full repertoire of voice frequency impairment measurements. Some systems even prompt the operator to answer a series of questions before suggesting which diagnostic routines to perform.

A network management system can be used to determine end-to-end and outbound error rates as well as overall circuit quality. Through the use of various loopbacks and tests, faults can be isolated to a particular line, modem, and terminal device.

Diagnostic self-tests on each hardware component on the network can be invoked from the operator console. In addition, some management systems can generate alarms to report a variety of equipment malfunctions originating from any location on the network.

A management system can tell, for example, when modems have recovered power so they can be put back into service. Invalid configurations and front-panel tampering on various kinds of equipment at remote locations can be detected. Out-of-control terminals can be put out of operation to prevent throughput bottlenecks. A network management system controls access to shared modems.

Voice frequency impairment measurements on analog leased lines include:
- Overall signal quality.
- Voice frequency receive and transmit levels.
- Loss of data carrier detect.
- Dropouts.
- Nonlinear distortion.
- Gain, impulse, and phase hits.
- Frequency offset.
- Phase jitter.

Alarms to report the loss of any of the following conditions:
- Modem or terminal power.
- Transmit or receive data.
- Transmit or receive clock.
- Data terminal ready.
- Request to send.
- Receive carrier.

Enhanced network control by detection of:
- Power recovery.
- Streaming terminals.
- Corrupt configurations.
- Front-panel tampering.

Capacity to perform the following tests:
- End-to-end error rate.
- Polling.
- Outbound error rate.
- Circuit quality.
- Loopback search.

Capacity to invoke diagnostic self-tests on remote devices.

Exhibit VIII-2-1. Summary of Diagnostic and Control Capabilities

---

The results of diagnostic routines and performance measurements are reported on a terminal or printer. Color displays are available to make it easier for the console operator to spot a problem and, through the use of multicolor alarm indicators, instantly obtain a reading on its severity. Red, for example, typically indicates a failure. Green may indicate normal operation, and yellow may be used to indicate a deteriorating condition. Low-end management systems typically use IBM or IBM-compatible microcomputers for this purpose, whereas high-end management systems may use sophisticated workstations.

LAN devices such as bridges also have fault detection capabilities. In addition to graphically representing the network topology at a workstation, bridges collect network performance statistics, receive alerts from other bridges and links, and allow the operator to disable faulty network elements remotely. Such management systems also make it possible for network managers to control access, set priorities for passing data over the network, and segment the network for maintenance and expansion purposes.

There are advantages to integrating the bridge into the multiplexer in wide-area networking environments. The multiplexer's existing management system can monitor and collect error and use statistics from the bridge, thereby simplifying overall network management. This arrangement also eliminates unnecessary startup costs because a separate bridge management software package typically sells for $6,000 to $10,000.

Maintenance Tracking

Maintenance tracking is related to fault detection and isolation. This is accomplished through a data base that accumulates trouble ticket information. A trouble ticket notes the date and time a problem occurred, the specific devices and facilities involved, and the vendor from which the device has been purchased or leased. It includes the name of the operator who responded to the alarm and any short-term actions taken to resolve the problem.

This kind of data base can be used for long-term planning and decision support. The network manager can call up reports on all outstanding trouble tickets, such as those involving particular segments of the network, those recorded or resolved within a given period, those involving a specific type of device or vendor, or those that have not been resolved within a specific time frame. With this information, a network manager can develop a better understanding of the reliability of a given operator, the performance record of various network components, the timeliness of on-site vendor maintenance and repair services, and the propensity of certain types of equipment and segments of the network to fail.

Performance Measurement

Another function of a network management system is performance measurement, which has two aspects: response time and network availability. Response time refers to how long computer users must wait for the network to deliver requested information from the host. The network management system displays and records response time information and generates response time statistics for a particular terminal, line, network segment, or the network as a whole.

This information can be reported in real time or can be called up as needed for a specified time frame. The systems can display very elaborate network schematics using specific colors to indicate various levels of response time. This information can be used to track down the cause of the delay. When an application overruns its allotted response time, the manager can decide whether to reallocate terminals, place more restrictions on access, or install faster equipment.

Network availability is a measure of actual network uptime, either as a whole or by segments. Such information may be compiled into statistical reports that summarize such measures as total hours available over time, average hours available within a specified time, and mean time between failure.

With long-term response time and availability statistics compiled and formatted by the network management system, managers can have objective tools at their disposal with which to establish current trends in network use, predict future trends, and plan the assignment of resources for specific present and future locations and applications.

Configuration Management

Network management systems also provide the means to configure lines at remote locations. If a WAN link becomes too noisy to handle data reliably, for example, the system automatically reroutes traffic to another line or sends it through the public network. When the quality of the failed line improves, the system reinstates the original configuration. Some integrated network management systems—those that unify the host (LAN) and carrier (WAN) environments under a single management umbrella—are even capable of rerouting data while leaving voice traffic where it is.

An integrated network management system permits the assignment of different priorities to voice and data traffic. This capability is very important on networks that serve multiple business entities and on statewide networks that serve multiple government agencies.

On a statewide network, for example, state police have critical requirements 24 hours a day, seven days a week, whereas motor vehicle branch offices use the network to conduct relatively routine administrative business only 8 hours a day, five days a week. The response time objectives of each agency are different, as would be their requirements for restoration in case of an outage. On the high-capacity network, there can be two levels of service for data and another for voice. Critical data has the highest priority in terms of response time and error thresholds and takes precedence over other classes of traffic when it comes to restoration. Because routine data is able to tolerate a longer response time and higher error rate, the point at which restoration is implemented can be prolonged. Voice is more tolerant than data of errors and delay, so restoration may not be necessary at all. Assigning priorities to traffic and rerouting only when necessary ensures maximum channel fills, improving the efficiency of the entire network and lowering its cost of operation.

In environments that combine LANs and WANs, routers are very efficient at bypassing link failures and congested nodes, which is critical for applications that cannot tolerate unnecessary delays. Bypassing is facilitated by the ability of routers to share information with each other through the OSI network layer. Bridges cannot do this because they do not have access to the network level through a routing protocol. Thus, when one bridge gets overloaded, the others never know about it.

If there is more than one path to a particular node, the router selects the most economical path. If the packet is too large for the destination node to accept, the router breaks it down into a manageable frame size. This capability is especially important in wide area networking, where telephone lines provide the link between LANs. With smaller packets, there is less chance that the data will be corrupted by noise on the line. Even if that occurs and a retransmission is necessary, having smaller packets results in less information delay.

There are two types of routing: static and dynamic. In static routing, the network manager configures the routing table, and once set, the paths on the network do not change. This may be acceptable for a LAN confined to a small geographic area, but not for wide area networking. Although a static router recognizes that a link has gone down and issues an alarm, it does not automatically reconfigure the routing table to reroute traffic. A dynamic router, on the other hand, reconfigures the routing table automatically and recalculates the lowest cost path. Some routers even rebalance the traffic load.

Because routers are protocol-specific, more than one may be needed to support all of an organization's networking needs. Some multiprotocol routers have recently become available; they are capable of routing several protocols simultaneously, thus approaching the level of gateways in terms of function.

Configuration management applies not only to the links of a network but to equipment as well. In the WAN environment, bridges may be enabled or disabled. The features and transmission speeds of software-controlled modems may be changed. If a nodal multiplexer fails, the management system can call its redundant components into action or invoke an alternate configuration. When nodes are added to the network, the management system can determine the best routing plan for the traffic it will handle.

Bridges have similar capabilities in the LAN environment. They support multiple bridging between the same two networks, providing the capacity required for high-volume traffic and the processing power to implement redundant, reliable configurations. Initial and continuous operations, as well as reconfigurations, are often automatic. For example, bridges that use the spanning tree protocol (part of the Institute of Electrical and Electronics Engineers's 802.1 standard) can facilitate the design and implementation of flexible and reliable networks. It allows networks of bridges to be instructed when to accept or reject particular messages so the data will flow only over specified routes. And, in the event of a failure on the network, the bridge can switch to an alternate path automatically, ensuring continuous network operation.

Applications Management

In the WAN environment, one applications management function is altering circuit routing and bandwidth availability to accommodate applications that change by time of day. For example, after regular business hours, voice traffic tends to diminish and data traffic may change from transaction-based to wide-band applications that include inventory updates and large printing tasks.

Applications management also includes changing the interface definition of a circuit so that the same circuit can alternatively support both asynchronous and synchronous data applications, and determining appropriate data rates in accordance with response time objectives, or to conserve bandwidth during periods of high demand.

In the LAN environment, access to the gateway may be controlled by assigning specific ports to certain microcomputers. When a microcomputer requests access to the gateway, it is given the port reserved for it. Since no other microcomputer can access the port, security is enforced. Under this scheme, each port may have access privileges associated with it. One port may provide access to all mainframe applications, for example, while another port may be limited to only one application.

Security

Network management systems have also evolved to address the security concerns of users. Terminals employed for network management may be protected by passwords to minimize disruption to the network through data base tampering. Various levels of access may be used to prevent accidental damage. A senior technician, for example, may have a password that allows him or her to make changes to the various data bases, whereas a less experienced technician's password allows only reviewing of the data bases without permitting any changes.

Individual users may be given passwords that permit them to make use of certain network resources but deny them access to others. A variety of methods are available to protect networks from intruders who may try to access network resources with dial-up modems.

A management system, for instance, can request a password and hang up if it does not obtain one within 15 seconds, or it can hang up and call back over an approved line before establishing the connection. To frustrate persistent hackers, the system can limit unsuccessful call attempts to three. All attempts at entry are automatically logged to monitor access and to aid in the investigation of possible security violations. Other possible points of entry (e.g., gateways, bridges, and routers) may be protected with hardware- or software-defined partitions that restrict internal access to available ports.

Inventory and Accounting

The network management system also allows users to inventory the network, tracking the number and types of lines that are serving various locations and determining what capabilities exist for alternative routing. Even the actual arrangements of cards in the equipment cabinets at remote locations can be accounted for. To facilitate corporate accounting some systems track the depreciation of components. All of this information may be displayed at a terminal and output to a printer.

SYSTEM COMPONENTS

The management system for each type of device on the network requires its own hardware and software. A minimal network management system consists of a system controller, central processor, storage device, printer, and operator's console—all of which tie into the vendor's own line of products.

The system controller, the heart of the network management system, continuously monitors the network and generates status reports from data received from various devices on the network. The system controller isolates network faults and restores segments of the network that have failed or are in the process of failing.

The central processor may consist of a mainframe, minicomputer, or microcomputer. There, stored information may be processed for on-demand reporting, batch retrieval, or comprehensive analysis.

As previously mentioned, the operator's console may consist of a workstation or a microcomputer. In most cases, any printer may be used with the vendor's network management system.

MANAGEMENT APPROACHES

There are three general approaches to network management: centralized, distributed, and a relatively new approach that combines the advantages of the first two: distributed management under centrally weighted control.

The centralized approach entails creating a strategic node, at which an operator administers the configuration data base and monitors the performance of the entire network through the receipt of alarms and the implementation of various diagnostic routines. When certain network elements fail, reconfigurations may be implemented automatically by the management system or manually by the operator. Changes may also be initiated automatically by event or time of day. Built-in redundancy can prevent the loss of network management capabilities resulting from the failure of critical components.

With the distributed approach, there is no master (i.e., strategic) node. Instead, each node is equipped with its own management capabilities. All diagnostic routines and configuration information are stored at each location so that the failure of any single node on the network does not affect the management of any other node.

A third approach combines the advantages of the centralized and distributed approaches. With a distributed management system, the operator at the master site can exercise management and control over the entire network in keeping with the efficiency, cost control, and disaster recovery objectives of the corporation as a whole. At the same time, each local site can exercise management and control over its own domain.

At the master site, the operator has responsibility for the data base that determines controller switchover priority, controller configuration, and network configuration. In the event the master site goes down, this data base contains all the information necessary to permit a subordinate node to take over as the master controller. If the primary master controller fails, a sequence of events is initiated automatically in which another site is selected to carry out the tasks of the master controller. The new controller is automatically downloaded with the most recent network configuration information. All other controllers on the network are automatically notified of the change.

INDUSTRY CONSOLIDATION

An integrated network management solution that embraces diverse product types is difficult to find. Vendors of T1 multiplexers, for example, typically do not make modems or data sets, and those who offer modems and data sets typically do not make T1 multiplexers. Neither type of company specializes in LANs or such interconnection devices as bridges, routers, and gateways. In addition, vendors usually fall into one of two camps: the host environment or the carrier environment. These camps speak different languages, employ different technologies, and approach network management in different ways. IBM, for example, approaches network management as if the network was merely a peripheral to the host, whereas AT&T focuses on the management of transmission facilities as if the host environment did not matter.

Yet users need network management systems that work in both environments to unify the management of the diverse components. In fact, it is the absence of an integrated approach to network management that has forced many computer and communications equipment manufacturers to pool their research and development efforts, either through joint ventures, mergers, or acquisitions.

To date, there is no clear evidence that these arrangements will benefit customers. This is because integrating diverse product lines cannot be achieved merely by a larger firm's acquisition of a smaller firm. At best, a hodgepodge of products are offered that were never intended to work together. This situation is particularly vexing for those who are in search of a unified network management solution. This is precisely the problem that the open systems interconnection (OSI) is intended to address.

AN EMERGING STANDARD

The key to successful management of an organization's network is to be able to mix and match equipment and services from different vendors and manage them from a central point of control. Toward this end, vendors are beginning to support OSI, an emerging set of standards designed to permit various degrees of interconnectivity among competing products. This will make it possible for different products to exchange network management information, such as

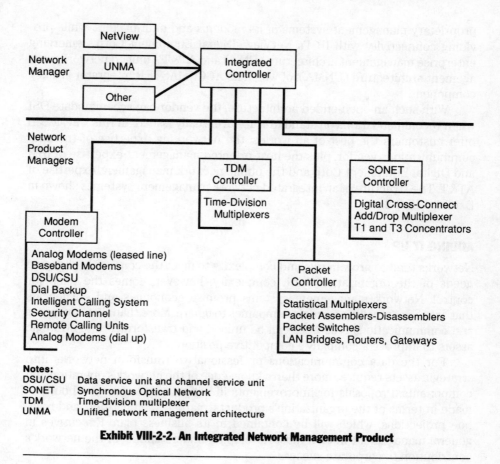

Notes:

DSU/CSU	Data service unit and channel service unit
SONET	Synchronous Optical Network
TDM	Time-division multiplexer
UNMA	Unified network management architecture

Exhibit VIII-2-2. An Integrated Network Management Product

alarms, performance measurements, use statistics, and diagnostic test results in a standard format so that every piece of the network can be more effectively monitored and controlled, possibly from a single terminal.

ADDRESSING IMMEDIATE NEEDS

Network management systems in compliance with OSI protocols are several years away, but there is an immediate need among users and vendors for an integrated network management solution. Instead of waiting for standards, therefore, many vendors are competing with each other in a new arena: that of supporting both the host and the carrier environments through their own proprietary management systems.

A vendor of data communications networks, for example, may offer an integrated network management system that provides connectivity among the proprietary management systems of its modems and multiplexers, while providing connectivity with IBM's NetView, Digital Equipment Corp's emerging enterprise management architecture (EMA) and AT&T's unified network management architecture (UNMA), of which its ACCUMASTER Integrator is a key component.

With such an open-ended architecture, the vendor can accommodate OSI when recommendations on standards are eventually issued. In this way, it can offer customers the best of all worlds: the networking expertise of the data communications vendor, plus the host-oriented management expertise of IBM and Digital Equipment Corp and the public network management expertise of AT&T. The structure of an integrated network management system is shown in Exhibit VIII-2-2.

ADDING IT UP

Networks tend to grow in size and complexity to meet the constantly changing needs of the organization. With complexity, however, comes the need for control. Network management systems promise economies and efficiencies that are too compelling for most companies to ignore. More than that, computer and communications resources can be unified and transformed into strategic assets to improve a company's competitive position.

For the data communications professional to transform networks into strategic assets requires more than a knowledge of the network's operation and components. Proposals for improvements in network management should be made in terms of the organization's products, markets, competition, and revenue projections, which will be contained in its business plan. Executives in general management in turn must develop an understanding of the network's contribution to corporate success.

VIII-3
OSI Systems Management Services and Protocols

WILLIAM COLLINS

Interest in open systems interconnection (OSI) has increased dramatically over the past several years. Progress on standards for OSI management is one of the main reasons behind the growing interest.

A communications manager's task is to facilitate the exchange of information among all the offices in a company's network, regardless of the type of computer system installed at each office. Connecting computer systems from different vendors has often been an extraordinarily difficult task; developments in OSI are helping to resolve this situation.

OSI will permit a communications manager to design a flexible communications system that will connect systems productively and efficiently throughout the corporate structure. The design will require the use of the comprehensive basic reference model of OSI, OSI management services and protocols, and OSI management applications. OSI leaves room for system growth and change in an elegant way: it standardizes the protocols between functions but not the design for implementing those functions, thus ensuring compatibility among different systems while encouraging innovative engineering.

BASIC REFERENCE MODEL

The OSI basic reference model provides substantial flexibility in designing communications systems. It defines seven layers of functions involved in data communications and the services and protocols required to perform these functions.

The basic reference model defines OSI systems management in terms of management applications that communicate with one another through application protocols. These management applications provide the following capabilities:

- Mechanisms for monitoring, controlling, and coordinating all managed objects within open systems.
- The ability to manage objects related to single or multiple layers.

- A framework for connecting open systems that allows suppliers to construct their individual systems in unique ways but still allows manageability across all open systems in the network.

Although the uniformity of many aspects of OSI simplifies the communications manager's job, it leaves many issues that must be resolved on a case-by-case basis. Managers have the responsibility not only for implementing the OSI layer services and protocols but for deciding which layers of the OSI reference model are applicable to a given problem, which OSI system management service and protocol is best suited for a specific implementation, and whether these services and protocols can be properly translated to a specific implementation.

ISSUES OF OSI SYSTEMS MANAGEMENT

OSI systems management provides a mechanism for the exchange of information about monitoring, controlling, and coordinating communications resources in open systems. The resources may be both real pieces of equipment and logical representations of real equipment. The OSI management framework uses the term *managed objects* to describe these resources and to distinguish the objects themselves from management information about them.

Most management information exchanged between open systems requires the same communications services as those for other application layer exchanges. Systems management communication is effected, therefore, through application layer protocols. The scope of OSI systems management includes the following:

- Defining mechanisms for monitoring, controlling, and coordinating all OSI resources across open systems.
- Modeling systems management application processes (SMAPs), which are the management functions in an open system.
- Specifying systems management application entities (SMAEs), which are the aspects of SMAPs that concern OSI communications.
- Using application layer services and protocols for the exchange of management information and control.

Exhibit VIII-3-1 illustrates the relationship among these aspects of OSI systems management in the context of a connection between two open systems.

SYSTEMS MANAGEMENT APPLICATION PROCESS

A systems management application process is an application process that performs management functions. A SMAP consists of an SMAE to carry out communications with other SMAPs, a management information base, and possibly one or more managers that provide various functions.

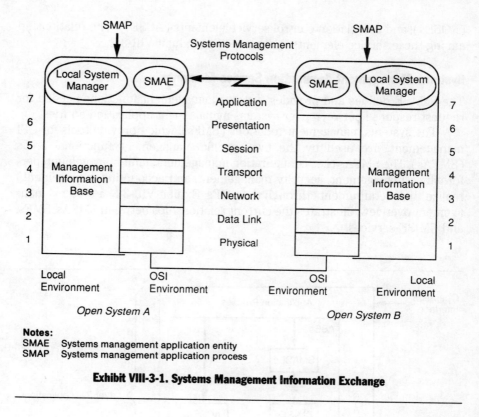

Notes:
SMAE   Systems management application entity
SMAP   Systems management application process

Exhibit VIII-3-1. Systems Management Information Exchange

A management information base is a conceptual repository containing the OSI systems management data in an open system that is available to the OSI environment. The management information base data may be provided by a local systems manager through a SMAP or by a remote open system through either system management protocols by way of the SMAE or through layer management protocols. The management information base data is available to all of these sources. It is organized according to the OSI systems management standard on the structure of management information, which defines the format used to identify the OSI management data.

SYSTEMS MANAGEMENT APPLICATION ENTITIES

In the application layer of the OSI reference model, application entities represent the communication aspects of an application process. Systems management application entities contain several service elements, including systems management application service elements (SMASEs), common management information service elements (CMISEs), remote operation service elements

(ROSEs), and association control service elements (ACSEs). The relationship among these service elements is illustrated in Exhibit VIII-3-2.

Systems Management Application Service Elements

The SMASE defines and provides systems management functions needed for request response between peer systems management application entities.

The systems management functions (SMFs), which provide tools for OSI management, are used by the five specific management functional areas (SMFAs). The SMFAs (i.e., configuration management, fault management, performance management, security management, and accounting management) realize their requirements through the SMFs. Exhibit VIII-3-3, a systems management overview, illustrates the current relationships between SMFAs, SMFs, and CMISE services.

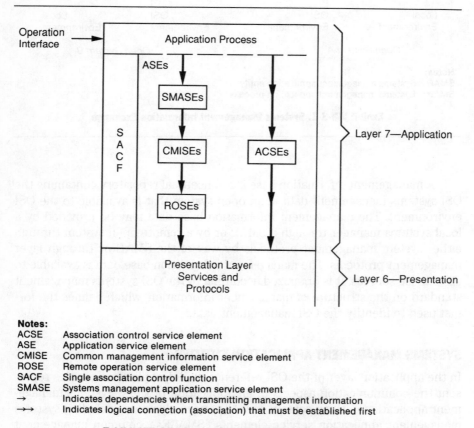

Notes:

ACSE	Association control service element
ASE	Application service element
CMISE	Common management information service element
ROSE	Remote operation service element
SACF	Single association control function
SMASE	Systems management application service element
→	Indicates dependencies when transmitting management information
→→	Indicates logical connection (association) that must be established first

Exhibit VIII-3-2. Example of Application Layer Structure

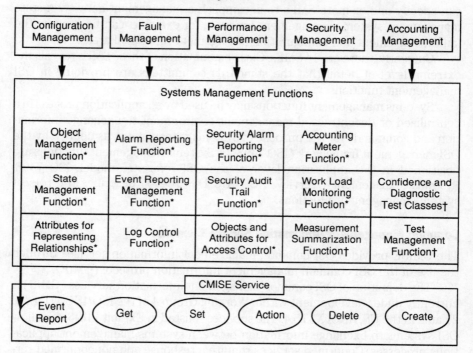

Specific Management Function Areas

Configuration Management	Fault Management	Performance Management	Security Management	Accounting Management

Systems Management Functions

Object Management Function*	Alarm Reporting Function*	Security Alarm Reporting Function*	Accounting Meter Function*	
State Management Function*	Event Reporting Management Function*	Security Audit Trail Function*	Work Load Monitoring Function*	Confidence and Diagnostic Test Classes†
Attributes for Representing Relationships*	Log Control Function*	Objects and Attributes for Access Control*	Measurement Summarization Function†	Test Management Function†

CMISE Service

Event Report   Get   Set   Action   Delete   Create

The systems management overview describes the relationships between SMFAs and SMFs. Each SMFA uses one or more SMFs.

Each SMFA has an FAD that describes the SMF that the SMFA develops.

SMFs describe a set of systems management functions that are developed by the SMFAs.

CMISE services describe CMISs that define a set of services used by management processes to act upon an agent process, and a CMIP that specifies an application layer protocol for exchange of management information.

Notes:
CMIP   Common management information protocol
CMIS   Common management information service
CMISE   Common management information service element
FAD   Functional area document
SMF   Systems management function
SMFA   Systems management functional area
* Committee draft or draft international standard
† Working document

Exhibit VIII-3-3. Systems Management Overview

Systems management functions (ISO/IEC 10164/1-11) carry out the management processes (activities) specified by the (system management user) requirements of the various specific management functional areas. Each SMFA can specify one or more SMFs to accomplish a management activity. A state management systems management function, for example, can be used by the fault management and configuration management functional areas.

Currently, there are 14 SMFs. Close examination of these SMFs reveals the extreme level of detail that the standards committees are providing in OSI management functions.

Systems management functions may be used by an application process in a centralized or decentralized management environment to exchange information and commands for the purpose of systems management, as defined by the OSI management framework (ISO 7498-4). Systems management functions are positioned in the application layer of the OSI reference model. ISO 7498, Systems Management Overview (ISO/IEC DIS 10400) describes the role of systems management functions.

Common Management Information Service Elements

The CMISE provides OSI common management information services through the use of the OSI common management information protocol (CMIP).

The definition of OSI common management information services (CMIS) is currently under development within Working Group 4 of the ISO/IEC JTC1/SC 21 and, in the US, ANSI X3T5.4. The services—listed in Exhibit VIII-3-4—allow OSI systems to exchange information between systems management applications processes. Confirmed services require a response and nonconfirmed services do not; some services require both.

M-Event-Report. The M-EVENT-REPORT service is used by a CMISE service user to report an event to a peer CMISE service user. It is defined as both a confirmed and a nonconfirmed service.

M-Get. The M-GET service, a confirmed service, is used by a CMISE service user to retrieve management information values from a peer CMISE service user.

Services	Type
M-EVENT-REPORT	Confirmed/nonconfirmed
M-GET	Confirmed
M-SET	Confirmed/nonconfirmed
M-ACTION	Confirmed/nonconfirmed
M-CREATE	Confirmed
M-DELETE	Confirmed

Exhibit VIII-3-4. Summary of Common Management Information Services

M-Set. The M-SET service is used by an invoking CMISE service user to request the modification of attribute values by a peer CMISE service user. It is defined as both a confirmed and a nonconfirmed service.

M-Action. The M-ACTION service is used by a CMISE service user to request a peer CMISE service user to perform an action on a managed object. It is defined as both a confirmed and a nonconfirmed service.

M-Create. The M-CREATE service, a confirmed service, is used by an invoking CMISE service user to request a peer CMISE service user to create a representation of a new managed object instance and simultaneously to register its identification. The representation should include the object's identification and the values of its associated management information.

M-Delete. The M-DELETE service, a confirmed service, is used by an invoking CMISE service user to request a peer CMISE service user to delete a representation of a managed object instance and to deregister its identification.

This limited set of CMISE services permits a variety of management communications.

Common Management Information Protocols

The common management information protocols are the protocols that provide the CMIS. Although a detailed discussion of these protocols is beyond the scope of this chapter, it is important to note that they use the connection-oriented remote operation service (CO-ROS) as an underlying service. The CO-ROS is itself being modified by ISO to relax restrictions that do not allow responders to invoke operations and to allow an alignment between ISO and International Telephone and Telegraph Consultative Committee (CCITT) versions of this service.

Although the CMIP specification requires CO-ROS, it is not desirable to use it for system management exchanges that do not require a transport connection when the traffic for CMIP operations is light. In this situation, a connectionless remote operation service (CL-ROS) is preferable. For example, when an SMAE is reporting events randomly, the high overhead would make it costly to maintain a transport connection. Although OSI has traditionally been connection oriented, work has begun in ISO to specify connectionless services for certain applications.

Remote Operation Service Element

The ROSEs provide remote operation services through the use of the remote operation protocol. Application entities that are interactive may require interactive protocols. If application process A, for example, requests that an operation be performed by application process B, application process B attempts to perform the operation and then reports the outcome of the attempt back to application process A. This interaction is illustrated in Exhibit VIII-3-5.

The specification and implementation of the interaction between application processes A and B is achieved by a ROSE. ROSEs provide a uniform mechanism for defining and representing operations and their outcome. They can support operations that always report results, operations that never report results, operations that report only success, and operations that report only failure.

One application process can perform operations provided by another by entering into an exchange of operation protocol data units. These units, defined by remote operations services as Invoke, ReturnResult, ReturnError, and Reject, can be described as follows:

- Invoke—Requests that an operation be performed and carries the description of the operation to be performed.
- ReturnResult—Reports the successful completion of an operation.
- ReturnError—Reports the unsuccessful completion of an operation.
- Reject—Reports the receipt and rejection of an invalid unit.

Because ROSE provides an environment for interactive protocols, the developer of an interactive application process that uses an interactive protocol must specify the nature of the operation, the results, and the errors that are specific to the application.

Association Control Service Element

The association control service element (ACSE) provides association control services through the association control protocol. It is concerned with providing a service and a protocol that supports the establishment and release of application associations, the identification of the application contexts applicable to the association, the selection of an initial application context, and the

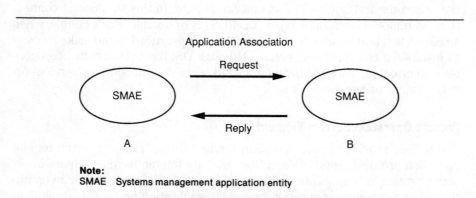

Application Association

Request

SMAE

SMAE

Reply

A

B

Note:
SMAE   Systems management application entity

Exhibit VIII-3-5. Remote Operations Model

transfer of user information between peer application entities. It also provides the means for identifying the presentation and session layer requirements for supporting the application association.

ISO/IEC JTC 1/SC21 Working Group 6 is currently defining a context management facility that supports the definition of more than one application context, the deletion of an existing defined context, and the selection of a current application context from a set of defined contexts. The management of application context and presentation context, however, requires further study.

Application Context Management

Some ISO/IEC JTC1/SC21 standards committees consider an application association to involve the defined application context list and the current application context. Each application association has one defined application context list that contains the names of all application contexts agreed on by both communicating application entities. Association control specifies three services for managing the defined application context list: A-ASSOCIATE, A-CONTEXT-DEFINE, and A-CONTEXT-DELETE.

Each transmission of the protocol data unit of an application association has exactly one current application context, which must be a member of the defined application context list. The A-CONTEXT-SELECT service specifies the current application context for transmission from the initiator of the service to its recipient peer application entity.

In an application environment with a single application association, context management is not required. In this case, the ACSEs are considered to be part of the application context of the user application and do not form a separate application context. Context is acquired through the A-ASSOCIATE service, can be relinquished through the A-RELEASE service, and can be aborted through either the A-U-ABORT or A-P-ABORT services.

In an application environment with more than one application service element, context management may be needed. In this case, the service elements used to acquire, relinquish, and abort the context depend on the circumstances. Context acquiring services include A-ASSOCIATE, A-CONTEXT-DEFINE, and A-CONTEXT-SWITCH. Context relinquishing services include A-U-ABORT and A-P-ABORT.

SPECIFIC MANAGEMENT FUNCTIONAL AREAS

The *OSI Management Framework* DIS 7498 includes standards for specific management functional areas (SMFAs) that define the procedures used to accomplish management tasks. These include configuration management, fault management, security management, performance management, and accounting management. Exhibit VIII-3-3 illustrates these specific management functional areas as service users of CMISEs.

Configuration Management. Configuration management facilities control, identify, and collect data from and provide data to OSI resources to permit continuous operation of interconnected devices. The facilities provide for setting the open system parameters, initializing and closing down OSI resources, collecting data about the open system state both on a routine basis and in response to a significant change of state, and providing specified data to open systems on request.

Fault Management. Fault management facilities permit the detection, isolation, and correction of abnormal operations in the OSI environment. Faults, which may be persistent or transient, cause open systems to fail to meet their operational objectives. Faults manifest themselves as errors in the operation of an open system; error detection provides the mechanism for recognizing faults. The facilities provide for maintaining and examining error logs, accepting and acting on error detection notifications, tracing faults, carrying out a sequence of diagnostic tests, and correcting faults.

Security Management. Security management facilities protect OSI resources. The facilities provide for authorization, access control, encryption and key management, authentication, and the maintenance and examination of security logs. An application service element might use the security management facilities to request authentication of a communication partner from a trusted third party. An implementation might request security facilities to provide the audit trails needed by fault management.

Performance Management. Performance management facilities evaluate the behavior of OSI resources and the effectiveness of communications activities. The facilities provide for gathering statistical data for the purposes of planning and analysis and for maintaining and examining the logs of system state histories.

Accounting Management. Accounting management facilities make it possible to set charges and identify costs for the use of system resources. The facilities provide for informing users of costs incurred or resources consumed, establishing accounting limits for the use of OSI resources, and permitting costs to be combined when multiple OSI resources are used to achieve a given communications objective.

STRUCTURE OF MANAGEMENT INFORMATION

The structure of management information refers to the logical structure of OSI management information. According to the *OSI Management Framework* and the *Management Information Service Overview,* this information is structured in terms of managed objects, their attributes, the operations that may be performed on them, and the notifications that they may issue. The set of managed objects in a system, together with its attributes, constitutes that system's management information base.

The structure of management information defines the concept of managed objects and the principles for naming managed objects and their attributes so that they can be identified in management protocols. It also defines a number of subobject and attribute types that are, in principle, applicable to all classes of managed objects. These include the common semantics of the object or attribute types, the operations that may be performed on them, and the notifications that they may issue. The structure of management information also defines the relationships that may exist between the various object types.

SUMMARY

OSI systems management services and protocols are a result of an effort to design concrete solutions to real problems. They permit communications managers to turn an ad hoc communications network system into a uniformly managed network, easily changing the configuration of a communications device or computer peripheral many miles away. Access to each open system in a network requires the use of the comprehensive structure of the OSI management services and protocols and their subcomponents. Attention to the intricacies of CMISE, ROSE, ACSE, and SMFA can result in clear benefits, most notably a standard way to manage communications between network components.

VIII-4
Standard Management Systems to Integrate 1990s Networks

PAUL J. BRUSIL

Today, most organizations realize that through effective network management practices, it is possible to avert the large-scale disruption of data communications networks that might be caused by equipment failure or breaches of network security.

This chapter describes network management problems, international activities in the standards community, the role of implementation agreements, and the aspects of today's network management problems that are not being addressed by standards or standards implementation groups.

THE NEED FOR NETWORK MANAGEMENT

Multivendor networks typically exist in nearly every organization's internal communications environment, in which voice, data, and video communications are provided by equipment from many communications vendors. Products include data and circuit switches; video, digital video, and video teleconferencing equipment; standards-based and proprietary LANs together with terminal and computer attachment devices as well as bridges and gateways; and remote data and telecommunications attachment devices, including T1 devices, modems, and statistical multiplexers.

Complex heterogeneous systems in any business environment cannot be maintained without management capabilities. Users of today's extensive, high-capacity, complex networks expect a certain quality of service from their distributed systems in terms of network bandwidth or delay, error rate, transparency, reliability, and protection. They need networks that adapt, without disruption, to changes in communications service requirements. Network management ensures that networks provide the requisite service and adaptability.

The use of standard communications protocols (e.g., Transmission Control Protocol and Internet Protocol) as well as de facto vendor standards (e.g., SNA and DECnet) fosters communication interoperability in such a heterogeneous environment, but true integration of multivendor devices into a comprehensive distributed system cannot occur until universal and harmonious management can be effected across all networking and networked resources that constitute the system.

The fact that US companies together spend an estimated $30 million annually just to attend, let alone prepare for, standards-related network management meetings attests to how critical, timely, and widespread is the need for network management in the communications and information processing industries.

NETWORK CONSTITUENCIES

Attitudes toward network management facilities and their importance vary depending on the viewpoint of the constituency—the positions of network service users, network service providers, and network maintainers are all different.

Users consider network management a mandatory network procurement item, primarily because they do not usually retain manual methods of conducting business once the new networking equipment is installed. When supermarket networks are down, for example, checkout lines stop. When high-volume stock market transactions cannot be made in a timely fashion, millions of dollars can be lost because of delayed order executions. Productivity plummets as clerks or stockbrokers, as well as businesspeople, bank managers, and the public in general wait for restoration of networking service.

Furthermore, users' emphasis on a variety of network performance characteristics can lead to the need for dynamic adjustments of protocol parameters. Fast response times may require network management systems to adjust timers deeply embedded into different network protocols, whereas the high throughput that others expect may require adjusting the maximum length of the information field of protocol data units.

For network service providers and vendors, poor network management—or worse yet, lack of network management—means lost sales. Furthermore, network outages and disasters lead customers to try other companies. For a service provider to maintain its promised bandwidth requires that network management systems support sophisticated rerouting and capacity planning capabilities, to circumvent congested or failed links, and to plan for installation of additional links.

For network maintainers, today's more complex, heavily loaded, multisubnetwork, multivendor environments are creating labor-intensive network maintenance problems as technicians struggle to learn how to use the ever-increasing number of heterogeneous network management products. To provide accurate measurements of aggregate channel throughput, availability, errors, and reserve capacity margins requires several different management systems.

OVERVIEW OF NETWORK MANAGEMENT TASKS

There is general agreement that network management must at least address a set of five partially overlapping operational and administrative tasks, namely, those needed to bring up, enroll, or reconfigure network devices; keep them operational; fine tune their operation or allow planning for expansion; keep records of network use; and protect the network from unauthorized use or tampering. In terms of standards, these functions are known as configuration management, fault management, performance management, accounting management, and security management, respectively.

Fault management provides the services to detect, log, isolate, test for, and correct problems in disabled network components.

Security management enables network managers to analyze audit trails of security-relevant events and supports the control of security services and mechanisms (e.g., deciding when to redistribute keys for encryption algorithms, when to reinitialize such algorithms, and when to isolate infected nodes).

Configuration management can foster continuous network operation by permitting observations and control of network system configurations. This includes determining the arrangement, relationships, characteristics, and state of network resources; detecting changes in such network configuration descriptors; and controlling such descriptors by changing existing network configurations.

Performance management, by providing the services to measure, track, store, analyze, and maintain network parameters related to communication quality of service objectives, can allow communications to circumvent emerging bottlenecks. By providing traffic generation test services, it can determine network capacities, thereby assisting network facility planning.

Accounting management can enable networking cost centers to identify or negotiate costs for communications resource use, to initiate or deactivate charging algorithms, and to monitor or report relevant information.

CURRENT NETWORK MANAGEMENT PRACTICE

Today's network maintainers are, in general, working with partial solutions to network management problems. Many vendors have (or have announced) products, but these are capable of managing only isolated groups of network components. Accounting management and security management are not well addressed by current products.

Current proprietary management equipment, such as the different types used for terminal servers, bridges, and gateways, employ many display formats and command languages, all of which network management personnel must remember and understand. For some organizations, the number of consoles associated with these management products causes their control center to resemble a spacecraft control facility. Coordination among the various management stations and the potentially conflicting decisions made by different personnel can be a serious problem. When some of the management consoles are scattered throughout the organization, coordination and synchronization are even more difficult.

Some organizations resort to using one vendor's networking management systems or a single network management product, such as IBM's NetView. Although the NetView/PC extension is making it possible for other vendors' products to be incorporated into the NetView environment, this does not guarantee total turnkey integrated network management through a single system.

Other organizations develop or procure unique systems to integrate the various autonomous management systems into a coherent whole. One such approach, recently prototyped by MITRE, has been to incorporate into different windows on a single workstation the information from several management consoles. The efficacy of this approach is questionable, because difficulties in integrating the independent data bases hinder the network maintainer's ability to digest, compare, and comprehend related network conditions needing management attention. The lack of common command languages, menus, icons, and display formats among the different windows is still a problem.

Network maintainers require extensive training and the ability to understand all communications protocols and devices used, as well as possible interactions between them. A maintainer may wish, for example, to make the network run more efficiently. Because efficiency is usually improved by transmitting long packets, the manager might decide to allow a high maximum length for the transport protocol's information field. In some cases, however, this decision does not have the desired effect because underlying protocols may need to do extra work to segment and subsequently reassemble these long packets.

Organizations urgently need easy, single-site management of the multiple classes and combinations of multivendor network components. The integration of universal network management functions into a multivendor environment, however, is an exceedingly complex process.

STANDARDS FOR MULTIVENDOR MANAGEMENT

Personnel managing and maintaining today's heterogeneous, mixed communications environments need a standard network management framework and tools with standard data formats and protocols. Production of multivendor, standards-compliant, interoperable network management products to support these needs is an interactive, multistep process, no single step of which can itself ensure success.

The process typically begins with user-oriented groups, such as the National Institute of Standards and Technology (NIST) or the International Federation of Information Processing (IFIP), providing requirements to international standardization bodies, such as the International Standards Organization (ISO), the International Telephone and Telegraph Consultative Committee (CCITT), and the Institute of Electrical and Electronics Engineers (IEEE) (see Exhibit VIII-4-1). These groups develop standards for particular environments (e.g., local or long-haul communications), particular devices (e.g., communications equipment, networked end systems such as computers, or intermediate network systems such as gateways), and particular communication protocol suites.

A common approach to communications systems management has been taken by these groups, bringing into the OSI standards community work being done on disparate devices (e.g., LANs, public and private WANs, communications devices, telephony, applications, and computers).

Benefits

There are many benefits to such a standard approach. Technical benefits are simplified procurement of interoperable equipment. Economic benefits are lower life-cycle costs. Once a vendor implements a standard, competition increases the size of the vendor pool implementing the standard. This improves industrywide product price-to-performance ratios as prices drop or capabilities and performance increase, decreases training and maintenance costs as differences between commercial network management tools narrow, and consequently lowers initial, maintenance, and upgrade costs. An overview of the ISO approach and a summary of the standards that specify the details follow.

Management Standards Concepts

Standards for network management govern the architecture, its functions, protocols for transferring management information, and the information itself. Management may be of two types: layer management, which acts directly on a single layer (e.g., media access control layer management of the packet flow through a LAN bridge), or systems management. The second type is currently receiving the most standards attention.

Network Management Standards

Standards are being created by many standards organizations (see Exhibit VIII-4-2), which are progressing at different rates. A complete set of standards to which comprehensive, ISO-based, network management products can conform does not now exist. Their completion is scheduled to occur throughout the early 1990s, most being scheduled to be finished by the end of 1991 and the most immature of the systems management standards scheduled for completion by 1993. The status of the core set of OSI systems management standards, as of late 1990, is referred to in Exhibit VIII-4-3.

Two standards documents provide the architectural information for the

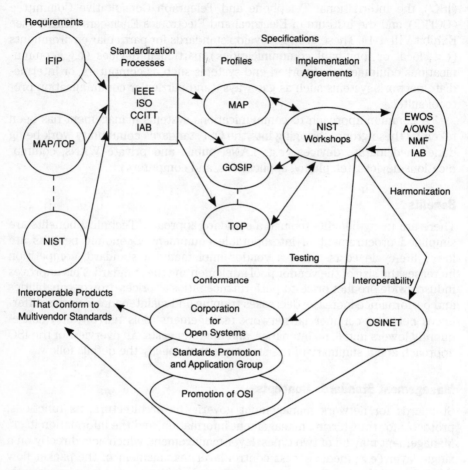

Requirements

Standardization Processes

Specifications

Profiles

Implementation Agreements

Harmonization

Testing

Conformance

Interoperability

Interoperable Products
That Conform to
Multivendor Standards

Notes:

A/OWS	Asian and Oceanic Workshop
CCITT	International Telephone and Telegraph Consultative Committee
EWOS	European Workshop for Open Systems
GOSIP	Government OSI Profile
IAB	Internet Activities Board
IEEE	Institute of Electrical and Electronics Engineers
IFIP	International Federation of Information Processing
ISO	International Standards Organization
MAP/TOP	Manufacturing Automation Protocol and Technical and Office Protocol
NIST	National Institute of Standards and Technology
NMF	Network Management Forum
OSINET	Open Systems Interconnection Network

Exhibit VIII-4-1. The Standardization and Commercialization Process

Management Area	Standards Organization	Work by Standards Groups
Architecture	ISO SC21/WG4	OSI management architecture
	ISO 802.1	LAN layer management architecture
	CCITT SG VII	Telephone network management architecture
Management Communications Services and Protocols	ISO SC21/WG4, CCITT SG VII, and IAB NetMan	Common management information service (CMIS)—To carry out a network control and monitoring function
		Common management information protocol (CMIP)—Bit patterns to transmit a request for a network management service
	IEEE 802.1	LAN layer management protocol
	IAB	Simple network management protocol—A transition protocol for managing the Internet before OSI's CMIS and CMIP are deployed
System Management Functions	ISO SC21/WG4, CCITT SG VII, and ANSI T1M1.5	Configuration and fault management
		Performance, accounting, and security management
		Common functions (e.g., state management or error reporting used in systems management)
Managed Objects	ISO SC21/WG4	Definition of structures, formats, and guidelines for managed object definitions (structure of management information)
	ISO SC21/WG4 & WG5	Definition of parameters to be managed for systems (e.g., WG4: systems identification and serial numbers) and ISO upper-layer protocols (e.g., WG5: determining which system is to initiate sending)
	ISO SC6/WG2 and ISO SC6/WG4	Definition of parameters to be managed for ISO lower-layer protocols (e.g., timers specifying retransmission time-outs and counters registering number of packets sent)
	IEEE 802.2 to 802.10	Definition of parameters to be managed for lower-layer protocols for LANs and metropolitan area networks; includes security

Exhibit VIII-4-2. Network Management Standards

Management Area	Standards Organization	Work by Standards Groups
Managed Objects (*cont*)	ANSI ASC X3T9.5	Definition of parameters to be managed for high-speed, fiber-optic LANs (fiber distributed data interface)
	ANSI ASC T1M1.5	Definition of parameters to be managed for such telecommunications devices as multiplexers
	CCITT and various study groups	Definition of parameters to be used in communications (e.g., for Integrated Services Digital Network, a standard network for combining voice, data, and other digital services)
	IAB MIB WG	Definition of parameters to be managed for Internet's Transmission Control Protocol and Internet Protocol

Notes:

ANSI	American National Standards Institute
ASC	Accredited Standards Committee
CCITT	International Telephone and Telegraph Consultative Committee
CMIP	Common management information protocol
CMIS	Common management information service
IAB	Internet Activities Board
ISO	International Standards Organization
MIB	Management information base
SC	Subcommittee
SG	Study group
WG	Work group

Exhibit VIII-4-2. (*Cont*)

development of all the system management standards. These are the systems management framework and the systems management overview. The systems management framework defines the major elements of OSI management—namely, systems management, layer management, the management information base, and the management functional areas such as fault and performance management. The systems management overview expands the framework's concepts. It addresses functional aspects of systems management, management domains, concepts of management processes acting in either a managing or an agent role, application layer concepts relating to systems management, and the systems management standards.

Next, a multipart standard, the systems management functions, defines the functions a management system must perform to support the requirements of fault management, configuration management, performance management, ac-

Document	Under Development	International Standard
Management Framework		✓
Systems Management Overview	✓	
Structure of Management Information:		
Part 1: Management Information Model	✓	
Part 2: Definition of Management Information	✓	
Part 4: Guidelines for Managed Object Definition	✓	
Common Management Information Service		✓
Addendum 1: CancelGet		✓
Addendum 2: Add/Remove		✓
Common Management Information Protocol		✓
Addendum 1: CancelGet		✓
Addendum 2: Add/Remove		✓
Systems Management Functions:		
Systems Management—Part 1: Object Management Function	✓	
Systems Management—Part 2: State Management Function	✓	
Systems Management—Part 3: Relationship Management Function	✓	
Fault Management:		
Systems Management—Part 4: Error Reporting and Information Retrieval Function	✓	
Systems Management—Part 5: Service Control Function	✓	
Systems Management—Part 6: Confidence and Diagnostic Testing Function	✓	
Systems Management—Part 7: Log Control Function	✓	
Security Audit Trail	✓	
Accounting Metering	✓	
Work Load Monitoring	✓	

Exhibit VIII-4-3. OSI Management Standards

counting management, and security management. The following are the first group of systems management functions being created within the ISO:

- Object management—For creating, deleting, examining, and changing sets of management information.
- State management—For monitoring the operability and use of communications resources and for restricting permission to use these resources or receive state-change notifications.
- Relationship management—For establishing and examining the relationships among managed objects and therefore for observing how the operation of one part of the system depends on other parts.
- Error reporting and information retrieval—For reporting the occurrence of events and information related to events (e.g., accumulated statistics).

- Management service control—For controlling the criteria that trigger event generation and the specification of destinations to which events are to be forwarded.
- Log control—For controlling the start and stop of event and error logging and the creation and modification of logging criteria.
- Confidence testing—For starting, stopping, and reporting results of specific diagnostic tests.
- Work load monitoring—For monitoring network resource use, reporting warning conditions as assessed by specifiable thresholds, and clearing such conditions.
- Security audit trail control—For controlling the start and stop of auditing and the creation and modification of auditing criteria.
- Security alarm reporting—For reporting security events.
- Security audit trail and alarm reporting control—For providing management service control functions to security management operations.
- Communications instance account—For reporting details of all communications.

The communication services and protocol used to manipulate the information values associated with remote managed objects and to transfer management information between open systems are similar to query languages. Addenda to each of these standards are being prepared to provide additional services and corresponding protocol extensions. The common management information service and common management information protocol standards provide the building blocks that define operations needed to perform the system management functions. The main services are:

- Initialize and terminate—For establishing and breaking association links between managing and agent processes.
- Get—For obtaining information (i.e., attributes) associated with remote managed objects from the agent processes representing these objects.
- Set—For changing such information.
- Event report—For sending event notifications from agent processes concerning the status of network components and communications.

Other services include creating and deleting specifiable instances of managed objects, adding and removing management information, canceling previous retrieval requests, synchronizing management operations across multiple objects, and linking multiple management operation replies with a specific request.

Structure of management information, a multipart standard, is intended for standards groups working to define managed objects. This standard provides:

- A management information model—This model sets forth naming and identification (location) principles for management information. It addresses object-oriented design principles, managed object classes and property inheritance relationships, naming principles (including object containment hierarchy and name structure), and polymorphism, a technique to extend object classes to support new equipment and technology types without making older management systems obsolete.

- Definitions of generic object classes—These support management activities for establishing event generation criteria and receiver criteria needed to select incoming remote management reports for processing.
- Definitions of generic types of managed object attributes—These include count, gauge, threshold, counter threshold, gauge threshold, and tide mark.
- Guidelines to layer standards groups—For defining management objects and attributes, according to universal template formats, to manage their layers.

Managed objects exist as high-level, composite objects (e.g., an end system or gateway) and lower-level atomic objects (e.g., a transport layer's retransmission timer). Attributes are the properties of managed objects that determine or reflect their behavior. Every standards group that specifies a protocol or a component of a communications system has the responsibility to specify, according to the relevant structure of management information rules, the managed objects and attributes associated with that resource. The number of such standards groups is very large. In addition, ISO is defining those managed objects that belong to open systems themselves and not to any particular protocol layer within such systems. The timetables for development of most of these management information standards have not yet been established, and to a major extent, completion of such standards cannot progress until the structure of management information standards are mature. As such, this aspect of the development of management standards may impede the availability of standards-based products for some time.

A number of vendors, while not currently working on standardization, are developing their own managed objects for areas that go well beyond networking. These developers are setting precedents for the eventual standardization of managed objects associated with many distributed system resources, such as operating systems (e.g., queue managers) and data base systems, as well as distributed applications (e.g., electronic mail).

COMMERCIALIZING OSI STANDARDS

Standards by themselves do not give rise to interoperable products; standards typically identify numerous options to suit the different needs of the many nations and industries that participated in their development. Standards also do not specify the conformance testing required to assure that applications will actually interoperate. The conformance criteria that standards contain specify only a minimal level of conformance.

To develop interoperable products, users and vendors need to agree on compatible subsets of the base standards. These also will specify implementation details that are outside the scope of the standards but that are required to facilitate multivendor interoperability. In the case of network management, such details include, for example, agreements on what to provide in the management protocol's access control fields. More precise conformance details are also specified. Implementation agreements may also identify the particular profiles or subsets of layered protocols that must be supported by compliant implementations. The Government OSI Profile (GOSIP) represents one constituency that requires implementation agreements.

OSI users and vendors from virtually all other constituencies have traditionally viewed the OSI Implementer's Workshop as the international focal point for developing implementation agreements for ISO, IEEE, and CCITT networking and distributed computing environment standards.

OSI IMPLEMENTER'S WORKSHOP OVERVIEW

The OSI Implementer's Workshop, a series of public, quarterly forums, brings together future users and potential suppliers of OSI protocols. The workshop accepts as input emerging OSI protocol standards and from them produces agreements on the implementation and conformance testing particulars of these protocols. The workshop, in conjunction with its ARPAnet-like (although significantly smaller in scale) Open Systems Interconnection Network (OS-INET) experiments, expedites the development of OSI protocols and promotes the interoperability of independently manufactured data communications equipment. The technical work of the workshop is performed by its 15 SIGs.

Ongoing agreements are published and distributed for comment after each quarterly meeting. Once these and their underlying base standards are deemed mature, the status of the ongoing agreements is elevated so that they become stable agreements. Stable agreements that are based on draft international standards (DISs) or international standards (ISs) and by workshop consensus are deemed mature enough for product development and procurement reference. New releases of stable agreements extend the functional level of these standards.

Network Management Special Interest Group

The network management special interest group (NMSIG) is chartered to develop product-level specifications for the common services and protocols for exchanging management information between OSI nodes and the specific system management functions that use these common services; to initiate and, as necessary, coordinate with other special interest groups to develop product-level specifications of layer-specific and system-specific management information; and to establish relationships with other standards bodies and related groups. As necessary, the NMSIG provides feedback to standards bodies regarding ambiguities and errors in standards, as well as any need for additions or enhancements to the OSI systems management standards.

The NMSIG represents more than 120 organizations; approximately 40 are user organizations, and the rest are vendors. Technical leadership is provided by nine section editors and five officers, who represent a broad cross section of industries, users, the US government, and vendors.

The NMSIG tracks emerging standards as closely as possible. As soon as the standards reach technical maturity (i.e., DIS status), the NMSIG incorporates companion agreements into a new phase of the stable implementation agreements. The new phases thus add to the function and capability of systems compliant with the NMSIG agreements; they do not represent changes in direction. This approach requires considerable planning to work properly.

The first phase of an agreement is scheduled for publication when a minimal subset of standards that can be implemented as useful products is available. The set of standards available will be sufficient to enforce multivendor interoperability, so that one vendor's managing system will be able to manage a small, agreed-on set of another vendor's managed objects.

The rapid pace of technological innovation has produced some discouragement with the traditionally slow standards development process. Accordingly, to satisfy the demand for network management products, some vendors, either alone or in alliances, have begun developing products using implementation agreements that are based on guesses about the standards' final form.

Examples include the Manufacturing Automation Protocol (MAP), the Internet Engineering Task Force, and the OSI Network Management Forum. These groups are less conservative than the NMSIG and, accordingly, are willing to develop implementation agreements that may not stand the test of time. Their motives are to foster the early arrival of useful products allowing for subsequent migration to the standards when the standards are fully mature.

The problem is that this premature commercialization can lead to products that have a limited useful life or are not useful at all. There is also the risk that a large installed base of products derived from premature standards could encourage vendors to either sway standards toward these early agreements or to impede the standardization process.

The OSI Network Management Forum agreements, emphasizing manager-to-manager interaction for telephone network management, is the set of early agreements most closely aligned with emerging ISO standards. To meet some multivendor, trade show demonstration requirements, however, the group has had to guess about the details of the mature standards. In the structure of management information area, the OSI Network Management Forum predictions are proving correct; however, its managed objects are not strictly based on current standards work.

The similarities and differences between the NMSIG and the OSI Network Management Forum are shown in Exhibit VIII-4-4.

Comparison Category	Group	
	OSI/NMF	NMSIG
Philosophical Orientation	• Phased approach	• Phased approach
	• 1990 demo of real products pacing phase 1 IAs	• Demo under discussion; not pacing phase 1
	• Phase 1 IAs slightly ahead of standards	• All phases slightly behind standards
	• Phase 2 IAs align with new and evolving standards	• All IA phases align with new and evolving standards
	• Commitment to manufacture product	• No product commitments
	• Open membership: —Full, $50,000 plus three staff per year —Associate, $10,000 per year	• Open membership ($150 per meeting)
	• Full members (currently 13) vote on agreements	• All knowledgeable participants vote on agreements
Participant Base	• Large international base: more than 70 organizations from 10 countries on three continents	• Large international base: more than 120 organizations from 12 countries on four continents
	• Exclusively vendors (without RBOCs, DEC, or IBM)	• More than 80 vendors
	• Heavy telephone and modest computer vendor support	• Modest telephone and heavy computer vendor support
	• Little current user involvement; efforts started to attract users	• Heavy user commitment: more than 40 organizations and one-third of leaders
	• No government participation	• Five governments participate
Technical Orientation	• Manager-to-manager focus	• Manager-to-agent focus (includes manager-to-manager focus)
	• Single domain	• Single domain
	• No directory dependence	• No directory dependence
	• MIB has few MOs	• No MOs yet
	• Telephony MO focus; growing number of computer and circuit MOs	• MIL open to all communities; initial focus is on computer, circuit, MAP, SMO, and TCP/IP
	• Unknown MO harmonization plans	• Multigroup MO harmonization underway to ease transition to OSI and integration of OSI into distributed computing environment
	• Registration authority not yet determined; possibilities include NMSIG and AT&T	• Registration authority delegated from NIST OSI Workshop

Exhibit VIII-4-4. Activities and Orientations of the NMSIG and OSI/NMF

Comparison Category	Group	
	OSI/NMF	**NMSIG**
	• Conformance test development and testing before complete set of management standards; includes SPAG and some COS funding	• Working with COS in a traditional way, leading to COS member decision to develop tests when standards mature (DIS)
Future Enhancements	Likely postdemo additions:	Likely mid-1990 additions:
	• Performance management focus	• Performance management work load monitor
	• Security management will be a low priority	• Security will be a high priority; the initial focus will be commercial-grade security of management and updating MIL to include 802.10, if mature
	• Other systems management functions (SMFs)	• Other SMFs will include log control, confidence and diagnostic test, and communication instance accounting
	• Will continue aligning IAs to maturing standards; alignment with NIST and other organizations' IAs will be considered	• Will continue aligning IAs to maturing standards (DISs and ISs)
	• Will extend MO base to include SC21 WG2/WG4 MOs (network and transport MOs)	• Will expand MIL with SC21 WG2/WG4 MOs; 802 collaborations will produce MO templates; guidance to FDDI and international space agencies

Notes:

COS	Corporation for Open Systems
DIS	Draft international standard
FDDI	Fiber distributed data interface
IA	Implementation agreement
MAP	Manufacturing Automation Protocol
MIB	Management information base
MIL	Management information library
MO	Managed object
NIST	National Institute of Standards and Technology
NMF	Network Management Forum
NMSIG	Network Management Special Interest Group
OSI	Open systems interconnection
RBOC	Regional Bell operating company
SMF	Systems management function
SMO	Systems managed object
SPAG	Standards Promotion and Applications Group
TCP/IP	Transmission Control Protocol and Internet Protocol

Exhibit VIII-4-4. *(Cont)*

International Considerations

In the short run, differences in products based on competing implementation agreements can lead to, or in some cases perpetuate, the lack of multivendor network management interoperability. The NMSIG is moving to correct this problem.

Each special interest group in the NIST-OSI Implementer's Workshop works to establish consistency between agreements being developed by regional groups, such as the European Workshop for Open Systems and the Asian/Oceanic Workshop serving the Pacific Rim nations, or by groups that serve other constituencies, such as the Internet Engineering Task Force of DARPA's Internet Activities Board and the Network Computing Forum, Open Software Foundation, and OSI Network Management Forum vendor consortiums. While the European Workshop for Open Systems and Asian/Oceanic Workshop currently do not support network management activities, the NMSIG has initiated efforts to foster alignment with many of those organizations working on network management. Through these collaborations, it will be possible to divide some of the remaining work, align the products of duplicated efforts, and bring more resources to bear on the implementation of OSI management standards. Such cooperation could ultimately lead to more, and better, interoperable network management products.

Beyond the NMSIG

The existence of several implementation groups demonstrates the importance of interoperable networks to the data communications and information processing industries.

One of the most important initial benefits of the NMSIG agreements is that NIST is developing plans to publish these agreements and the accompanying Management Information Library as a Federal Information Processing Standard. First-generation network management products conforming to this FIPS specification will have widespread applicability to GOSIP and similar environments.

Any transitional network management problems associated with the migration from TCP/IP to OSI protocol environments will be eliminated through cooperation between the Internet Engineering Task Force and the NMSIG. The reduction in the number of implementation agreement differences will lower life-cycle costs, because vendors will reduce the number of different implementations.

The ultimate benefit of the NMSIG agreements is that conformance tests for products built to these agreements will be developed and conducted by such organizations as the Corporation for Open Systems or its European and Japanese counterparts, the Standards Promotion and Application Group and the Promotion of OSI Group respectively. Conforming products will be certified by these groups. In addition, the Corporation for Open Systems mark signifies that the vendor will work with other certified vendors to resolve interoperability problems that may arise at user sites.

The final step for proving interoperability is to conduct multivendor tests and demonstrations using such vehicles as the recently announced NIST network management interoperability research facilities or the OSI Implementer's Workshop–sponsored OSINET.

After completion of all these steps, shown in Exhibit VIII-4-1—standards development, implementation agreements consensus, conformance test development, conformance testing, and interoperability testing—network management products can be considered multivendor, standards-compliant, interoperable, and interchangeable.

WHAT STANDARDS DO NOT ACCOMPLISH

Network management standards provide the tools to make integrated and interoperable network management systems, but they do not guarantee this. Implementor groups, conformance testing groups, and interoperability testing groups are essential to the development of interoperable products.

Furthermore, standards do not dictate how management is to be accomplished. That is, the algorithms for processing network resource observations, manipulating them to decide whether management control actions are necessary, and deciding how to effect and sequence any resulting control actions to accomplish a complex management scenario are not standardized. Standards provide no assurance that network management systems (acting either autonomously or cooperatively) from different vendor product lines will make consistent decisions and maintain network service stability in response to a given situation.

A standard application program interface (API) would help. An API is a method for specifying the interface an application program uses to interact with a service. A standard graphic interface known as GKS, for example, specifies exactly how objects are to be drawn on graphics devices. Similarly, operating system calls are being standardized by POSIX. The benefits of interface standardization for network management are compelling. Portable, third-party graphics, data base management, report generation, and expert system applications for network management could become a reality. By recompiling conformance test systems, the testing of different vendor's management systems could be simplified. It is unfortunate that such API standardization is not receiving any attention.

It should be noted that some implementations will outperform others, and the standards do not, and should not, provide any constraints in this area.

Common ergonomic specifications for the user-system interfaces of multivendor network management systems would minimize problems and costs associated with learning and using different network management products. Because this is not necessary to achieve multivendor interoperability, it is not part of the standardization process. Expert systems and knowledge-based technology are also, therefore, not part of current network management standards, even though they could lower the level of expertise required of network maintenance personnel. Furthermore, standards do not address organizational policy issues, such as who controls the integrated resources.

The last issue is the open management that standards provide. Without adequate security provisions in open management tools, networks are subject to deliberate damage.

SUMMARY

Buyers of network management systems will face difficult choices as standards evolve through the early 1990s and vendors introduce incompletely standardized products. The life of these products depends on whether it will be easy to upgrade them to full standards compliance—something that is currently unknown. The completion of systems management standards will eventually make the total integration of management resources for multivendor distributed computing environments possible.

Section IX
Security

A s has been shown throughout the *Handbook*, local area networks based on industry standards are highly effective at promoting connectivity between equipment of different types. LANs also give users control of their own information processing systems. With accessibility, connectivity, and distributed control, however, comes vulnerability. Systems that allow or encourage open connections are, by design, open to connection by unauthorized users; there are other security concerns as well. How does a LAN manager address this apparent paradox? Is it possible to continue to promote openness and at the same time protect those elements of the LAN that need protecting?

The answers to these and many similar security-related questions are the subject of this section of the *Handbook*. The first three chapters identify and define the types of security problems found in LANs and present several suggestions for performing security risk assessments and taking corrective action. The next three chapters discuss security activities occurring in several national and international standards bodies, both for LANs and for more general applications. The last two chapters present case studies of actual LAN security products and implementations.

Securing any automated system requires a comprehensive set of procedures, both automatic and manual. Such procedures can be conceptually viewed as concentric layers of protection surrounding the ultimate object of protection, the information itself. Chapter IX-1, "Evaluating Security Controls in LANs," presents a comprehensive methodology for ensuring and evaluating LAN security controls. A detailed checklist is included to facilitate a security review.

In many respects, the concept of security extends well beyond protection from intentional harm or compromise. Damage can occur in a number of unintentional ways, including accidental execution of the wrong command, hardware or software problems, or natural disasters. Chapter IX-2, "Security and Controls of Microcomputer Networks," discusses how all of these security factors can be incorporated into a risk assessment.

Similarly, Chapter IX-3, "A LAN Security Review," considers these same types of factors for the purpose of conducting a risk assessment. Specific examples of control measures are given as implemented in a NetWare environment, although the general principles can be applied to any LAN.

Security features in data communications standards permit the use of standards-based security solutions. These usually allow the exchange of authentication information or the protection of data elements during transmission between open systems. Chapter IX-4, "General Communications Security Services and Protocols," focuses on current security standards and features and describes what can be expected in emerging standards. Chapter IX-5, "Application-Specific Communications Security Services and Protocols," discusses standardization of security mechanisms in financial applications as well as message handling and directory systems.

Of all the committees currently developing security standards, only one—the IEEE 802.10 LAN security working group—is actively developing security standards specifically for LANs. Chapter IX-6, "OSI-Based LAN Security Standards," discusses security considerations unique to LANs and describes the work to date within 802.10. Relations with other standard security groups are also examined.

IX-1
Evaluating Security Controls in LANs

LORNE A. DEAR

This chapter presents one approach to understanding the internal control and security needs for LANs. Specifically, it addresses the need to know what data and what users will be on the network, how the network architecture should be designed, how overall network security involves layers of control, what access controls are necessary and who is responsible for them, and how controls can be enforced by the message format on a network. The chapter includes a detailed control checklist that may be adapted to meet a company's particular needs. It concludes with how to evaluate security deficiencies and recommend corrective actions to management on the basis of the results of the completed security checklist.

IDENTIFYING NETWORK TRAFFIC

The first step in evaluating the internal control and security needs for a LAN is to determine what data and what users will be on the network. This information is critical to determining the number and types of security controls needed. The more sensitive the data, the more controls are needed; the more users and organizational activities on the network, the more controls are needed.

Sensitive data is information that must be protected because its unauthorized disclosure, alteration, loss, or destruction could cause damage to the organization. For example, such data could include financial, private, official, source-selection sensitive, or corporate strategic planning information. The amount of such data, the types of transactions that will contain such data, and the time of day most of the transactions will be processed should be identified.

The number of personnel and their locations should also be identified to determine control requirements. Before controls on an existing LAN can be evaluated, the following questions regarding network users should be answered:

- Are all network users authorized?
- Do some users require special security clearance?

- Are all users authorized to see accounting information, corporate planning information, and all other types of information on the network?
- Are contractor personnel allowed on the network?
- Can foreign nationals obtain access to the network?
- Is dial-up access possible?

The number and type of internal controls and security on a LAN will depend on the answers to these types of questions.

LAN ARCHITECTURE

LAN architecture can greatly enhance security. The effectiveness of such techniques as clustering users and layering controls depends on the network architecture.

Clusters

After specific data and users are identified, controls and security evaluation can be performed. This involves determining which users will share the same files or frequently communicate with each other. On the basis of this analysis, users who communicate often or share the same files can be clustered on the network. Clustering increases network performance and greatly enhances security. Users who communicate frequently are usually located close together (e.g., on the same floor in a building) so they do not create traffic on other clusters on the network. The network channel used by persons in one cluster can then be used by persons in another cluster without mutual interference, thus increasing network efficiency.

The communications bridges between the clusters can be used to provide security by preventing specific data from leaving a particular cluster. The bridges can also prevent unauthorized access to a cluster. Cluster users can maintain private files and share common files with the other network users. Additional security is possible by logically separating users (i.e., assigning them different network channels within each cluster). Exhibit IX-1-1 depicts one such cluster architecture.

As shown in the exhibit, the network is divided into three communications clusters. All sensitive corporate data is processed on one cluster, and the bridges that connect the cluster to other network users prevent any of the data from leaking out. File accessibility can be restricted to individual users, or to all users on that cluster. Users outside the cluster cannot access the files. Other files contain data common to all network users. Similarly, sensitive personnel data is controlled within the accounting and personnel cluster. Data and file access restrictions are placed on any sensitive data in this cluster.

An unlimited number of controls can be placed in the network's communications bridges. Additional controls can be placed on the gateway, which connects the LAN to other short- or long-haul networks. The isolation between general users, how they define links, their access, and between the associated access controls help provide control to the network, if audit and security require-ments are met.

AUTOMATED AND MANUAL CONTROLS

(partial text obscured) automated controls are necessary to protect data on a *(text obscured)* networks, software, storage media, and internetworked networks also *(text obscured)* allow *(text obscured)*-wide access to data. To protect data in these networks also involve *(text obscured)* the issues involved with the unauthorized use and manipulation of data, *(text obscured)* prevention, detection, and recovery for the *(text obscured)* environment in them.

Large clusters might...

(text obscured) can be configured in large or small clusters or a network accessible *(text obscured)* IX-1-1). The large, complex environment needs automated controls. The controls *(text obscured)* these sophisticated clusters are tied to the center of the traffic *(text obscured)* by the file processor.

(text obscured) points are the roles the principal or administrator so strong that each *(text obscured)* application(s) accessed at all times. These may include local or remote controls, security *(text obscured)*, and identification of procedures. As one *(text obscured)* are user identification, these persons in particular as to system components. These *(text obscured)* controls include the user security, authorization, portable access. *(text obscured)*

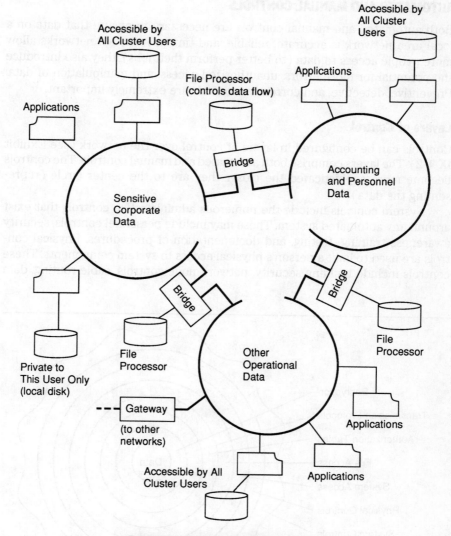

Exhibit IX-1-1. Communications Clusters

The diagram shows:
- **Applications** (top left) connected to **Sensitive Corporate Data** cluster
- **Accessible by All Cluster Users** (storage) connected to **Sensitive Corporate Data**
- **File Processor (controls data flow)** connected via **Bridge**
- **Accessible by All Cluster Users** (top right, storage) connected to **Accounting and Personnel Data**
- **Applications** connected to **Accounting and Personnel Data**
- **Accounting and Personnel Data** cluster with **File Processor** and connected via **Bridge**
- **Sensitive Corporate Data** cluster with **Private to This User Only (local disk)** and **File Processor** connected via **Bridge**
- **Other Operational Data** cluster with **Gateway (to other networks)**, **Applications**, **Accessible by All Cluster Users**

cluster users, between channels within a cluster, and between the associated access controls provide a means to enforce data integrity and security requirements.

AUTOMATED AND MANUAL CONTROLS

Both automated and manual controls are necessary to ensure that data on a local area network is accurate, reliable, and timely. Although networks allow more people access to data (to better perform their jobs), they also introduce the potential for more errors, unauthorized access, and manipulation of data. Preventive, detective, and corrective controls are extremely important.

Layers of Control

Controls can be configured in layers of control over the network (see Exhibit IX-1-2). The layers comprise both automated and manual controls. The controls become more sophisticated the closer they are to the center circle (representing the data).

System controls include the numerous administrative controls that exist around any automated system. These may include personnel controls, security awareness training, testing, and documentation of procedures. Physical controls are used to limit a person's physical access to system components. These controls include building security, network node controls, cable routing, data

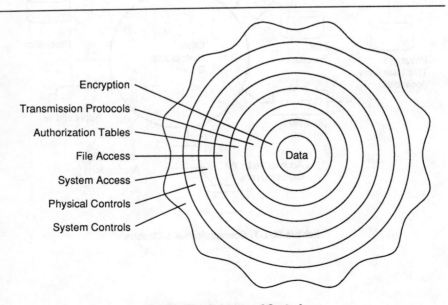

Exhibit IX-1-2. Layers of Control

backup, and even separation of work areas and users' duties. Access controls, because of their importance, are discussed separately, in a following section.

Transmission protocols include the communications controls that should exist within a LAN. These include, in part, protocols to identify and authenticate users and their messages. The use of these message formats for evaluation of the security controls is discussed in a later section.

Encryption (i.e., the scrambling of data before transmission or storage) is another security control. The extent of the use of encryption on a network should be determined on the basis of the cost versus the sensitivity of the data and the risks involved.

Access Controls

Adequate access controls, which include authorization tables, are essential for LAN security. Varying levels of access control will be necessary depending on the sensitivity of the data, the clearance level of the users, and the architecture of the network.

Different people are responsible for access control. Executive management, data security administrators, system developers, EDP auditors, and network users should understand that the network manager is not solely responsible for protecting corporate data. Data security is a team effort; network users also must protect data within their own clusters and areas to ensure that the entire network is secure.

Sign-on access to the network itself and to the other systems connected to the network can be controlled by the network manager. Specific security packages and software controls can be built into the network control center, network interface units, and bridges to allow only authorized users access to the network itself or any part of the network.

After a user has reached any system connected to the network, the access controls in that system take over. The data security administrator must include any necessary controls to allow or prevent access to specific applications, files, records, or fields within records. The network users play a primary role in securing data on a local area network. The access controls in the individual systems connected to the network and the centralized network access controls together make up the total access control protection for a network.

Control Through the Message Format

Security controls can also be enforced by the message format designed for the network. The message format can be used to record as much or as little user information as desired, and the information can be automatically stored in a network audit file. Such information can then be reviewed as often as wanted by management personnel, the data security administrator, EDP auditors, or other authorized personnel. Exhibit IX-1-3 shows a sample message format for a network.

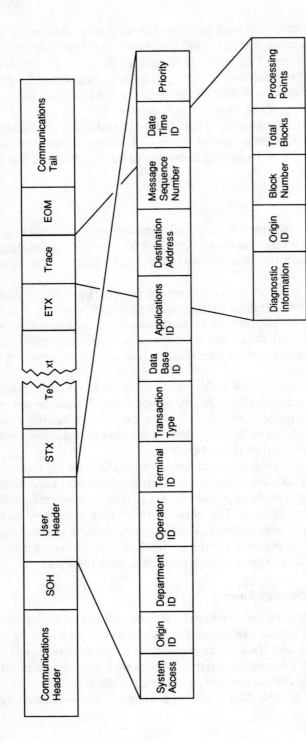

Exhibit IX-1-3. Message Format for LAN Security

Notes:
EOM   End of message
ETX   End text
SOH   Start of header
STX   Start text

The message format includes the communications header, user header, text, trace, communications tail, and various **start** and **stop** codes. The communications header establishes a circuit, synchronizes the equipment, and performs other preliminary routines. The trace includes diagnostic information, such as the number of retransmissions necessary and the number of operator-generated errors. The communications tail checks the message integrity and ends the message. The number and type of security controls to be tracked, however, can be built into the user header.

The user header can contain fields for system access and various levels of access identification. Organization and department identification codes can be used to provide greater control than just the system access code. A manufacturing department, for example, might not be given access to financial data from a different department. Further control can be provided by requiring additional operator and terminal identification codes. Operator identification codes can be used to prevent access by unauthorized users. Special codes can be used to limit users to specific files or applications. Such codes can also be used to evaluate training needs, such as too many unsuccessful access attempts by authorized users. Terminal identification can be used to identify origin points for transactions. The origination of payroll transactions, for example, may be limited to terminals in the accounting department.

SECURITY CHECKLIST

The checklist in this section is designed to help data security administrators and corporate management evaluate the automated and manual controls on a local area network. The checklist can be a supplement to any checklists currently in use.

The checklist is divided into five sections. The first four sections deal with controls over the LAN itself. They are used to evaluate the security policy, transaction accountability, assurance, and documentation of security controls. The fifth section deals with general controls that affect network security. The questions are answered by checking yes or no, identifying where the control is located (e.g., in the network control center, network interface unit, or authorization table), and identifying what document the control is described in. The purpose of the description document is to minimize the time required for any subsequent security evaluation and to provide a permanent record. The person performing the evaluation should initial each completed question so he or she can be contacted if additional information is necessary.

Security Policy

The LAN security policy is the total set of security rules enforced by the network. One security rule for a LAN, for example, is to control access to records so only properly authorized persons will have access to read, write, create, or delete data in the records. The entire set of rules (i.e., the security policy) should be documented, and the documentation should be made available only to those persons with a need to know. The following questions address specific areas that should be included in a LAN security policy.

Question	Response		Control Location	Description Document	Evaluator Initials
	Yes	No			
Are all the security control mechanisms within the LAN (i.e., hardware, software, firmware, and communications) documented?					
Does the LAN security policy define and control access between authorized users and LAN components (e.g., systems, programs, directories, files, records, and fields)?					
Does the LAN security policy allow users to specify and control access to and sharing of their personal components (i.e., as in the previous question)?					
Do the LAN security controls limit the unauthorized sharing of users' access rights?					
Do the LAN security controls protect LAN components, either by direct user action or by default, from unauthorized access?					
Can the LAN security controls provide access control by one user?					
By a group of users (other manual controls necessary for individual control)?					
Do the LAN security controls allow only authorized users to grant access to LAN components for new, unauthorized users?					
Do the LAN security controls allow network components to be isolated?					
Does the LAN security policy provide for data encryption or physical protection of the communications medium?					

Question	Response		Control Location	Description Document	Evaluator Initials
	Yes	No			
Do the LAN security controls ensure that data transmission accuracy requirements are met?					
Do the LAN security controls include tests, detection, and reporting of errors (e.g., bit error detection and correction)?					
Do the LAN security controls clear storage space (i.e., memory) before initial assignment or reassignment of such space to users?					
Do the LAN security controls revoke users' authorizations to data in LAN storage components before initial assignment or reassignment of such components?					

Transaction Accountability

Transaction accountability involves the identification of individuals who access the network, what data they are authorized access to, and what processing capabilities they have for such data. It also involves the recording of any security-related event in an audit log. The identification and authorization information must be securely maintained by the LAN and must be associated with every component that performs some security-related action in the LAN. The audit information must be kept and protected so that actions affecting security can be traced to the responsible party. The audit information must also be protected from modification and unauthorized destruction in order to permit detection and after-the-fact investigation of security violations.

Question	Response		Control Location	Description Document	Evaluator Initials
	Yes	No			
Do the LAN security controls require that entities (i.e., persons, devices, or processes) be identified before requested actions are initiated?					
Does the LAN maintain authentication data that includes information (e.g., passwords and security levels) for verifying entity identifications?					

Question	Response Yes	Response No	Control Location	Description Document	Evaluator Initials
Is the authentication data used by the network security mechanism to authenticate the identity of entities?					
Is the authentication data used by the network security mechanism to verify the security level and authorization of the entities?					
Do the LAN security controls protect authentication data from access by unauthorized entities?					
Can the LAN security controls uniquely identify each network entity?					
Can the LAN security controls associate each network entity with all its auditable actions?					
Can the LAN security controls create and protect audit records containing identification, access, and authentication data?					
Does the LAN security mechanism forward audit data to the LAN component responsible for maintaining audit trail information?					
Does the LAN security mechanism limit audit data (read access only) to those authorized?					
Does the LAN security mechanism record the following events:					
• The use of identification and authentication controls?					
• The introduction of components (e.g., programs and files) into a user's address space?					
• The deletion of components from a user's address space?					
• Actions by the LAN operator, administrator, and security officer?					
• Other security-relevant events?					

Question	Response		Control Location	Description Document	Evaluator Initials
	Yes	No			
Does the audit record for each recorded event identify: • The date and time of the event?					
• The user?					
• The type of event?					
• The success or failure of the event?					
For identification and authentication events, does the LAN security mechanism record the origin of the request (e.g., terminal ID) in the audit record?					
Is the capacity of the audit file and any security alarm file adequate for the number of users and transactions processed on the LAN?					
Are the communications ports properly balanced so audit and alarm files are consistently used and data is not lost?					
Will the audit and alarm files record required information when a user attempts multiple actions during a single connection?					
Can the audit and alarm files be bypassed by resetting LAN components to invoke a default configuration?					
If dial-up access to the LAN is possible, do adequate controls exist to record user access and prevent unauthorized access?					
Does the LAN security mechanism prevent users from using system commands (to bypass controls) instead of menu choices?					

Assurance

Assurance is the independent validation, by hardware, firmware, software, and communications controls, that the LAN security policy is being enforced. The hardware, firmware, and software controls should perform the tasks of identification, authentication, and other security-related actions in a secure manner. Typically, the controls are embedded in the LAN operating system. The controls must be protected from unauthorized changes and tampering throughout the LAN's life span.

Question	Response Yes	Response No	Control Location	Description Document	Evaluator Initials
Does the LAN security mechanism maintain memory space for its own execution?					
If so, is that space protected from external interference or tampering?					
Does the LAN security mechanism maintain distinct address spaces under its control to isolate its processing?					
Do hardware controls exist to adequately separate LAN elements that require protection from those that do not?					
Is the LAN security mechanism specified in terms of an industry standard?					
Does the LAN security mechanism grant the least set of privileges needed by a user?					
Is the order of priority for protocols specified for each hardware and software component?					
Are the locations and contents of any security-related controls within the protocols specified?					
Is there direct correspondence between the security-related controls within communications protocols and the security features in the LAN security mechanism?					

Question	Response		Control Location	Description Document	Evaluator Initials
	Yes	No			
Do hardware and software controls exist to periodically verify the correct operation of the LAN security mechanism?					
Has the LAN security mechanism been tested and found to work as claimed in the documentation?					
Has periodic testing for unauthorized access, erroneous communications, denial of service, or other security weaknesses been performed?					

Documentation

The LAN security mechanism must be adequately documented to allow for effective security and use of the network. The documentation should cover the security features built into each component of the network and how the components interact with each other. The documentation should also include an explanation of how security privileges should be controlled, how security in each LAN component was tested, and the results of those tests.

Question	Response		Control Location	Description Document	Evaluator Initials
	Yes	No			
Have all LAN component developers provided a summary, chapter, or manual that describes the security mechanisms in the component?					
Have the LAN component developers provided guidelines on the use of the security mechanisms and how they interact with other LAN security components?					
Does a manual for the LAN security administrator present cautions about functions and privileges that should be controlled when operating the network?					
Does a manual describe the detailed audit record structure for each type of audit event?					

Question	Response		Control Location	Description Document	Evaluator Initials
	Yes	No			
Have the LAN component developers provided documentation that describes the security test plan, test method, and test results for each LAN component?					
Does the documentation include tests and results for unauthorized access, denial of service, and erroneous communications?					
Is documentation available that describes the LAN component developers' approach to protection against compromise and how such an approach works in the component?					
Does any documentation describe the interfaces between the LAN security mechanisms?					

General Controls

General controls are those controls that may exist outside the automated LAN components. In this checklist, general controls are broken into four sections. These sections are organizational controls, developmental controls, network management controls, and network protection controls. The controls include manual controls that are a key supplement to the automated controls previously covered. Such manual controls are essential to securing any information system, including LANs.

Organizational Controls. The organizational controls include separation of duties and personnel policies.

Question	Response		Control Location	Description Document	Evaluator Initials
	Yes	No			
Is the LAN management function independent from other operations?					
Are LAN administrators and security officers prohibited from having authority or duties in other departments?					

Question	Response		Control Location	Description Document	Evaluator Initials
	Yes	No			
Are the following LAN functions performed by a different individual or group:					
• LAN systems analysis and design?					
• LAN systems programming?					
• LAN program testing?					
• LAN equipment operation?					
• LAN data base management and update?					
• LAN assignment of user interface units and identification codes?					
If not, do adequate compensating controls exist?					
Is there a clear line of responsibility between supervisors and subordinates?					
Is there a personnel rotation policy within the LAN department?					
Are LAN department personnel required to take regular vacations?					
Does the LAN department have a low turnover rate?					
Low absentee rate?					
Are LAN department employees who resign or are terminated relieved of their duties immediately and denied access to all LAN resources?					
Are there security screening policies for LAN employees?					
Are there security screening requirements for contractor and service personnel?					

Developmental Controls. Developmental controls include system design and acceptance practices.

Question	Response Yes	No	Control Location	Description Document	Evaluator Initials
Does the organization follow a formal methodology for systems development?					
Does the LAN development process include:					
• User requirements definition?					
• Conceptual system design?					
• Cost/benefit analysis?					
• LAN vulnerability analysis?					
• Detailed test plans?					
• Acceptance testing based on performance specifications?					
• Implementation and conversion plans for operation?					
• A postimplementation evaluation plan?					
Do users prepare and submit properly authorized requests for new or revised LAN capabilities?					
Are test results reviewed by systems analysts and designers?					
Are procedures effective to ensure that no data is lost or erroneously changed during system conversion?					
Was the LAN adequately tested in parallel with the old system?					
Does the LAN have adequate backup power for all components?					
Does the LAN program manager have senior management support regarding security controls?					
Does the user actively participate in the LAN development?					

Question	Response		Control Location	Description Document	Evaluator Initials
	Yes	No			
Are all LAN subnetworks and components subject to acceptance testing?					
Does such subnetwork and component testing evaluate whether both manual and automated security processes perform in accordance with total LAN specifications?					
Was the LAN acceptance test performed by a group independent from those who designed and installed the network?					
Did such testing represent true operating conditions (i.e., live data in expected peak volumes)?					
Did such testing include examples of routine, complex, and illogical transactions?					

Network Management Controls. Network management controls include resource accountability, errors, malfunctioning reporting, and preventive maintenance.

Question	Response		Control Location	Description Document	Evaluator Initials
	Yes	No			
Is there a formal LAN control center?					
Does the center maintain a formal inventory of network interface units (e.g., serial number, user, and data assigned)?					
Have all LAN users been formally authorized to use the network?					
Does the LAN security officer regularly check the LAN configuration to ensure that all components are authorized?					
Does the LAN administrator verify network interface unit configurations after a unit has been serviced by maintenance personnel?					

Question	Response		Control Location	Description Document	Evaluator Initials
	Yes	No			
Is the logical address of each network interface unit recorded?					
Do LAN control center personnel periodically verify the network interface unit user and logical address?					
Do LAN control center personnel have a policy to deny LAN access to users who do not have a valid interface unit address?					
Does the center have a priority scheme to allow more critical users LAN access before less critical users?					
Does the LAN control center maintain logs of all LAN processing actions?					
If so, does the log record:					
• Device log-on time?					
• Device errors?					
• Files accessed or used, by device?					
• Device log-off time?					
• Other recording? (describe)					
Does the LAN controller automatically produce a log of all LAN operation?					
If so, does the log list:					
• Date of operation?					
• Job name and number?					
• Job start and stop times?					
• All files accessed or used?					
• Record counts?					
• The user-network interface unit performing the actions?					

Question	Response		Control Location	Description Document	Evaluator Initials
	Yes	No			
Are all logs reviewed by LAN center management daily and filed as a permanent record?					
Are security-related events immediately posted to alarm files and acted on?					
Are disposition notes entered on audit and alarm logs to show the corrective action taken?					
Are all audit and alarm log pages and entries sequentially numbered?					
Are all logs independently exam-ined to detect operator problems and unauthorized interventions?					
Are all LAN malfunctions recorded and reported?					
Are the solutions to malfunctions recorded, matched to the malfunction reports, and permanently retained?					
Does the LAN center maintain a regular preventive maintenance schedule for LAN components?					
Is there documented evidence of the time and type of maintenance that was performed?					
Is all sensitive data removed from all online storage devices before the equipment is turned over to maintenance personnel?					

Network Protection Controls. Network protection controls include physical security and access controls.

Question	Response		Control Location	Description Document	Evaluator Initials
	Yes	No			
Has responsibility for conducting periodic risk analyses been formally assigned?					

SECURITY

Question	Response Yes	No	Control Location	Description Document	Evaluator Initials
Has a risk analysis been performed?					
If so, did it measure the network's vulnerability to:					
• Inadvertent error or improper disclosure of information?					
• Fraud or theft?					
• Financial loss?					
• Harm to individuals from infringement of privacy rights?					
• Loss of proprietary data and harm to organizational activity?					
Are the time periods between risk analyses commensurate with the sensitivity of data processed or changed in the LAN?					
Do procedures require a risk analysis to be performed before approval of design specifications for the LAN?					
Do procedures require a risk analysis to be performed whenever significant changes to the LAN (e.g., to the physical facility, hardware, software, or communications) occur?					
Has responsibility for the LAN security been formally assigned?					
Do the individuals responsible for LAN security have both LAN and security experience?					
Are all employees required to attend training and sign an agreement regarding security responsibility, ownership, and use of data on the LAN?					
Do procedures exist to handle an employee who becomes a suspected LAN security risk?					

Question	Response Yes	Response No	Control Location	Description Document	Evaluator Initials
Is physical access to the LAN control center limited to authorized personnel?					
Are access controls adequate?					
Are LAN center personnel trained to challenge improperly identified visitors?					
Are all other LAN components adequately protected from unauthorized access?					
Are all LAN center and user personnel counseled to report all cases of security intrusion (either inadvertent or intentional) to security personnel?					
Are LAN center personnel present when maintenance personnel work on LAN components?					
Are all unused LAN connections disabled, physically monitored, or otherwise controlled?					

EVALUATING DEFICIENCIES

After the security checklist is completed, evaluation of the security deficiencies must be performed. Such an evaluation requires the consideration of compensating controls, possibly some testing of actual controls to ensure proper functioning, and estimating potential financial losses and exposures from security breaches.

Compensating controls reduce the likelihood of unauthorized access to, or modification or loss of, data. Each weakness in security policy, transaction accountability, assurance, or other type of control should be analyzed to determine whether other controls adequately protect data despite that security weakness.

If such weaknesses are found, even with compensating controls, actual testing of the deficiency should be done to provide convincing evidence of the security weakness. Such testing may also provide insight into other potential weaknesses not identified by the checklist.

If a security weakness is confirmed, a risk assessment of the particular weakness should be performed. The assessment should determine the potential financial losses from the unauthorized access of, or modification or loss of, data. This will enable the data security administrator to make informed decisions on whether additional security measures are warranted.

SUMMARY

Application of this security checklist should help a corporation evaluate the existing or planned security controls for a LAN. After the security deficiencies are evaluated, compensating controls are considered, and the risks are quantified, informed recommendations to executive management can be made regarding the need for additional security controls to adequately protect that key corporate asset—data.

IX-2
Security and Controls of Microcomputer Networks

FREDERICK GALLEGOS • THOMAS R. HALSELL

Although a LAN can consist of such devices as intelligent terminals, minicomputers, and supermicrocomputers, this chapter emphasizes the networking of microcomputers. Any references to LAN and personal computer networks (PCNs) refer to the networking of microcomputers.

A network represents a substantial investment in microcomputer equipment, network equipment, network operating software, shared software, individual user software, data, personnel, administration, and training. The network or the information contained in the network files may represent an organization's major assets. Therefore, an organization must evaluate the security and controls to be used in the LAN. A control is anything that reduces or eliminates the potential loss of an asset. Security and controls can be classified as physical security and access controls, environmental controls, software and data security controls, and administrative security controls.

PHYSICAL SECURITY AND ACCESS CONTROLS

The objective of physical security and access controls is to prevent or deter theft, damage, and unauthorized access and to control movement of PCN equipment and attached devices. Some physical controls also prevent unauthorized access to data and software.

General physical controls that can be used to protect office equipment and PCNs include personnel badges, which help employees identify unauthorized personnel, and alarms and guards, which deter theft of PCN equipment. In addition, placement of the PCN equipment and office design will further secure the PCN. For example, PCN equipment should be placed in areas where office traffic is light. If possible, the microcomputers, printers, and other equipment should be placed behind locked office doors. Network managers may want to use combination locks to prevent duplication of keys; another alternative is to use a locking device that operates on magnetic strips or plastic cards—a convenient device when employees regularly carry picture identification badges.

The PCN equipment should be attached to heavy immovable office equipment, permanent office fixtures, special enclosures, or special microcomputer workstations. The attachment can be achieved with lock-down devices, which consist of a base attached to permanent fixtures and a second interlocking base attached to the personal computer equipment. The bases lock together, and a key, a combination, or extreme force is necessary to remove the equipment. All PCN equipment must be locked down to prevent unauthorized movement, installation, or attachment.

Many microcomputers and other equipment attached to the network may contain expensive hardware and such security-sensitive devices as hard disks, encryption boards, added memory, graphics and color cards, print spoolers, software cards, and PROM, EPROM, EEPROM chips. The removal of these devices not only incurs replacement costs but could cause software to fail and may be a means of circumventing security or allowing for unauthorized disclosure of such company-sensitive information as customer lists, trade secrets, payroll data, or proprietary software. Internal equipment can be protected by lock-down devices, as previously discussed, and special locks that replace one or more screws that secure the top of the equipment. These special locks are called CPU locks because they prevent access to the CPU area.

Cabling enables the various users and peripheral equipment to communicate. However, cabling is also a source of exposure to accidental or intentional damage or loss, which can be caused by the weather, by cutting the cable, or when someone is detaching or attaching cable to and from equipment. In many networks, if the cable is severed or damaged, the entire system will be impaired.

Cabling should not be accessible to either the environment or individuals. The network manager may want to route and enclose cabling in an electrical conduit. If possible and if the exposure warrants the cost, cabling can also be encased in concrete tubing. By encasing the cable, unauthorized access through attachment is lessened. In addition, unauthorized movement of the cabling will not occur easily and will enable the network manager to more efficiently monitor and control the network and access to it.

To alleviate potential downtime, cable may be laid in pairs. If one set is damaged, the alternate set can be readily attached. The second pair is usually protected in the same manner as the original but is not encased in the same tubing to prevent the same type of accident from damaging the second cable.

ENVIRONMENTAL CONTROLS

All PCN equipment operates under daily office conditions (e.g., humidity, temperature, smoke, and electrical flow). However, a specific office environment may not be suited to a microcomputer because of geographic location, industrial facilities, or employee habits. A primary problem is the sensitivity of microcomputer equipment to dust, water, food, and other contaminants. Water and other substances can not only damage the keyboard, CPU, disk drive, and floppy disks but also may cause electrocution or a fire. To prevent such occurrences, the network manager should adhere to a policy prohibiting food and liquids at or near the microcomputer.

Although most offices are air-conditioned and temperatures and humidity are usually controlled, these conditions must nonetheless be evaluated by the network manager. If for any reason the environment is not controlled, the manager must take periodic readings of the temperature and humidity. If the temperature or humidity is excessively high or low, the microcomputer equipment and the network should be shut down to prevent loss of equipment, software, and data. When microcomputer equipment is transported, either inside or especially outdoors to a new location, the equipment should be left idle at its new location to allow it to adjust to the new environmental conditions.

Airborne contaminants can enter the equipment and damage the circuitry. Hard disks are susceptible to damage by dust, pollen, air sprays, and gas fumes. Excessive dust between the read/write head and the disk platter can damage the platter or head or cause damage to the data or programs. If there is excessive smoke or dust, the microcomputers should be moved to another location. Small desktop air filters can be placed near smokers' desks to reduce smoke, or the network manager can limit smoking to specific locations away from microcomputer equipment.

Static electricity is another air contaminant. Static electricity can be reduced by using special sprays that can be applied to the bottoms of shoes, by placing antistatic carpeting and pads around the microcomputer area, and by using antistatic chair pads and keyboard pads. Machines can also be used to control static electricity in an entire room or building.

Major causes of damage to PCN equipment are power surges, blackouts, and brownouts. Power surges, or spikes, are sudden fluctuations in voltage or frequency in the electrical supply by the public utility. They are more frequent near an electrical generating plant or power substation. The sudden surge or drop in power supply can damage the electronic boards and chips as well as cause a loss of data or software. If power supply problems occur frequently, special electrical cords and devices can be attached to prevent damage. These devices are commonly referred to as power surge protectors.

Blackouts are caused by a total loss of electrical power and can last seconds, hours, or days. Brownouts occur when the electrical supply is diminished to below-normal levels for several hours or days. Brownouts and blackouts occur infrequently but are disruptive to continuing operations. If microcomputer use is essential and the organization's usual backup power is limited to necessary functions, special uninterruptible power supply (UPS) equipment can be purchased specifically for the microcomputer equipment. UPS equipment can be either battery packs or gas-powered generators. Battery packs typically are used for short-term tasks only (e.g., completing a job in progress). Gas-powered generators provide long-term power and conceivably could be used indefinitely.

SOFTWARE AND DATA SECURITY CONTROLS

Data and software security and access controls are the key controls over a microcomputer network. (Software and data security controls are referred to as data security throughout this chapter because both controls provide security.) A microcomputer network has two levels of data security. The first is access and use of local standalone microcomputer capabilities; the second is access and use of the network system and its capabilities. These two levels can be integrated through the installation of certain security software and hardware. However, the organization must be aware that these two levels exist to provide the security for all the network's functions as required.

The objective of data security is to prevent access by unauthorized users and restrict authorized users to needed data and functions. Authorized users should be restricted to the use and access of specific data, screens, software, utilities, transactions, and files.

Password and Data Access

The key to PCN security is user authentication. Although badges and personal identification are common authentication tools, they can fail at all levels of security. Other methods of authentication can be obtained by the computer system itself. Special software and hardware are available that allow authentication of users through the entering of an ID number and a password.

A PCN has two levels of password and user ID security requirements. The first protects local microcomputer access and use, and the second protects network access and use. The user ID and password used for the local microcomputer will be a double safeguard to network access. To access the PCN, the user must have a valid user ID and password for local use, and that password can be set up to restrict access to the network user ID and password screen. In addition, this double security can be used to restrict users to specific computers and limit specific computers to the network.

On a PCN, the first user ID and password entered control the use of the standalone capabilities of the microcomputer and related equipment. The second user ID and password control use of and access to equipment and software shared by all users interconnected through the network software and cabling. If the user ID matches the standalone microcomputer authorization table and the user's access includes network use, the user will be allowed to enter a network user ID or password. The user's network password and ID will be validated by the network software, and network capabilities will be limited as instructed by the network software.

User IDs and passwords are practical and economically feasible in most situations. If the risk of loss is high and the cost can be justified, card IDs or a voice authentication system can be added to the user ID and password system.

Password and user ID design and secrecy are key factors in the effectiveness of the user ID and password system. Passwords must not be written down by employees or shared with others. A major benefit of passwords is traceability of the use and misuse of the system. Employees are responsible for their own passwords and user IDs and can be held accountable for the actions taken on them. Because it must not be easy to guess or decipher user IDs and passwords, the network manager should discourage the use of nicknames, acronyms, birth dates, social security numbers, department names or numbers, or personal characteristics.

A password system should never allow passwords to be displayed on the log-on screen. Any individual who is present would then have knowledge of the password and could, ultimately, access the system. The only acceptable printing of a password should be for the network manager's permanent record, and even that listing must be retained in a highly secure vault to prevent unauthorized viewing. An effective security system will protect the actual user ID and password file from other users' access. The password system should disable a user ID in the event a correct password is not entered in three attempts. The user ID and password will be reestablished only after the security administrator has been notified and satisfied that the error was accidental. Any willful or potentially fraudulent problems require swift resolution. At times it may be appropriate to lock the microcomputer from use when user IDs or passwords appear to be randomly guessed by a user.

In addition to the use of passwords and user IDs, a security system must list the user IDs and microcomputer locations of all security violations. The actual violation (e.g., an attempt to use an incorrect password or to access unauthorized systems) must be logged, and the security administrator must investigate and resolve the problem.

Passwords and user IDs can be used to segregate duties by limiting access to systems, files, read or write capabilities, screens and screen displays. Segregation of duties can be achieved at both the standalone microcomputer and the network. Duties must be segregated in microcomputer networks as they are with local microcomputer use, because the traditional separation of duties seen in mainframe systems is circumvented. Computer operations, systems development, systems programming, and application programming in a microcomputer environment are usually at the hands of the user, who can perform various programming, operations, and application functions by simply reading a book and applying the knowledge.

To segregate duties on the PCN, security software must be in place. The software limits not only access to specific programs and data but also the user's capabilities to DO commands and programming tools. In addition, the software must monitor what a particular command or program is doing—such as formatting disks or making global copies or deletes. The security software will prevent accidental errors and possible theft of sensitive data.

Encryption

Encryption is a technique of creating unintelligible information (i.e., cipher-text) from intelligible (i.e., cleartext) information. The same algorithm is used to create the ciphertext from cleartext and convert the ciphertext back to cleartext. The algorithm uses a key to tell the mathematical equation where to start producing the ciphertext. The key must be given to the program that will decipher the text. For encryption to be effective, the passage of the key and the algorithm must be kept secret. Programs must not be hard coded with the key, nor should the key be written down. The key and the algorithm are often encrypted or written in machine language to prevent the casual user from intercepting code messages.

Encryption is useful in protecting sensitive information (e.g., password, user ID, and payroll files). Any sensitive message or transmissions must be encrypted to prevent interception either by someone on the network or by someone using highly sophisticated electronic equipment (all microcomputers emit electromagnetic signals that can be detected by other electronic equip-ment). Another way of protecting transmissions is to use fiber-optic cabling in place of twisted-wire cabling. A combination of encryption and fiber optics ensures transmission security.

Encryption can be provided by either hardware or software. It can be as uncomplicated as a simple algorithm or as complex as the National Institute of Standards and Technology's Data Encryption Standard. The choice depends on the level of security required or desired by the organization. If encryption is widely used within the organization, the public key system should be used. The public key system requires that the sender create the ciphertext on the basis of the receiver's public key. The receiver will decipher the information using his or her private key. The public key system eliminates the passing of the key, which can threaten its secrecy.

Backup, Recovery, and Data Storage

Data and software on local microcomputers and on the network need to be copied and archived periodically. Backup copies can quickly and accurately restore misplaced diskettes and erased files and diskettes. The backup method must allow the restoration of individual files, directories, partitions, and disks. Tape backups that allow restoration of the entire hard disk only can cause data integrity errors on data for files and directories that do not require restoration. If one file requires restoration on the basis of a previous day's backup, any files updated since the backup will not reflect those updates after the restoration.

Users should perform the backups for shared data. The data backup should be in the same format as that on the original disk. Encrypted files must be backed up as encrypted files, and files that require a password to be accessed must be stored in that manner. This prevents circumvention of security by accessing the backup and copying its contents. Moreover, if the backup format is not the same as the original, a backup tape that is used to restore information there will weaken security until the files are reprotected.

At least two backup copies should be made of all data and software. One copy is filed for permanent off-site storage to protect against some damage that would possibly destroy the PCN and the software, and the second is stored on site for quick and ready access in the event of data or software loss. Backup must be frequent if control is to be effective.

The method of backup and master copy storage chosen is critical to efficient and effective PCN management and control. One copy of data should be stored off site daily. All on-site backup and master copies should be protected from fire, theft, water, and accidental loss. The on-site copies must be stored in fireproof and waterproof vaults designed for the protection of magnetic media. The network manager must implement a library and backup checklist to ensure that backups are made and accounted for regularly.

Software and Other Controls

Software that accesses shared data on the network must be designed specifically for a multiuser environment. Single-user software may cause data integrity problems, data access problems, or network crashes. For example, if user A accesses a file and begins changing information, the applications software does not actually change the data on the disk; rather, it changes the data in the memory of user A's microcomputer. If, however, while user A is editing or inputting, user B edits the same file, when users A and B then save their copies of the same file, the only changes made to the file will be user B's—all of user A's changes will have been overwritten by user B's version of the file.

One method of avoiding the previously mentioned access problems is to design access locks. These locks do not allow a user to update specific data while another user is already updating that data. Locks can be provided by either applications or network operating system software. These locks can be user requested or automatically implemented. They limit access to data fields, records, file transaction types (read or write), directories, or software systems.

Access locks must be used for all files accessed by applications that are used on the network. Applications must lock data that is necessary to complete a particular task to prevent deadlock, which occurs when application A has locked access to a file or piece of data and then requires a second item. Meanwhile, application B has locked application A's desired second item and now requires A's locked data. Neither application will release the data until the other releases its data, resulting in both applications waiting for the other to release its data. Applications software and the network operating system software must provide a method of releasing inaccessible files or data without stopping the application.

Data and software used in the PCN can be controlled by using diskless microcomputers. The major loss of data, security, controls, and privacy occurs through the availability of diskettes. Users can copy data or software to or from the PCN. However, without diskettes, microcomputer users would require extensive time to type in programs that could be damaging. If applications already exist on diskettes, the diskettes could be given to the network manager, who would review their contents and load the software. Thus, the PCN would be controlled from loss of privacy of sensitive data. The diskless microcomputer can provide greater control over local and network access but does require greater administrative and organizational controls.

ADMINISTRATIVE SECURITY CONTROLS

The administration of the PCN is similar to the management of any data processing facility. The network manager's main objective is to prevent, detect, and correct unauthorized access to the network's hardware, software, and data to ensure the network's sound operation and all security surrounding the local microcomputer and the microcomputer network processing.

Before any security controls can be implemented, the network manager must perform a risk assessment of the PCN. Risk assessment is the task of identifying the assets, the threats to the assets, and the probability of loss of the assets as a result of a particular threat. The loss is determined by quantifying the dollar value of the assets lost and multiplying that value by the probability that the loss will occur. After risk assessment is complete, the organization will have the information to determine the security and safeguards that must be implemented. The safeguards and controls will lessen the loss in the event of a disaster or control violation.

After implementation of the necessary controls, daily management of the network is required. Daily management ensures that security controls are maintained, though changes occur in the software, applications, and personnel. Daily management can be classified into various categories, which are discussed in the following sections.

Physical and Environmental Controls Management. All such controls in active use must be tested periodically. Such testing includes the evaluation of the effectiveness of current controls and the implementation of additional controls as determined to be necessary. The results of testing of physical and environmental controls should be reported to senior management.

Data Access Management. The network manager must assign and maintain user IDs and passwords and associated file and data access schemes as well as receive computer-generated reports of attempted unauthorized accesses. Reports on data access and traffic analysis should also be reviewed. These reports will allow the administrator to manage network growth and help foresee future security needs.

Policy and Procedures Documentation Review. The objectives here are to provide standards for preparing documentation and ensuring the maintenance of the documentation. The network manager must set documentation standards so that when employees change jobs, become ill, or leave the organization, replacement personnel can perform the tasks of that employee. The manager must also periodically test the documentation for clarity, completeness, appropriateness, and accuracy.

Data and Software Backup Management. Backup media must be labeled, controlled, and stored in an appropriate manner. The network manager must maintain control logs of all backups as well as provide documentation on how to recover files, data, directories, and disks.

Other Management Controls. Internal and external audits, contingency and disaster recovery planning, personnel background checks, and user training are included in this category. Auditors can aid in establishing proper testing requirements and in reviewing, testing, and recommending the proper controls to establish the necessary safeguards. Contingency planning or disaster recovery is essential to the proper maintenance of the PCN. The contingency plan establishes the steps to recover from the destruction of hardware, software, or data.

Personnel background checks must be performed on all employees who have access to key organizational information. The background check should involve a review of credit history, financial health, personal problems, and other areas that may identify potential risks. This information can help establish potential integrity breaches before they occur.

User training must be established for all network functions. Users must be trained in microcomputer use, general computer knowledge, security, policies and procedures, consequences of noncompliance, and general network use. In addition, users should undergo more specific training for the different software on the network as required. Such basic training can prevent many problems from occurring.

OTHER RISK CONSIDERATIONS IN A MICROCOMPUTER NETWORK

Assessing risk in a LAN should also include how the system is connected. Three areas of concern are media, topology, and software and protocols.

Media

Media are the cables with which computers are connected. Three types of cables are found in today's LANs: twisted pair, coaxial, and fiber optic. Twisted-pair wire is individually coated copper wires twisted together. They are encased in plastic and may contain up to 24 pairs. Twisted-pair wire is used as telephone wire. In fact, because telephone wire has two sets of wires, one of which is not used, some LAN installations may ride on the currently installed line. Twisted-pair wire is generally the least expensive of the three types of cabling. However, the IBM PC Network LAN uses twisted-pair wire that must meet IBM specifications, adding considerable cost to this medium.

Coaxial cable is a copper or multistrand wire encased in an insulator (e.g., Teflon). The insulator is surrounded by a mesh wire, which is then encased in plastic. This type of cable is much more resistant to electromagnetic interference but is more expensive than twisted-pair wire.

Two types of transmission can be supported by coaxial cable: baseband and broadband. Baseband is a single flow of data and is also supported by twisted-pair cable. Broadband combines the flow of data with a carrier signal by means of a modem. A modem at the other end of the transmission translates the carrier signal back to the data transmission.

Coaxial cable supports a wider bandwidth than twisted-pair wire. Bandwidth is the speed capacity for transmitting data. For example, to transmit 10 million bits per second, the medium requires a bandwidth of 10 MHz. The user should be wary, however, of judging the speed capacity of a LAN by the media and bandwidth used. Other factors in LAN design have more significant impact on performance. For example, coaxial cable also supports voice and radio transmission, an important consideration for departments that desire future flexibility.

Fiber-optic cable is the most expensive medium. With this medium, computer transmissions are converted to light transmissions, which are reconverted to electronic transmissions at the receiving end. This new type of medium has the widest bandwidth and is resistant to electromagnetic interference. In addition, it is the most resistant to tapping.

Exhibit IX-2-1 summarizes the risk characteristics of twisted-pair, coaxial, and fiber-optic cable.

Each LAN vendor specifies which medium is to be used. For example, the AT&T StarLAN uses standard twisted-pair cable, the Orchid PC Net uses coaxial, and the IBM PC Token-Ring Network uses the IBM cabling system, which uses a variety of high-performance cables. However, IBM has stated that standard telephone wiring can be used under some conditions.

The potential LAN user should carefully evaluate media requirements. Such issues as cost, interference, and future expansion needs should be con-

	Cost	Installation	Bandwidth	Interference	Susceptible to Tap
Twisted-Pair Cable	Low	Easy	Low	Susceptible	High
Coaxial Cable	Medium	Moderately difficult	Medium	Susceptible	High
Fiber-Optic Cable	High	Difficult	High	Not susceptible	Low

Exhibit IX-2-1. Media Risks

sidered. However, a LAN configuration should not be purchased solely on the basis of an evaluation of media. Other system features substantially affect the performance of the selected LAN. Most important, the potential user should not be overly influenced by the speed rating or bandwidth.

Topology

Topology refers to the configuration by which the workstations are interconnected. The three basic topologies include bus, star, and token ring. Risks in this area focus on their application and use.

In a bus topology, a single cable runs past every workstation and the ends of the cable are terminated with special equipment. In the token-ring configuration, the cable runs past all workstations but the ends are joined, forming a ring. In the star topology, each workstation is connected directly to a server or hub. Variations of these topologies include distributed stars, in which two or more star configurations are linked together, and the star-wired ring topology, which combines the star and ring schemes.

Topologies are determined by the network vendor, and each has advantages and disadvantages. The bus topology is simple; however, a faulty workstation may be difficult to isolate. The star topology enables the user to locate cable faults easily because each workstation is connected to the server by an individual cable; this type of system requires more cabling than the other two configurations. If the workstations are located in dispersed locations, this can add considerably to the cost of cable and installation. An overview of topology risk factors is shown in Exhibit IX-2-2.

	Bus	Token Ring	Star
Application	Small networks	Few workstations at high speeds	Integrate voice and data
Complexity	Uncomplicated	Relatively complex	Very complex
Performance	Excellent in light load	Average transmission delays are long	Direct function of central node
System Overhead	Low	Medium	High
Vulnerability	Workstation failure does not affect network	Workstation failure can cause system failure	If server fails, system fails
Expandability	Easy	Modification cost low but temporarily disrupts network	Severely limited; server may support limited number of workstations

Exhibit IX-2-2. Topology Risks

Software and Protocols

One of the most important tasks of the LAN is to traffic requests from the workstation for files and network resources. This control task is accomplished by software protocols, which are formal rules that govern the exchange of information between computers and provide reliable, effective, and efficient transfer of information. Without protocols, the system would be in chaos with unanswered requests, improperly routed data, and workstations monopolizing resources.

Major software protocols include contention, polling, and token passing. Contention includes simple contention and carrier-sense multiple access (CSMA). In simple contention, the system performs in the manner of a meeting when people talk at will. What happens, however, when two people talk at once? Or when two workstations send messages simultaneously?

In the network, messages are converted to packets. If packets are sent by two workstations at the same time, they will collide and the packets will be destroyed. Although contention does not check whether another station is transmitting at the same time, it does provide a system by which the receiving station sends an acknowledgment that the packet has been received. If the sending station does not receive an acknowledgment, it will assume that the packet was not received and will retransmit.

CSMA is an access method that can be likened to a business meeting in which participants wait for a break in the conversation to make their contributions. In CSMA, a workstation monitors the transmission channel to determine whether any other workstation is transmitting and transmits when the line is free. As with contention, the station awaits an acknowledgment that the packet has been received. This is necessary because collision is still possible in the situation in which two stations sense a free line and transmit at the same time. A workstation waiting to send a packet can continually monitor the line for an opportunity to transmit, which is known as persistent carrier sense. Or in another scheme, the workstation can wait for a random period to reinitiate transmission. The scheme is known as nonpersistent carrier sense. Nonpersistent carrier sense results in fewer collisions.

Two subsets of CSMA are used in LAN technology: CSMA with collision detection (CSMA/CD) and CSMA with collision avoidance (CSMA/CA). In collision detection, the workstation continues to monitor the line after transmission. If a collision is detected, transmission is halted, and retransmission occurs after a random or unique delay for each workstation. This reduces the risk of two stations retransmitting at the same time. In collision avoidance, workstations wait for an opportunity to transmit and then transmit their intention to send a packet when the line is clear. If two workstations are contending for access, their precedence is determined by a preestablished table. In this mode, features must be implemented to ensure that an individual workstation does not dominate the network. For example, in some implementations, the recipient station has the first right to transmit.

The polling protocol performs very much as a moderator at a meeting would, calling on participants for contributions. In a polling network, primary workstations call on secondary workstations to determine whether they have information to transmit. If a workstation does, it may be allowed to transmit immediately or be assigned a time to transmit. To avoid work degradation, packets to be sent are stored in a buffer in the secondary workstation. In some polling implementations, priority can be assigned a workstation by polling it more than once a cycle, polling it less than once for each cycle, or polling it according to a recently established activity level.

The token-passing protocol is similar to a meeting in which the gavel is passed and a participant may speak only when the gavel is in hand. In the network implementation of this arrangement, a bit pattern known as a token is passed among the workstations. When a workstation receives the token, it has the right to transmit. The message and routing information are written to the token and passed through the network.

An empty token consists of a header, data field, and trailer. A token that has been assigned a message contains a new header, destination address, source address, routing, data message, and new trailer.

Each workstation determines whether the passed message is intended for its use. If not, it is passed. The recipient workstation reads the message and marks it as copied or rejected. The token is eventually routed back to the originating workstation. Only the originator may remove the message. This protocol reduces the risk of colliding packets.

Exhibit IX-2-3 summarizes protocol risk evaluation factors.

	Contention	Polling	Token Passing
Message Length	Short packets	Tends to be larger than contention	Moderate to long
Traffic Volume	Low	Moderate to high	Quite high
Network Length Constraints	Length increases risk of collision	Limited by media	Limited by media
Performance	Excellent under light-to-medium loads	Excellent for moderate loads	Excellent for most conditions
Overhead	High	High	High
Access Delay	Moderate to long	Relatively long	Moderate delay in heavy traffic
Station Failure	Station failure does not affect network	Secondary station failure does not affect network	Station failure disruptive only in older LANs

Exhibit IX-2-3. Software Protocol Risks

SUMMARY

Personal computer networks are becoming increasingly popular in business settings. PCN implementations must include security controls to provide protection of physical and information assets. The level of protection required must be established through risk assessment. The risk assessment team must include members of senior management in order to establish the priority of asset protection.

Once risk assessment has been completed, the level of security can be achieved by implementing physical, environmental, and software and data access management controls. Any controls implemented must not cost more than the potential loss that the control was established to prevent, deter, detect, or correct.

The key control over a PCN is the use of passwords. Passwords establish data and software access schemes that provide for segregation of duties. This key control must be rigorously maintained.

IX-3
A LAN Security Review

ROBERT KLENK • PETER CLUCK

The introduction of a LAN into a computing environment introduces some security and reliability concerns. In the single-user microcomputer environment that usually precedes a LAN installation, the protection of data is simpler: one user controls a microcomputer, including that computer's physical security, data backup, and the reliability of the information in the system. In a LAN environment, resources are shared. The system may have a central file server that contains such applications as spreadsheets, word processing, and data base management as well as critical and sensitive data. A LAN turns each system location into a miniature data center, complete with data center security concerns.

This chapter discusses the control measures Novell Inc implemented in its LAN operating system, called NetWare. General examples apply to most LAN operating systems, and implementations specific to NetWare are pointed out.

The network manager's review of security and control in the LAN will estimate the level of:

- Confidentiality of information on the LAN.
- Reliability of information on the LAN.
- Reliability of the network (e.g., is the data backed up periodically as needed?).
- Performance of the network.

THE LAN ENVIRONMENT

The LAN hardware includes the cables and circuit boards that physically connect the microcomputers or mainframes to the LAN and carry messages around the system. The software is the LAN's operating system.

Most LANs transmit data over coaxial cable or twisted-pair wires. Fiber-optic technology has great potential for very high speed data transmission and combined data and video service, but it is more expensive. Optical fiber has a higher bandwidth, better security, no electrical interference, and fewer installation problems.

The network topology is the physical design or structure of the system. In general, topologies can be described as trees, stars, or rings, but in large networks, a combination of these architectures may be used. A star LAN has a central hub and a point-to-point communications circuit to every other device on the network. If the central controller stops working, the entire network stops. This architecture has high overhead cost and vulnerability. Ring LANs pass messages from node to node until they reach their destinations. Each element plays an active role in transmission, so failure of two or more elements can isolate sections of the ring. The tree architecture arranges elements like leaves on a tree, and the devices share the main transmission medium, also called a bus. Messages are transmitted along the bus to other attached devices. Each topology presents different control considerations.

One role of the LAN software is to provide services directly to the user; another role is to support the applications that run on the network. NetWare designates one machine in the network as the file server. It contains the shared hard disk and runs the network operating system. This ensures data integrity for the network and allows for proper control and management of all network resources.

NetWare's fault tolerance increases the dependability of the LAN by safeguarding against failure in critical parts of the network hardware. For example, NetWare makes two copies of the file allocation tables (FATs) and directory entries and stores them on different disk cylinders. If a failure occurs in a directory sector, NetWare automatically switches to the duplicate directory. When the system is turned on, NetWare automatically performs a complete consistency check on each duplicate directory and FAT. Every time data is written to the network disk, the network automatically performs read-after-write verification to guarantee that the data is legible.

LAN SECURITY REVIEW

The first step in performing a security review is to obtain an understanding of the LAN and its applications. NetWare structure and commands are described in several volumes of product documentation.

NetWare is similar to MS-DOS in that both provide commands that allow manipulation of stored data. MS-DOS manages data stored locally in the microcomputer and supports the applications running on the microcomputer; NetWare manages network access and data stored on the network hard disk. NetWare does not replace the operating system of a workstation that is still needed for running applications.

LAN software has three major components: the operating system (DOS in this case), the shell, and the file server. The shell and file server are NetWare components in this case. DOS and the shell are present at most workstations. The file server software manages the network resources and synchronizes disk access so that there are no conflicting file requests. The network server runs the file server software; workstations run only the shell and DOS.

A virtual console function, called **FCONSOLE**, lets authorized users perform file server console operations from any workstation on the network. The user may have the security level equivalent to supervisor to execute commands that affect more than one workstation. The activities performed by **FCONSOLE** include controlling and shutting down the file server, viewing the server's status, monitoring file-locking activities, broadcasting console messages, purging salvageable files, viewing software product information, viewing a station's console privileges, restricting access of management features to certain users, listing a connection's open files, listing connections using an open file, and viewing the system mapping table, physical disk statistics, and disk channel statistics.

User Rights and Access

The NetWare **SETLOGIN** utility is an important tool for customizing the LAN environment. It enables the network manager to automatically set up drive mapping, run programs, display messages, and perform other functions. The functions executed with **SETLOGIN** determine the chain of events that take place during log-in. **SETLOGIN** can be used to customize the network log-in procedure for each user.

NetWare permits use of the **MAP** command to map a particular drive letter to particular directories during log-in (e.g., the Lotus 1-2-3 directory can be mapped to drive C, or the WordPerfect directory can be mapped to drive D). Mapping also sets up the search-drive facility, which is similar in function to the DOS **PATH** command.

The NetWare commands are usually in **SYS:PUBLIC**; most default scripts include this as a search drive. Only the system supervisor should have access to all NetWare commands, and only those commands that are needed by a user should be available to that user.

Certain files can be executed during the **SETLOGIN** script. Those files will be executed during log-in (e.g., # **WP** will execute WordPerfect). Similar to executing a .**BAT** file in DOS, this can be done using the **INCLUDE** command from **SETLOGIN**. All or part of a log-in script can be stored in an ASCII text file. This is usually done to facilitate standard log-ins for certain groups of users.

Additional variables in the **SETLOGIN** script are based on three elements: user names, workstation attributes, and the data and time. The script can be customized to display the date and time and a user's name. Tests can be performed on the workstation or user ID using the script's if-then programming features.

Restricted Commands

Each network operating system has certain commands that are so powerful they must be restricted to authorized individuals. Such commands:

- Add, change, or delete users.

705

- Establish connection to other LANs.
- Powerfully affect files across the networks (e.g., hide files).
- Powerfully affect the security of the LAN (e.g., alter read or write access in directories).

In NetWare, these commands typically are restricted:

- SYSCON—Enables a system supervisor to modify a file server's directory and security structure and add users, groups, and directories to a server.
- HIDEFILE—Hides a specified file so that it does not appear in a directory search and cannot be deleted or copied.

Exposures and Threats

During a LAN security review, the network manager should classify the exposures and threats to the LAN. A major exposure is a network user who is not properly identified. The most common means of identifying users is to issue a user ID and password to each user. Controlling user IDs (e.g., requiring periodic password change requirements) is necessary. In addition, restrictions can be placed on user log-ins, as shown in Exhibit IX-3-1.

NetWare provides a specific security function—the SECURITY command—that lets the system supervisor check for possible holes in the network security, identify who has been given the security level of supervisor, and check conformance to password rules. Occasionally, this utility can supply useful and surprising results. The command must be executed by someone with a supervisor security level.

Unauthorized Devices. To prevent an unauthorized device from transmitting on the LAN, the network manager should verify the configuration and periodically visit the locations.

Unauthorized Commands. It is possible to store unauthorized commands on the microcomputers that are used for workstations, and some of these workstations may have hard disks with other copies of the NetWare commands. Nevertheless, the user's overall system security level still indicates what the user can do. For example, if the user has a SYSCON security level, that user can access files only at that level.

Unauthorized File Sharing. A LAN might allow unauthorized file sharing or resource sharing if the network is not secure. Some users may not have the proper security level assigned to them, or they may have update capabilities for files that should be restricted to read-only access. The available NetWare rights include READ, WRITE, OPEN, CREATE, DELETE, CHANGE (directory rights), MAKE (new subdirectories), ERASE (existing subdirectories), SEARCH (directories), and MODIFY (file status flags).

NetWare System Configuration V2.12   Monday June 10, 1991 11:06 am
User CLUCK __P On File Server PENN5

	Account Restrictions For User CLUCK__P	
	Account Disabled:	No
	Account Has Expiration Date:	No
AL	Date Account Expires:	
AR	Limit Concurrent Connections:	Yes
BA	Maximum Connections:	1
BI	Allow User To Change Password:	Yes
BI	Require Password:	Yes
BR	Minimum Password Length:	6
BR	Force Periodic Password Changes:	Yes
CA	Days Between Forced Changes:	60
CA	Date Password Expires:	August 9, 1991
CL	Limit Grace Logins:	Yes
CL	Grace Logins Allowed:	1
CO	Remaining Grace Logins:	1
CO	Require Unique Passwords:	Yes
	Limit Disk Space:	Yes
	Maximum Disk Space (in kilobytes):	5,000

Exhibit IX-3-1. User Log-In Setup Screen

Applications

LAN applications include those usually run on a microcomputer (i.e., word processing, data base management, spreadsheet, graphics, and communications). Communications applications may include dial-up access to outside services and a gateway to mainframe sessions.

NetWare provides application program interfaces (APIs) for network applications. For example, a resource accounting API allows applications to use information generated by the accounting portion of the operating system. A network management utility that bills for resource use is one example. The queue management API is used to manage print jobs for a print server or a script for an archive or for a batch job server. The network diagnostics API creates information for applications that depend on statistical information from the network. File server function calls are accessible from the virtual console API. Any applications that are designed to monitor system security can use the security API. This interface permits the review of unauthorized access.

NETWORK ADMINISTRATION

The NetWare system has the ability to limit a user's access to designated directories, to specific workstations, or during certain times of day. The number of resources that one user can tie up during a period of time can also be limited. The system uses nonreversible password encryption to store passwords, and an optional capability requires users to change their passwords after a specified period, to not reuse previous passwords, and to use passwords of a minimum length. In addition, the system has a parameter to specify the number of invalid log-in attempts before the system locks the user out. These optional controls are highly recommended.

Physical Security

Safeguarding a LAN starts with physical protection of the LAN hardware. The degree of physical security depends on the risk analysis that identifies threats and exposures. The main LAN server requires special protection because it can act as a system console in which commands can affect the entire network. The LAN workstations might require a limited-access area if, for example, the data accessible to its users is sensitive. Components of the LAN and their locations and intended uses should be evaluated carefully.

Media for carrying the LAN communications include:

- Copper cable.
- Fiber-optic cable.
- Wireless transmission equipment (i.e., microwave, radio, and infrared transmission).

If the information on the LAN is sensitive, the most secure medium to use is fiber-optic cable; the least secure is wireless transmission. Physical protection from wiretaps should be installed with sensitive data. For example, communications involving national security are often sent over wires. The pipes carrying these wires are filled with a liquid that, if the pipe is cut, sets off a pressure-sensitive alarm.

Ordinary LAN installations will not require this extreme physical protection. However, the degree of physical protection of a network from wiretapping depends largely on the medium used to carry the data transmission. It is easy to passively wiretap (i.e., just listen to) a copper cable. It is much more difficult to listen in on fiber-optic cable. Regardless of the transmission medium, few problem-solving technicians have devices to listen to data as it crosses the network.

Access Control

User names and passwords are part of the LAN log-in procedure. During log-in, NetWare asks for a user name; when the name has been accepted as an authorized user of the network, NetWare asks for a password. When a password has been accepted, the user is recognized as a particular profile. According to the profile, the user is given access to certain applications, data files, commands, and network resources and is given specific rights to the applications and data files on the appropriate access list. In NetWare, such rights are specifically defined as read, write, open, create, delete, parental, search, and modify.

Password security controls access to the file server. Trustee rights specify the degree of access a user has to files in a directory. Directory security determines what a user can do within a directory. File attributes determine what access is available to individual files.

Security Limitations. Many LANs have components that are outside the immediate physical premises. To verify the components and connections of a network, the network manager might have to visit several locations. To view all the security parameters, the reviewer must have a supervisor security level.

Audit Trails

Audit trails are the record of LAN activities. Because the record of which user did what may be crucial to security, the audit trail should include invalid log-in attempts and attempts to access data outside a user's restrictions. These logged items require follow-up to determine whether security policies are being violated.

The recent versions of NetWare have the **ACCOUNTING** option, which enables the system to record log-ins and system use. Other NetWare products, such as **LTAUDIT**, are available to provide more flexible audit trails of system use.

Backup and Disaster Recovery Planning

A disaster recovery plan should ensure that essential applications are restored as quickly as possible after a disaster. System backup is always a necessity.

External devices (e.g., tape drives, removable disks, cassettes, parallel drives, cartridges, and optical disks) can be used to provide backup capability for files. Other backup and contingency plan aids include uninterruptible power supplies, redundant processors, inventory of additional equipment, and problem-detection tools.

A review of the LAN should include a check to see that backups are performed regularly. Evidence should substantiate this; the backup tapes or disks should be tested on another system.

Concurrency

LANs introduce the problem of record concurrency (i.e., when two or more users try to access the same file or record simultaneously). In NetWare, there is a system utility called **HOLDON/HOLDOFF**, which can hold a network file open so that it cannot be accessed by two or more users simultaneously. Most LANs have a comparable utility.

SPECIAL RISKS AND CONCERNS

Special security concerns are introduced with the LAN environment. Some LANs permit an open port on the file server, allowing portable or laptop computers to link to them. This should be eliminated if it is not acceptable for a particular situation.

In addition, all LANs are not standalone networks. Other networks may be accessed from a LAN, or a LAN may tie into others. The LAN security review should determine what other networks are accessible and whether they access the LAN in a secure manner. Asynchronous bridge software is included with the NetWare operating system. This allows bridges to take LANs beyond local-distance boundaries. It makes connecting with another LAN as easy as changing a computer's disk drive.

Another special risk is server-to-server communication. This should be reviewed in the same manner as network-to-network communication.

A link to a mainframe always raises the question of information integrity. The token-ring attachment enables a LAN supporting IBM's token-ring topology to include a 3174 mainframe with the token-ring support option as if it were another workstation on the LAN. Some early LAN gateways did not properly disconnect a user from a mainframe session. That is, when a user logged out of a mainframe session, the LAN did not disconnect the host session. The LAN then accepted the next user requesting a mainframe session as the first user, which created a security problem.

Dial-up access presents another concern. There are many products that enable a remote user to dial up and gain access to a LAN. Once this is done, a remote user may have the same capabilities as a local user. The network manager should treat the dial-up access as another application and should review who can use it and what characteristics those users have once they are connected to the LAN.

ACTION PLAN

A step-by-step approach to the LAN security review must be tailored to the specific needs of the organization. The review should include steps to:

- Identify the users with supervisor system privileges.
- List all users on the system and what they can access.
- Evaluate the exposures (e.g., mainframe access, system utilities, directory sharing, and trustee rights).
- Run the SECURITY (or equivalent) utility to identify vulnerabilities in the system—This will help identify any users with supervisor privileges, who do not require passwords and are not required to change them.
- Identify the file server on the LAN and review the overall physical security.

- Review the system for external connections (i.e., ports and modems) and draw a schematic diagram of the LAN.
- Use SYSCON (or an equivalent utility) to review the existing controls.

Performing the Review

The LAN security review should include steps to:

- Determine the scope of the system, including what external devices the LAN can use—The NETGEN (or equivalent) file should be reviewed.
- Use the SYSCON command to identify who the system users are—The groups existing in the system should be identified and the account restrictions for users listed.
- Identify the critical resources on the system—SYSCON can be used to determine who has access and whether it is authorized.
- Use SYSCON to determine what other LANs can be attached—If possible, the users of the other LANs should be determined.
- Have the SECURITY utility executed—The output from the screen should be printed and reviewed for any holes in security.
- Identify the system administrator and review how users are given access and granted rights—System defaults should be verified.
- Review any disaster recovery plans that exist for the LAN (assuming that it is critical enough to warrant one)—The availability of backup devices should be considered.
- Review the backup of files and software, determine its location, evaluate its environmental security, and verify that the proper files are being retained.
- Observe the physical security of the file server, cabling, modems, and location of any external devices.
- Review the logical process of connecting to mainframes (dial-up or gateway)—These connections can support file transfer with CICS, VM/CMS, or MVS/TSO environments.
- Review some of the log-in scripts to determine whether certain users have automatically signed on to applications during their log-in process.
- Review the list of network users who are currently logged in, using the USERLIST command-line utility.

Interpreting the Results

The results of the review should be presented to management, who will determine the action to be taken on outstanding security and control issues. On the basis of the criticality of the applications running on the LAN, the following recommendations can be made:

- Users should have only the access levels required to perform their routine job functions.

- All users should be required to use log-in passwords and to have them changed regularly—Passwords should be a minimum of five characters and should not be reused.
- System software and critical files should be backed up regularly and stored in a secure location.
- Additional critical hardware devices should be obtained to provide a secure level of redundancy in case of primary device failure.
- There should be a formal procedure to add users and resources to the LAN.
- Because of the critical nature of the file server, the access to this component should be properly controlled.

IX-4

General Communications Security Services and Protocols

JOSEPH J. TARDO

Data communications standards promote the widespread interconnection of large numbers of geographically dispersed, heterogeneous computing elements. This ability to access information and resources, however, can introduce major security problems and risks if it is not suitably controlled. It is therefore important for data communications standards to include appropriate security features and mechanisms.

The need for security is becoming increasingly acute as larger networks become commonplace. Early standardization forestalls the proliferation of proprietary approaches to security that tend to negate the benefits of a standards-based solution.

Security problems are generally complex and are best approached methodically. High-level requirements and goals should be expressed in terms of security policies that indicate criteria for identification of and access to sensitive or critical information and resources. These policies should also detail circumstances under which individuals can be held accountable for their actions and specific procedures (e.g., dual control) that are designed to institute a set of continuous internal checks or audits.

To plan for and eventually configure a secure system on the basis of standards, a network manager needs to know which security features are necessary to support security policies, which standards exist (or are likely to exist soon) that specifically address security, and which of the standards have (or are likely to have) the needed security components or extensions. This chapter offers guidelines for assessing specific security needs and focuses on security in general communications facilities, including open systems interconnection (OSI). The standards field is constantly changing as new standards are approved and new groups are formed. The emphasis in this chapter is therefore on approved standards, with a brief mention of ongoing developments.

STANDARDS BODIES ACTIVE IN SECURITY

Almost all standards bodies that are developing data communications standards have some security activity or interest. Some standards bodies, however, exist primarily for the purpose of producing security standards. Representatives of computer manufacturers and communications service providers are the major contributors in these committees, although a number of user groups are also represented.

Within the US, the American National Standards Institute (ANSI) Accredited Standards Committee X3T5.7—Information Processing Security—and the Institute of Electrical and Electronics Engineers (IEEE) standards committee 802.10—Interoperable LAN Security—focus primarily on encryption. Internationally, the International Standards Organization/International Electrotechnical Commission Joint Technical Committee 1, subcommittee 20 (ISO/IEC JTC 1 SC20)—Data Cryptographic Techniques, for which ANSI X3T1 is the US Technical Advisory Group (TAG)—has developed standards for encryption algorithms and for the standardized application of these algorithms.

ISO/IEC JTC 1 SC20 developed procedures for the registration of cryptographic algorithms and standards for both physical link encryption and modes of operation for 64-bit block ciphers. ANSI X3T1—Data Encryption—developed the standard for the data encryption algorithm (DEA), which is essentially the same as the data encryption standard (DES) algorithm published by the US government. Maintenance responsibilities for this algorithm are at present being reassigned within ANSI. ISO, mostly for political reasons, has elected to publish standards for applications of encryption only, not for actual cryptographic algorithms.

ISO/IEC JTC 1 SC21 Working Group 1—Security Rapporteur Group—focuses primarily on communications security architectural questions relating to OSI and other communications models. This committee was responsible for drafting the OSI security architecture, ISO 7498/2, and is actively working on other security models and frameworks. The US technical advisory group is ANSI committee X3T5.7.

ISO/IEC JTC 1 SC21 Working Group 6—Security Rapporteur Group—is primarily focused on OSI upper-layer security issues. This committee drafted the authentication amendment to the association control application service element (ACSE) standard, ISO 8649/AM 1, and is working on other upper-layer security components, including the security exchange application service element (SA-ASE). The US TAG is also ANSI committee X3T5.7.

ISO/IEC JTC 1 SC21 Working Group 4—Management Security Rapporteur Group—focuses primarily on security issues in the management of OSI networks. The US technical advisory group is the security management ad hoc group within ANSI committee X3T5.4.

JTC 1 security work was reorganized in 1989. A new subcommittee, ISO/IEC JTC 1 SC27, is expected to assume the work program of SC20 but with a broadened scope, permitting it to address some security issues beyond cryptography. This group should provide a focus for coordinating all the security standards development work within JTC 1.

The European Computer Manufacturers Association (ECMA) technical committee (TC) 32 technical group (TG) 9 considers security in distributed open systems and has produced a report on a security framework for open systems. It has also published ECMA 138, Data Elements and Service Definitions. TC32 TG9 is developing a distributed system security architecture.

The International Telephone and Telegraph Consultative Committee (CCITT) Study Group VIII considered placement of security in the telematic services during the study period that ended in 1988. CCITT Study Group VII drafted the directory authentication framework and the specifications for security teleservices in directory systems and message transfer systems included in the 1988 X.500 and X.400 recommendations. During the 1992 study period, security standards are being developed jointly with ISO by the distributed applications security group.

Most standards interpretive bodies have elements dealing with security as well. Examples of these subgroups include the Security Special Interest Group of the National Institute for Science and Technology (NIST) Implementer's Workshop, the security working group within the Manufacturing Automation Protocol (MAP) and Technical Office Protocol (TOP), and the European Open and Secure Information Systems (OASIS) committee.

A table of international standards organizations with their respective responsibilities is given in Exhibit IX-4-1.

OSI SECURITY ARCHITECTURE (ISO 7498/2)

Any discussion of data communications security standards invariably begins with the OSI security architecture. Familiarity with this standard is recommended for anyone in the security field; in particular, its extensive list of security definitions is very useful. This section provides a brief overview of ISO 7498/2 and assumes a familiarity with the seven-layer OSI reference model (ISO 7498) shown in Exhibit IX-4-2.

General Description

ISO 7498 provides a reference model architecture that serves as the conceptual basis for the development of standards for open systems. ISO 7498/2 extends this basic model to include security-related concepts and architectural elements for circumstances in which communications must be protected against threats to security. It identifies basic security services and mechanisms and describes where each should be placed within the seven-layer OSI model. It also provides guidelines for and identifies constraints on the use of these services and mechanisms in an attempt to provide a consistent security approach within OSI.

Standards Organization	Committee	Subcommittee	Responsibility
ISO/IEC	JTC 1	SC6	Transport and network encryption and lower-layer security model
		SC18	Secure messaging
		SC20	Cryptographic techniques, digital signatures, and physical-layer encryption
		SC21	OSI security architecture, presentation encryption, application authentication, higher-layer security model, and frameworks
	TC68		Financial message authentication, wholesale and retail, and bank cards
ECMA	TC32	TG9	Open systems security
CCITT	SG VII		Directory authentication and secure messaging
	SG VIII		Security in telemetric services
IEEE	802.10		LAN encryption

Exhibit IX-4-1. Principal International Standards Organizations Involved in Security Standards

Basic Security Goals

The network manager must be concerned with controlling access, protecting data, and providing individual accountability and auditing throughout the information processing environment. OSI focuses only on the visible aspects of a communications path, not on end-system measures. The basic communications security goals of the OSI security architecture, therefore, include:

- The prevention of unauthorized disclosure of information.
- The prevention or detection of unauthorized tampering with or modification of information or services, including the substitution, destruction, or corruption of information or services (i.e., masquerading) or the reordering or replaying of messages.

Layer 7	Application
Layer 6	Presentation
Layer 5	Session
Layer 4	Transfer
Layer 3	Network
Layer 2	Data Link
Layer 1	Physical

Exhibit IX-4-2. The OSI Reference Model

- The prevention or detection of the unauthorized use of resources or services.
- The prevention or detection of unauthorized denial of service or interruption of service attempts.

The precise definition of authorization in all of these goals depends on the particular security policy in effect. Two forms of authorization policy are identified in the OSI security architecture:

- Identity-based authorization—Permission is based ultimately on the identity of the requestor, including his or her membership in a group.
- Rule-based authorization—Permission is based on matching security labels and attributes associated with the requestor and the resource.

Identity-based policies are usually discretionary in nature; the granting of access rights is generally under the control of the owner or creator of the resource rather than the system administration. The familiar access controls used to determine individual, group, and organizationwide privileges are an example of a mechanism that can be used in conjunction with an identity-based authorization policy. Rule-based policies, which are generally mandatory and imposed by the system administration, operate so that security-access attributes are always determined by the system according to the rules. Military classifications and clearances are an example of a mandatory, rule-based policy mechanism.

Security Services and Mechanisms

The OSI security architecture identifies a number of security services and mechanisms. These are discussed in the following sections.

Authentication. There are two forms of authentication services. The first, peer-entity authentication, applies only to connection-oriented services and peer entities named within OSI. When service is provided by layer n, it provides corroboration to the next higher layer $(n + 1)$ that its peer entity $(n + 1)$ in a particular connection or association is the one claimed. For example, the transport layer can vouch for the identities of session layer entities communicating through a transport connection because these entities are uniquely determined by transport service access points.

The second form of authentication service, data-origin authentication, is similar to the first except that it applies on a connectionless (i.e., single data unit) transfer basis. A distinction is made between these two forms of service because more effective mechanisms can sometimes be employed for peer-entity authentication.

Authentication mechanisms rely on an exchange of information or credentials to prove or substantiate a claimed identity. One familiar mechanism uses secret passwords, in which both ends know the password and one proves its identity to the other by producing the shared secret. The secret is lost if a third party is able to eavesdrop or if the password is presented to the wrong challenger.

A more robust authentication mechanism uses some form of shared secret function, in which one entity challenges another by presenting some data that only the correct remote entity could properly transform. Cryptographic techniques, such as data encipherment or digital signatures, can be used in place of a password to demonstrate the knowledge of a secret key without disclosing the secret. It is important to note that each challenge could be made effectively unique so that every response would match exactly one challenge. These responses could not then be replayed, as can encrypted passwords or even encrypted time vectors.

The bidirectional data exchange inherent in connections and associations permits authentication by means of challenges and responses, whereas the single one-way transfer inherent in connectionless data does not. At best, data-origin authentication permits an assumed challenge, such as a time-varying quantity or sequence number, to be used to approximate an identifier that can only be used once. Peer-entity authentication can also provide resistance to the unauthorized replaying of authentication exchanges, whereas data-origin authentication provides only limited indications of misuse.

Access Control. Access to systems or applications is usually granted on the basis of the authenticated identity of the remote system or application. The OSI security architecture provides access control services at the application, transport, and network layers; some of the security mechanisms available include access control lists, capabilities, and security labels.

Data Confidentiality. The data confidentiality service protects against the inadvertent or unauthorized disclosure of data in transit. A number of forms of the basic service are identified in the OSI security architecture.

Connection-oriented and connectionless services may be appropriately provided at any layer except the session layer, depending on the particular configuration, because no one layer can provide protection for all contingencies. For example, the most effective protection against an external threat on a single link is usually link encryption. For point-to-point links, encryption at the physical layer usually suffices. Encryption at the physical layer is also the basis of the traffic-flow confidentiality service, which protects against the possibility that an intruder might observe such patterns in communications traffic as the length of messages.

For multiparty links and LANs or LANs interconnected through bridges, encryption at the data link layer may be sufficient. When relatively secure LANs are interconnected using public packet-switched data networks (PPSDNs), network layer encryption between points of subnetwork attachment may be more appropriate. In other circumstances (e.g., for end-to-end encryption over multiple subnetwork hops), confidentiality should be established at the transport layer or above. Selective encryption of fields within a message (rather than the encryption of entire associations or connections) can be provided only by a combination of mechanisms at the presentation and application layers.

Confidentiality can also be provided by mechanisms other than encryption. In the OSI security architecture, the only alternative specifically discussed is routing control. A measure of traffic-flow confidentiality can also be realized by traffic padding—either within messages or with dummy messages transmitted at regular intervals—at the network and application layers.

Data Integrity. The data integrity service protects against the unauthorized alteration of data in transit. As with the data confidentiality service, the basic service takes several forms.

The connection-oriented integrity service may be applied at the network, transport, and application layers. In addition, connection-oriented data integrity may include automatic recovery (i.e., retry) at the transport and application layers. The connectionless integrity service may be provided, without recovery, at the network, transport, and application layers. As with data confidentiality, data integrity can also be provided for selected data fields by a combination of mechanisms in the application and presentation layers. Specific data integrity mechanisms can include the use of a cryptographic checkvalue, possibly with security sequence numbering or time stamps.

Nonrepudiation. The nonrepudiation service provides protection against a denial that communication took place. This service may be provided on behalf of the recipient (i.e., proof of origin) or the sender (i.e., proof of delivery). Because it depends on particular application semantics, it is provided only in the application layer. Nonrepudiation may be mechanized using a combination of data integrity and digital signature techniques in conjunction with key management (e.g., the archiving of keys). Implementing nonrepudiation will most likely involve the use of at least one trusted third-party notary.

Management. The OSI security architecture also provides a section outlining security management concepts. Primary among these is the security management information base, a conceptual aggregate of all relevant security information necessary to provide OSI security services and mechanisms. The security management information base is a logical concept whose elements may be implemented in various ways in real open systems; it is not itself a specified component. Another concept introduced in the management section is that of the security domain. Although not defined precisely, a security domain is a collection of entities that are under a common security administration and subject to the same security policy.

The OSI security architecture identifies several specific systems security management activities, including security event-handling management, security audit management, and security recovery management. It also describes a number of security mechanism management functions, including the management of cryptographic key material, access control, authentication, and routing control.

Impact and Acceptance

The influence of the OSI security architecture standard was felt even before it was formally published in the spring of 1988. The standard is considered by many to be a landmark public document on network security. It provides an extensive list of definitions, but more important, it also provides a basis for other work in the area, most notably the Department of Defense (DoD) Secure Data Network Study (SDNS) and OASIS, as well as continuing work in security frameworks and models within ISO.

THE ECMA AND STANDARDS FOR SECURITY IN OPEN SYSTEMS

As the ISO was developing the OSI security architecture, the ECMA published technical report TR/46 on security in open systems. TR/46 was developed by ECMA task group TG9 on security under ECMA technical committee TC32, whose overall area of responsibility is communications, networks, and system interconnection.

TR/46 identifies the following functional requirements for security:

- Access control, including authentication, authorization, and proxy access (permitting entities to act on one's behalf).
- Resource protection.
- Information protection in processing and storage as well as during an actual interchange.
- Management, including administration, auditing, and recovery.

TR/46 focuses on security functions necessary for building secure distributed open systems applications. In particular, its security model is based on the approach of subjects accessing objects, with access mediated by security facilities according to user and application policy requirements. Conceptually, it identifies 10 security facilities:

- The subject sponsor—The processing element or elements acting directly on behalf of the user.
- Authentication.
- Association management.
- Security state.
- Security attributes management.
- Authorization.
- Interdomain.
- Security audit.
- Security recovery.
- Cryptographic support.

The report also identifies supportive security applications as possible mechanisms for developing components within a security architecture. Supportive security applications are application processes that follow the client-server model described in TR/42's framework for distributed office applications. These processes may be used to provide or manage security functions within a security domain or to provide support for secure interactions between domains.

This work is in ECMA-138, which describes data elements and services used to implement the concepts in TR/46. It provides a much more detailed model based on security policies and domains, including security services interfaces and protocol security attributed data structures. These are described using abstract syntax notation, in ASN.1, per ISO 8824. The authentication service has six primitive operations (i.e., **AA-Authenticate, AA-ChangeAuthentication, AA-TerminateAuthentication, AA-CheckID, AA-Recovery,** and **AA-Management**) that use security attributes such as privilege attribute certificates and integrity class.

Relation to ISO 7498/2

The ECMA work builds on the ISO work by providing a conceptual basis for addressing security in the upper layers as well as specific protocol definitions to support this model. It also deals with distributed (multiparty) applications. Many felt that the OSI security architecture was limited by the scope of the reference model, which stresses the pairwise aspects of the interconnection of open systems.

Network managers should consider TR/46 as containing mostly valuable tutorial information for understanding the problem and a potential solution methodology for eventual distributed application security. The definitions in ECMA-138 will eventually be candidates for inclusion by reference in other applications protocol standards.

CRYPTOGRAPHIC TECHNIQUES

The first published standards dealing with security techniques defined a particular encipherment algorithm, the data encryption algorithm (DEA). DEA (ANSI standard X3.92-1981) was essentially the ANSI version of the US government's data encryption standard (DES), published by NIST; subsequent ANSI standards were initially based on this particular algorithm. Once work on cryptographic techniques moved into the international arena, however, the focus shifted to multiple algorithms.

In addition to encryption algorithms, integrity mechanisms, digital signatures, authentication exchanges, encryption in communications protocols, and key management have been the subject of standardization work.

DEA and DES

Considerable controversy has surrounded the data encryption standard and data encryption algorithm since their inception. Detractors have claimed that the algorithm was deliberately weakened during its review process so that the length of the key is shorter than originally proposed and that it has a trap door that allows knowledgeable parties to easily decipher transcripts. No hard evidence has emerged, however, that the DES is vulnerable to any form of known cryptanalytic technique other than the brute force method of trying all possible keys. Furthermore, the US Department of State, which controls the export of all encryption equipment under the International Traffic in Arms Regulations, tends to impose tighter constraints on the export of the DES than on other proprietary algorithms. NIST continues to reaffirm the DES whenever it comes up for periodic review; it is published as Federal Information Processing Standard 46 (FIPS-46) and is available from the National Technical Information Service.

The general concept of standardized, public encryption algorithms itself has been controversial. Proponents argue that because a standardized algorithm is used by vast numbers of experts, it is more likely that any weaknesses will be discovered early on. Opponents, pointing to the experience of the Allies in World War II, claim that knowing the algorithm gives the cryptanalyst a major advantage. Furthermore, opponents insist that it is ill-advised to rely solely on one algorithm given the increasing processing power of today's computers. For the DES in particular, the possibility of winning a brute force attack against its 56-bit key becomes more realistic with each advance in supercomputer technology.

Within the international standards community, the opponents of the DES have prevailed; political considerations intervened when ISO JTC 1 SC20 attempted to publish the DES as ISO 8227 in 1986. Efforts to publish the draft international standard, although approved through the usual technical balloting process, resulted in an ISO Central Secretariat decision not to standardize cryptographic algorithms. Even without an official ISO document, however, the DES has been incorporated into a number of subsequent standards, in particular for financial applications.

Modes of Operation

The DES is a block cipher that provides a functional one-to-one mapping for each key from 64-bit vectors onto 64-bit vectors. Problems arise when larger blocks of data are enciphered because repeated patterns in the data that span 64-bit blocks (e.g., sequences of null or blank characters) produce repeated ciphertext patterns.

The modes-of-operation standards extend the usefulness of DES to such situations as data communications streams. Modes of operation are essentially procedures for combining plaintext and ciphertext using simpler operations, such as bitwise conditional vector complementation (exclusive-OR). NIST initially published three modes of operation in FIPS-81, and these were carried over intact to ANSI X3.106-1983. These modes are electronic codebook (ECB)—obvious block-by-block encryption—and two chaining modes that mask repeated data patterns—cipher-block chaining (CBC) and cipher feedback (CFB).

In cipher-block-chaining mode, the previous ciphertext block is combined with the current plaintext block using bitwise complementation (exclusive-OR) before the DES block encryption function is applied. The decryption process requires the two reverse steps: the ciphertext blocks are first passed through the DES and then undergo bitwise complementation with the immediately preceding ciphertext block. Cipher-block chaining can be applied only to messages that are a multiple of the 64-bit block size. To encrypt arbitrary-length messages, a form of padding is generally used. To process the first block of a message, a value known as an initialization vector is used in place of the ciphertext. In CBC mode, either the initialization vector can be sent encrypted in ECB mode as the first block of ciphertext or the same initialization vector can be used for all messages to save transmission. In the first case, a new initialization vector could be chosen for each message, thereby masking repeated transmissions of the exact same message. In the second case, the initialization vector is generally considered key material and is protected as if it were the actual DES key, although its effect is mainly on the first 64-bit block of text.

The CFB mode uses two similar steps but applies them in a different order. Cipher feedback first passes part or all of the previous ciphertext block through the DES and then combines the result with the next plaintext block using exclusive-OR. A new initialization vector is used to initialize each message cipher stream and is usually added to the beginning of each message. Cipher feedback can be applied on data that is blocked into sizes smaller than a DES 64-bit block, as is required for cipher-block chaining. In fact, because CFB block size can be as small as 1 bit, cipher feedback is often preferred for certain kinds of communications applications—for example, those that require encrypting 1 bit at a time.

The ECB, CBC, and CFB modes of operation were extended into the international standards arena after they were published by NIST and were published as ISO 8372 after they were generalized to apply to 64-bit block cipher algorithms. Standards for modes of operation for general bit-length block ciphers are described in ISO draft-proposed standard 10116.

Registry of Cryptographic Algorithms

Following the ISO Central Secretariat's decision not to standardize cryptographic algorithms, SC20 introduced a work item to develop a registry of these algorithms, published as ISO/IEC 9979:1990. The registry provides formal ISO names for registered algorithms, and although it does not require that details of the algorithms be divulged, it does require that the intended application area, interface requirements (i.e., whether it is a block or stream cipher), and a battery of test words be supplied. The registry is intended to provide an alternative to algorithm standardization by encouraging the development of algorithm-independent standards. Appointment of the National Computing Center in the UK as Registration Authority is being finalized.

Integrity Mechanisms and Digital Signatures

A block cipher such as the DES can be used to compute a cryptographic checkvalue analogous to the way addition and accumulation are used to compute a checksum. ISO 9797:1989 describes such a procedure using an n-bit block cipher as the function block and exclusive-OR for accumulation, much like the CBC mode of operation. Essentially the same procedure is used in ANSI X9.9-1987 for computing checkvalues on electronic funds transfer messages, but X9.9 specifically requires the use of the DES algorithm.

The ISO Central Secretariat ruling also prevented public-key algorithms, such as the Rivest-Shamir-Adleman (RSA) algorithm, from becoming standardized. ISO distinguishes public-key algorithms from such conventional algorithms as the DES by referring to them as asymmetric rather than symmetric. Asymmetric algorithms have two keys—an encryption key and a decryption key—whereas symmetric ciphers have essentially one key.

Asymmetric algorithms are useful for digital signatures. For example, the RSA algorithm permits encryption and decryption to be performed in either order. Assuming that the decryption key is kept secret, anyone with the corresponding public-encryption key can verify the source of a decrypted data buffer.

ISO is currently drafting two digital-signature standards. Proposed standard DP 9796 computes a digital signature with message recovery, in which the text to be signed is completely included in the signature and can be recovered during the signature verification procedure. The original text is encoded in a redundant form, making it unlikely that a random string of bits would be considered a valid signature. DP 9796 is self-contained in that it includes the description of the cryptographic procedures for signature computation and does not refer to any other document.

Digital signature with message recovery can be used only to sign data that is no longer than half the block length of the public-key algorithm. Another proposed standard computes a digital signature in which a hash or compressed encoding is signed rather than the actual data, thereby permitting arbitrarily long data (e.g., entire files) to be signed. To verify such a signature, the alleged original text is used to compute the hash, and then the public key is used to recover the hash as originally computed by the signer. The ISO is preparing committee draft 10118 to provide one or more standardized hash functions suitable for use in signature with shadow and other standards.

Peer-Entity Authentication Mechanisms

Several draft-proposed standards are under development for cryptographic peer-entity authentication mechanisms. DP 9798 uses an n-bit symmetric key algorithm and permits a challenge-response exchange. By enciphering a received challenge with its secret encryption key, one entity can demonstrate that it knows the commonly held key without divulging that key directly, as would be the case if a simple password scheme were used. Furthermore, if the challenge is chosen at random so it cannot be reused, the response cannot be recorded and then replayed later. DP 9798 also accommodates the use of a third-party authentication server. DP 9799 is similar to DP 9798 but uses asymmetric algorithms.

Choice of Encryption Algorithm

It may be necessary to decide whether to specify a standard algorithm (e.g., DES) or a proprietary algorithm. Despite continued controversy, DES remains cryptographically strong, and files and communications encrypted using DES are unlikely to yield to direct cryptanalysis. Usually it is the keys that are compromised or subverted, not the cryptographic system itself.

The decision rests on two main issues: interoperability and export. Although the use of DES cannot guarantee interoperability, use of nonstandard algorithms effectively precludes it. Export issues are of greater concern because, except for financial applications, proprietary algorithms are often easier to obtain outside the US and may often be exported or imported with fewer restrictions.

LINK ENCRYPTION

Many well-established standards cover encryption at the lowest two layers of OSI. These are primarily limited to providing the data confidentiality service. Physical-link encryption represents the most generally available form of communications encryption today, with equipment readily available from several vendors. Many such devices comply with existing standards to some extent, providing a useful gauge of their quality, but conformance to standards does not necessarily guarantee interoperability.

For example, none of the standards described in this section address key management procedures (e.g., the secure exchange of working keys). In general, easy key management tends to be the strongest motivation for selecting a particular manufacturer's offering over another, but reliance on proprietary provisions works against multivendor interoperability goals.

FIPS 139 (Federal Standard 1026)

FIPS 139, formerly Federal Standard (FED-STD) 1026, applies to the physical layer only and specifies the use of DES in 1-bit CFB mode to provide data confidentiality. FED-STD-1026 was originally developed by the National Communications System and published by the General Services Administration in 1983. As with other federal standards, FED-STD-1026 was developed primarily to meet the needs of government purchasing. It has since been taken over by NIST and republished as a Federal Information Processing Standard.

Essentially, FIPS 139 covers the minimal requirements for interoperability with security during actual data exchange. In particular, it dictates lengths and formats for initialization vectors and describes when to send the vector to resynchronize cryptographically after reestablishing communications. This standard, though not developed for this purpose, can provide confidentiality with data integrity if a higher-layer protocol provides suitable error detection. For example, if the high-level data link control protocol—described in ISO 4335 and ISO 3309—is used, its cyclic redundancy check might provide the necessary integrity mechanism.

FIPS 139 applies to simple point-to-point environments. It includes provisions for both synchronous and asynchronous (i.e., start-stop character) framed transmission, including specifications for partitioning the initialization vector when various asynchronous transmission character lengths are used. To an external observer, synchronous physical-layer encryption provides a continuous stream of random bits, masking the presence of data on the line.

ANSI X3.105-1983

The ANSI link-encryption standard, X3.105-1983, applies to both the physical and data link layers. Like FIPS 139, it provides only the data confidentiality service. Most of the physical-layer provisions are compatible with FIPS 139 but differ in certain details. For example, the ANSI standard places fewer restrictions on the choice of initialization-vector lengths and permits the use of 8-bit cipher feedback, which can be more quickly implemented than a 1-bit cipher feedback.

X3.105 introduces the concept of data enciphering equipment (DEE) situated between the data terminal equipment (DTE) and the network interface data communications equipment (DCE). In most cases, the DCE is connected to a local modem; X3.105 specifies how the DEE should interact with Electronic Industries Association (EIA) RS-449 and RS-232 interchange circuits.

X3.105 also covers encryption with data link protocols. At the data link layer, encryption is on a per-message basis, which permits multipoint physical links in which multiple stations share the same physical link and transmit at different times, using different cryptographic key relationships. Physical-layer encryption alone does not support multipoint links. Data link protocols may be preferable to physical link protocols for certain line conditioning techniques (e.g., statistical multiplexing) or when only a portion of the traffic needs to be protected. The major drawback to the use of data link encryption is that it leaves message pattern and header information exposed; physical-layer encryption provides better protection against traffic analysis.

X3.105-1983 accommodates various options for encryption at the data link layer. The preferred approach simply replaces the contents of the data information field (the I-field) with encrypted data, leaving header fields in the clear. The encrypted data includes a control byte and initialization vector in addition to the actual encrypted data; the I-field is handled as if it were to be transmitted transparently by whatever link protocol is in use, and the data enciphering equipment computes a new frame check-code trailer. No integrity check code is performed. This form was advocated by manufacturers who had designed their DEE products to receive data according to the link protocol, encrypt it, and forward the encrypted data to the decrypting device in what amounted to a cascaded data link connection.

An alternative protocol-sensitive approach to data link–layer encryption is full-frame encryption. In this approach, encryption begins at a specified point in the frame and continues to the end. The encrypted portion can include the block check code, which can then function as a form of integrity check. This type of operation is more complicated than the preferred approach because in certain circumstances it can generate bit patterns that can confuse data link equipment. The standard does not specify a solution to this problem, and individual manufacturers of data enciphering equipment have provided their own. Full-frame encryption was advocated by manufacturers who had taken a bit or byte cut-through approach to the design of data enciphering equipment.

ISO 9160

The ISO link-encryption standard, ISO 9160, published in 1987, is essentially consistent with FIPS 139 and the physical-layer components of ANSI X3.105. The ISO standard goes into great detail about the interface between DEE devices and the operation of the data communications equipment and the interface between DTE devices and DEE devices relative to internationally standardized protocols and CCITT-recommended protocols (e.g., V.24). The ISO document also discusses additional initialization-vector signaling methods.

ISO 9160 is algorithm independent, reflecting the ISO Central Secretariat's decision against standardizing encryption algorithms, and is therefore perhaps overly generalized in places. The annex to the standard, however, refers to the operation of the standard with the ANSI DES algorithm and contains most of the provisions of FIPS 139.

FIPS 140 (FED-STD-1027)

FIPS 140, formerly FED-STD-1027, covers the physical security of implementations of link-encryption equipment using the DES. For example, it describes the types of indicators that must be provided and how they should be controlled by a physical lock and key. It also addresses such things as emanation limits, antitampering requirements, battery-backup operations, continuous self-test procedures, and requirements for key protection, including conditions under which key material is to be zeroized.

FIPS 140 is essentially the same as FED-STD-1027, which was originally developed by the Communications Security Organization of the National Security Agency and published in 1982 by the General Services Administration. The National Security Agency used FED-STD-1027 as a basis for certifying commercial-grade DES algorithm link-encryption devices as suitable for use by such government agencies as the Treasury Department or the Federal Bureau of Investigation.

Starting in 1988, the National Security Agency shared responsibility for certifying commercial-grade encryption equipment with NIST. NIST is in the process of revising and updating FIPS 140. Much of the National Security Agency's earlier certification process was transferred to its commercial communications security endorsement program, to which a new set of documents applies. The program applies mainly to high-grade products that are capable of protecting both government-sensitive and DoD national security–classified information using proprietary, classified algorithms of the National Security Agency other than the DES. Documents produced by the program will not be published as standards but will, instead, be made available to qualified vendors on an as-needed basis by the National Security Agency.

FIPS 140 remains perhaps the only document of its type and is often cited in discussions concerning the physical security of encryption devices. Because it primarily addresses standalone DEE devices, its provisions tend to be overly restrictive for other types of devices (e.g., embedded option module and board-level devices).

DEVELOPMENTS TO WATCH

OSI Frameworks and Models

ISO/IEC JTC 1 SC21 has embarked on an ambitious program of security frameworks and models that are intended to provide the basis for a uniform, consistent implementation of security mechanisms in layer standards. As currently defined, frameworks describe a general service available in many layers that can be distributed among many systems. Work has begun on frameworks for authentication, access control, nonrepudiation, confidentiality, integrity, and security auditing.

Models, on the other hand, address both the implementation of services within particular layers and the interaction of these layer services. The upper-layer architecture security model, as its name implies, details how such security mechanisms as encryption, authentication, and key management are to work in the upper three OSI layers (i.e., the application, presentation, and session layers). The model will address such areas as when and how authentication procedures are to be invoked in setting up and maintaining associations and will define the security relationships between various system and subsystem entities. An analogous model is under development for the lower layers.

End-to-End Encryption

Activities are planned or are already under way that define end-to-end encryption protocols at the OSI presentation, transport, and network layers. These are discussed in the following paragraphs.

Presentation Encryption. Presentation encryption services are expected to be characterized as under the control of a particular application and will apply to selected data fields rather than to entire connections. SC21 WG6 is studying the issue of how to specify the type of protection to apply to elements in the data stream and how to specify the associated cryptographic keying parameters in each instance.

Transport Encryption. Transport encryption services are expected to apply to entire connections on an end system–to–end system basis. The minimum level of protection would be specified at the service boundary using arguments to service primitives. Administration-imposed protection policies and keying, however, will probably be implemented by means of network management functions.

Of the three layers for which encryption protocol extensions are planned, standards for the transport layer will probably be available first. Two ISO committees—SC20 WG3 and SC6 WG4—are addressing transport encryption; the work in SC6 will be conducted under an approved joint work item involving CCITT as well. The SP4 protocol, published as the result of the National Security Agency–sponsored secure data network study, is a likely candidate for this work.

Network Encryption. Network-layer encryption can protect all communications between a pair of systems, whether between end systems or intermediate systems (i.e., routers or gateways). Network encryption, therefore, can be applied between entire subnetworks. When applied between end systems, network-layer encryption is much like transport-layer encryption: it uses a system-to-system keying relationship, as does SP4, rather than a new cryptographic key for each connection. Protocols for other applications of network-layer encryption—the National Security Agency's SP3 is an example—tend to be more complicated. SC6 is considering drafts for network layer encryption.

IEEE committee 802.10 is developing a standard for confidentiality, integrity, and access control services for LANs. The standard will most likely operate between the logical link control and media access control sublayers. Compatibility with the suite of 802 protocols is expected. The standard will also include key and layer management provisions.

Security Management

ISO committee SC21 WG4 has an active rapporteur group that is in the advanced stages of developing part 7 of the management information services definition dealing with security management. This document addresses a number of security-related management services, including security event logging and audit management, security recovery reporting, key management, access-control management, routing-control management, and data confidentiality and integrity protection management. The document also details the concept of the security management information base.

Kerberos Authentication

As part of the trend toward open operating system architectures, many organizations have been formed with the goal of standardizing existing implementations of the UNIX operating system. Prominent examples of such organizations are X/Open, the Open Software Foundation (OSF), UNIX International, and IEEE POSIX. These groups generally prefer to incorporate existing designs rather than develop new ones, and as they become more interested in security mechanisms for distributed applications, it seems likely that they will consider Kerberos, the network-authentication and key-distribution service developed under the Massachusetts Institute of Technology's project Athena.

Kerberos requires that a client user first contact the trusted, online Kerberos key-distribution service (KKDC) to obtain a ticket for a designated service. This ticket contains a DES key that is generated by the service for this session, encrypted under the secret key of the service, and bound to additional information, including the identity of the client and the time of the request. The service also returns the session key encrypted under the client's master key. On Athena workstations, the client key is obtained as a function of the user's password, thereby granting a granularity of authentication to the individual user rather than to a system. This key is subsequently used by the client to create an authenticator that, together with the ticket, authenticates the client when the client accesses the remote service.

SUMMARY

Except for physical-layer link-encryption devices, few if any products covered by existing security standards are yet available. Consequently, at least in the short term, a company committed to a standards-based solution to its security problems may have to install nonstandard security products or extensions. This is especially true in the area of authentication, in which a plethora of expensive and incompatible devices is currently being marketed. A company's policy statements should make it clear that such solutions represent temporary solutions to immediate, acute security problems. The emerging security features in standards should be carefully considered when planning long-term solutions.

IX-5
Application-Specific Communications Security Services and Protocols

JOSEPH J. TARDO

C hapter IX-4 describes the security features of general communications standards. This chapter describes security features in two important application areas: financial services and messaging and directory systems.

FINANCIAL SERVICES STANDARDS

The standards discussed in this section were written specifically for financial services applications, not for general applications. These documents, however, have often been cited in a wider context. Financial services standards are developed in the US by ANSI committee X9 and internationally by technical committee TC-68, which is at the same level in the International Standards Organization (ISO) hierarchy as JTC 1.

ANSI X9.9: Message Authentication Code

ANSI X9.9, the most widely known financial services standard, is used for computing a Data Encryption Standard (DES)–based cryptographic check-value on wholesale (e.g., interbank) electronic funds transfer messages. This checkvalue is known as a message authentication code. X9.9-1987 is often cited as the source for the definition of the message authentication code, even though it also includes quite a few operations specific to electronic funds transfer processing.

In the standard, electronic funds transfers are specified—in a form analogous to an abstract syntax (i.e., independent of representation)—as strings of uppercase characters, numerals, and certain punctuation marks. These characters can be sent coded in many ways (e.g., by teletype), and a single electronic funds transfer might be coded according to several schemes as it is relayed through an interbank network. It is still recoverable, however, as a string of characters, with special characters delimiting the different message fields.

X9.9 contains editing rules that specify how fields are to be selected and encoded into a buffer of bits for the message authentication code computation. It includes a table that provides an 8-bit ASCII encoding for each character. The actual message authentication code computation uses the DES in cipher-block chaining (CBC) mode with a zero initialization vector and performs all the encryption steps, discarding all but the final ciphertext block. In effect, computing the message authentication code is analogous to computing a checksum except that the DES algorithm is used as the function instead of addition and exclusive-OR is used to accumulate the running checkvalue.

The ISO version of X9.9, ISO 8731/1, reflects an earlier version of the standard. Both ANSI X9.9 and ISO 8731/1 provide for data origin authentication with single datagram data integrity (in ISO 7498/2 terminology) but without confidentiality.

X9.17: Key Distribution

ANSI X9.17-1985 defines key-distribution procedures and protocols that allow wholesale interbank electronic funds transfer systems to support X9.9 and companion standards. As with X9.9, X9.17 is often cited outside of the financial services context as an example of a general approach to key distribution and has as a result occasionally been required in circumstances in which not all provisions of X9.17 were desirable or appropriate.

Because key-distribution messages must use the same communications links as electronic funds transfers, they are specified in the same abstract syntax form. The standard defines message-exchange types for three environments:

- Point-to-point—A message exchange in which one terminal requests a data encryption or authentication key from a peer with which it already shares a master key-encrypting key. The peer generates the working key and then returns it encrypted under the shared key-encrypting key.
- Key-distribution center—A message exchange in which peer terminals do not share a key-encrypting key with each other but share their own key-encrypting key with a third party service, the key-distribution center. On receiving a key request, a terminal requests that the key-distribution center generate a working key and return it encrypted twice, once under its own key-encrypting key and once under the initiating requestor's key-encrypting key. The terminal decrypts its part to recover the working key and forwards the other part to the initiator.
- Key-translation center—A message exchange in which the receiving peer terminal does not share a master key with the initiator but generates the working key and sends it encrypted under a key shared with the key-translation center. The key-translation center, which knows the initiator's master key, reencrypts it for the initiator and then relays it back to the peer.

X9.17 also defines ancillary procedures that support key management. These include the use of double-length keys, triple encryption, key notarization, and the use of key counters and offsets.

ANSI X9.23: Message Confidentiality

ANSI X9.23 provides for confidentiality, without integrity or origin authentication, for an electronic funds transfer communications environment. Essentially, X9.23 provides rules for encoding characters into ASCII, padding messages to multiples of 8 bytes, and encrypting using the DES algorithm in CBC mode. The procedures apply either to entire messages or to selected, delimited fields. Of particular importance in this standard are its filtering rules for the transparent transmission of 8-bit quantities over traditional interbank, character-oriented media (e.g., teletype).

ANSI X9.26: Access Management

ANSI X9.26, issued in 1989, standardizes the use of the DES algorithm for node authentication and for encoding personal authentication information, such as account numbers and personal identification numbers (PINs). An international version, DIS 10126-1, is being prepared.

ANSI X12.42: Electronic Document Interchange Authentication

This document was jointly produced by the X9 committee and the X12 committee on electronic document interchange (EDI). It provides editing rules for X12-standardized EDI message formats that are analogous to those of X9.9 and X9.23. It defines ways to include message-authentication codes in EDI messages, for encrypting designated fields, and for including X9.17 cryptographic-service messages in electronic documents. The standard provides for mechanizing message protection—which may be applied at the functional group level, the transaction set level, or some combination of the two—using security header and trailer segments defined in X12.42 (which refers to X9.9, X9.23, and X9.17 for service and mechanism definitions).

CCITT RECOMMENDATIONS

The International Telephone and Telegraph Consultative Committee (CCITT) is empowered, by international treaties, to produce documents that member countries are committed to follow, whereas compliance with ISO standards is purely voluntary. In practice, however, when CCITT makes recommendations, compliance may often be negotiable, and many countries adopt ISO documents rather than develop their own compulsory national standards—as, for example, in government purchasing. ISO and CCITT have agreed to avoid duplication of work and to avoid issuing technically incompatible standards when their respective standards and recommendations overlap in scope. Achieving this goal, however, has sometimes been complicated by differences in the organizational structure and work programs of the two organizations.

CCITT gave serious attention to security considerations when formulating its 1988 recommendations. In particular, CCITT added extensive security services and mechanisms to its recommendation on directories and message-handling systems. It also added cryptographic-authentication exchange to a protocol for accessing public packet-switching data networks.

In certain areas, CCITT has taken the lead in developing standards, although with full ISO participation. However, because the two organizations operate under very different procedures—CCITT is on a four-year cycle, whereas ISO uses a ballot-by-ballot procedure with different member body organizations authorized to approve items at different levels—the text of the corresponding ISO and CCITT documents is not always exactly equivalent.

CCITT X.500 and ISO 9594: Directory Systems

The CCITT X.500 series of standards for directory services is also issued as ISO 9594. Optional security services are specified in X.500 through X.507. A framework for authentication is presented in X.509 (also ISO 9594-8).

The goal of the X.500 standards is to make possible a large-scale, globally distributed data base of information to facilitate communication. Part of the goal is to provide a basis for developing a worldwide, automated directory assistance containing network terminal addresses for sending electronic mail.

X.500 directories have two major architectural components: directory agents and a directory information base. To access information, the end user makes requests to a directory user agent. The directory user agent functions as a client accessing a directory system agent, which has access to the actual information. The address information is intended to be distributed among many directory system agents, and the standards define protocols permitting a variety of ways for the agents to process requests.

Information in the directory information base is indexed using a hierarchical naming scheme. Each entry is a collection of attributes, certain of which are distinguished as the key fields for accessing a data base record. The directory information tree conceptually includes all such distinguished attributes, so a set of distinguished names of entries can be derived by following the vertices of the tree. In practice, the directory should contain one global name hierarchy that branches from a common root into different country names, then through registration authorities and subauthorities to leaf entries that are the actual objects being accessed.

X.509 augments X.500 by adding cryptographically derived authentication information as optional attributes of the object in the directory. These attributes take the form of certificates—collections of information about the actual object named in the entry (e.g., the values of certain attributes) that have been bound together in a certified way using a digital signature. Certificate values are included as attributes of entries. For example, it can be shown that a particular certificate correctly represents the binding of a distinguished name to a public key by virtue of the fact that it has been digitally signed by some mutually trusted administrative entity. X.509 introduces the concept of a certification authority to represent such an administrative entity. Directory user agents and directory system agents include procedures for assembling one or more certificates as needed to support authentication.

Optional Security Services. The optional security services specified in X.500 through X.507 include:

- Control of access to directory entries.
- Authentication of users accessing the directory.
- Authentication of retrieved values to users.

The standards are written to allow these services to be used for applications other than directory applications. In particular, the CCITT standards for message-handling systems—the X.400 series—rely heavily on these same services for security features.

Although access control is specified as a service, X.500 stops short of defining a particular mechanism for accomplishing it, leaving this implementation to the local system. The 1992 recommendations are expected to standardize the protocols for the exchange of access-control information but will most likely not standardize the access-control mechanisms themselves. Implementations of the 1988 X.500 recommendations will probably provide only minimal support for access control to directory entries.

X.500 accommodates digital signatures to provide authentication of data origin and to ensure data integrity. The standard allows users to request digital signatures for retrieved values in order to verify that they indeed come from legitimate service components. Similarly, users can sign local directory service agent requests to enable the service agent that is the actual custodian of the requested information to enforce its access controls. This is possible because X.500 permits directory system agents (DSAs) to obtain information from a chain of other DSAs rather than directly. X.500 does not provide for confidentiality of information, nor does it provide for authentication of error returns or referrals (as when a DSA that does not have the information returns a hint about its location rather than passing the request on to another DSA).

CCITT X.509 and ISO 9594-8: Authentication Framework. X.509 is one of the few standards that applies public-key encryption technology to the problems of distributing security-related attributes for authentication and controlling the distribution of cryptographic keys in a very large user community. X.509 defines two kinds of authentication: simple, password-based and strong, cryptographic-based. Simple authentication, though much less secure, was included in X.509 because it can be implemented in the short term. Its use is not, for example, affected by export control laws. Password-based systems, however, are vulnerable to a variety of attacks. A system could, for example, misrepresent itself to trick unsuspecting users into revealing their passwords.

For simple authentication, the directory does not maintain the cleartext password; rather, it supports a version transformed by a one-way hash function. The hash function, known by any verifying entity, can be applied so that the password would appear in cleartext only on the local system where it was entered.

Because a well-chosen hash should be irreversible in any practical sense, it should prevent untrusted components in the directory from recovering the password, thereby preventing an intruder from gaining service on a local system. However, there is little or nothing to prevent a determined entity from masquerading as a legitimate directory service component and merely replacing the hashed password.

Strong authentication is resistant to such attacks, permitting identities to be verified without their learning enough to later masquerade as a different entity. In strong authentication, a challenge that need never be reused is selected by the object entity and sent to the subject entity requesting authentication, encrypted under the subject entity's key. This key will be accurate because it appears in a certificate digitally signed by a trusted certification authority. Each entity can look up the other's certificate attribute in the directory information base, or each can exchange certificates directly with the other. An entity is considered authentic if it can prove it knows the private encryption key that will reverse the transform performed with the public key, thereby returning the decrypted challenge. In addition to the two-message challenge/response exchange, X.509 defines one-way and two-way authentication procedures that use time stamps and random number values to prevent the replay of authentication information.

X.509 contains both informal and formal (i.e., abstract syntax) descriptions of certificates and of the service parameters that affect simple and strong authentication. Certificates contain effective dates and expiration dates, algorithm identifications, the issuer's name, and the subject's name and public key. Certificates holding certificate authority or issuer certificates are associated with the names of certificate authorities.

To verify a certificate, an entity needs the public key associated with the certificate authority that issued it. If both the subject and object entities subscribe to the same authority, verification is immediate. In other cases, X.509 provides algorithms to establish an unbroken chain of trust—a chain of certificates that begins with a trusted key and continues with each key verifying the next public key in the chain until a trusted version of the certificate authority key for the sender's certificate is obtained.

Certification authority entries also have a blacklist attribute for listing all the revoked certificates, much the way a credit card company lists invalid or stolen cards. User and certification authority certificates that have been revoked are listed on separate attributes. No foolproof method of revocation exists, however; the approach adopted in the standard represents a compromise. An intruder could, for example, prevent access to the blacklist with an effective denial-of-service attack. The NIST-OSI Implementer's Workshop has provided additional definitions for hash functions and digital signatures suitable for use with X.509.

Although X.509 is intended to be algorithm-independent, only one public-key encryption algorithm is actually known to supply the described services— the Rivest-Shamir-Adleman (RSA) algorithm, which is computationally intensive. Annex C of X.509 describes the use of the RSA algorithm with various key parameters, one of which is a short, common, public-verification key component that reduces the computing required for signature verification.

CCITT X.400 and ISO 10021: Message-Handling Systems

The 1988 series of CCITT X.400 recommendations for message-handling systems includes a rather extensive set of optional security services. Message-handling systems provide a facility for users to exchange messages on a store-and-forward basis. The originating user interacts with the message-transfer system (MTS) by submitting and retrieving messages through a local user agent (UA), which in turn acts as a client to a message-transfer agent (MTA) server. An MTA can store and forward messages on behalf of users. The MTS consists of a set of MTAs that cooperate to eventually deliver messages to the MTA that services the addressed end user's UA. User agents, in addition, can interact with the MTS through a message store, the primary purpose of which is to accept delivery of messages on behalf of a particular end user for later retrieval by that end user's UA.

User agents can request that information be returned from the MTS in the form of a receipt—or report—indicating whether or when the message was actually delivered. Users can also submit probes, or dummy messages, simply to obtain a report.

When servicing a request, MTAs can expand distribution lists, split requests (i.e., submit a probe or message to multiple recipients), redirect or reroute messages, and convert to alternative encodings.

The X.400 Security Services Model. The X.400 security services rely in large part on X.509 security definitions and mechanisms. Secure-access management services provide support for controlling access within the MTS. Peer-entity authentication services can be applied on UA-to-MTA or MTA-to-MTA links using either X.509 simple or strong authentication and are used for access-control decisions. The security-context service matches security labels on messages and agents to restrict the flow of information to unauthorized or untrusted transfer or user agents.

X.400 provides data-origin authentication services for messages, probes, and reports; these are mechanized using digital signatures as specified in X.509. During X.400 message-origin authentication, the originator of a message or report supplies a certificate along with a token that contains such items as security labels, integrity-check fields, proof of delivery requests, and content-confidentiality keys. Some fields of the token are encrypted, whereas others are integrity protected. The originator digitally signs the messages when submitting them.

Proof of submission and proof of origin are included as part of the origin-authentication services; they take the form of reports originating from within the message transfer system. These reports include such items supplied by the MTS as the originating MTA's certificate and a token containing a digitally signed message-submission identifier, the time of submission, and the arguments of the submitted message. The user can use the token and certificate to verify the report.

X.400 includes three data confidentiality services: the connection-confidentiality service, the content-confidentiality service, and the message-flow confidentiality service. The standard does not, however, specify mechanisms for implementing these services.

The connection-confidentiality service protects protocol exchanges between MTS components and is provided by the underlying communications service. The content-confidentiality service is applied on an end-to-end basis between originator and final recipient. Message-transfer systems support this service by providing the parameters for transferring key information securely and by providing indications that the data needs to be decrypted on receipt. The message-flow confidentiality service essentially provides double enveloping and message padding to hide address and size information from untrusted components of the MTS.

Three data integrity services—the connection-integrity service, the content-integrity service, and the message-flow integrity service—function similarly to their data confidentiality service counterparts. A fourth data integrity service—the message-sequence integrity service—assures recipients that the messages they receive have not been reordered or replayed.

The data integrity and data confidentiality services are mechanized either in the UAs or in the underlying communications subsystem, not in the message-transfer system.

Nonrepudiation services provide information that can be used to prove to a third party that a particular form of communications took place. These services are directly provided from within the MTS by trusted components. The service protects against three threats: denial by the originator that the message was sent, denial by the recipient that the message was received, and denial by the MTS that the message was ever submitted for delivery. The implementation of nonrepudiation is perhaps the least understood of all of the X.400 services and involves the potential addition of trusted entities (e.g., third-party notaries).

X.400 also identifies a message-security labeling service, intended to be used with the security-context service, that permits messages to be individually labeled on a limited basis. The security-management services primarily support labeling and context services but also permit entities to change their authentication credentials. The register security-management service allows the security administration authority to set allowable user labels in the MTA; an analogous service is provided for the message store. A change-credentials service is also provided.

Security Aspects of CCITT X.32

CCITT recommendation X.32 defines a protocol by which a data terminal equipment (DTE) device establishes access to a data communications equipment (DCE) device on public packet-switched data networks. The motivation for X.32 was to provide dial-up X.25 service. It includes an optional cryptographic challenge/response exchange using public key encryption, which is mechanized in both the layer 2 high-level data link control (HDLC) exchange information (XID) frame and in the layer 3 X.35 protocols. The appendix of the recommendation includes a description of the algorithm and certificate format, which is not necessarily compatible with X.509.

The intention of the X.32 security recommendation appears to be that the service providers managing DCE devices should provide certificates to subscribers. The burden of computation for authentication rests with the subscriber in that the DTE device must encode a digital signature whereas the DCE device performs a much simpler verification computation.

It is not clear to what extent the X.32 authentication procedures will be supported in basic product offerings for private X.25 networks.

Privacy-Enhanced Mail

The Internet Engineering Task Force (IETF) issued three documents that defined privacy-enhanced mail protocol elements and procedures for the Internet community. RFC1113, RFC1114, and RFC1115 provide for message authentication and encryption, primarily using the DES algorithm. They also include public key–based key distribution provisions that use the X.509 syntax for public key certificates.

SUMMARY

Achieving a secure system—one that adheres to and enforces stated security policies—requires that policy requirements be taken into account in such diverse areas as physical plant planning and personnel as well as in the selection of communications protocols and services. The use of available security features and mechanisms provided in communications standards must similarly be motivated by policy requirements.

Standardized security mechanisms provide at best only the necessary components within an overall security strategy. Such features do not, merely by their incorporation, guarantee security, nor can one expect standards developers to derive a simple, complete, nonredundant set of security mechanisms sufficient for all or even a majority of circumstances.

IX-6
OSI-Based LAN Security Standards

KIMBERLY E. KIRKPATRICK

T he committees developing security standards for networks generally base them on the open systems interconnection (OSI) reference model. The use of OSI protocols has been accepted by both private industry and the government as the way to ensure interoperability in the future. In spite of the proliferation of committees developing network security standards, however, only one committee—the Institute of Electrical and Electronics Engineers (IEEE) 802 standards subcommittee—is working on the problem of security standards specifically for LANs at layers 1 and 2. Although other committees are working on layers 3 through 7, this chapter addresses only layer 1 and 2 security standards, with the exception of key-management standards, which involve the distribution of keys to layer 2. The chapter also provides an overview of the committees developing OSI-based security standards to show how the 802 committee's security work fits into and complements other OSI-related network security standards efforts. Finally, the chapter discusses the scope and objectives of the 802 committee's security work along with conclusions about the future of LAN security standards.

LAN SECURITY THREATS

Many kinds of threats can potentially violate the security of a LAN. These threats may arise from the information and data on the LAN or its communication and data processing services, equipment, and facilities.

Compromise. Broadcast LANs, in which every node can read all the data on the LAN, are the most vulnerable to compromise. It is also easy to tap baseband coaxial cable or twisted-pair wires, install a traffic monitor, and read all the traffic on a LAN. Some LAN architectures define a mode of operation—often called promiscuous mode—that allows a node to receive all data frames transmitted on the LAN regardless of the destination address of the frame. LAN adapters that implement this feature make eavesdropping or unauthorized access to data easy to accomplish and difficult to detect.

LANs can also be compromised by traffic analysis, which is the inference of information about the data on a LAN from the observation of traffic flows on it (i.e., the presence, absence, amount, direction, and frequency of transmissions). Because all nodes have access to all traffic, traffic analysis is easy to accomplish. Traffic analysis is possible even if the data on the LAN is encrypted, because header information remains unencrypted.

Loss of Integrity. Loss of integrity occurs when a system is exposed to accidental or malicious alteration or destruction. Data integrity can be lost in three ways, which are discussed in the following paragraphs.

Data Modification. Data modification is the altering of data in an unauthorized and undetectable manner, as can happen when nodes modify frames sent on the LAN and then transmit the modified versions. Such an attack can compromise communication between trusted nodes even when some level of authentication is used.

Replay. Replay is the repeating of a message or part of a message to produce an unauthorized effect, as when nodes copy messages destined for a different node and replay them at a later date. If the replay is not detected, the contents of the message will be acted on by the node receiving the replayed message. If the content of the message were, for example, to shut down the network, this could have very serious consequences.

Masquerade. A masquerade is one entity pretending to be another entity. An unauthorized node, or an authorized node that is untrusted or compromised, can masquerade as an authorized node with little difficulty. Many LAN adapters allow the source address of LAN frames to be selected or changed by the node, making masquerading easy.

Denial of Service. Denial of service occurs when an authorized entity cannot gain access to LAN resources or when time-critical operations are delayed. Denial of service can result from physical damage to LAN components (e.g., a cut cable), from disruption caused by the use of incorrect protocols (e.g., the wrong signals being transmitted or signals being sent at the wrong time), or from overloading.

Unauthorized Use of Resources. An unauthorized use of a resource is a use that is not consistent with defined security policy. Because conventional LAN technology cannot restrict to whom a node sends information or the data to which a node can listen, a legitimate node has access to all data and resources on a LAN.

Flooding. Flooding, also referred to as jamming, is the generation of data by a node that interrupts the services provided to other nodes. Flooding can be caused by a LAN node that is broken and is transmitting messages continuously or by a node that has been altered maliciously to achieve the same effect.

METHODS FOR COUNTERING SECURITY THREATS

Although many methods for mitigating security threats to LANs exist, none provide a complete solution. Achieving a secure LAN therefore requires a combination of methods determined by the environment in which the LAN resides. As Exhibit IX-6-1 shows, security methods can be divided into layers, extending from the system itself to governmental legislation and policies.

All security methods would be more useful if standards for applying them were available. Standardization would relieve users of the need to rely on proprietary, vendor-unique methods. It would also save users money because standardized solutions cost less than unique solutions.

Security Legislation. When determining how threats to the security of a LAN can be addressed, the network manager must be aware of the legislation that has been enacted for computer security. Although legislation cannot physically prevent people from breaching the security of a LAN, it can deter them and provide a way to prosecute them if they are caught.

It has always been a felony to compromise data pertaining to the national security of a government, even if that data resides on an accessible computer.

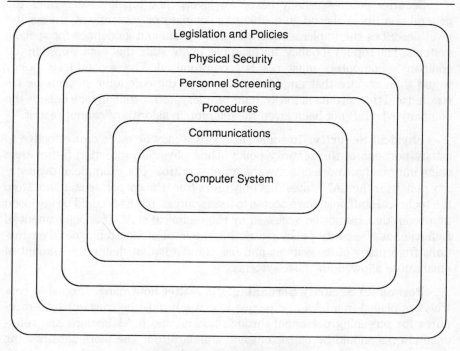

Exhibit IX-6-1. Layers of Protection

However, three significant laws have been enacted in the US that make it a crime to access data without authorization. These are:

- The Computer Fraud and Abuse Act of 1986—Makes it a federal crime to gain unauthorized access to data in any financial institution, federal government, or interstate computer.
- The Electronic Communications Privacy Act of 1986—Prohibits the unauthorized interception of electronic communications and defines privacy for stored, wired, and electronic communications.
- The Computer Security Act of 1987—Establishes a governmentwide security program, reasserts civilian control over information policy, defines sensitive information, provides for a computer standards program within the National Institute of Standards and Technology (NIST), establishes a computer research effort at NIST, and requires security training of federal employees involved with computers.

Security Policy. The security policy or policies to which a LAN must conform are as important as the legislation governing its use. For example, if a LAN is used to process classified US government data, it must conform to US Department of Defense (DoD) Directive 5200.28—Security Requirements for Automated Information Systems.

Security policies usually have two levels. The top level describes the general security goals and guidelines of a company or government; the second level describes the implementation of those goals and guidelines for specific systems. The top-level policy, for example, might state that data stored in the company's computers must not be compromised. The second-level policy would then require that employees' access to the computer systems be restricted and that all data in the systems be encrypted so that anyone outside the company who has not been given the decryption algorithms cannot read it.

Physical Security. In some situations it may be more cost-effective to satisfy portions of the security policy using physical protection rather than using internal hardware or software system controls. For example, if the security policy for the LAN states that only users from the corporate staff, not from the technical staff, may have access to its resources, the LAN could be enclosed in a room that cannot be accessed by the technical staff. The Department of Defense has a security policy restricting the level of electromagnetic emanations from many of its systems and has standards that define the amount of emanations allowed for those systems.

Personnel Security Screening. No matter how many automated controls are placed in a LAN, the people who use it must be trustworthy. Procedures for screening personnel through background investigations and reference checks should be consistent and standardized. The more sensitive the data to which employees are to have access, the more closely they should be investigated, with care always taken not to violate their privacy rights. Just as the Department of Defense has standards for the physical security of systems, it also has standards for performing background investigations of personnel who require access to classified data.

Security Procedures. Defining and faithfully executing procedures is extremely important to the security of any system. A few simple procedures have a better chance of being followed than many complicated ones. Security procedures that are appropriate to LANs include turning off microcomputers attached to the LANs when not in use for extended periods of time, locking up diskettes, storing diskettes in fireproof containers, and using programs taken from public electronic bulletin boards only when they have been approved by the company.

Communications Security. Communications security is the set of network security controls that protect data while it is on the network or accessible from the network. Various services, mechanisms, and design guidelines can enhance the security of a LAN. Some of the most common security services include confidentiality, access control, integrity, prevention of replay, prevention of denial of service, and data origin authentication.

Computer Security. Computer security is the set of operating system controls that protect data while it resides on a system. The collection of the various design guidelines for these controls is known as a trusted computing base. Computer security is very important to the overall security of any LAN because the data on the computers is the resource to which the LAN provides access. The proper integration of computer and communications security is critical for effective system security.

SECURITY STANDARDS COMMITTEE OVERVIEW

Several international and national standards bodies as well as US government organizations are working to develop security standards for the OSI basic reference model and the OSI security architecture. All of these organizations exchange information about their work through specific, well-defined channels. Exhibit IX-6-2 illustrates the various organizations and their official working relationships.

The international standards organizations working on security in open systems are the International Standards Organization (ISO), the European Computer Manufacturer's Association (ECMA), the International Telephone and Telegraph Consultative Committee (CCITT), and the IEEE. The ISO contributes standards for security architecture and security management. The CCITT contributes to the development of OSI security standards through liaisons. ECMA has developed a security architecture for distributed systems by addressing security at layer 7 of the OSI model. The IEEE is the only standards body concentrating on LAN security standards specific to layer 2. Although it

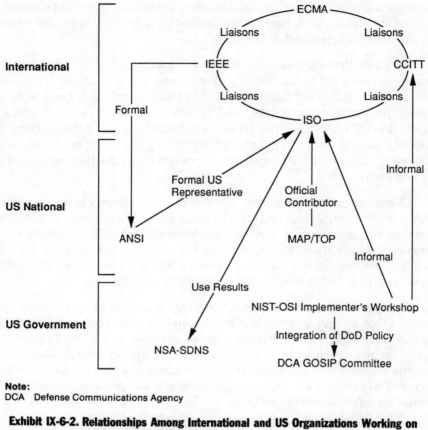

Note:
DCA   Defense Communications Agency

Exhibit IX-6-2. Relationships Among International and US Organizations Working on ISO/OSI Security Standards

has liaisons with all of the international organizations and creates international standards, the IEEE must submit its standards to ISO through the American National Standards Institute (ANSI).

ANSI is the formal US representative to ISO. The Manufacturing Automation Protocol and Technical Office Protocol (MAP/TOP) Users Group, which represents user organizations worldwide, has the status of official contributor to the ISO committees. The MAP group represents a consortium of factory automation users headed by General Motors. The TOP group, headed by Boeing, represents the office automation community. Together they are developing specifications for specific subsets of ISO standards.

NIST and the National Security Agency (NSA) are US government organizations developing network security standards based on ISO standards. The NIST-OSI Implementer's Workshop has much the same goals (and many of the same participants) as the MAP/TOP group. The workshop aims to promote multivendor interoperability quickly by developing implementer's agreements for a specified subset of international security standards options. These agreements are to form the basis for security specifications in the government OSI profile (GOSIP). GOSIP will be required by the Defense Communications Agency for use in Internet.

An NSA research program called Secure Data Network Systems (SDNS) promotes the design of the next generation of secure computer communications networks. The program is currently focusing on next-generation architecture, services, protocols, and products. It has been proposed that SDNS products be developed and introduced under the NSA's commercial communications security endorsement program.

The many committees working on OSI security issues attempt to work together through consultation and liaisons committees to avoid unnecessary duplication. Despite all the activity in these organizations, the development of security standards based on the ISO/OSI model has far to go. Although work has begun on these standards, much remains to be done before they are accepted internationally. Exhibit IX-6-3 summarizes the current security focus of the standards bodies shown in Exhibit IX-6-2. Many of the standards these groups have developed are in preliminary draft form. Additional work must be done before they can be useful even as guidelines for the way specific security protocols are to fit into the OSI security architecture.

Group \\ Layer	ISO	ECMA	CCITT	IEEE	ANSI	MAP/TOP	NIST	NSA
Application	✓	✓	✓	✓	✓		✓	✓
Presentation	✓	✓			✓			
Session								
Transport	✓	✓			✓			✓
Network								✓
Data Link				✓				✓
Physical								

Exhibit IX-6-3. Security Standards Activity of Various Standards Organizations

IEEE 802 STANDARDS SUBCOMMITTEE SECURITY WORK

The IEEE 802 standards subcommittee has two committees working on security standards: 802.2, the Logical Link Control Working Group, and 802.10, the LAN Security Working Group. The 802.2 working group has developed a security sublayer proposal for placing a security label on each logical-link control protocol data unit. The 802.10 working group is developing the Standard for Interoperable LAN Security (SILS). The two groups coordinate their work closely.

The IEEE 802.10 working group was formed to address the urgent need for secure communications on LANs. As new products for encrypting data transmitted between hosts on a LAN were introduced, vendors and users realized that they could satisfy a larger market if they conformed to a standard for secure communications.

In March 1988, 42 LAN vendors and users met to declare their support for a LAN standard and determined its scope. They agreed that the processes to be standardized were the secure exchange of data at the data link layer, the management of cryptographic keys, and the specification of network management objects associated with secure data exchange and key management. At subsequent meetings, the group agreed to include security and system management because these enable the secure management of the defined objects. Exhibit IX-6-4 shows the relationship of these processes in the OSI reference model.

In addition, the group decided that the standard should include guide-

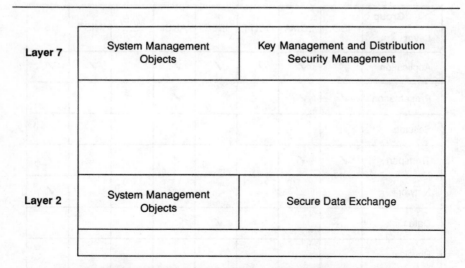

Layer 7	System Management Objects	Key Management and Distribution Security Management
Layer 2	System Management Objects	Secure Data Exchange

Exhibit IX-6-4. Security Standardization and the OSI Reference Model

lines or recommended practices for the use of particular cryptographic algorithms—for example, the Rivest-Shamir-Adleman (RSA) algorithm or the Data Encryption Standard (DES) algorithm—and for key distribution. These guidelines are intended to make the protocols developed as independent as possible of the algorithms used to encrypt data. The ability to use particular algorithms in the public domain is essential to the successful implementation of the standard. The protocol for key management should permit both manual and automated key management, and the purpose of the guideline for key distribution is to describe secure ways of distributing keys manually. Exhibit IX-6-5 summarizes the scope of SILS.

Once the scope of the project was defined, the IEEE Technical Committee on Security and Privacy and the IEEE 802 standards subcommittee of the IEEE Technical Committee on Computer Communications were approached as potential sponsors. Cosponsorship was agreed on, and the group officially became the IEEE 802.10 Working Group. The group meets and works with the 802 standards subcommittee to draw on its expertise and to ensure that the resulting standard will be compatible with existing LAN standards. The sponsorship of the Technical Committee on Security and Privacy allows the working group to develop a key-management protocol at layer 7 of the OSI model despite the fact that the 802 project is limited to layers 1 and 2 of the OSI model.

Objectives of IEEE 802.10

The overall goal of IEEE 802.10 is to develop security protocols that are independent of any particular algorithm, that are compatible with existing 802 LAN standards, and that incorporate existing ISO protocols—for example, the common management information protocol for key management and security management. The specific objectives developed by 802.10 to guide the development of SILS can be divided into four categories: general objectives, key-management objectives, secure data exchange objectives, and security management objectives.

Areas for Standardization
- Secure data exchange
- Key management and distribution
- System management objects
- Security management

Recommended Practices
- Use of particular encryption algorithms: RSA or DES
- Philosophy of key distribution
- Rationale for the selection of SILS security services

Exhibit IX-6-5. The Scope of SILS

General Objectives. The general objectives of IEEE 802.10 are to:

- Define a standard that will be accepted by the IEEE, ANSI, ISO, and the Department of Defense and that will serve as a Federal Information Processing Standard.
- Incorporate work on security standards by other standards organizations.
- Make data exchange independent of key management.
- Minimize options.
- Ensure that the standard requires no change to other 802 standards except addenda.
- Use only proven technology.
- Ensure that life-cycle costs of systems incorporating the standard be reasonable.
- Ensure that the performance-to-cost ratio of systems incorporating the standard be reasonable.
- Make nonrestrictive patent licensing available for specified mechanisms.
- Make the standard applicable to both private and government applications.
- Define a set of minimum essential requirements that a device must implement to ensure interoperability.
- Ensure that mandated protocols be exportable.
- Assess the impact the protocols would have on the size of the trusted computing base during the protocol specification.

Key-Management Objectives. SILS establishes tools (e.g., protocols) that are used for key management but does not define the key-management application. Key-management objectives are to:

- Support automatic (i.e., electronic) key management.
- Allow centralized key management, distributed key management, or both.
- Make the core protocol for key management exportable.
- Specify at least one interoperable key-management protocol.
- Make key management independent of encryption algorithms and explore the possibility of making it independent of the key-management environment (i.e., method or architecture).
- Ensure that traffic encryption be applied only between layer 2 peers, even though the management occurs at layer 7—The key-management protocol should provide pairwise, group, or network traffic keys.
- Provide compromise containment to prevent the compromise of one device from compromising the entire LAN.
- Provide rapid compromise recovery.
- Allow the same interface to key-management services in 802 as are provided by ISO.
- Support security service and mechanism management (as defined in ISO 7498/2) by specifying appropriate objects for the key-management protocol.

Secure Data Exchange Objectives. The objectives of secure data exchange are to:

- Make the data-exchange protocol independent of the encryption algorithm.
- Provide for SILS-protected broadcast and multicast transmission.
- Choose security mechanisms that permit exportability.
- Allow protected and unprotected traffic to coexist on a LAN.
- Avoid reliance on layers above those addressed by 802 to provide SILS security services.
- Support security service and mechanism management (as defined in ISO 7498/2) by specifying appropriate objects.
- Maintain the interface between the media access control and logical-link control.
- Allow encryption in both transparent and nontransparent implementations.
- Allow support of multiple media access control addresses through a media access control relay device that implements the SILS secure data exchange.

Security Management Objectives. The objectives of security management are to:

- Make the standard compatible with 802.1 and the ISO's common management information services and protocols.
- Address the issue of configuration management (e.g., addresses and location).
- Coordinate definitions with the ISO security management group.
- Address the protection of the transfer of system management objects.

The expectations of the 802.10 working group are that SILS will become an IEEE standard and will then be submitted to ISO through ANSI for consideration as an ISO standard. To that end, members of the appropriate ANSI and ISO bodies have been kept informed about the direction of the working group and the objectives of the standard. In addition, every effort has been made to keep the standard compatible with the ongoing security work in ANSI and in ISO, especially that of the ANSI X3T5.4 and X9.9 groups and the ISO/IEC JTC1 SC20 and SC21 groups. The overriding goal of the working group is to ensure that when the standard is presented as an IEEE standard, neither the ANSI nor the ISO committees will encounter any surprises.

Exhibit IX-6-6 lists the various standards committees with which the 802.10 working group maintains contact. Exhibit IX-6-7 illustrates the process by which the working group expects SILS to achieve general acceptance. It should ultimately gain acceptance as an ISO standard that can be used in GOSIPs. The working group also expects it to be accepted as a security protocol for LANs at layer 2 in the SDNS program of the NSA.

ECMA TC32/TG9 Security in Open Systems

ANSI X12 Electronic Data Interchange: Joint Finance Project Team

ANSI X9 Financial Services: X9.E9 Wholesale Key Management and X9.A3 Retail Key Management

OSI Implementer's Workshop: Security SIG, Lower Layers SIG, Network Management SIG

NSA-SDNS

ISO/IEC JTC1 SC21 Information Retrieval, Transfer, and Management for OSI; ISO/IEC JTC1 SC20 Information Processing Systems Data Cryptographic Techniques; ISO/IEC JTC1 SC6 Telecommunications and Information Exchange Between Systems

CCITT Special Rapporteur Group for Question 18/VII (Distributed Application Framework) and Special Rapporteur Group for Question 19/VII (Directory Authentication Framework)

Notes:
IEC   International Electrotechnical Committee
SIG   Special interest group

Exhibit IX-6-6. Committees with Which the IEEE 802.10 Working Group Maintains Contact

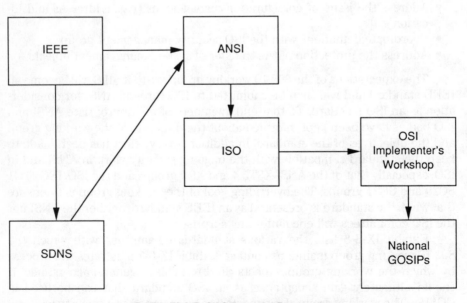

Exhibit IX-6-7. SILS Potential Progression

SUMMARY

Current LAN technology makes LANs exceptionally vulnerable to security breaches. This vulnerability must be overcome if LANs are to reach their full potential. The technology for providing security on LANs has matured, making secure LANs feasible. The completion and acceptance of the standard for interoperable LAN security being developed by IEEE 802.10 should help lower the cost of security, increase the market for secure LANs, and ensure the interoperability of secure LAN components, all of which will facilitate the design and implementation of secure LANs.

Section X
New Directions

A s with any dynamic technology, the evolution of LANs continues at a dramatic rate. A manager today must be aware of future developments to make intelligent decisions about the present. This section of the *Handbook* is devoted to the exploration of a number of important trends.

The first trends discussed are those responsible for fueling LAN growth. Next considered are several developments that will extend LAN capability far beyond anything that could be considered local. Considered last are the management challenges produced by increasing LAN complexity and the growing number of available resources. These challenges include ensuring that users have the ability to access all the needed and available resources and that LAN resources are maintained at their maximum operational level.

One of the most exciting software trends is the development of true distributed computer environments. Network operating systems, as known today, can be considered somewhat rudimentary forerunners of what is to come. Chapter X-1, "Distributed Computing Architectures for LAN Computers," discusses three types of distributed computing technologies, including network operating systems, distributed languages, and distributed operating systems. Examples of each are discussed and compared, and general guidelines for comparing distributed architectures are presented.

It is not necessary to wait for distributed languages to emerge from the laboratories. Chapter X-2, "The Network Computing Architecture and System: An Environment for Developing Distributed Applications," discusses in detail the language constructs and other attributes associated with network computing architecture (NCA) and network computing systems (NCS), the system for remote procedure calls developed by Apollo Computers (now part of Hewlett-Packard) and subsequently placed in the public domain. While the long-term market outlook for NCA/NCS is the subject of much debate (primarily because of competing systems), this system is representative of the type of distributed application development tools that should be widely available by the mid-1990s.

As LANs begin to span continents, applications and other resources grow in terms of features, complexity, and sheer numbers. It is unreasonable to expect users to keep up with the status of the LAN using today's ad hoc, informal methods. Even on small LANs, the grapevine often fails to keep users fully aware of the services available, much less how to access them. Fortunately, there is a solution.

In late 1988, the International Telephone and Telegraph Consultative Committee (CCITT) and the International Standards Organization (ISO) finished their joint development of the base standard for an open systems interconnection (OSI) directory, referred to by the CCITT as the X.500 series of recommendations and by ISO as 9594. Contrary to popular belief, the directory's applicability goes far beyond use simply as an electronic mail directory similar to the telephone white pages. In fact, in many respects, the directory standard represents one of the most advanced, far-reaching OSI layer 7 applications developed to date. Chapter X-3, "Open Systems Interconnection Directory Systems," presents a detailed look at this standard and briefly discusses several extensions to the base standard currently under development.

A final LAN direction worthy of study is in the area of network management. With LANs and their resources becoming more numerous and complex, management of these resources becomes increasingly difficult. At the same time, competent professionals with the needed management expertise remain scarce. The solution to this problem, at least in part, relies on the development and deployment of expert systems for network management. Chapter X-4, "Expert Systems in LAN Management," explores the basis of expert systems and discusses how such systems can be developed to support LAN management. A fault scenario is depicted, illustrating how an expert system could be used to diagnose the problem and relieve the LAN administrator of the burden of responding to multiple alarms triggered by a single event.

X-1
Distributed Computing Architectures for LAN Computers

VICTOR A. DUARTE

A s the computational power of microcomputers increases and LANs capable of data rates of 100M bps or more come into use, the need for constant access to a host mainframe declines. The computing requirements for a given task can be distributed among the networked components, and improvements in computing performance, the ability for a system to grow in smaller, more manageable increments, enhancement of data integrity and availability, and more cost-effective use of computing resources all result.

This chapter examines the types of distributed computing configurations possible when computers are connected over a LAN backbone. The basic architectural requirements of distributed systems are studied, and examples of existing distributed systems are presented.

Distributed computing fundamentally involves dividing the execution of a process among multiple processors, which may operate on the tasks either sequentially or in parallel. Dramatic improvements in throughput are achieved through multiple processors executing instruction sequences in parallel; processing of different portions of a task can overlap, and communications delays are minimized because of reduced context switching between processes. Parallel processing, while not necessary to distributed computing, is a desirable quality.

High-speed microprocessors coupled with 100M-bps LANs provide a solid hardware platform for the development of parallel distributed computing systems. The controlling software for such systems is discussed later in this chapter.

ADVANTAGES OF DISTRIBUTED COMPUTING

Performance. Distributed computing decreases the time required to execute computing tasks, thereby improving execution throughput. Distributed computing can also provide increased system availability because multiple processors are available for use in the event that some of the processors fail.

Resource Use. With storage devices, files, printers, data, and programs available simultaneously to multiple users, resource use is much higher than with single-user computer systems. In the event of processor failure, distributed computing systems can provide even greater resource use than multiuser mainframe systems because some of the computer resources will still be available. In centralized systems, a processor failure interferes with access to other computing resources.

Fine-Grain Scaling. In centralized systems, increasing processing power by small increments (e.g., 10%) is often impossible. The available performance increments of mainframe systems are too coarse; boosting system performance capacity on large computer systems involves large leaps in performance. It is also more expensive and requires considerable planning to ensure the system upgrade is done smoothly.

System Reliability. By distributing users and processes across multiple processors, and through software that diverts work from a failed processor, the reliability of the computing system is improved. Disk duplicating and file replication are also used to minimize the effect of disk or file corruption on a distributed system.

Price/Performance Ratio. Because computing costs are lower on smaller-scale computers compared with large models, a trend toward the downsizing (i.e., the porting of mainframe software for microcomputer use) and decentralization of systems was expected. Decentralization has occurred but not downsizing. Instead, new applications have been written for the networked, high-performance microcomputer environment.

TECHNICAL CHALLENGES

Distributed computing has many benefits, but it also entails problems when traditional operating and networking systems are adapted to multiple-processor, distributed systems. Managing computer resources (e.g., virtual memory) over a local network is a formidable task. Maintaining the availability of the entire system, facilitating process recovery in the event of failure, and handling deadlock situations are well-understood areas in traditional computing but involve unique difficulties in distributed computing systems.

Resource Management

Control of multiprocessor distributed computing systems, which may involve parallel execution of communicating processes, can be very complex. In computing theory, the Undecidability of the Halting Problem states that it is impossible to decide whether a Turing machine will halt when presented with a certain input. Simply determining at any instant which processors in a distributed system are available, which is a basic requirement, is therefore impossible.

In a distributed computing environment, scheduling processors and processes is complicated by the dynamic nature of computing tasks. Numerous scheduling algorithms exist for traditional single-instruction, single-data computers; distributed computing systems complicate such scheduling decisions because numerous processors (some, possibly, in failure state) with potentially different computing facilities and capabilities must be considered. Processes that communicate heavily should execute simultaneously on different processors to increase their processing overlap as well as their communication throughput. The task of efficiently and effectively managing such resources is extremely challenging.

Fault Tolerance

Two different approaches to fault tolerance are used in distributed computing systems. One approach is to provide atomic transactions; these are done in an all-or-nothing fashion. If a failure occurs during the atomic transaction, the system returns to the beginning of the transaction. The other approach is to operate critical resources in a redundant fashion. In the event a critical resource fails, it is likely, although not certain, that backup resources will still be operational.

Software failures that cause the host processor to crash, such as those caused by a computer virus, are the most difficult to handle because the traditional approach to failures is to allocate another processor and rerun the failed program. The subsequent, repeated processor and program failures can devastate a system, unless the cycle is detected and broken by the controlling software of the distributed system. Still, the loss of a processor in a distributed system is not as damaging as in a centralized system.

Deadlock Detection

Distributed systems can suffer from the effects of resource and communications deadlocks. Resource deadlocks are similar to those present in centralized computer systems, with the additional complexity implicit in the nature of the distributed environment. Specifically, because a system is distributed, resource allocation tables are also distributed, making the gathering of resource information more difficult. Also, a deadlock cycle can form as processes wait for messages from one another. If, for example, X waits for Y, Y waits for Z, and Z waits for X, a deadlock occurs. These situations require the detection of a cycle in a communications graph that can become as unwieldy as complex network routing algorithms.

IMPLEMENTATIONS OF DISTRIBUTED SYSTEMS

Network Operating Systems Versus Distributed Operating Systems

Before the development of the microprocessor, a basic operating system provided filing, memory management, CPU and concurrent process scheduling, deadlock prevention or detection, and resource protection. All of these functions were, and are, provided by operating systems for minicomputers and mainframes.

The operation of the filing system varies. In some systems (e.g., Prime PRIMOS) the domain can be limited to a single computer; other systems provide tools (e.g., UNIX's UNIX-to-UNIX Copy) to copy files from one computer to another over a network, and others provide for global file access, as exemplified in IBM's shared direct access storage device (DASD) concept. The level of transparency provided by the file systems varies considerably.

Operating systems also perform memory management, which can be static or dynamic. With dynamic memory management, the operating system performs all virtual-to-real address translation and paging functions. In both static and dynamic memory management, the operating system has total control over where programs and data are loaded into memory as well as how much memory is available. In a multiprocessor system, the operating system has the entire system memory at its disposal.

Another basic function of the operating system is to schedule and dispatch concurrent processes in conjunction with CPU scheduling. The necessary system control blocks are created for this purpose and, on the basis of such a CPU scheduling algorithm as multilevel feedback queue, the processes are scheduled for a given amount of CPU time. In multiprocessor systems, the operating system schedules processes on all CPUs.

Because the operating system schedules multiple processes simultaneously, it must also provide a means of serializing access to system resources such as files, printers, service routines, and even program code and data. This is provided by the operating system semaphore facility. IBM provides the **COMPARE** and **SWAP** instruction for single CPUs, and the **TEST** and **SET** instruction for multiple CPU systems.

The operating system controls the system resources in a way that is transparent to the programs using the system. Processes do not have control over which CPU actually executes the instruction stream, nor should they need to. It is the responsibility of the operating system to insulate the user from such details. Processes can also serialize access to resources across multiple CPUs. In a multiprocessor system, the operating system provides transparent file access regardless of which CPU channel actually feeds the disk drives. IBM allows multiple CPUs, each with an independent operating system (e.g., MVS/XA), to transparently access files in the shared DASD pool.

Network operating systems provide some of these capabilities, but not to the extent provided by a true operating system. Specifically, file access on a network operating system is not transparent. A file server machine usually has a bank of disks that network users can access. Another approach is to define a network disk name for each network user, allowing network users to access one another's disks. This is quite different from having the operating system control access to all network disks at its discretion.

CPU scheduling by a network operating system is neither dynamic nor transparent. True distributed systems execute the process dynamically. Those that are less distributive require the user to specify which CPU should receive the process. Similarly, programs can be run dynamically on any CPU, or the CPU is implicitly specified as the one in which the file is locally stored.

Network Operating System Attributes

Network operating systems allow access to disks that are connected over a network. They provide a security system as well as an auditing facility. The security system controls user access to network disks and files as well as user access to the network services (e.g., mail). The auditing facility logs access and use of selected network resources.

Novell NetWare. NetWare differs from other commercially available systems in that it is a true operating system rather than an interface to an underlying operating system, as is 3+Open by 3COM Corp. NetWare is based on the client-server computing model, with the operating system kernel residing on the server and the workstation user or process being the client. The kernel is centrally located in a dedicated or nondedicated workstation; the entire system depends on the operation of the server. This centralization of the kernel contradicts a basic principle of truly distributed operating systems; a true distributed system should have a distributed kernel (i.e., one that is distributed among all the cooperating processors).

NetWare is a multitasking operating system, exploiting the capabilities of the Intel 80286 and 80386 CPUs. Through file directory hashing, it maps a file name to a specific index table, which reduces the time required to determine file location and attribute information. Frequently used file directories are cached, thereby reducing access time. File allocation tables (FATs) are indexed to improve access time by as much as 75%. Disk access is optimized using a technique called elevator seeking, which organizes disk requests on the basis of the current position of the disk head. Directories and FATs are duplicated in the event of a system failure. Read-after-write I/O verification is performed to ensure that write requests are successful. An emergency I/O area on disk is provided for data blocks in which the read-after-write verification fails. The impact of a power failure is minimized by use of an uninterruptible power supply.

NetWare supports LAN-to-LAN, LAN-to-host, and LAN-to-remote micro-computer connections. The LAN types supported are IEEE 802.3 and 802.5. Host connections are supported using Transmission Control Protocol/Internet

Protocol (TCP/IP) for program-to-program communication and System Network Architecture (SNA) gateways for terminal-based host communications. Both asynchronous and synchronous data link control (SDLC) host connections are supported.

Server processes can be created using the value-added process facility, which extends NetWare's services to the server process. The server can allocate memory, create and destroy processes, and process operator input. Although NetWare extends these services to server processes, it does not extend them to client processes as do true distributed operating systems. Process management is not handled by the NetWare kernel. Servers manage specific processes—the ones they created—resulting in a minimal level of process management that has no influence on system load and availability.

Banyan VINES. VINES is a network operating system based on the UNIX and MS-DOS operating systems. Its servers operate as a UNIX process and communicate with client processes on microcomputers running MS-DOS. The server is supported on any processor that runs UNIX and can be connected to microcomputers, minicomputers, and mainframes. IEEE 802.3 and IEEE 802.5 LANs are supported as are X.25 connections, high-level data link control (HDLC) and binary synchronous communications (BSC) data link controls, and SNA networks. Disks and printers connected to the server can be shared by client processes.

Multiple servers may be operational on a VINES system; users log into the network rather than into an individual server. Client processes have access to resources on all servers on the basis of access rights declared when they were configured. Servers may be dedicated to such specific functions as printer or file sharing so that system load balancing can be controlled.

System resources (e.g., files, printers, communication servers) are located by a distributed directory service called StreetTalk, using a global naming scheme. (The location of a resource is not part of the global name. A distributed naming system needs the location to be part of the name, because the locations of resources can change, causing access problems otherwise.) StreetTalk stores all group level name information on all servers; detailed information is split and distributed among multiple servers. This replication of group-level information enhances the availability of the name service in case a server fails.

VINES provides support for socket-connection and client-server models of interprocess communication. A socket is an object that manages communications flow between a process and the underlying communications subsystem. The underlying communications can be an X.25 logical link control (LLC) connection, Transmission Control Protocol/User Datagram Protocol (TCP/UDP), or native VINES communication (LLC 1 and LLC 2) protocol. The socket interface can be handled as a blocked or nonblocked call. Communications over a socket can occur between VINES processes or may include an application on another network that supports the socket model. The client-server relationship is implemented as a remote call procedure for communication between VINES client and server processes. A remote call procedure includes the name of the target service, which is resolved by Matchmaker using StreetTalk and is generated using the Matchmaker compiler.

The VINES communication protocol supports port-based communications on two port types: well known and transient. A well-known port is a port number built into the operating system that is reserved for processes that provide the same function on multiple nodes of the network. Transient ports are assigned to processes by the operating system when needed, and the assignment is not predetermined or predictable.

VINES provides base servers for security, file access, printing, semaphore, mail, and network management.

Distributed Language Attributes

Distributed languages provide language constructs specifically for process or task distribution in either homogeneous or heterogeneous computing environments. They allow the development and execution of distributed programs but differ from distributed systems in that process distribution is application based rather than systemwide.

Distributed languages are easier and safer to use than distributed systems. However, they also make using operating system facilities more difficult by virtue of their insulating the application from operating system details.

Conic. The Conic environment provides facilities for compiling, configuring, executing, and debugging distributed programs. A major strength of the Conic language environment is its configuration facility, which partitions applications into logical processing nodes. Logical nodes may be dynamically created, connected, and controlled using the configuration manager.

The Conic language environment supports heterogeneous computer architectures because it transforms data types between different machines. Each machine may run the UNIX operating system, or the Conic Executive may be run on a machine that does not have a separate operating system. If UNIX is present on a target machine, a logical node is implemented as a process. Logical nodes are connected in a peer-to-peer fashion rather than as the usual client and server.

The Conic language is an extension of Pascal. With the language, a task module type (an independent instruction stream that is instantiated at configuration time) is defined. A module's communication interface is defined using the **EntryPort** and **ExitPort** statements. **EntryPort** defines the location at which messages are received, and **ExitPort** is used similarly for outgoing messages. Both associate a local name and local type with their respective messages. This allows modules to be site independent, because all references are to local variables with no machine, source or target, specified.

Two types of messages are used in Conic. The **NotifyTransaction** message type provides unidirectional message passing through a nonblocking **Send** primitive. Bidirectional message passing is accomplished with the **RequestReply** message type, which uses a blocking **Send** primitive. The sender of the message is blocked in the **RequestReply** case until a response is received from the target process. A wait time-out can be used to declare a process failure and initiate transaction back-out procedures.

Object types are declared using definition units, which allow common constants, types, functions, and procedures to be declared and separately compiled and used by task modules and definition units. Exclusive use of data is provided using message-based synchronization primitives.

A logical node is formed by defining a group module as a grouping of task modules. The interface used by both a task module and a group module is the same, as is their instantiation. Message types between groups or tasks are declared with **Use**, and instantiations of each are declared using **Create**. Interconnections between entry and exit ports are declared with the **Link** statement.

Using the above constructs, Conic allows the formation of complex processing nodes organized in a concise and comprehensible manner. The logical node is the unit of processing distribution and is therefore specific to the computing environment in which it executes. The Conic compiler generates the appropriate executable code on the basis of the machine that executes the logical node.

A distributed application consists of instances of logical nodes at specific nodes in the computer network. The interconnection of these logical node instances forms the logical (i.e., virtual) Conic application. Logical nodes communicate using the Berkeley UNIX (BSD 4.3) Internet datagram protocol over an Ethernet backbone. DEC VAX, DEC PDP-11, Sun Workstation, Motorola 68000, and LSI11/73 machine architectures are supported.

A name server registers the addresses of all logical nodes in the Conic execution environment. Each time a logical node is instantiated, it sends the server a message containing its User Datagram Protocol/Internet Protocol (UDP/IP) address. The logical nodes also send messages at intervals to the controlling servers to inform the servers of the nodes' status. The server is the main failure point of the system, but the system provides additional robustness by allowing simultaneous operation of multiple servers. Servers also maintain a file of the registered logical nodes; if the system crashes, the file can be re-created in 10 to 20 seconds. This minimizes the impact of server crashes on the entire Conic environment.

Conic also includes commands that allow an operator to list the applications currently running, the nodes in the system, a node's ports and types, and the links to a node's ports.

Network Command Language. Network Command Language (NCL) is a distributed language specifically designed to operate in a distributed heterogeneous system environment. It is based on the client-server model, with a common data representation and common interface paradigm.

Heterogeneous distributed systems introduce a layer of complexity not present in homogeneous environments. By virtue of the system's heterogeneity, one part may provide a particular service function not present on a different part of the system. NCL overcomes this obstacle by viewing the heterogeneous computer system in the same way a compiler views source code: the code is generated for a specific computer system and can be generated on any computer system. The important thing is that the generated code execute on the appropriate target machine. NCL is, essentially, a network language.

NCL is based on LISP and allows functions and data to be used interchangeably. Since functions are evaluated remotely, using remote procedure calls, it is possible to have nested function calls in parameter lists, with each function executed on different server machines. The specification of expressions in using request-response mode operation forms the syntax of the language.

A collection of one or more elements, denoted using a common descriptor notation, forms an NCL expression. The descriptor encodes class, type, size, and structure information for each expression. No limit on expression size is imposed by NCL. Return values are designated in each expression, and the values are returned by means of a response message.

Six element classes are defined in NCL: input value, return parameter, local variable, session variable, environment variable, and reference variable. The common descriptor format consists of a 64-bit structure, with the first 8 bits specifying the class of the element and the second 8 bits designating the element type. The next 16 bits are used to indicate the size of the element. The meanings of the remaining bits in the descriptor vary on the basis of the type and class fields.

The element types possible are list, function, link, integer, byte vector, and nil. A list is a collection of items (e.g., a Pascal record), and the link type allows physically contiguous list structures to be used as a linked list. The remaining element types are self-descriptive.

NCL provides atomic and parallel functions, which execute sequences of expressions as an atomic unit or run them in parallel on multiple processors.

Distributed Operating System Attributes

The ability to insulate processes and computer users from the execution location of an instruction stream clearly distinguishes a distributed operating system from network operating systems and distributed languages. The distributed operating system functions as a true operating system in that target processors are not specified when a new process is spawned. The distributed operating system uses its own criteria to determine which processor or groups of processors execute the process. Some distributed operating systems may even shuffle processes among processors in the middle of their execution to improve the load balance of the processor pool.

The location of files and disks in a distributed operating system is equally transparent. Processes need not know the processor on which a file or disk is located. This is a detail handled by the operating system.

The overriding distinction between a distributed operating system and a network operating system or distributed language is whether the process or computer user must specify the details of resource location and use. In a distributed operating system, such details are not required.

Examples of distributed operating systems and the unique approaches in their implementations follow.

V Kernel. The V Kernel operating system supports an array of Sun workstations, each running a copy of the operating system software. The kernel is a software backplane, in that it facilitates communication between hardware and software resources. The kernel consists of an interprocess communications handler, kernel server, and device server.

Communication between client and server is accomplished using **Send**, **Receive**, and **Reply** primitives. The client process issues a **Send** operation resulting in the transmission of a 32-byte message to the server. This blocks the client until the server responds with a **Reply** message overwriting the 32-byte message area. These calls can be embedded in stubs to give them the appearance of procedure calls. A **Send** message can contain a pseudopointer; this points to a segment in the client memory space to which the server may read or write if the appropriate access is granted. In addition, the first 1K byte of data pointed to by the pseudopointer is transmitted to the server on the assumption that this information would otherwise have been requested. This piggybacking of information is similar to the X.25 fast select feature, in which the call connect packet also contains user data that otherwise would have been transmitted after the call connect had been processed.

The V kernel does not dynamically allocate processors to tasks but rather assigns a specific function (e.g., user machine, file server) to each processor. The kernel provides memory and process management with the device driver performing I/O management using the V I/O protocol. All I/O is performed at the block level.

A group of processes is called a team. These share the address space of the user and therefore must run on a single processor. Although the processes are related, they may operate independently of one another so that if a process is blocked while awaiting a reply from a server, other processes may continue to execute.

The V kernel has three levels of naming: the process ID (PID) name, the symbolic ASCII service name, and the symbolic object name. The PID, the lowest-level name, identifies the port address to be used for communicating with the process. The service name is used to register a service process with the kernel, allowing clients to access the service using an ASCII string rather than a PID. The highest-level name is the object name, which is always used in context and identifies such an object as a file. Each server manages its own contexts, which consist of a symbolic name, server PID, context number, and object identifier.

The central file server supports hierarchical file access. It is not included as part of the V kernel but rather operates as a team of processes running as a user process. The workstations are connected by a 10M-bps Ethernet LAN, which allows the file server to provide reasonably fast file access to the client processes. Measurements show that 7.8 msec, which includes network overhead, is required to read a 1K-byte block cached in the file server. If the block is not cached in the file server, 35.5 msec is required.

The V system essentially provides no fault tolerance capability. If a system problem arises while a process is running, the request must be retried when the system returns.

Cambridge Distributed Computing System. The Cambridge distributed computing system is based on a slotted-ring LAN. As such, it contains a fixed number of small frames continuously circulating the ring and is very effective in networks for which network latency times must be short. The Cambridge ring does not lend itself to situations in which stations on the ring have large transmission requests, because it does not make good use of available media bandwidth. Since so much of each packet consists of overhead information, the effective bandwidth of a 10M-bps slotted ring is 4M bps.

The Cambridge ring system consists of two major components: the servers and the processor bank. A processor is allocated to a user for the duration of a terminal session and is returned to the processor pool when the user logs out of the system. Processors are not dynamically allocated to work on pieces of a task but are used as personal computers.

Although processors are not dynamically allocated by the Cambridge system, a process can request the resource manager to allocate a specific type of processor for a task. The process can also request a specific operating system to be loaded onto the allocated processor.

Both LLC 1 and LLC 2 modes of communication are provided by the system. LLC 1 is used by the remote procedure call facility and LLC 2 is used for the byte-stream facility, primarily for terminal emulation and file transfer. Packet sizes vary, with each packet consisting of a 2-byte header, a 2-byte PID, and up to 2K bytes of user data.

Dedicated server machines are available and provide basic services such as file service, name service, boot service, terminal service, and log-in service. The name server provides a means of identifying other servers on the system by associating an ASCII string with the corresponding machine ID of the computer providing the requested service. The address of the name server is fixed so client programs can have this address hard coded. A process that intends to use a particular service must first identify itself to the active name server by presenting a user name, session key, user class, and control key. The session key is the primary means of access control and is based on the idea that a user cannot guess the session key of another user if the session key is very large and created randomly at log-on time.

The system supports two variations of the same unstructured file type. The file consists of 0 to a maximum number of 16-bit words sequentially organized. One file type can perform atomic updates to the file; the other has a file index capability. A 64-bit permanent user ID (PUID), composed of a 32-bit disk address and a 32-bit random number, uniquely identifies each file in the system. When a file is created, a parent index file is associated with the new file and a slot containing the file PUID is constructed. Since the same is true for index files, a directory file system is realized.

The ability to easily boot servers on the Cambridge system facilitates recovery from system failures. This is the basic approach the system takes to fault tolerance and is somewhat unsatisfying. A consolation is that atomic operations are supported and therefore the incidence of files broken due to system crashes can be minimized.

LOCUS. The LOCUS distributed operating system connects 17 DEC VAX/750s over an Ethernet LAN. It allows programs and files to be relocated transparently and without interrupting the operation of the system. It is compatible with the UNIX operating system and provides support for UNIX named pipes and signals over the network. A hierarchical file system with replicated files for enhanced file availability is used. The kernel traps requests for system service and then determines if the request will be executed locally or remotely. The user is completely unaware of the machine servicing the request.

Processes are created using **Fork** and the UNIX **Exec** command. The calling process contains a dynamically controlled **Advice** list that determines where the new process will be created. LOCUS allocates space on the target machine for the body of the process and then initializes the process environment.

Access to memory resources is controlled by a token mechanism, granting the owner of the token access to the desired resource. Large amounts of data are usually transferred with each system call, resulting in acceptable performance overall.

Access to files through the LOCUS file system is transparent. In no way does the path name of a file indicate the location in the network of the file. LOCUS replicates files to provide greater file availability in case of failure and to improve performance by accessing files on the basis of their proximity to the requesting process. As network bandwidths increase, accessing files on the basis of their proximity to the requesting service becomes less important.

Each node in the LOCUS system can operate as a full-function node. During file access, the system recognizes three types of sites: using site (US), storage site (SS), and current synchronization site (CSS). US and SS are self-defining. The CSS node handles global file access synchronization for the file group and, receiving a **FileOpen** request, selects the SS.

LOCUS maintains absolute file synchronization across multiple copies of a file within a partition. The difficulty arises when multiple partitions occur because of physical or logical (i.e., communication) breaks in the network. To ensure high data availability, a data object appearing in more than one partition should be updated during the partitioning of the network.

Accent. Accent is a communications-oriented operating system in that the underlying communications system implements the abstraction between processes. The system can be viewed as a network of loosely coupled processors (i.e., the user has access to either a single processor or, if the task requires them, multiple processors). The Accent kernel controls the bare machine (i.e., no separate operating system is required) and provides virtual memory management, interprocess communication, and process management.

The Accent interprocess communication facility allows access to call services and objects available in the system. Messages are sent and received from abstractions called ports, to which processes refer indirectly. A kernel port and data port are automatically assigned to a process; these allow the process to send and receive information with the kernel. At a given time, a single process can be authorized to receive messages that are queued in a port. This authority can be transferred to another by means of a capability message. The local name associated with a port is converted by Accent to the corresponding name on the receiving process. Intermediary processes can be used to control message flow between processes because the Accent kernel allows the transfer of receive access to ports. This means the kernel can be removed from process networking details, which can instead be relegated to server processes designed specifically for this purpose. This makes the system more robust by reducing the size and complexity of the kernel.

The **Send** and **Receive** primitives allow unblocked buffered operation. Consequently, a port may become full of messages that have not yet been sent or received. Accent allows a process that is sending a message to a full port to wait for the message to be queued, receive an error notice, or have the kernel access the message and notify the process when the message has been placed in the queue of the designated port.

An Accent mechanism that makes it remarkably different from a network operating system (as the term is used in this chapter) is its ability to transfer a process from one machine to another in the network. This can be done without the knowledge of the processes. Only the network servers need to make adjustments for the new network address of the relocated process. All of the state information for a process, of the last checkpoint operation, is encapsulated in a message that is sent to the target machine.

Another basic operating system mechanism provided by Accent and missing in network operating systems is the ability to manage virtual memory remotely from another process. The Accent host machine uses a flat address space of 4G bytes, partitioned by Accent into segments. The segment is the basic unit of virtual memory allocation and secondary storage management.

Temporary segments are used by processes on the basis of their memory needs, whereas permanent segments are used for files. Permanent segments remain allocated by Accent until explicitly deleted, whereas temporary segments vanish once all links to them are released.

Processes can reference one another's virtual memory pages because Accent passes page references in messages. The system can designate pages as copy-on-write so that the kernel copies them only if they are modified. Similarly, one process wishing to copy another's memory pages on the same page boundaries can simply have the kernel add them to its memory map. This approach to memory management allows local memory access to be simulated over a network. This is essential for a distributed operating system to truly operate as such.

Accent provides a complete process management facility. **Fork** and **Terminate** primitives are used to spawn and terminate processes and can be suspended with **Suspend** and resumed with **Resume**. The **SetPriority** primitive is used to dynamically change the priority of an executing process. Microcoded context switching can switch Pascal processes in about 50 microseconds. The kernel includes a primitive process scheduler with 16 priority levels. Processes can be interrupted by the kernel using the pseudointerrupt mechanism, which drives the process on receipt of a message.

REVIEW OF DISTRIBUTED SYSTEMS

Distributed computing can reduce process execution time, increase system throughput, improve resource use, minimize scaling increments, and improve system availability. The extent of these improvements depends on whether the system is a network operating system, a distributed language, or a true distributed operating system. Distributed operating systems provide the greatest degree of work distribution. They allow processes and processors to be dynamically assigned and provide file access that is transparent to file location, along with other powerful features. They are also the most complex systems to develop.

By comparison, network operating systems provide static work distribution and host-cognizant file access, but they are simpler than distributed operating systems and offer some of the same features. Distributed languages provide a way for an application to request work distribution through language constructs. Such languages provide the simplest way to distribute work among multiple processors but limit distributed computing to specific applications rather than the entire computing system. All three of these systems are distributed computing systems because they all provide facilities for distributing work over multiple processing nodes.

The extent to which a system is distributed can also be described by referring to the following properties: granularity of parallelism, communications pattern, communications granularity, and ability to be scaled. Fine-grain parallelism is achieved if the average instruction block length without interprocessor communication is 17 to 256 instructions. A rich communication pattern is one in which many processors communicate in nonfixed patterns. It indicates the extent to which a distributed system can dynamically change interprocess and interprocessor communication. Fine communication granularity is achieved when communication message size ranges from 1 to 16 bytes. Messages of this size typically indicate moderate to fine-grain parallelism. Fine-grain scaling is facilitated by employing many small processors in a distributed operating system. If additional capacity is required, more processors are added to the system. Ideally, a distributed system would have open-ended scaling so that thousands of processors could be used by the system.

DISTRIBUTED SYSTEMS OVER LANS

The extent to which a distributed system can achieve fine-grain distribution (i.e., fine-grain parallelism, fine-grain communication, rich communications pattern, open-endedness) is directly influenced by the qualities of the communications medium. LANs are ideal for distributed computing because they offer high-speed communications with low bit-error rates and low communications latencies. Token-protocol (as opposed to contention protocol) LANs offer the additional quality of providing deterministic access to the network. Given the high throughput of FDDI, its deterministic access to the media, and its fault-tolerant design, it is the LAN of choice for moderate to fine-grain parallelism. Open-ended scaling is also more feasible using FDDI than other LANs.

The connection of microcomputers, minicomputers, and mainframes to a LAN offers diverse computing capacities, which distributed systems can exploit. Communication adapters used to connect microprocessors to a LAN offer throughput of up to 40M bps (using 32-bit data transfer coupled with such sophisticated bus schemes as Multibus II). Channel-attached adapters (e.g., the IBM 8232) offer mainframe access to the LAN at channel speeds of up to 4.5M bps. T1 connection to a LAN provides host computing power that is remote from the LAN.

LANs, especially FDDI, provide a powerful, flexible communications system on which moderate to fine-grain parallel distributed computing systems can be implemented. Distributed operating systems provide the richest capabilities of all distributed systems.

LIMITATIONS OF CURRENT SYSTEMS

Although fault tolerance is an important aspect of distributed systems, these systems typically handle faults by facilitating process restart from the beginning or the last checkpoint. Ideally, process-state information should be instantly available to an active backup processor in the event the node fails.

All of the systems discussed are small to moderate in size and are limited in their ability to be scaled. Larger systems would provide greater computing capacity and insight into problems associated with the growth of such systems.

X-2

The Network Computing Architecture and System: An Environment for Developing Distributed Applications

TERENCE H. DINEEN • *PAUL J. LEACH* • *NATHANIEL W. MISHKIN* •
JOSEPH N. PATO • *GEOFFREY L. WYANT*

The network computing architecture (NCA) is an object-oriented framework for developing distributed applications. The network computing system (NCS) is a portable implementation of that architecture that runs on UNIX and other systems. By adopting an object-oriented approach, application designers are encouraged to think in terms of the data structures their applications should operate on, not what server the applications should make calls to or how those calls should be implemented. This design increases robustness and flexibility in a changing environment.

NCS currently runs under Apollo's DOMAIN/IX, 4.2BSD and 4.3BSD, and Sun Microsystems Inc's version of UNIX. Implementations for the IBM PC and VAX/VMS are under development. Apollo Computer has placed NCA in the public domain.

In addition to its object orientation, NCS supplies a transport-independent remote procedure call facility using Berkeley UNIX sockets as the interface to any datagram facility. It provides at-most-once semantics over the datagram layer, with optimizations if an operation is declared to be idempotent. (That is, NCS ensures that a call will be executed no more than once, but a less overhead-intensive protocol can be used if it is asserted beforehand that repeated execution of a call will be harmless.) It is built on a concurrent programming support package that provides multiple threads of execution in a single address space, although versions can be made for machines that just have asynchronous timer interrupts. The data representation supports multiple scalar data formats, so that similar machines do not have to convert data to a canonical form but can instead use their common data formats. The remote procedure call interface definition compiler is extensible. Procedures for client-

773

server binding can be attached to data types defined in the interface. In addition, complex data types can be marshalled by user-supplied procedures that convert such types to data types the compiler understands. There is a replicated global location data base; using it, the locations of an object can be determined given its object ID, its type, or one of its supported interfaces.

There are several reasons for the development of NCA. Large, heterogeneous networks are becoming more common. Users of systems in such networks are often frustrated by the fact that they cannot get those systems to work cooperatively. Advances have been made in allowing data sharing between systems, but not sharing of computing power. Tools to allow the effective use of the aggregate computing power have not been available. This has become even more irritating as more specialized processors (e.g., ones designed to run numerical applications fast) have become more widespread. Current technology obliges users of those processors to resort to file transfer protocol and Telnet. Even in an environment of systems of relatively similar power, a network computing architecture is called for. There are applications that can take advantage of a parallel configuration of multiple systems. (Parallel make, a version of the UNIX software development tool that invokes the C compiler multiple times in parallel, is an example.) Also, replicating resources over a number of machines increases the reliability seen by users of the network.

It is important to understand that there is almost no network application that requires NCA/NCS. However, without NCA/NCS the application is bound to be more difficult, less general, and harder to install on a variety of systems. Experience has shown that some obviously useful network applications are not written because of these problems. The existence of NCA/NCS helps to solve these problems and expand the set of network applications as a result.

ARCHITECTURE

The structure of NCA is illustrated in Exhibit X-2-1.

Heterogeneous Interconnect

The lowest NCA level provides the basic interconnection to heterogeneous computing systems. At this layer, NCA currently defines a remote procedure call protocol (NCA/RPC), a network interface definition language (NIDL), and a network data representation (NDR). Remote procedure call is a mechanism that allows programs to make calls to subroutines in which the caller and the subroutine run in different processes, most commonly on different machines. NIDL is a high-level language used to specify the interfaces to procedures that are to be invoked through the remote call procedure mechanism. NCS includes a portable NIDL compiler that takes NIDL interfaces as input and produces stub procedures that, among other functions, handle data representation issues and connect program calls to the NCS remote procedure call runtime environment

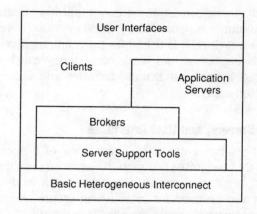

Exhibit X-2-1. NCA's Overall Structure

that implements the NCA/RPC protocol. The relationships among the client (i.e., the caller of a procedure offered by some remote server), server, stubs, and NCS run time is shown in Exhibit X-2-2.

Server Support Tools

Augmenting the heterogeneous interconnect layer are the server support tools. These tools simplify the writing of complex applications in a distributed envi-

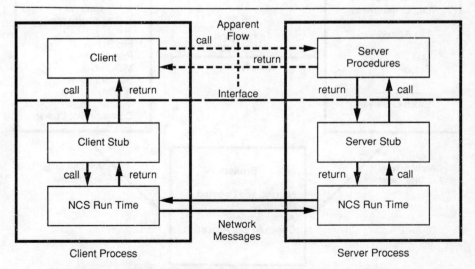

Exhibit X-2-2. Relationships Among Client, Server, Stubs, and NCS Run Time

ronment. Currently, these consist of the data replication manager (DRM) and concurrent programming support (CPS). DRM provides a weakly consistent, replicated data base facility. It is useful for providing replicated objects when high availability is important and weak consistency can be tolerated. CPS provides integrated lightweight tasking facilities and allows multithreaded servers to be written easily.

Brokers, Clients, Servers, and User Interfaces

Built on top of the server-support tools are a set of brokers. A broker is a third-party agent that facilitates transactions between principals. In a network computing environment, brokers are primarily useful in determining object locations but can also be used for establishing secure communications (i.e., authentication), associatively selecting objects, issuing software licenses, and performing a variety of other administrative chores not directly related to the operation of the principals. The role of brokers is shown in Exhibit X-2-3.

Client programs and application servers make use of the three base layers. Application servers produce services; clients are the consumers. Servers invoke brokers to make their existence known. Clients can invoke brokers to locate application servers and then use the underlying RPC mechanism to make use of the services provided. The application server may in turn be a client of other distributed services.

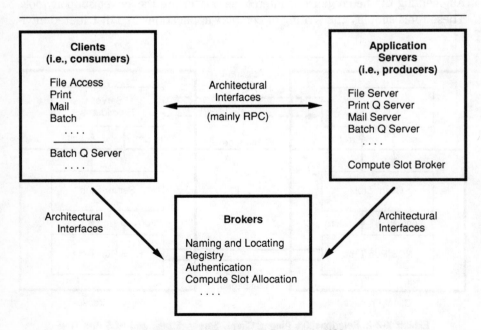

Exhibit X-2-3. The Role of Brokers in NCA

From the user's perspective, user interfaces tie all the pieces together. User interfaces are not part of NCA, however, and therefore will not be discussed in this chapter.

Unique Identifiers

An important aspect of NCA is its use of universal unique identifiers (UUIDs) as the most primitive means of identifying NCA entities (e.g., objects, interfaces, operations). UUIDs are an extension of the unique identifiers (UIDs) already used throughout Apollo's system. Both UIDs and UUIDs are fixed-length identifiers that are guaranteed to refer permanently to just one entity. The principal advantages of using any kind of unique identifiers over using string names at the lowest level of the system are their small size, ease of embedding in data structures, location transparency, and the ability to layer various naming strategies on top of the primitive naming mechanism. Also, identifiers can be generated anywhere, without first having to contact some other agent (e.g, a special server on the network or a person who is responsible for issuing the identifiers).

UIDs are 64 bits long and are guaranteed to be unique across all Apollo systems. Embedded in them are the node number of the system that generated the UID and the time that the UID was generated. To make it possible to generate unique identifiers on non-Apollo systems, UUIDs are 128 bits long and the encoding of the identity of the system that generates the UUID is more flexible.

THE OBJECT-ORIENTED APPROACH

NCA is object-oriented, meaning that it follows a paradigm used by distributed systems development environments such as Smalltalk (Xerox Corporation), Eden (University of Washington), and Hydra (Carnegie-Mellon University). The basic entity is the object. An object is a container of state (i.e., data) that can be accessed and modified only through a well-defined set of operations (what Smalltalk calls messages). The implementation of the operations is completely hidden from the client (i.e., caller) of the operations. Every object has some type (what Smalltalk calls a class). The implementation of a set of operations is called a manager (what Smalltalk calls a set of methods). Only the manager of a type knows the internal structure of objects of the type it manages. Sets of related operations are grouped into interfaces. Several types may support the same interface; a single type may support multiple interfaces.

For example, an interface called directory, which contains the operations **add__entry, drop__entry,** and **list__entries,** might be supported by two types: **directory__of__files** and **print__queue.** There are potentially many objects of these two types. That there are many objects of the type **directory__of__files** should be obvious. By saying that there are many **print__queue** objects, it is meant that a system (or a network of connected systems) might have many print queues, perhaps one for each department in a large organization.

Motivation

The reason for using the object-oriented approach in the context of a network architecture is that it allows the user to concentrate on what is to be done, not where and how something is to be done: objects are the units of distribution, abstraction, extension, reconfiguration, and reliability.

Distribution. Distribution addresses the question of where an operation is performed. The answer is that the operation is performed where the object resides. For example, if the print queue resides on system A, an attempt to add an entry to the queue from system B must be implemented by making a remote procedure call from system B to system A. (This implementation fact is hidden from the program attempting to add the entry.)

Abstraction. Abstraction addresses the question of how an operation is performed. In NCA, the object's type manager knows how the operation is performed. For example, a single program list_directory could be used to list both the contents of a file system directory and the contents of a print queue. The program simply calls the list_entries operation. The type managers for the two types of objects might represent their information in completely different ways (possibly because of the different performance characteristics required). However, the list_directory program uses only the abstract operation and is insulated from the details of a particular type's implementation.

Extension. The object-oriented approach allows extension (i.e., it specifies how the system is enhanced). In NCA, there are two kinds of extensions allowed. The first is extension by creation of new types. For example, users can create new types of objects that support the directory interface; such programs as list_directory that are clients of this interface simply work on objects of the new type, without modification. The second kind of extension is extension by creation of new interfaces. A new interface is the expression of a new function.

Reconfiguration. Because of partial failures, or for load balancing, networked systems sometimes need to be reconfigured. In object-oriented terms, this reconfiguration takes place by moving objects to new locations. For example, if the system that was the home for some print queue failed because of a hardware problem, the system would be reconfigured by moving the print queue object to a new system (and informing the network of the object's new location).

Reliability. The availability of many systems in a network should result in increased reliability. NCA's approach is to foster increased reliability by allowing objects to be replicated. Replication increases the probability that at least one copy of the object will be available to users of the object. To make replication feasible, NCS provides tools to synchronize multiple replicas of an object.

Although NCA is object-oriented and applications that use the object-oriented capabilities of NCA are more robust and general than those that do not, it is easy to use NCS as a conventional remote procedure call system, ignoring its object-oriented features.

NETWORK INTERFACE DEFINITION LANGUAGE

The network interface definition language (NIDL) is the language used in NCA to describe the remote interfaces called by clients and provided by servers. Interfaces described in NIDL are checked and translated by the NIDL compiler.

NIDL is strictly a declarative language—it has no executable constructs. NIDL contains only constructs for defining the constants, types, and operations of an interface. NIDL is more than an interface definition language, however. It is also a network interface definition language and, therefore, it enforces the restrictions inherent in a distributed computing model (e.g., lack of shared memory).

NIDL Language Constructs

A NIDL interface contains a header, constant and type definitions, and operation descriptions. The header provides the interface identification: its UUID, name, and version number. The UUID is the name by which an interface is known within NCA. It is similar to the program number in other remote procedure call systems except that it is not centrally assigned. The interface name is a string name for the interface that is used by the NIDL compiler in naming certain publicly known variables. The version number is used to support compatible enhancements of interfaces.

A standard set of programming language types is provided. Integers (signed and unsigned) come in 1-, 2-, 4-, and 8-byte sizes. Single- (4-byte) and double- (8-byte) precision floating-point numbers are available. Other scalars include signed and unsigned characters as well as Boolean constructs and enumerations.

In addition to scalar types, NIDL provides the usual type constructors: structures, unions, pointers, and arrays. Only discriminated unions are supported (i.e., nondiscriminated unions are not permitted; the actual data values must be known at run time so that they can be correctly transmitted to the remote server). Pointers, in general, are restricted to being top level (i.e., pointers to other pointers, or records containing pointers are not permitted, although this restriction can be relaxed). Arrays can be fixed in size or have their size determined at run time.

Operation declarations are the heart of a remote interface definition. These define the procedures and functions that servers implement and to which clients make calls. All operations are strongly typed. This enables the NIDL compiler to generate the code to correctly copy parameters to and from the packet and to do any needed data conversions. Operation declarations can be optionally marked to have certain semantic properties (e.g., whether they are idempotent).

All operations are required to have a handle as their first parameter. This parameter is similar to the implicit self argument of Smalltalk-80 or the this argument of C++. The handle argument is used to determine what object and server is to receive the remote call. NIDL defines a primitive handle type named handle_t. An argument of this type can be used as an operation's handle parameter. Clients can obtain handle_t by calling the NCS run time and providing an object UUID and network location as input arguments. Use of more abstract kinds of handles is described below.

Handle arguments can be implicit. An interface definition can declare that a single global variable should be treated as the handle argument for all operations in the interface. While this style conflicts with some of the goals of the object-oriented approach (e.g., it makes it harder to make calls on different objects using the same interface), it can be useful in cases in which an existing local interface is being converted to work remotely.

NIDL Example

Exhibit X-2-4 is a short example of an interface described in NIDL. The example is of an interface to a bank object that supports a single operation: depositing money into an account.

Line 1 defines the UUID by which this interface is known. This is the first version of this interface. If new operations are added in the future, the version number should be incremented. Line 2 declares the interfaces on which this

```
[uuid(334033030000.0d.000.00.87.84.00.00.00), version(1)]        (1)
interface bank {
    import
        "nbase.imp.idl";                                          (2)
    typedef                                                       (3)
        long int bank$acct_t;
    typedef
        char bank$acct_name_t[32];
    void bank$deposit(                                            (4)
        [in]      handle_t        h,
        [in]      bank$acct_t     acct,
        [in]      long int        amount,
        [out]     status_$t       *status
    );
};
```

Exhibit X-2-4. Example of an Interface

interface depends. The import statement is similar to #include in C language, except that the named interface is not textually included. The contents are made available for the importer to refer to types and constants defined in that interface. This allows factoring out a common set of types into a base interface. Line 3 defines a set of types (account and account name types) that are used by the bank operations. Finally, line 4 defines the operation itself.

A variant of NIDL that looks like Pascal (as opposed to the C-like version of which Exhibit X-2-4 is an example) is also available. Regardless of the variant used as input to the NIDL compiler, the output is the same.

Object-Oriented Binding

One drawback of the language as described so far is that all operations are required to have a primitive handle_t as their first argument. This means clients need to embed these handles in their programs and to manage the binding to servers themselves. It would be better to achieve as much local-remote transparency as possible (i.e., to make programs insensitive to the location of the objects on which they operate). Embedding primitive handles in client programs destroys much of this transparency. To relieve clients of the need to manage these handles, we introduced the notion of object-oriented binding.

Object-oriented binding comes into play when the first parameter to an operation is not a handle_t. In this case, the type is taken to represent some more abstract, client-oriented handle. Because a handle_t is required to actually make remote calls, some way is needed to translate the abstract handle into a handle_t. The person who creates the abstract type is thus obliged to write a procedure for the conversion. This procedure is assumed to have the name type_bind (where type is the type name of the abstract handle) and is automatically called from stubs when the remote call is made. The abstract handle can be viewed as an object (in the Smalltalk sense) that supports the bind operation.

To make this more concrete, the previous bank example could be reformulated in terms of object-oriented binding. Instead of taking a handle_t as its first parameter, bank$deposit could take a bank name of type bank$name. The NIDL compiler would generate a call to bank$name_bind to translate from a bank name to the primitive handle_t. This routine would probably call on a naming server to look up the bank location. The bind routine might also choose to cache location information to make later translations faster.

Object-oriented binding hides the details of handle binding from the client and allows interfaces to be designed in a more abstract, client-oriented fashion. This provides a higher level of local-remote transparency than other systems that always require the client to manage handles or explicitly name the remote host on each call.

Marshalling Complex Types

The reason that pointers cannot be nested is that such nesting would require the NIDL compiler to generate code to transmit general graph structures. However, permitting only top-level, nonnested pointers can be a severe limitation in the design of an interface. For example, it excludes passing tree data structures to remote procedures.

To provide an escape from this restriction, NIDL allows a type to have an associated transmissible type. The transmissible type is a type that the NIDL compiler knows how to marshal. Any type that has an associated transmissible type must have a set of procedures to convert that type to and from its transmissible type. In the example of the binary tree, the transmissible type could be an array. The **tree$to_xmit_rep** procedure would examine the contents of the tree to build a representation of it in the array, and the **tree$from_xmit_rep** procedure would reconstruct the binary tree from the array.

Transmissible types may be associated with any type, not just types using nested pointers. Bit maps are an example. A bit map may be represented internally as a fixed-size array of integers. Even though the NIDL compiler is capable of marshaling this, it may be more efficient to have it transmitted in a run-length-encoded (RLE) form. The bit map type could therefore have an associated **RLEBitmap** type and a set of procedures for converting to and from the RLE form.

NETWORK DATA REPRESENTATION

Communicating typed values in a heterogeneous environment requires a data representation protocol. A data representation protocol defines a mapping between typed values and byte streams. A byte stream is a sequence of bytes indexed by nonnegative integers. Examples of data representation protocols are Courier and XDR. A data representation protocol is needed because different machines represent data differently. For example, VAXs represent integers with the least significant byte at the low address, and 68000s represent integers with the most significant byte at the low address. A data representation protocol defines the way data is represented so that machines with different local data representation can communicate typed values to one another.

NCA includes a data representation protocol called network data representation (NDR). NDR defines a set of data types and type constructors that can be used to specify ordered sets of typed values. NDR also defines a mapping between ordered sets of values and their representations in messages.

Under NDR, the representation of a set of values consists of two items: a format label and a byte stream. The format label defines how scalar values are represented (e.g., VAX or IEEE floating point) in the byte stream; its representation is fixed by NDR as a data structure representable in 4 bytes.

NDR supports Boolean, character, signed integer, unsigned integer, and floating-point scalar types. Boolean types are represented in the byte stream with 1 byte; false is represented by a zero byte and true by a nonzero byte. Characters are represented in the byte stream with 1 byte; either ASCII or EBCDIC codes can be used. Four sizes of signed and unsigned integers are defined: small, short, long, and hyper. Small types are represented in the byte stream with 1 byte, short types with 2 bytes, long types with 4 bytes, and hyper types with 8 bytes. Either big- or little-endian representation can be used for integers; two's complement arithmetic is assumed for signed integers. The two sizes of floating-point type are single and double. Single floating-point types are represented with 4 bytes and double floating-point types use 8 bytes. The supported floating-point representations are IEEE, VAX, Cray, and IBM.

In addition to scalar types, NDR has a set of type constructors for defining aggregate types. These include fixed-size arrays, open arrays, zero-terminated strings, records, and variant records.

Arrays of fixed size have a known number of elements. Their values are represented in the byte stream simply as a sequence of representations of the values of the elements. Each element value is represented according to the element type of the array. Open array types have a fixed first index value and element type, but their final index value is not known from their type. Therefore, it is necessary to represent the value of the index of the last element in the array immediately before the values of the array elements are represented.

Zero-terminated strings can be viewed as a special case of open arrays; they are open arrays of characters whose last index value is defined by a terminating zero byte. To support this common data type in an efficient manner, NDR represents such values with an explicit length value followed by the characters of the string, including the terminating zero character.

Record values are represented in the byte stream by representations of the values of the records' fields in the order defined by the record type. Variant records are assumed to have an initial set of fixed fields, which includes a tag field used to discriminate among the possible variants. Representations of the values of the fields of the selected variant follow the representations of the values of the fixed fields of a variant record value.

Some types may appear to be missing from NDR. NDR has no enumerated or bit-set types and no pointer-type constructor. The definition of NIDL maps such types onto their representations in an NDR byte stream. For example, NIDL maps enumerated types and bit sets onto the NDR unsigned integer type of the appropriate size. Typed pointer values are mapped onto the NDR type that represents the type that the pointer references.

NDR is abstract in that it does not define how the format label and the byte stream are represented in packets. The NIDL compiler and the NCA/RPC protocol are users of NDR; they work together to generate the format label and byte stream, encode the format label in packet headers, fragment the byte stream into packet-sized pieces, and put the fragments in packet bodies.

The important features of NDR are its flexible representation of scalar values, its use of natural alignment, and its extensibility.

By using a format label to specify an interpretation of the scalars in a byte stream, NDR supports a multicanonical approach to data conversion in a heterogeneous environment. A sending process can use its preferred encoding of scalars when constructing a byte stream, providing that it is one of the defined options. A receiving process needs to convert data representations only when the format specified in the incoming format label differs from its own preferred format. Thus, two compatible machines can communicate efficiently without needing to convert to a conventional network format and back again on each transmission. NDR defines a broadly useful but not universal set of scalar formats. The choices are reasonable for promoting heterogenous network computing combining workstations and special-purpose server machines. Conversely, it is important to keep the space of possible formats to a reasonable size because each recipient needs to convert any incoming scalar format to its own format.

NDR requires that values be naturally aligned in the byte stream. Natural alignment means that all values of size 2^n are aligned at a byte stream index that is a multiple of 2^n, up to limiting values of n; NDR chooses this limit to be 3. That is, scalars of size up to 8 bytes are naturally aligned. This permits, but does not require, implementations of NCA to align buffers for the byte stream so that stub code can use natural operators to manipulate values in the byte stream efficiently and without alignment faults. This also helps to promote communication ease between different kinds of machines in a heterogeneous environment.

By its use of a format label, NDR is an extensible data representation protocol. The format label could be extended to specify other such aspects of the data representation as packing disciplines, dynamic typing schemes, new encodings of scalars, or new classes of scalars.

THE NCS NIDL COMPILER AND STUB FUNCTIONS

NCS includes a compiler that mediates between NIDL on the one hand and NDR and the NCS run time on the other. The functions of the compiler include checking the syntax and semantics of interface definitions written in NIDL, translating NIDL definitions into declarations in such implementation languages as C, and generating client and server stubs for executing the remote operations of an interface.

The NIDL compiler is organized as a front-end component and a back-end component. The front-end parses and checks an interface definition and produces an abstract syntax tree (AST) intermediate form. If the interface definition is sound, the front end then passes this tree to the back end, which generates the implementation language include files and stub code files for the interface.

784

NCS's NIDL compiler is implemented for portability in C, using the standard UNIX compiler-building utilities **YACC** and **LEX**. It is available in source form to encourage its use and extension in heterogeneous networked environments.

NIDL Compiler Functions

Distributed object-oriented programming imposes certain restrictions on the semantics of interfaces. It is part of the compiler's job (along with the design of NIDL) to enforce these restrictions. Some examples illustrate the front end's semantic checks. All types used in a definition must be well defined. All parameters and fields whose type is an open array require the use of a **last_is** attribute to give their size at call time. Every remote interface requires a UUID. Every operation of an interface requires an implicit or explicit handle parameter to support object-oriented programming.

The second major function of the NIDL compiler is to derive files that declare the interface's constants, types, and operations in the languages in which client applications and servers are written. These files are included in client and server programs that use or implement the remote operations of an interface. For the current implementation, the supported languages are C and Pascal. Generating these files is done by a fairly straightforward pass over the abstract syntax tree; adding the capability to generate include files in other ALGOL-like languages would be a simple exercise.

In addition to declaring the constants, types, and operations of an interface, the derived include files declare two important statically initialized variables defined for each interface. One is the interface specification (ifspec), which encapsulates the identity of the interface and its salient properties (e.g., number of operations, well-known ports used). The ifspec variable is used in the binding and registering operations of the NCS run time. The second variable is the server entry point vector (EPV), which holds pointers to the server side's stub routines. This EPV variable is used when a server registers for an interface; it is used by the NCS run time to dispatch incoming calls.

The third major function of the NIDL compiler is to generate files of stub code for the operations defined in an interface. There are two such files—one contains client-side stub routines and the other contains server-side stub routines. This emitted code is in standard C, which is used as a universal assembler to promote portability. Each operation in an interface gives rise to a client stub routine and a server stub routine. The following section discusses the functions of these routines.

Stub Functions

Client stub routines are called by clients of an interface; they have the same interface as the operation for which they stand in. Server stub routines are called by the server-side NCS run time; their interface is defined by NCS. Client stub routines call the client-side NCS run time to perform remote calls. Server stubs call the manager's implementation of an operation to provide the actual service. Thus, the first function of stubs is to hide the NCS run time from users and implementers of remote interfaces and to create the illusion of accessing a remote procedure as though it were local.

To communicate input and output arguments and function results between callers and called routines, the stub must marshal and unmarshal argument values into call and reply packets. This is done in accordance with NDR and the conventions of NCS. Unmarshaling code is also responsible for detecting and performing necessary data conversions by comparing the incoming format label with the local formats. Data conversion is done by a combination of inline code and support operations in the NCS run time.

The stubs also need to calculate the size requirements for call and reply packets on the basis of the dynamic size of input and output arguments. The size information is used to determine whether a predeclared packet on the stack is large enough. If not, the stubs need to allocate and free storage for packets. It is not the job of the stub to decompose a large packet into pieces that can be sent over the network—the NCS run time provides the capability to handle arbitrarily sized packets.

Client-side stubs map the operations of an interface to the operation number used by the NCS run time to identify operations; they also pass options designating the desired calling semantics and the ifspec derived from the NIDL declaration of an operation to the NCS run time's remote call primitive.

On the server side, the stub routines are responsible for managing storage to be used as the server side surrogates for dynamically sized arguments. This is necessary to support the server's illusion of large data structures passed to it.

The stubs also manage the more elaborate features of NIDL previously described. Client stubs support automatic binding by calling users' binding and unbinding routines when necessary. Implicit handles are made explicit to the NCS run time by client stub routines. Users' marshaling routines are invoked as necessary by both client and server stubs as part of marshaling input and output arguments of the appropriate types.

In summary, the NIDL compiler accepts an interface definition as input and produces a large amount of protocol code. This is important because the code is complex enough to make its manual coding very error prone and tedious. Manually producing this kind of code has been a major impediment to building distributed systems in the past.

LOCATION BROKER

A highly available location service is a fundamental component of a distributed system architecture. Objects representing people, resources, or services are transient and mobile in a network environment. Consumers of these entities cannot rely on a priori knowledge of their existence or location but must consult a dynamic registry. When consumers rely solely on a location service for accessing objects, it becomes essential that the location server remain available in the face of partial network failures.

The NCA location broker (NCA/LB) protocol is designed to provide a reliable networkwide location broker. This protocol is defined by a NIDL interface and is thereby easily used by any NCA/RPC-based application.

The NCA/LB, unlike such location services as Xerox SDD's Clearinghouse or Berkeley's Internet Name Domain service (BIND), yields location information based on UUIDs rather than on human-readable string names. The advantages of using UUIDs were described previously.

Locating

An object's type manager must first advertise its location with the location broker (LB) for that object to be located. A manager advertises itself by registering its location and its willingness to support some combination of specific objects, types of objects, or interfaces. A manager can choose to advertise itself as a global service available to the entire network or it can limit its registration to the local system. Managers that choose the latter form of registration do not make themselves unavailable, but rather limit their visibility to clients that specifically probe their system for location information.

Clients find objects by querying the location broker for appropriate registrations. A client can choose to query for a specific object, type, interface, or any combination of these characteristics. When operations are externally constrained to occur at a specific location, a client can choose to query the LB at the required system for managers supporting the appropriate object.

Location Broker Organization

The location broker is divided into two components. The global location data base is a replicated object containing the registration information of all globally registered managers; the processes that manage this data base are called the global location broker. The NCS run-time implementation of the global location broker uses the data replication manager (DRM) to maintain the data base. DRM provides a weakly consistent replicated data base package. Weak consistency implies that replicas of the global location data base object may be inconsistent at any time but that in the absence of updates, all replicas will converge to a consistent state within a finite amount of time. This form of consistency provides a high degree of both read and update availability to the global location data base. It is not necessary to be able to communicate with all replicas of the object to effect a change in the registration data base. The DRM assumes the responsibility of propagating updates to the replicas in a timely fashion.

A local location broker supports managers that wish to limit their registration to the local system. Access to these registrations is provided in two ways. A client can directly query the location broker at a specific node to determine the objects and managers that are registered there. Alternatively, a client can simply execute a remote operation while supplying an incompletely bound handle (i.e., one that specifies only an object and system, not a particular server process). Remote calls made using such a handle are delivered to the local location broker, which serves as a forwarding agent if an appropriate manager has registered itself locally. This mechanism obviates the need for users of the NCA to use well-known ports.

The division of the location broker into two distinct entities is, to a large degree, an NCS run-time implementation decision. Logically, the local location data base object and the global location data base object are a single partitioned object; in fact, access to these data bases is provided through a common set of operations that select the target based on look-up keys.

THE NCA/RPC PROTOCOL AND NCS IMPLEMENTATION

The NCA/RPC protocol is designed to be low cost for the common cases and independent of the underlying network protocols on which it is layered. The NCS run-time implementation of the NCA/RPC protocol is designed to be portable.

Protocol

The NCA/RPC protocol is designed so that a simple RPC call will result in as few network messages and have as little overhead as possible. It is well known that existing networking facilities designed to move long byte streams reliably (e.g., TCP/IP) are generally not well suited to being the underlying mechanism by which RPC run times exchange messages. The primary reason for this is that the cost of setting up a connection using such facilities and the associated maintenance of that connection is quite high. Such a cost might be acceptable if, for example, a client were to make 100 calls to one server. The possibility of one client making a call to 100 servers in turn should not be precluded, however. In general, we expect the number of calls made from a particular client to a particular server to be relatively small. The reliable connection solution is also unacceptable from the server's perspective. A popular server may need to handle calls from hundreds of clients over a relatively short period of time (e.g., 1 to 2 minutes). The server does not want to bear the cost of maintaining network connections to all those clients.

One way of establishing reliable network connections is to make the remote procedure call implement exactly the reliability it needs, layered on an unreliable network service (e.g., the user datagram protocol/internet protocol [UDP/IP]). This approach has the additional advantage that some systems (e.g., embedded microprocessors) cannot or do not support any reliable network service; however, if they are connected to a network at all, they will at least supply an unreliable service. Further, unreliable services tend to be more similar across protocol suites than reliable services. (For example, some reliable protocols might return errors immediately if the network partitions even though a virtual circuit is currently idle, and others might defer until the next time I/O is attempted.) This similarity means that the RPC protocol can be accurately implemented in more protocol suites than would be possible if it assumed a reliable service.

All that the NCA/RPC protocol assumes is an underlying unreliable network service. The protocol is robust in the face of lost, duplicated, and long-delayed messages; messages arriving out of order; and server crashes. When necessary, the protocol ensures that no call is ever executed more than once. (Calls may execute zero or one times and, in the face of network partitions or server crashes, the client may not know how many times the call was executed.)

The NCA/RPC protocol operates roughly as follows. The client side sends a packet describing the call (a request packet) and waits for a response. The server side receives and dispatches the request for execution and sends a packet in response that describes the results of executing the call (the response packet). If the client does not receive a response to a request within a certain interval, it can send a ping packet to inquire about the status of the request. The server either sends back a working packet, indicating that execution of the request is in progress, or a no-call packet, which means that the request has been lost (or that the server has crashed and rebooted) and the client needs to resend it. The protocol gets slightly more complicated if the input or output arguments do not fit into one packet.

If a called procedure is nonidempotent, the protocol ensures that the server executes the call one time at most. To detect old (duplicate) requests, the server keeps track of the sequence number of the previous request for each client with which it has communicated. However, the server considers this information to be discardable and it may discard it if it has not heard from the client in a while (i.e., there is no permanent connection between the client and server). Thus, it is possible for a long-delayed duplicate request to arrive after the server has discarded the information about the requesting client. To handle this case, the server calls back to the client (using an idempotent remote procedure call) to ask the client for the client's current sequence number. The server then uses the returned sequence number to validate the request. For calls to nonidempotent procedures (with input and output arguments that fit in a single packet), a total of two message pairs are exchanged between client and server for the simple case.

Subsequent calls between the same client and server require just one message pair. The extra message pair in the first case could conceivably be eliminated if the server were willing to retain client sequence number information long enough to ensure that all duplicate requests had been flushed from the network. This approach was not taken, because any time interval considered long enough (e.g., 1 minute or more) seemed too long to obligate the server to hold the information.

In addition, for nonidempotent procedures, the server side saves and periodically retransmits the response packet until the client side has acknowledged receipt of the response. If the server side receives a retransmission of the request, it resends the saved response instead of reexecuting the call. The client side acknowledges the response either implicitly, by sending a new request, or explicitly, by sending an acknowledgment packet. The protocol also handles the case in which the server has executed the nonidempotent call but, because of network partitions or a server crash, fails to send the response packet.

If a called procedure is idempotent, the protocol does not guarantee how many times the procedure is executed. On idempotent requests, the server side does not save the results of the operation once it has sent back the response packet. In addition, the client side is not required to acknowledge the receipt of responses to idempotent requests.

Run Time

The NCS/RPC run time is written in portable C and uses the Berkeley UNIX socket abstraction. (In terms of the socket abstraction, it uses SOCK_DGRAM-style sockets.) This abstraction is intended to mask the details of various protocol families so that it is possible to write protocol-independent networking code. (A protocol family is a suite of related protocols; e.g., TCP and UDP are part of the Department of Defense Internet protocol family; PEP and SPP are part of the Xerox NS protocol family.) In practice, however, the socket abstraction has to be extended in several ways to make it possible to write truly protocol-independent code. The socket abstraction has been extended by using a set of operations implemented in a user-mode subroutine library; the NCS run time uses these extensions so that it can be truly protocol independent. Bringing up the NCS run time on a new protocol family should not require any changes to the NCS run time itself. All that should be required is the addition of some relatively trivial routines to the socket abstraction extension library.

NCS is careful about creating sockets. Because sockets are a fairly scarce resource, monopolizing many of them for a long period is to be avoided. NCS keeps a small private pool of sockets. One is pulled from the pool when a process makes a remote call. When the call is completed, the socket is returned to the pool. The pool need contain only one socket for the entire process if the system supports only one thread of control per process (as is the case in standard UNIX).

The use of the socket abstraction at all could be considered too specific to Berkeley UNIX, thus reducing the portability of the run time. Fortunately, two factors argue against this point of view. First, AT&T System V Release 3 will support at least a sufficient subset of the socket calls (layered on top of their own networking model). Second, even if the target of a port does not have anything resembling the socket interface, NCS use of the interface is fairly simple and it would not be too hard to implement the Berkeley UNIX calls in terms of whatever the target system supplies.

SUMMARY

NCA and NCS represent the first step in a complete network computing environment. One of the guiding goals in the development of NCA has been transparency. This has a number of aspects: replication, failure, concurrency, location, and name transparency.

With replication transparency, all copies of an object can be considered equivalent. The user of an object cannot tell whether it consists of a single copy or many copies. The DRM provides replication transparency in the case in which some short-lived inconsistencies can be tolerated. Future versions of NCA will include support for strongly consistent replication.

Location transparency allows users to access objects without specifying where the objects are. Objects are free to be moved around the network to adapt to changing load conditions and the availability of new hardware. The location broker provides the ability to find the location of objects before their first use. It should be possible to have objects move at any time during program execution.

Concurrency transparency supports the illusion that a given client is the sole user of an object. NCS addresses this partially through concurrent programming support, which provides a simple locking facility. In the future this, and to some degree, failure transparency, will be addressed through the use of an object-oriented atomic transaction facility.

Failure transparency (i.e., the ability of components of a distributed system to fail and recover transparently to their users) is largely a function of location and replication transparency. By replicating objects, when a given replica fails, another is available to takes its place. Location transparency hides the switch from one replica to another from the user.

Neither NCA nor NCS addresses the issue of name transparency. A general-purpose name server will be built in a future version of NCS. In addition, a higher-level form of naming will be addressed. In many instances, it is more convenient to find an object by attribute rather than by a text name. An attribute broker provides this ability. Thus, for example, a client is able to query the attribute broker for a list of 26-page-per-second laser printers rather than managing the mapping between machine names and attributes itself.

Most of the focus in the NCA development so far has been on getting the basic model right. Once the object-oriented model is in place, these higher-level services will evolve naturally. If development had started with a more traditional process-oriented model, the desired level of integration and transparency would be much more difficult to achieve.

X-3
Open Systems Interconnection Directory Systems

LELAND W. SEETON, JR

Today's networks are complex, quantitatively, in terms of the large numbers of installed LANs and WANs and the proliferation of applications exchanging information over these networks, and qualitatively, with respect to the problem of unambiguous identification of network resource consumers and providers. (This includes direct and indirect consumers and providers.) For the purposes of this chapter, consumers and providers, both direct and indirect, are termed objects. Unambiguous identification also involves the naming of these objects and the publication of information about their characteristics or attributes.

The introduction of the Open Systems Interconnection (OSI) reference model and the related development of distributed processing require a standardized means of identifying, registering, and publishing information about these objects and their users. Some key attributes used to identify objects by name are the functions, services, and protocols necessary to manage the access, retrieval, and transfer of information identified with a named object. The registration of names is another important function. A repository for information about objects is generally referred to as a directory facility.

This chapter presents some of the significant elements of a directory facility in the OSI environment. It discusses some of the international standards that apply to such a facility and their relation to other components of the OSI model. The primary focus is on parts 1 to 8 of the international standard ISO 9594, The Directory. This standard addresses the directory facility requirements of a broad segment of OSI applications. Its model identifies the relevant application layer components of a directory facility. It specifies a means for identifying and publishing information about named objects based on a standard set of services and protocols. These services and protocols are used by the component entities of this facility to exchange information on behalf of the clients of the directory. These component entities of the directory do not represent a registration authority or perform any of the activities associated with a registration authority.

CONCEPTS AND TERMINOLOGY OF THE OSI DIRECTORY

The OSI reference model defines the framework for naming and addressing. This framework provides a conceptual model for describing the terms *directory function* and *directory facility*. Furthermore, the conceptual definition of these terms sets forth a general specification of requirements for the associated information processing and communication functions. The material presented here assumes some familiarity with the OSI model and the components of the application layer.

DIRECTORY FUNCTION

A directory function defines a general mechanism by which OSI layer entities may identify and access the capabilities of adjacent layer entities. A directory function can be thought of as a processing activity of an n-layer entity that makes use of identifiers and addressing information to provide mappings among these types of information. Directory functions are used during the establishment of an association between n-layer entities. These functions are used to support instances of connection-based and connectionless communications. The procedures used to provide these mappings are consistent and well defined in the context of the local system.

The information pertaining to these mappings consists of n entity titles, n and $n-1$ addresses, and n protocol addressing information. A directory function may make use of additional, locally derived information to provide these mappings. It is the responsibility of local systems management to make these types of information available to the directory function. Some of this information and the derived mappings may reflect the morphology of the local system and is therefore held locally. Other components of this information may influence the generation of protocol addressing information. These may be held locally or remotely by a directory facility.

One example is the processing of incoming protocol addressing information (e.g., a t-selector) to identify the correct mapping to the local session layer access point. Another is the use of the p-selector in the incoming protocol to derive the mapping to an application entity.

DIRECTORY FACILITY

A directory facility, in comparison, is a repository for the mapping information consumed by n-layer directory functions. Local systems management is responsible for retrieving and making this information available to n-layer directory functions. The directory facility has several primary tasks. It provides a repository for directory information. This information is made available to and is processed by the directory functions to provide these mappings. It provides the means for binding a name of an object to information representing identifiable specified characteristics of the object as well as the services necessary for information retrieval and transfer, and management of directory information.

Some of the information processed to provide these mappings is relevant to the structure or operation of the local system and is held locally. Other information used to provide these mappings is relevant to the construction of n-layer protocol addressing information that may reflect the internal structure of the remote system. This information may be stored locally or remotely but must be acquired from the remote system. If it is stored locally, no particular constraints are placed on the mechanism used to access this information. If it is stored remotely, specific services are provided by a directory facility to access the information remotely using OSI protocols. There are two types of directory facility identified in OSI (within the specific context of naming and addressing): the network address directory facility and the application title directory facility.

Network Address Directory Facility

The network address directory facility processes a network address according to a specified set of rules, to provide the routing and underlying layers with the information necessary to access the remote system through its network service access point. These functions may make use of various procedures to access and manage the information used in processing network addresses as part of the routing function of layer 3. A distinguishing characteristic of the information contained in this type of directory is its highly dynamic nature, which changes depending on the degrees of reachability and accessibility among the routers. This is one characteristic that differentiates the network address directory facility from the application title directory facility.

Application Title Directory Facility

The application title directory facility provides the means to access and process naming and addressing information and make it available to a directory function as part of establishing an application association between application entities. This may include, specifically, information that identifies by name a number of structural components in the application layer. Significant among these are application-process titles, application-entity titles, and application context titles. Moreover, other types of identifiers may be used in the process of establishing or changing the context of an association. Some of these identifiers may be more dynamic in nature than others, reflecting particular instances of communications within a specific context.

Association invocation identifiers, for example, exist only during the lifetime of an association. Information reflecting the dynamic state of associations between applications is perhaps better suited for local storage and retrieval by local systems management. (There is no requirement for employing any particular mechanism to achieve this capability, although OSI services and protocols may be used.) There is nothing, however, that precludes the storage of and access to both static and dynamic information, using the services of a single directory facility.

The application layer directory facility is either a local or remote facility or a combination of both. There is no requirement for an OSI end system to include or make use of a remote directory facility.

Local Application Title Directory Facility. The local application title directory facility furnishes local naming and addressing information to a directory function to derive the associated mappings. No requirement is placed on the local facility to support any standardized capability to share or manage this information in a unified manner with other local directory facilities on other systems.

It may be necessary to publish certain aspects of the locally held information (such as the semantics) to support the procedures for establishing an association with a remote peer application entity. Although the syntax of this information is meaningful only in the context of the local system that is publishing it, the semantics need to be understood by the remote system using this information. A local facility is not required to employ OSI services and protocols to provide access to this local information, irrespective of the perceived source of such access (local or remote). Similarly, publication or management of this local information does not require the use of OSI protocols.

Isolation from other directory systems (on other end systems) is an inherent constraint of a local directory facility. This type of facility therefore cannot make any guarantees about the overall consistency or reliability of information pertaining to the names or addresses of remote applications, other than perhaps some notion of short-term reliability. Certain aspects of objects—for example, an object's name—may have long lifetimes. Other aspects of an object—for example, the location (i.e., the address) of the application or the set of services an application is capable of supporting—may change more frequently.

The OSI standards do not preclude, however, the provision and use of non-OSI services and protocols to support the exchange of information between local directory facilities.

Remote Application Title Directory Facility. The remote application title directory facility, on the other hand, does furnish a model incorporating the use of OSI services and protocols for the distributed exchange of directory information among other remote directory facilities in an OSI environment. The OSI services may include those to create, access, extend, and maintain the directory information about objects located on cooperating OSI systems. The protocols used to support these services are application layer protocols exchanged between application-entity components of remote application processes. This makes it possible to maintain a consistent view of object information in an OSI environment.

The remote application directory facilitates communication between a diverse (and potentially large) population of objects (i.e., applications) in an OSI environment. Again, there are certain types of information that may not be well suited for retrieval from a remote directory facility. Highly dynamic information (e.g., association identifiers) would not be suitable candidates for holding in a remote directory facility. Information that has greater longevity and that is less prone to frequent changes (e.g., information that is used for identifying objects) is suitable for storage in a remote facility.

Structure of Information in a Directory Facility

Local Facility Information. As mentioned previously, a directory facility (local or remote) contains information identifying various objects of interest. Logically, an object can be represented in a directory facility as a set of assertions about the object's characteristics; these characteristics can be represented in several ways (e.g., by using either the object's attributes or its properties). In any case, the information contained in a directory facility is not the same as the information contained in or presented by the object. The information in a directory facility may be thought of in terms of distinct entries, each of which reflects reference information about an object but does not contain the actual object.

The physical representation and storage of directory information may employ any number of techniques. Use of a particular technique is a local system decision. The logical structuring of this information in the context of a local directory facility is relatively unconstrained because there is no requirement to exchange either the information or the supporting structure with other directory facilities. It may be necessary, however, to preserve the semantics of key information associated with an object. This key information would have an interpretation specific to the remote system supporting communications with applications residing therein. Information about an application on a remote system may, for example, include the application's presentation address on the remote system. Preserving the semantics of this address allows the remote system to realize the significance of this information and how it will be used in the remote system. The actual syntax of this address information is meaningful only to the remote system to which it applies, because it is the remote system that is the sole consumer of this address information.

Remote Facility Information. In a remote directory facility the situation is different, because the information about objects is available for exchange with other remote directory facilities. For the participating systems to have a logical view of this information requires that they understand the syntax and semantics describing the information. More precisely, this applies to a standard protocol's representation of the information about objects. Extending the semantics of these characteristics to set relations can provide relational assertions about these objects and a notion of object class.

Relations between objects can be stated in many ways (e.g., domains, neighborhoods, predecessor, successor, superior, and subordinate). Similarly, there are many techniques that, by an isomorphic description of the relations among entries in the directory, represent the relations among the objects.

Identification of an object requires associating a name with the object, and identifying an entry contained in a directory requires that the entry have a name. The naming requirement is a significant directory feature—the binding of a symbolic name to a set of attribute assertions (i.e., an entry). The name is constructed as a set of assertions about an entry's specific attributes. The particular syntax and semantics defined for representing the structure of this information to a large extent depends on the requirements of the users of the directory facility. The logical definition of this structure is reflected in the exchange of directory information in an application protocol between remote directory entities. In other words, to exchange information between remote directory facilities there must be a well-defined understanding of what the protocol information represents with respect to the requested operation and its relation to the structure of the directory information.

Support of a remote directory facility does impose a special requirement on the information contained in the local directory facility. Specifically, it requires the local directory facility to contain bootstrap information identifying at least one remote directory facility. The acquisition and maintenance of this bootstrap information is not specified.

Provision for Name Binding in a Directory Facility

A directory must provide a means of binding an object's symbolic name to the object's attributes and values. This binding is the creation of a named entry and its associated set of attributes in the information base. Binding may be considered a form of publishing the names of registered objects and other information related to these objects.

Name Forms

The form of a symbolic name can follow several types of linguistic constructs (e.g., primitive, simple, distinguished, descriptive) that identify one or more objects. In a directory context, the primitive, simple, and distinguished name forms have the property of unambiguously identifying a single object (i.e., a specific instance of a name cannot identify more than one object). It is permissible, however, to have more than one name form indirectly reference a single object entry. This is referred to as aliasing. Consequently, the name-to-object relation is a one-to-one or many-to-one mapping function for these three name forms (including aliases). Descriptive names, in comparison, may be distinguished from the other name forms on the basis of the characteristic of identifying none or more objects.

Regardless of the name form, a critical activity of the name resolution process is provided by the concept of a name resolver. This component governs the actual decomposition of a purported name. There are several possible outcomes of the decomposition process.

One possible outcome is that the purported name does not identify an existing object. Another possibility is the purported name identifies a single existing object, in which case the purported name is a simple name. A final possibility is that the purported name turns out to be a descriptive name and the decomposition produces a set of simple names or a composite set of simple and descriptive names. This last case may involve additional, recursive processing to reduce the descriptive elements of the set into simple names. At this point, the descriptive name is completely reduced and the resultant set can be viewed as a distribution list. Whatever the name form, the identity of objects represented in a directory can be quite diverse and may include people, systems, application processes, and application entities.

THE OSI DIRECTORY—ISO 9594

ISO 9594 is an eight-part international standard developed as a collaborative effort between ISO and CCITT. It is technically aligned with the CCITT 1988 X.500 recommendations and consists of the following documents:

- ISO 9594-1 (X.500)—Overview of concepts, models and services.
- ISO 9594-2 (X.501)—Models.
- ISO 9594-3 (X.511)—Abstract service definition.
- ISO 9594-4 (X.518)—Procedures for distributed operation.
- ISO 9594-5 (X.519)—Protocol specifications.
- ISO 9594-6 (X.520)—Selected attribute types.
- ISO 9594-7 (X.521)—Selected object classes.
- ISO 9594-8 (X.509)—Authentication framework.

This standard describes the basic model for the remote application directory facility. The principal requirements and functional components are defined in terms of the OSI basic reference model. The functional components of this standard are positioned as an application layer service for use by other OSI applications.

The access and transfer of directory information make use of the services and protocols of the supporting OSI layers. The information is stable; consequently, access is primarily passive, consisting of such retrieval operations as read, compare, and search. (These operations are passive in contrast to such operations as add, remove, and modify that change the information.) Because directory information is long-lived, retrievals constitute the majority of operations.

Directory information is globally distributed, and the mechanisms that support this distribution are transparent to the users of the directory. Because of the information's global nature, transient inconsistencies in directory entries are tolerated. The directory still behaves consistently from a user's perspective: it provides a consistent view of its information independent of the logical origin of the user's request.

Furthermore, this standard defines several functions, in particular the organization of the information elements into a logical structure called the directory information tree (DIT) and the definition of the information and protocol processing elements called the directory user agent (DUA) and the directory system agent (DSA). Authentication is provided by this standard, and several levels are specified along with their associated procedures (including strong authentication).

Some functions are not covered in the initial standard. These include replication of entry information, distribution of knowledge, remote management of access control information, and the publication and distribution of schema information.

Functional Components

The retrieval, transfer, and management of directory information is based on a client-server model comprising two entities and the associated information structures:

- The directory user agent (DUA).
- The directory system agent (DSA).
- The directory information tree (DIT).

The model is based on a remote directory facility (in contrast to a local directory facility) and distinguishes between an application's access to the directory and the distribution of information by the directory. The intent is to give the application transparent access to directory information, regardless of the logical or physical distribution of the actual information contained in the directory. The single most important goal of the standard is to provide the users of the directory with a consistent view of the directory's entry information— except as regards any access control constraints. Another goal is to guarantee that a user's request to the directory will produce the same results (or errors) wherever the request originated (i.e., location independence of the requester). This standard also provides for the integrity of directory information in that the directory will not inadvertently change the information on its own.

The model specifies a distinct set of OSI services and protocols to provide access to and distribution of the directory information base (DIB). One set of services and protocols supports application access to the directory. These are incorporated into the model of the DUA, as part of the remote directory facility. The other set of services and protocols supports the resolution of DUA requests when the directory information is distributed among more than one DSA. These services are incorporated into the DSA. An associated protocol provides for the exchange of directory information between two or more DSAs in support of resolving a DUA request. The dialogue between DSAs occurs only in the context of an underlying request from a DUA.

Administrative requirements are not standardized. There are, however, operational aspects that may require such administrative activities as local management of object class definitions, local configuration of DUA or DSA operational modes, and local management of access control information. Although the services and operational characteristics of the DUA and DSA appear similar on the surface, they are in fact quite distinct.

Exhibit X-3-1 depicts the positioning of the DUA, the DSA, and the DIB relative to one another and the application process in a composite network environment. This is a simple illustration. More complex configurations, with many DUAs on an end system servicing a variety of applications, are possible. This standard does not preclude the existence of more than one DSA on an end system.

DIRECTORY INFORMATION TREE

The directory's name constructs are currently based on a hierarchical model called the directory information tree (DIT). Names are constructed to indicate a positional relationship among the components of the name (i.e., a structure with superior and inferior components and a root). Thus, the directory information structure is modeled on a mathematical tree in which the entries are located at the vertices and the arcs connecting the vertices represent the topological ordering (hierarchy).

The path from the root down to a leaf node in this tree is based on the sequence of partial names, which together constitute the full name. This path has to be unambiguous. A single named path from the root cannot reference two distinct leaf entries. It is possible for there to be more than one named path from the root to a leaf entry (one or more of these named paths are referred to as aliases), but to avoid ambiguity, a single named path must not refer to two distinct objects.

The hierarchy allows the partitioning of the DIT into any number of subtrees; naming the items in the subtrees is the responsibility of a naming authority. A naming authority may designate subauthorities to allocate names for one or more subtrees in the DIT. To avoid generating name ambiguities in the DIT, the allocation must follow a set of agreed-on procedures. The activities of the naming authorities are distinct and separate from that of administrative authorities for the directory.

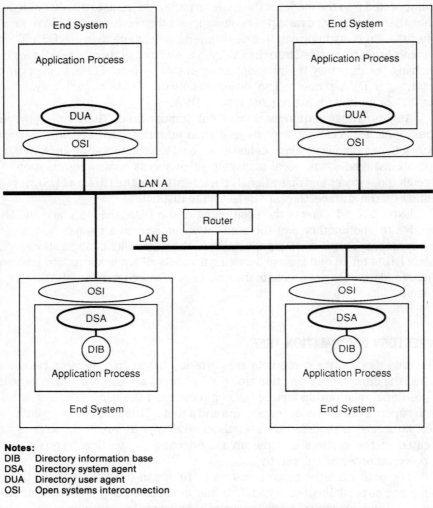

Notes:
DIB   Directory information base
DSA   Directory system agent
DUA   Directory user agent
OSI   Open systems interconnection

Exhibit X-3-1. Components of Directory Information Services

Directory Information Base

The actual realization of the directory information tree is the directory information base (DIB). A single DIB represents the instantiation of all the information contained in the global directory. The model is careful to refine this concept in a manner that logically considers the DIB as comprising various fragments (i.e., subtrees). These fragments represent naming contexts that are logically connected in a hierarchical but disjoint manner (i.e., these fragments do not contain overlapping naming contexts). The concept of the DIB conveys the notion of distribution of directory information; this accommodates partitioning on the basis of naming contexts. In the simplest (i.e., degenerate) case, there is one centralized DIB. In the more complex case, there may be many logically distributed fragments of the DIB (i.e., subtrees) making up the total information base. The base standard makes no provision for services and protocols to maintain the infrastructure of the DIB.

Entries in the DIB. Information in the DIB is organized to reflect the hierarchical ordering of the entries in the DIT. Specifically, this ordering is based on the hierarchical structure of directory distinguished names (DNs). A typical example of a DN reflecting this hierarchical ordering of name components might be: US USDA Dept—of—Biotechnology File—Transfer FTAM. Each of the components of this name is hierarchically specified, with US being closer to the root than FTAM. The actual specification and allocation (i.e., registration) of name components is the responsibility of a naming authority.

The hierarchical decomposition of a distinguished name is termed a relative distinguished name (RDN). Each of the name components in the example is modeled in the directory as attribute value assertions (AVAs). The AVAs consist of an attribute type and value. The attribute type is defined as an Abstract System Notation One (ASN.1) object identifier. The relative distinguished name AVAs are modeled as vertices in the DIT directory information tree. Thus, a DN is precisely an unambiguous sequence of RDNs denoting a particular path, starting at the root and proceeding downward to an object entry. Alias entries are constrained by the directory model to residing only at the leaf vertices of the tree.

There may be other attributes than type and value associated with an entry, to identify other characteristics of the object. Consequently, a primary function of the directory is to provide services supporting the retrieval or modification of the attributes associated with directory entries. One of these attributes of particular importance for OSI objects is the presentation address, which provides a means of identifying and supporting the establishment of communications between OSI application entities.

Therefore, the directory must provide access and management for the binding of the application entity's distinguished name to its presentation address. The name may be bound to such additional attributes of the object as its application context.

THE DIRECTORY USER AGENT

The DUA exists to provide its local application (client or user) with a means of accessing directory information located in a remote facility. A DUA cannot exist by and of itself. DUA instances exist only as part of the remote directory facility, as an application entity, and in the context of its associated application process. Consequently, when one OSI application elects to form an association with a peer application, it first queries the directory for the presentation address (and perhaps additional information) of the peer application. Once the information is obtained from the directory, the application can make it available to its local association services to initiate association establishment.

The DUA comprises services that are described in terms of the procedures it carries out to establish, use, and terminate an association with a DSA to access the information in the directory on behalf of its user. All of the DUA services generate protocol exchanges with a DSA. These services, protocols, and related procedures are discussed in more detail in the following sections.

Abstract Interface

In a very general sense, from the directory user's perspective there is a single abstract interface to the information contained in a directory facility. Viewed through this abstract interface, the components that make up a directory facility and their associated activities are transparent to the user of the directory.

A directory facility minimally contains the functions of the local directory facility and may also contain the functions provided by a remote directory facility. If the user's request cannot be satisfied by the information contained in the local directory facility, the request is presented to the remote directory facility, if one is present.

The DUA represents the local component of the remote directory facility. In the model, an application's request to access directory information is conveyed in a lcoal manner to the DUA. The DUA presents the user's request to one or more directory system agents for resolution. DSAs represent the application processes that contain the directory information base and that provide access to this information.

A DUA's access to the directory is modeled as a single abstract interface. The model for this interface to the directory is based on the abstract concept of ports. The ports provide a distinct view of the directory services available to the directory users. These services in turn represent real operations that generate the protocol necessary to convey an application's request to the directory and the procedures needed to interpret the results (or errors) returned by the directory. The port abstractions or the operation definitions do not describe or standardize a common application interface to the DUA. They do describe the information the DUA provides in the protocol conveyed to the directory for each defined service and the information (in the protocol) the DUA expects back from the directory.

The protocol that is used by a DUA to convey requests to a DSA (i.e., the directory) and return the corresponding results or errors is termed the directory access protocol (DAP). There are several situations that deviate slightly from the expected; these are discussed later in this chapter. In any case, the DAP is an abstract transfer syntax whose information is specified and encoded in ASN.1.

Operational Interface to the Directory

The model of the DUA's operational relationship to the directory is asymmetric. It is not bidirectional with respect to invocation of its services; the DUA is defined as a consumer of the services provided by the directory (i.e., the DSAs) rather than a supplier of those services.

Association Control. The DUA initiates the establishment of an association with a DSA. Subsequent requests to access the directory are conveyed to the DSA using the directory access protocol (DAP). The model does not provide for one DUA to form an association with another DUA, nor does the model allow a DSA to initiate the establishment of an association with a DUA.

The orderly termination (i.e., release) of an association is initiated by the DUA. Abrupt termination (i.e., abortion) of an association can be initiated by either the DUA or the DSA for any reason. Its use, however, is envisioned for circumstances in which it is not possible to continue an orderly dialogue.

Furthermore, in the context of an association between a DUA and a DSA, only the former can invoke requests on the latter. The DSA cannot use this existing association to invoke requests on the DUA. The DSA always conveys a response back to the DUA.

The model does not define (or restrict) the number of associations a DUA can establish with one or more DSAs at any time or over the lifetime of a DUA instance, nor does it constrain a DUA to the number of requests it can invoke on a DSA using one or more associations between them.

Operational Modes. In the context of an association between a DUA and a DSA, the DUA can convey directory requests to the DSA in either an asynchronous or a synchronous manner. Synchronous operation refers to a paired ordering of request-response protocol exchanges between these entities in a serial manner. The burden of synchronous operation is placed on the invoker (the DUA), which invokes a request and waits for a response before invoking the next request. In contrast, asynchronous mode permits the DUA to invoke multiple requests without waiting for the DSA to respond to a previous request.

The provision or use of one operational mode over another in a DUA is an implementation decision. Nothing precludes several instances of DUAs in a particular end system from executing requests using any combination of operational modes. For example, the DUA could provide its user with the option of selecting a particular operational mode. Conversely, the DUA could provide only a single operational mode as an administrative or configuration default.

The provision of synchronous or asynchronous operational modes by the DUA is orthogonal to the provision of a synchronous or asynchronous application interface to the services available in a directory facility. There is no implicit or explicit dependence between the specific type of DUA operations (i.e., services) that may be invoked and the operational modes selected to perform those operations.

Service Interface to the Directory. The DUA services supporting the various types of access to directory information using the DAP include:

- Read—Retrieves information on one entry in the directory.
- Abandon—Provides the capability to quit a previous operation.
- Compare—Tests the information provided against that of the entry.
- List—Retrieves name of the entry's immediate subordinates.
- Add entry—Creates a new entry in the directory.
- Remove entry—Deletes a specified entry in the directory.
- Modify entry—Changes the specified attributes or values of an entry.
- Modify RDN—Changes the name of a specified entry in the directory.
- Search—Retrieves information on one or more specified entries.

Each service is distinguishable from the others by an integer that denotes precisely one service of the directory access context. This integer, in turn, is used by underlying services to establish the context for interpreting the operation argument information.

Each of these services has associated service arguments. Some are common to all the services. Specific service arguments are used to control the behavior of the service interface to generate protocol requests or interpret protocol results. Other arguments are conveyed in protocol and may influence the operational behavior of the receiver or sender (such as time or size limits, referral use, and use of cache information). All of the services expect to receive a result or error back from the DSA.

The standard defines a single application context for the DUA that includes all of these services. Although there is no provision for identifying a subset of these services in the application context, nothing precludes an implementation from selectively supporting specific services depending on the anticipated needs of the application.

Bootstrapping. Another aspect of the DUA's service interface relates to an implicit activity in accessing the directory (i.e., the DSAs). This activity is initiated by the DUA before binding to a DSA. It is the process used by a DUA to acquire the presentation address of a DSA. The actual process is not specified in the directory standard.

Without this address, the DUA is not able to establish an association with a DSA. Consequently, no remote directory facility capability can be provided by the DUA. This specific activity on the part of the DUA is referred to as directory bootstrapping. The bootstrapping activity implies the DUA's use of the local directory facility to obtain the name of the DSA and its associated presentation address. This is the one instance of local directory facility use that must resolve the request locally and cannot invoke the capabilities of the remote directory facility. The actual procedures used in this special case activity are local to the implementation. There are no further constraints placed on the contents of this local bootstrap information in terms of the numbers or locations of the DSAs.

Caching of Entry Information. The term *caching* refers to creating and maintaining a local list of directory entry information obtained from prior operations. This information would typically be made available to the application by a local directory function. Although this particular activity is more likely to be used by the DSAs, the standard allows the DUAs to selectively enable DSAs to use or disable DSAs from using cached information. The standard does not preclude DUAs from caching directory entry information, inasmuch as this is considered an implementation decision. It may also be the case that the application invoking the services of the DUA is in a better position to determine how current the cached information is and when a read request needs to be issued to update its cache.

Use of Upper-Layer Services

In addition to the DAP–based services defined for the DUA, there are additional metaservices used by the DUA. These metaservices are coupled to specific application layer services of the remote operations service element (ROSE), the association control service element (ACSE), and presentation services.

Bind and Unbind. These metaservices are DUABIND and DUAUNBIND. The intention of these metaservices is to provide an abstract description of a DUA's establishment and termination of an association with a DSA.

The DUABIND and DUAUNBIND map onto the associated metaservices in ROSE termed BIND and UNBIND. The ROSE BIND and UNBIND, in turn, map directly on the A-Associate and A-Release services provided by ACSE.

The capability for a DUA to terminate an association abruptly is provided by the ACSE service, A-Abort, which is available for use by the DUA. The ACSE service provider may generate a provider abort that abruptly terminates an association. In either case, aborting an association may result in the loss of directory information being exchanged over that association.

In addition to A-Abort, the DUA has a similar service termed Abandon. This service may be used at any time. The intention of Abandon is to provide a control service to the DUA such that the DSA can be signaled to stop processing a request. Because of the distributed nature of directory operations, the Abandon operation can operate only on a best-effort basis. If the DUA's request has been passed on to a chain of DSAs, the ensuing Abandon operation may or may not effect the processing activities of these additional DSAs.

Remote Operations. In addition to the BIND and UNBIND metaservices, ROSE provides the operations of RO-Invoke, RO-Reject, RO-Result, and RO-Error to carry the directory operations. These ROSE operations are conveyed in protocol between the DUA and DSA using the presentation service P-DATA. The ROSE operations generate protocol that contains an invoke identifier, an operation identifier, and the operation argument.

The operation identifier distinguishes the specific type of DUA service requested from the set of services supported by the DUA. This identifier is an integer and in the directory access context uniquely identifies the operations supported in this context.

The invoke identifier is used by the DUA and DSA to unambiguously identify multiple requests and responses carried over a single association. It is used by the DUA to distinctly identify each request the DUA invokes. It is used by the DSA to identify possible duplicate requests from a DUA when the DUA is operating in the asynchronous operational mode.

The DUA uses the operation argument to represent all of the operation-specific protocol arguments encoded using the directory access protocol. It is used by the DSA to represent the result or error (encoded using the DAP) associated with the DUA request.

The DUA uses the **RO-Invoke** service to form the protocol data representing a DUA request and convey it to the DSA. The **RO-Invoke** contains the DAP operation identifier and all of the encoded arguments associated with the specific operation.

The DSA uses **RO-Result**, **RO-Error**, and **RO-Reject** to report on the outcome of DUA requests. The **RO-Result** and **RO-Error** may include the invoke identifier for correlation with the request.

The **RO-Result** is used by the DSA to return directory information in response to a DUA request. This information is encoded in the DAP and varies according to the operation requested by the DUA as well as the arguments specified in the request.

The **RO-Error** contains additional information specific to the directory service. These errors are from the set of errors specified by the standard. They are encoded in the DAP by the DSA.

RO-Reject is used by the DSA or DUA to respond to a previous **RO** operation that may have contained a duplicate invoke identifier, an unknown operation identifier, or possibly a malformed ROSE protocol data unit.

Exhibit X-3-2 presents one traditional view of the relationship between the application process, the local directory facility, the DUA component of the remote directory facility, and the supporting OSI upper-layer services.

DIRECTORY SYSTEM AGENT

The directory system agent is an application process that represents the more substantial pieces of the directory. It contains and governs access to directory information. The standard makes provisions for both a single DSA containing the entire directory information base as well as multiple DSAs, each of which holds a nonoverlapping fragment (i.e., partition) of the DIB. A substantial part of this standard addresses distributed directories. The handling of DUA requests is based on a distributed name resolution process to identify the target entry. The distributed operations consist of a set of services and protocols termed the directory system protocol (DSP). They are analogous to the ser-

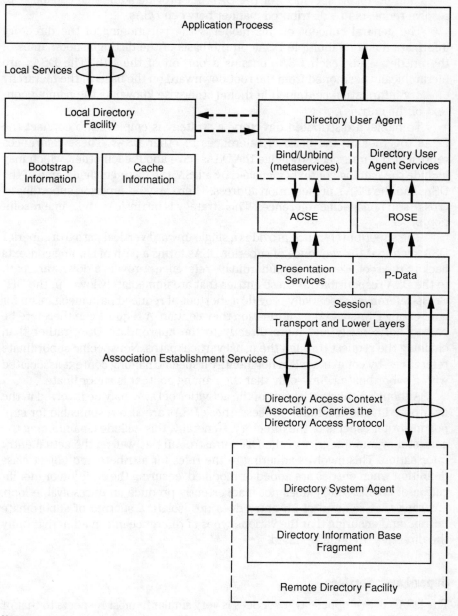

Notes:
ACSE   Association control service element
P-Data Presentation data service
ROSE   Remote operations service element

Exhibit X-3-2. Application Process, Directories, and OSI Upper-Layer Services

vices and protocols specified for the DAP but provide additional capability to resolve requests in a distributed manner between DSAs.

The general concept of this model is the partitioning of the directory information among multiple DSAs on the basis of the distinguished names of the entries. Thus, each DSA contains a portion of the DIB. The DSAs are hierarchically positioned from the root downward on the basis of the hierarchy of entry information contained in them (otherwise known as the naming context of the entries).

To model a distributed directory, a strategy is employed to connect the DSAs together on the basis of references to other DSAs. These references represent the internal knowledge the DSAs have about each other, which may include the naming contexts managed by a DSA, the distinguished name of the DSA, and the DSA's presentation address. There may be superior, subordinate, cross-, and nonspecific references. This strategy is intrinsic to the name resolution process.

The superior reference provides a single upward vertical path to a superior DSA such that the sequence of superior DSAs forms a path of naming contexts back to the root. Conversely, subordinate references provide a downward path to the DSA responsible for these entries that are immediately lower in the DIT. Cross-references essentially provide a shortcut of reduced path mechanism for connecting DSAs and the information they contain. A request can therefore be passed horizontally and more directly to the appropriate DSA, rather than chaining the request through the usual vertical paths. Nonspecific subordinate references, by comparison, do not identify a specific naming context associated with a subordinate DSA—only that the naming context is subordinate.

Although a substantial part of the activities of DSAs may be involved in the distributed name resolution process, these DSAs are also responsible for supporting other aspects of the directory. Generally, this includes maintaining the consistency and integrity of the DIT infrastructure as well as the actual entry information. This involves adhering to the rules for attribute and object class definition when entries are added or modified, ensuring the addition or modification of an alias entry does not inadvertently produce an unresolvable loop, ensuring that removal of an entry does not isolate a subtree of subordinate entries, and ensuring that the various types of reference information that unify the directory are kept updated.

Upper-Layer Services

The DSA's use of upper-layer services is very similar in most respects to that of the DUA. Both synchronous and asynchronous operational classes are available to the DSA for remote operations. The association class is different than that of the DUA. DSAs can initiate the formation of associations with other DSAs. An existing association can be used by either DSA to invoke operations on the other DSA. The standard does not limit the number of associations or outstanding operations between DSAs. The protocols defined for the distributed directory are termed the directory system protocol. The distributed services are identified by the directory system context. A DSA can support either the directory access or directory system contexts, or it may support both. In any case, the DSA must support all the services associated with one of these contexts.

Caching of Directory Information

Caching and the subsequent use of cached information by a DSA may be controlled by local administrative management. An optional parameter common to all DUA services provides an application with explicit control over the use of cached information to resolve a DUA request. In this situation, caching refers to a DSA maintaining local copies of directory information obtained from another DSA. Cached information may consist of selective or total entry information or it may be more extensive and include the names of other DSAs, their presentation addresses, and associated naming contexts.

One advantage of using cached information is quicker resolution of requests, because the request can be handled locally. Another advantage is a reduction in protocol traffic over the network. The disadvantage is that the cached information may become outdated (i.e., stale), although there are a number of nonstandard mechanisms that compensate for this situation.

Processing Modes

As previously mentioned, some service parameters can control the behavior of the DUA or DSA. Following a successful bind between a DUA and a DSA and after the DUA sends a service request to the DSA, there are four basic procedures the DSA can follow to formulate a response.

The simplest procedure is the direct resolution of the DUA request by the bootstrap DSA. This is expected when a single DSA contains all of the directory information. It involves only two directory access protocol exchanges—namely, the DUA-to-DSA request and the DSA-to-DUA response.

The DSA may have three alternative procedures available to process the request. One is for the bootstrap DSA to respond to the DUA with referral information. Referral information comprises the name and presentation address of another DSA presumably better suited to satisfy the request. The DUA (now in possession of the referral information) may bind to the DSA identified in the referral. Subsequent binding and requesting the services of the first referral DSA may result in additional referrals to other DSAs. The DUA needs to recognize that this process may generate multiple referrals. The use of referrals by the DUA or its application is a local matter. The use of referrals by DSAs may also be controlled by local administrative policy. Consequently, it is possible for the DUA to request the DSA return referrals, but the DSA may be unable to comply because of local management policies.

Another alternative is for the initial DSA to chain the DUA's request to another DSA it has knowledge of and which is better able to resolve the request. Chaining is the activity undertaken by one DSA to forward the DUA's request to another DSA. Subsequent DSAs may continue to chain the request. The results are returned through the chain of cooperating DSAs to the initial DSA and finally to the DUA. This is termed the distributed form of name resolution. It is possible that referrals may be involved in some intermediate phase of a chaining procedure. The chaining procedure involves additional protocol exchanges beyond the initial exchange between the DUA and the DSA. These exchanges are based on the directory system protocol.

The third alternative is termed multicasting. This is not synonymous with or used in conjunction with any processing activity used in OSI layer 2. Multicasting by DSAs is an application layer activity in which one DSA concurrently sends a request to several DSAs. The initiating DSA selects only those DSAs that are contained in a nonspecific subordinate reference. It is only in the case of the nonspecific subordinate reference that a DSA must forward a request without knowing the naming contexts supported by the nonspecific subordinate reference DSAs. The DSAs receiving this request respond back to the initiating DSA.

The underlying assumption of the referral or chaining mode of directory operations is that more than a single DSA contains the directory information base. In the single DSA environment (termed standalone), referrals and chaining do not apply to resolving DUA requests. This is because the single DSA has no knowledge about other DSAs. Consequently, the service parameters and DAP control information may or may not contain information to control referrals or chaining operations that are appropriate for the configuration of the directory. Provisions to control these options are present in the DUA services and protocol. The standard recognizes that it may be necessary to administratively control a DSA's use of any or all of the four procedures. The important idea is that the processing modes of the DSAs directly support the name resolution procedures used to identify the target objects specified in the DUA's request.

Exhibit X-3-3 presents a view of the major components in the directory model and the positional relations between them. The components are the application process, the local directory facility, the DSA element, the directory information base, and the supporting OSI upper-layer services. The two directory protocols are identified to show the flow of information between DSAs and a DUA.

EXTENSIONS TO THE BASE STANDARDS

There are several functions not addressed by the base standard. These include:

- Remote management of access control information.
- Replication of directory information.

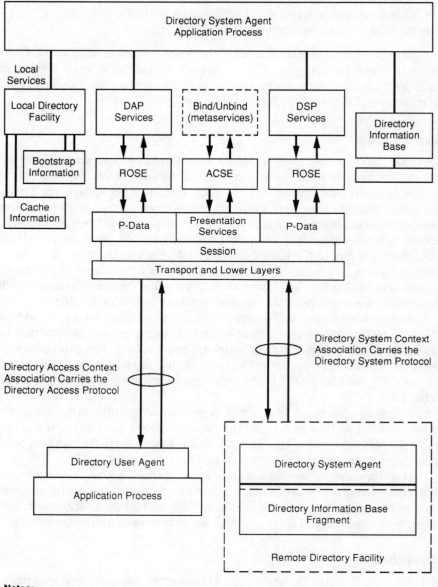

Notes:

ACSE   Association control service element
DAP   Directory access protocol
DSP   Directory system protocol
P-Data   Presentation data service
ROSE   Remote operations service element

Exhibit X-3-3. Directory Model Components and Their Relationships

- Distribution of directory knowledge.
- Extensions to the structure of information models.
- Publication of schema information.

The creation of standards in all of these areas is proceeding as a collaboration between the ISO and CCITT. Much of the extension work is complex because there are often subtle dependences on the base architecture. Brief descriptions of these added functions follow.

Access Control

The base standard essentially treats access control as a local matter. Nevertheless, it does provide some useful insights into the application of access control to the directory and has guided the establishment of requirements for the extension work in this area. Consequently, access control in the directory primarily focuses on the access to entry information held in the directory. This access is further described in terms of granularity and levels of protection. (Granularity refers to the size of directory information structures that can be subject to access controls. Several initial reports have stated the need for access control down to attribute values, a very fine degree of granularity. In contrast, other works posit that access control to the entry is sufficient.)

Beyond the enforcement of access control, the extension work will address the requirements for remote management of access control information for entries in any fragment of the directory information base. The extension work will take into account the fact that some of the information in the directory (specifically held by a DSA) may represent information replicated from another DSA.

Directory-specific access control is contrasted with the other aspects of access control as they pertain to the basic reference model (i.e., the access control applied between end systems and the access control applied to an association between application processes).

Directory-specific access control, access control between end systems, and access control between application processes do not work at cross-purposes. In fact, it would be reasonable for an OSI application such as a directory to make use of access control facilities in each of these contexts.

Replication

Replication is the distribution of copies of directory information among one or more DSAs. Some of the requirements for this capability are scalability, integrity and consistency of directory information (including access control), granularity of replicated information (the smallest and largest unit of information that can be replicated), procedures for establishing replication agreements among DSAs, and the associated services and protocols to support the exchange of these agreements and information to be replicated. Scalability refers to how well a model can accommodate increases in the quantity of information and the activities that process and exchange this information. Scalability is a key requirement for components of a distributed systems architecture.

Knowledge Distribution

Knowledge distribution addresses the need to formalize the definition of the directory knowledge information structure and provide the ability to exchange this knowledge among DSAs. Knowledge is essentially the information DSAs have about other DSAs—specifically, the other's name, presentation address, and supported naming contexts. The extension work will formalize the procedures (including the services and protocols) DSAs use to acquire, update, and pass on knowledge concerning the infrastructure of the directory.

Information Models

The basic information model will be extended to provide new functions—for example, structural identification of one or more specific values in a multi-valued attribute. The base standard does not provide a suitable method for meeting this need. Another new function will be refinement of the semantics of entry information in a way that allows properties (in addition to attributes) to be associated with an entry. (Property, used in this context, refers to information characterizing some aspect of an entry. It is distinguishable from an attribute in that an ordinary read operation does not return property information. Properties are not usually visible or accessible to the casual user of the directory.) Additional efforts will improve the capability for viewing collections of entries in the directory by providing refinements to permit arbitrary subtree definitions.

Publication of Schema

The base standard allows just the static and fairly simple definition of schema; procedures for publishing the schema in a formal manner will be introduced. The intention is to standardize the rules for interpreting basic information elements constituting entries in the directory and how the entries are organized into various collections (named classes). Furthermore, this extension will facilitate the acquisition of schema definitions by DSAs, allowing DSAs to dynamically support new classes of directory schema information.

SUMMARY

A directory system provides services that enable an end-user application to retrieve and manage information about objects. The basic concepts of directory systems have been part of communications technology for a long time, but international standardization of a specification for globally interconnected, cooperating directory systems for access to open, distributed systems is new. End users and developers of distributed applications need to be aware of the architecture of directory systems and how distributed applications can make use of the information contained in the directory.

X-4
Expert Systems in LAN Management

CELIA A. JOSEPH

This chapter examines the potential applications of expert systems to LANs. Expert systems, the subject of much research, are automated systems that, in dealing with a specific problem, can perform as well as humans whose experience with that problem would allow them to be viewed as experts.

Automated expert systems cannot emulate the performance of a human expert in every area. Unlike human experts, for example, automated expert systems have a limited ability to handle new situations, to reason at several levels of abstraction, and to learn new concepts, relationships, or strategies. Expert systems are appropriate, however, when human experts are unavailable or hard to find or the features of the problem, such as its complexity or the need to solve it in real time, make solutions difficult for humans (even experts).

This chapter provides a brief overview of expert systems in general, explores the applicability of expert systems to LANs, presents an example of an expert system for a specific application (i.e., LAN fault management), and examines future directions for expert systems in data communications.

BACKGROUND ON EXPERT SYSTEMS

Many conventional computer programs reach high levels of performance in specific application domains. The main difference between these programs and what is considered an expert system is in their organization, the way knowledge is incorporated, and the way they execute. In an expert system, for example, problem-solving knowledge is explicitly separated into a knowledge base, as opposed to being implicitly coded as part of the program's procedures. The knowledge base is manipulated by a separate, clearly identifiable control strategy called an inference engine. Thus, as generally defined, an expert system contains two main parts: a knowledge base and an inference engine. Exhibit X-4-1 depicts this structure.

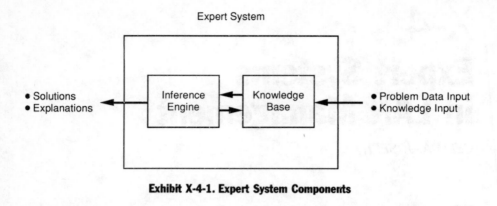

Exhibit X-4-1. Expert System Components

The Knowledge Base

The knowledge base consists of an encoded representation of the domain expertise that a human expert would have. The two basic types of information it contains are problem-solving knowledge and declarative knowledge.

Problem-solving knowledge is general knowledge about the problem domain. It can consist of facts, rules and procedures, logical relationships, algorithms, or heuristics.

Declarative knowledge consists of facts pertaining to the state of the problem domain. The declarative section of the knowledge base may contain current data on the problem being solved or an example of an abstract data model that can be used to represent the general categories of information pertinent to the problem domain. Such an example, or instantiation, usually represents the abstract data through the use of object-oriented definitions. In a network management expert system, for example, the data model contains information on the network objects that can be managed. The data model also includes containment and inheritance information. Containment defines logical structure relationships (e.g., a network management domain contains managed systems), and inheritance provides a means to pass definitions of characteristics between objects without requiring new definitions for each object (e.g., a protocol sublayer may inherit the characteristics of the protocol layer to which it belongs).

There are several methods for representing this knowledge in the knowledge base. Exhibit X-4-2 shows examples of three of the most commonly used representation methods: frames and slots, first-order predicate logic, and semantic networks.

A frame is a data structure that describes an object, and a slot is a data element in that structure that describes a characteristic of the object. Frames and slots can provide a great deal of flexibility in data representation. In some systems, for example, the selection of the slots that a particular instance of an

Name of frame: drill press 10
Type of frame: managed station
MAC address: 10 00 01 01 20 45
Slot time: 1800

a. Frames and Slots

ELEMENT-OF(drill press 10, managed station)
MAC address(drill press 10, 10 00 01 01 20 45)
Slot time(drill press 10, 1800)

b. First-Order Predicate Logic

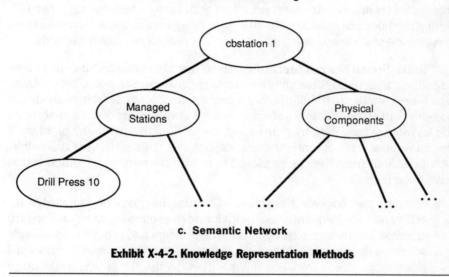

c. Semantic Network

Exhibit X-4-2. Knowledge Representation Methods

object needs can be done dynamically. A frame could be used to describe a system attached to a LAN. The slots in the frame would contain such information about the characteristics of that system as the type of system it was, its location, and its network address.

In first-order predicate logic, logic formats are used to express information. A request to open a transport layer connection between system A and system B could be represented in this way, for example: open (A, B, transport connection).

In semantic networks, knowledge is shown pictorially, using objects and relationships between the objects, with meaning embodied in the symbols and in the symbol arrangements. The characteristics of a network system, for example, could be depicted as shown in Exhibit X-4-2.

The representation methods provide only an abstract framework in which to place knowledge. The knowledge associated with a particular problem is called an instance. Using Exhibit X-4-2 as an example, the frame that describes a general object called managed station could include slots for all basic characteristics of all types of managed stations. A particular instance of a managed station, for example, drill press 10, may only require a subset of these slots to describe its actual characteristics.

Inference Engine

The other main part of the expert system, the inference engine, provides the control and reasoning techniques used to extract knowledge from the knowledge base to reach a solution for an instance of a given problem. Although rule-based techniques are most prevalent with current technology, other reasoning methods are possible. The two basic categories in use in current expert systems are state space search methods and problem reduction methods.

State Space Search Methods. These are used for searching the knowledge base to find possible solutions and, given these solutions, determining which best fits the particular problem being solved. Many search methods are possible, with various degrees of complexity. A small system could step through the knowledge base item-by-item to find the solution to a particular problem. If the knowledge base is large or complex, however, this method is unfeasible. Other methods must then be employed to reduce the number of solutions that have to be considered:

- Forward and backward chaining—Chaining methods tie knowledge together and are frequently used with knowledge encoded as rules. Forward chaining begins with expressions of the problem and proceeds to possible solutions. If symptoms X and Y are present, conclude state Z. Backward chaining proceeds from possible solutions to the states that could cause that solution: If the system is in state Z, look for symptoms X and Y to occur.
- Statistical inferencing—These techniques can be used to infer meaning from trends over time that show statistical significance when compared with a goal or baseline.
- Modeling—Various modeling techniques (e.g., discrete event modeling) can be used to infer the possible states that an object may be in, given knowledge of the events that have occurred to the object. Conversely, given knowledge of the object's state, the events that have occurred may be deduced.
- Optimization methods—These methods provide algorithms for synthesizing combinations of input into a meaningful form. Mathematical programming techniques for finding optimal solutions are an example of these methods.
- Propagation of constraints—This is an iterative method, in which every potential solution must satisfy all the constraints produced at each step. Thus, at each iteration, the possible solutions are further limited until the final solution is reached.

Problem Reduction Methods. These begin by partitioning the problem into subproblems that can be solved separately. When the separate subproblems are solved, these solutions are then combined to find the solution to the original problem.

Expert System Construction Methodology

The construction of an expert system is still something of an art. Although more expert systems are beginning to appear, expert system engineering (as contrasted with software engineering) is still in its infancy.

The basic steps used at the Industrial Technology Institute (Ann Arbor MI) in building expert systems are as follows:

1. Finding a human expert—Unless human expertise is available, the system cannot be built.
2. Defining the application requirements—With the expert's guidance, the main requirements that the application must satisfy are documented.
3. Defining an architecture—The architecture must be appropriate for the application and the environment in which the application will operate, and it must be possible to build with the tools available. A key issue is whether a centralized or distributed architecture is required.
4. Selecting the platform—This entails choosing the hardware and software base for the system. Hardware considerations include reliability, fault tolerance, and real-time requirements. A key software decision is whether to use an available expert system shell (e.g., ART, KEE, or Knowledge-Craft) and whether the shell is supported on the desired hardware. Shells may speed implementation but also incur a high processing overhead if their features are not needed. If a shell is not used, a programming language must be selected. Typical choices are object-oriented languages (e.g., LISP, C + +, or Prolog).
5. Acquiring the knowledge—Structured interviews, unstructured interviews, or observation of the expert in action are possibilities. Regardless of the methods used, this step tends to be a bottleneck because several iterations will be needed. The transfer of knowledge between the domain expert and the expert system developers is typically slow and fraught with misunderstanding. The domain expert, for example, tends to take things for granted that others, who are not as familiar with the domain, will be unaware of. The terminology of the two groups will be different. The expert, relying on long experience, may not be able to spell out the explicit steps used to solve problems. Artificial intelligence researchers are investigating techniques that will ease this process.
6. Encoding the knowledge—The expert system developers must determine how to represent the different types of knowledge that will be used in the system and then encode knowledge as it is acquired from the expert.
7. Selecting the reasoning methodology—The expert system developers

choose one or more methods to select knowledge from the knowledge base for specific problems. This step also requires interaction with the expert to ensure the reasoning is correct.

8. Test and tune—Each problem that the system handles should be tested to ensure that a correct solution has been reached. The expert must again work with the artificial intelligence staff to ensure the system works properly.

Building an expert system for a complex application can be time-consuming and labor-intensive; a system with large numbers (hundreds to thousands) of rules and facts in its knowledge base can take many years to develop. Once built, the system must be maintained as new knowledge is acquired. However, the results produced by a properly implemented system can pay large benefits.

EXPERT SYSTEMS FOR LOCAL AREA NETWORKS

Expert systems for LANs can be divided into three basic categories. First are those expert systems that run over a LAN, such as distributed applications that use a LAN-based communications mechanism. Second are those expert systems that help to design the LAN, such as topology design tools. Third are those expert systems that help to run the LAN, such as network management tools.

Distributed expert system applications can be separate distributed expert systems or a single expert system distributed over multiple network nodes. In either case, a key characteristic is the use of a LAN-based mechanism for communication between the expert system components. Some examples of this type of distributed application are a security system for determining when an access control policy must be enforced, a data base assistant that records the type of information contained at any time in each data base, and an integrated planning system for manufacturing.

LAN design tools are expert system–based tools for determining the physical structure, station placement, and station configuration for a LAN. Some design tools of this nature have been developed for WANs; these methodologies appear to be applicable to LANs as well. The Industrial Technology Institute's MAPCon is an expert system tool for configuring Manufacturing Automation Protocol (MAP) networks.

Network management tools are a growing application for LAN expert systems. Although most work done so far has focused on telecommunications networks, the concepts can be adapted to LANs. A major focus for expert systems is fault management in networks. The next section explores this topic in more depth. Other network management applications for expert systems include performance management, particularly performance tuning; configuration management for maintaining consistent parameter settings; security management, such as determining when security has been breached; and accounting management, including determining how to apply charges on the basis of client, time of day, and resource consumption.

EXAMPLE: EXPERT SYSTEMS FOR LAN FAULT MANAGEMENT

The International Standards Organization (ISO) has defined five basic areas of network management: accounting, configuration, fault, performance, and security management.

Fault management is an ideal application for an expert system for several reasons. First, the number of potential symptoms that may occur in a layered protocol stack is large, and the relationship between the symptoms can be complex. Second, experts who understand the interaction between the protocols in a layered communications architecture are rare. Therefore, this expertise is not likely to be readily available each time a fault needs to be diagnosed. Third, with the growing reliance on LANs for communications in many organizations, most failures cannot be tolerated for long. Thus, the diagnosis and correction must be done quickly.

Building a fault management expert system entails understanding the requirements for fault management in a LAN.

Fault Management Requirements

Fault management, as defined by ISO, consists of three main functions: fault detection and prediction, fault isolation, and fault correction.

Fault detection and prediction determines when a fault has occurred or is about to occur somewhere in the LAN. The network management specification for a specific open systems interconnection (OSI) profile defines the types of information that the managed systems supply to their manager. For example, for Manufacturing Automation Protocol/Technical Office Protocol (MAP/TOP) 3.0 systems, this information includes protocol error counters and event reports. The fault management system must be able to detect faults using this information.

Fault isolation determines where the fault occurred (i.e., which network resource has failed somehow). After it has detected a fault, the fault management system uses current information to locate it. If the current information is insufficient, the fault management system can request additional information by sending a common management information protocol (CMIP) m-Get operation request to specific systems for selected counter updates or by running tests. Some of the tests that ISO currently defines are connectivity, data integrity, response time, and diagnostic tests.

Fault correction provides information on how to fix or bypass the fault. In some cases, the fault management system can automatically correct the fault without human intervention. In other cases (e.g., if a board needs replacement), this is not feasible, and the system could provide suggestions for how to fix the fault.

Building a Fault Management Expert System

Once steps 1 through 4 of the construction methodology have been completed, the next phase is to build the knowledge base. The fault management expert system needs the following types of information:

- General information about the objects being managed.
- Information about fault symptoms and their meanings.
- A description of the LAN's logical and physical topology.
- Fault relationships between the managed systems.
- A fault correction data base.
- Current LAN operating data.

General information on the objects that are being managed includes the object's attributes and relationships with other managed objects. This basic information should be defined in the data model. The data model contains, for example, information on the protocol layers being used in the LAN, the layer management entities each protocol layer contains, and the characteristics of each layer management entity. The data model indicates the layer management entity's type (e.g., counter, gauge, or threshold), the type of access management has to it (e.g., read, write, or no access), and the possible range of values that the layer management entity may take.

Fault symptoms and their meanings describe what can fail and its failure symptoms, as well as the relationship between symptoms (e.g., this failure will cause this primary symptom followed by these secondary symptoms later).

The LAN's logical and physical topology as well as the fault relationships that are possible between managed systems (e.g., this fault will also cause these symptoms in another system) are needed for fault isolation. The system must be able to distinguish between the primary symptoms of a fault and the follow-on symptoms caused as a consequence of the fault.

A fault correction data base contains two basic types of information. First, it must indicate how to fix a specific fault (e.g., repeated protocol errors are fixed by replacing the protocol layer). Second, it must indicate the types of fixes possible for a specific system (e.g., if all of the protocols are on a single board, replacing a protocol layer means changing protocol boards).

Current data describes the state of the LAN using information related to the problem being diagnosed at the time the problem was noted. This information includes the configuration characteristics of the managed systems involved, their protocol error counter values, any event reports received, and the results of any tests performed. The current data contains, for example, the values of the layer management entities pertinent to the problem for the systems involved.

The next step after building the knowledge base is developing the reasoning methodology. Some of the methods commonly used in fault diagnosis applications are diagnostic reasoning, statistical analysis, models, human interaction, and optimization techniques.

Diagnostic Reasoning. Work in traditional artificial intelligence diagnosis has determined that fault diagnosis takes place on several levels. At the highest level, behavior can be summarized by symptom-diagnosis heuristics, sometimes called experiential, or shallow, knowledge. Alternatively, the diagnostician can reason about the interactions of the subsystems that make up the overall mechanisms to explore its behavior. This level of reasoning is commonly called deep, or functional, reasoning. These subsystems can in turn be decomposed further. At the lowest level, reasoning is in terms of basic physical principles, using qualitative models.

Statistical Analysis. Techniques exist in the manufacturing industry to use statistical process control to monitor the quality of processes and products and make corrections before the system drifts out of acceptable bounds. Such techniques can be adapted to network fault management to monitor trends in error parameters and detect suspicious patterns that can in turn be passed to fault detection analysis functions for more detailed analysis.

Models. Discrete event modeling permits detailed dynamic experiments with complex systems that can answer hypothetical questions about possible faults and proposed solutions. The stochastic activity net technology developed at the University of Michigan and the Industrial Technology Institute is a generalization of petri nets that has been used to model computer backplanes, communications protocols, and other complex distributed systems. It incorporates both simulation and analytical methods to permit detailed, flexible exploration of the behavior of such systems in the presence of faults. Model-based reasoning can use a stochastic activity net model of the LAN to confirm diagnoses (e.g., cause a LAN resource in the model to fail and see if the LAN exhibits the same symptoms) and to test fixes (e.g., change the model and see if the symptoms are corrected).

Human Interaction. The human component is a frequently overlooked aspect of expert systems. When the expert system cannot solve the problem, the human can suggest new avenues for the system to explore. Furthermore, the human still has capabilities that an automated system does not possess; for example, the human can walk over to a failed system and tighten a loose connector.

Optimization Techniques. Mathematical programming offers efficient mechanisms for exploring problem spaces with certain constrained structures. Although not widely used for fault management functions, these techniques can be superior to heuristic techniques for domains that meet their presuppositions.

These methods are commonly used as state space search strategies—that is, they are used to select sets of rules appropriate to a specific problem. One or more of these techniques can be adapted to a fault management expert system. Systems can employ single or multiple modes of reasoning. Those employing multiple modes are more complex to build but can provide more powerful reasoning results.

Fault Management Example

To give a better feeling for how the fault management expert system might work, the diagnosis of a broken modem in a MAP 3.0 carrier band network is presented. Exhibit X-4-3 depicts the LAN used for this scenario. The LAN is a manufacturing cell with five stations: robot 1, robot 2, robot 3, controller 1, and the network manager.

At the beginning of this scenario, all operations are regular. All of the robots have manufacturing message specification application associations established with controller 1. The network manager performs a poll to request current values of the station's counters. All stations respond typically and the counter values reflect usual operations.

Suddenly, robot 2's modem jams while it is transmitting (resulting in modem jabber). After a short time, the modem automatically shuts itself off. While the modem was jammed, nothing but noise could be heard on the network; thus, the other stations all recorded noise bursts in their **modemErrors**

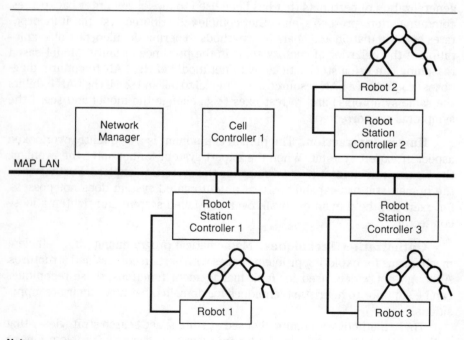

Note:
MAP   Manufacturing Automation Protocol

Exhibit X-4-3. Example of a Manufacturing LAN

counters. Because MAP 3.0 defines modem jabber as a specific physical layer error that should be reported in an event report, robot 1, robot 3, and controller 1 send event reports to the network manager station. Because denoting specific physical layer errors is optional for this event report, controller 1 sends only an unspecified error event report.

At the receipt of the event reports, the network manager requests an ad hoc poll for counter values from the managed stations, although this is not a usual polling cycle time. This gives the network manager up-to-date information on who is capable of responding, network connectivity, and counter values.

Only robot 1, robot 3, and controller 1 respond to the ad hoc poll, because robot 2's modem is off. Some time later, the transport connection between controller 1 and robot 2 times out, causing controller 1 to send a **transportTimeoutThld** event report to the network manager, indicating that its number of transport layer time-outs has exceeded its preset limit. When the next polling occurs, robot 2 again does not respond.

Following MAP 3.0 requirements, the stations are only required to report a limited amount of information to the network management station. The expert system's job is to deduce as much as possible from this limited information.

The expert system's basic procedure is to look for meaningful events. The key events are receipt of event reports, nonresponse to a network manager request (e.g., a regular or ad hoc poll), and a change of statistical significance in the counter values obtained from a station. The first two items are externally generated events; the third item is generated internally by the expert system.

Given that one or more events have occurred that cannot be considered typical, the expert system begins to look for the most likely explanation for the combinations of symptoms it sees. When it receives the event reports in the scenario, the expert system proposes a hypothetical diagnosis of modem jabber and informs the network administrator of this. Because it received event reports from more than one system, it can be reasonably sure that the event reports' senders are not generating spurious event reports. It still has to determine where the problem occurred. To do this, it requests the ad hoc poll for more information. When robot 2 does not respond to the ad hoc poll, it proposes the diagnosis of failed modem at robot 2 and informs the network administrator.

The expert system's job is not over, however, once it makes a diagnosis. This single failure will produce a number of other symptoms. Given its diagnosis, the expert system predicts the follow-on symptoms that it will see. These include noise (indicated by the **modemErrors** counter), a break in the logical ring (indicated by the **claimToken** counter), a token pass failure (indicated by the **noResponse** counter), transport retransmissions (indicated by the **numberTPDURetransmitted** counter), transport connection time-outs (indicated by the **transportTimeoutThld** event report), and continued nonresponse from the failed station, either to network manager requests, or to requests from other stations on the subnet, for example, transport connection failures (indicated by the **unsuccessfulCRTPDUThld**).

Exhibit X-4-4 provides a step-by-step listing of this fault scenario.

One of the main benefits of the expert system is to avoid flooding the network administrator with all of the symptoms of each fault. As this scenario shows, even a simple fault can produce several symptoms. Without the expert system, the network administrator would have to keep track of the state of all managed systems and the symptoms they produce over a period of time. The expert system filters out the symptoms that add no new information and informs the network administrator only of major events. If further explanation of a diagnosis is wanted, however, the administrator can still access the expert system's internal event log.

SUMMARY

One area in which expert systems will continue to advance is network management. Each of the five network management functions is an appropriate application for an expert system, and expert system tools will be developed for each area. These tools will be integrated in various combinations to address the needs of such specific environments as manufacturing. The work so far in this area has been mostly in configuration management and fault management.

Event ID	Event	Observed Symptom
0	Normal operations	—
1	Polling results	Usual counter values
2	Modem jabber at robot 2	—
3	Modem shuts off	—
4	Event reports sent: Physical jabber (robot 1, robot 3) Unspecified pleError (controller 1)	Event reports received: Physical jabber (robot 1, robot 3) Unspecified pleError (controller 1)
5	Net manager requests ad hoc poll	m-Get requests to all managed systems
6	Poll results received	No response from robot 2 Counter values elevated for: modemErrors (robot 1, robot 3, controller 1) claimToken (robot 1, robot 3, controller 1) noResponse (robot 3) numberTPDURetransmitted (controller 1)
7	Controller 1's connection with robot 2 times out	Event report received: transportTimeoutThld (controller 1)
8	Normal poll	No response from robot 2 Counter values elevated for: noResponse (controller 1) numberTPDURetransmitted (controller 1)

Exhibit X-4-4. Fault Scenario Events

Tools for performance, accounting, and security management can be expected to be developed in the future.

As more experience is gained with expert systems for LAN management, these techniques will be adapted to managing the applications themselves. For example, such applications as file transfer, access, and management or the manufacturing message system could be managed so that they could be automatically configured to meet changing performance objectives according to a user's priority or the time of day.

LAN-based expert systems will change from centralized tools to distributed tools, with each piece able to work and reason autonomously. A decentralized network management scheme would support self-diagnosing and self-tuning LANs. To configure the network and tune individual parameters, the autonomous management systems in the network would negotiate among themselves. To detect and diagnose faults, the systems would plan appropriate cooperative actions, while still remaining responsive to their individual domains.

Index

O

P

DATE DUE

SEP 2 8 '91			
GAYLORD			PRINTED IN U.S.A.